The
Armchair
SCIENCE
Reader

EDITED BY

Isabel S. Gordon

AND

Sophie Sorkin

1959

SIMON AND SCHUSTER • NEW YORK

LIBRARY OF CONGRESS CATALOG CARD NUMBER: 59-13134

MANUFACTURED IN THE UNITED STATES OF AMERICA
BY H. WOLFF, NEW YORK

To Ralph and Myron Gordon
who showed us, each in his own sphere, that:

Science is wonder
As number is music, if we can
But read our thought back to the high listener
Whose language in us, overheard,
Creates the mind.

FOREWORD

◇◇◇◇◇◇◇◇◇◇◇◇◇◇◇◇◇

THE *excitement of science! Who, today, is not constantly and increasingly aware of it? Yet there was a time when the scientist kept his discovery secret or, at most, took only a few, the inner circle, into his confidence. Thus Galileo, in order to establish the priority of his discovery, sent this anagram to Giuliano de' Medici:*

SMAISMRMILMEBOETALIPVMVGTTAVIRANS

Giuliano sent it on to Kepler, who, himself an explorer of the skies, knew at once that Galileo had seen the moons of Saturn, for he unscrambled the message and read: "Altissimum planetam tergeminum observavi" — "I have seen that the highest planet is a triplet."

Today, however, news of science is no longer restricted to the inner circle. Our books and journals, our popular periodicals and daily newspaper — all bring us stories of the adventures of science.

In The Armchair Science Reader, *we have tried to assemble an anthology that conveys this excitement of science in writings that are a delight to read. It is not primarily to the reader who is already well informed about science, nor yet to the one who wishes to add to his scientific knowledge, that this book is addressed. The reader we have in mind throughout is the one who, first and foremost, enjoys good writing and then is enough a child of his time to be interested in the way thoughtful men have reckoned with science.*

As we explored the rich storehouse of the literature of science, we soon passed beyond the obvious staples of science-fiction or biographies of scientists to discoveries — yes, and rediscoveries — of a wealth of plays and poems and realistic stories on which science had had an effect. As Wordsworth foresaw, when science becomes part of our lives, it inevitably becomes part of our literature as well. In the past as well as the present, science has colored the way writers see the universe and, consequently, has colored their representation of it in their works. Our problem was never one of finding enough examples; it was always rather one of choosing from the boundless wealth and still staying within the confines of two hard covers. That there will be complaints about omissions as well as inclusions is certain; to this we are resigned. Our answer to such complaints is that we were making selections to illustrate certain themes and progressions of thought.

In Section One we have brought together a group of stories that show man in his various relationships to nature and science: using science to combat unfriendly elements of nature; falling victim to his own creations; triumphantly setting himself free from the limitations of our here-and-now to voyage in the worlds of space-time. In Section Two we turn to the past for fascinating accounts of those great men and events that have changed the course of science and thus of civilization. In Section Three we attempt to examine more closely the methods and tools of the scientist, after first considering man himself. What sort of man is it to whom the scientific pursuit becomes a passion and a way of life? And how — by means of what modes of thought, what tools of testing — has science taken us beyond the first simple steps of observation and induction to more and more elaborately co-ordinated systems of putting questions to nature?

In Section Four we present some of the classics of science-writing and especially of writing about nature. Overwhelmed by the riches available in this field, we made our selections for variety of topic, giving preference to those essays which, in addition to color and charm, offered some specific scientific generalization.

Section Five may at first glance surprise the reader of a science anthology. So much poetry! And poems so well known! True enough; but here we have tried to indicate by the groupings how, in every age, the pursuit of truth — ultimate truth, poetic truth — is conditioned by underlying scientific concepts; how the poet who seeks to resolve and express man's relationship to his universe and its ultimates must work in terms of the images his time furnishes him, and reason from the premise his science offers him. As a result many familiar and well-loved poems, reread in the framework of the scientific setting of their time, take on new meaning and depth.

In Section Six, finally, we share in the thinking of those men — men of years past, men of today — who are concerned with the goals of science. For us, as always, the question remains: What shall we do with the power science has given us?

This has been the plan we held before us as the book took shape.

This, together with our own feeling for a piece — its readability, its literary worth, its scientific value — determined the choices. We know you will find many old friends here; we hope you will make new ones as well. If you have stayed with this foreword thus far, you undoubtedly realize that each section has its own progression; the various captions indicate this. But each selection also stands alone. So, whether you read the works in the order presented, or browse pleasantly at will, your way will be right for you. Putting this book together has been fun for its editors; we hope it will be for its readers too.

NEW YORK   I.S.G.

JUNE 1959   S.S.

A WORD OF THANKS

In addition to authors whose courtesy we acknowledge elsewhere, there are many to whom we are indebted for help of various kinds. It was Dr. Morris Meister, president of Bronx Community College, who, in the days when he was still principal of the Bronx High School of Science, made us aware how vast a store of pleasant and non-technical reading is to be found in the field of science; and how important it is for the general reader to keep abreast of scientific ideas. For this initial impetus and for many fruitful suggestions, our first and sincerest thanks go to Dr. Meister.

We would also thank those well-read friends who have brought us materials; science-trained friends who have made valuable suggestions; librarians who have helped us trace fragments to their sources and to find lost texts. Miss Ettie Goldberg and Mrs. Ruth Handel of the library of the Bronx High School of Science have been especially kind and helpful in every way.

Finally, an apology and a thank-you to both our husbands and all four of our children, who were so often called upon to fend for themselves during the days and weeks and months that have gone into the framing of this book.

I.S.G.
S.S.

CONTENTS

Foreword   vii

1. Science Sparks the Imagination

MAN AMONG THE STARS

Invasion from Mars   HOWARD KOCH   3
Flight to Malacandra   C. S. LEWIS   23
Our Distant Cousins   LORD DUNSANY   31

MAN UPON THE SEAS

The *Nautilus* Reaches the Pole   JULES VERNE   52
A Descent into the Maelström   EDGAR ALLAN POE   63

MAN AND HIS EARTH

John Thomas's Cube   JOHN LEIMERT   78
In Hiding   WILMAR H. SHIRAS   86
"Creative Evolution —"   GEORGE BERNARD SHAW   117
Split Cherry Tree   JESSE STUART   123
"Cabinet Decision"   NIGEL BALCHIN   134
Dr. Southport Vulpes's Nightmare   BERTRAND RUSSELL   142
The Portable Phonograph   WALTER VAN TILBURG CLARK   147
By the Waters of Babylon   STEPHEN VINCENT BENÉT   153

2. Eureka!

SOME GENERAL OBSERVATIONS

On Sharing in the Conquests of Science
                                         HARLOW SHAPLEY   167
Science and the Imagination   WALDEMAR KAEMPFFERT   170
From First Step to Last   HANS ZINSSER   172

FOUNDERS AND FINDERS

TWO EUREKAS
  The Golden Crown: Archimedes   ZSOLT DE HARSANYI   173
  Swing of a Pendulum: Galileo   ZSOLT DE HARSANYI   174

A BOY PLAYING: ISAAC NEWTON
  In the Elaboratory   HUMPHREY NEWTON   177
  An Apple Falls   LOUIS TRENCHARD MORE   182

THROUGH THE MICROSCOPE
  On Certain Animalcules   ANTONY VAN LEEUWENHOEK   185
  Even a Lady's Teeth   ANTONY VAN LEEUWENHOEK   188

LIGHTNING STRIKES
  Mr. Franklin: Philadelphia Prometheus   CARL VAN DOREN   189

A CANDLE BURNS
  The Discovery of Oxygen   JOSEPH PRIESTLEY   194

IN TRANSIT
  In a Carriage   CHARLES DARWIN   196
  On a Bus   FRIEDRICH KEKULÉ   197

"CHANCE FAVORS THE PREPARED MIND . . ."
  Chickens, Dogs . . . And a Child's
    Life Is Saved   RENÉ VALLERY-RADOT   198

TEAM WORKERS

THE AIR AGE BEGINS
  The Campers at Kitty Hawk   JOHN DOS PASSOS   209

HUMAN GRANDEUR
  Portrait of Madame Curie   ALBERT EINSTEIN   214
  The Discovery of Radium   EVE CURIE   214

CONTROLLED NUCLEAR REACTION
  Landing in the New World   ARTHUR H. COMPTON   225

"THE LAWS OF PHYSICS ARE THE DECREES OF FATE"
  The Great Theory Tested   PHILIPP FRANK   230
  The Order of Nature   ALFRED NORTH WHITEHEAD   234
  Self-Portrait   ALBERT EINSTEIN   235
  $E=mc^2$ MORRIS BISHOP   236

3. Monuments of Method

THE MAN OF SCIENCE

The Blood of the Martyrs   STEPHEN VINCENT BENÉT   239
Portrait of a Scientist   SINCLAIR LEWIS   254
A Letter to Charles Kingsley   THOMAS HENRY HUXLEY   258
The Life of Solitude   ALBERT EINSTEIN   261
"In Silent Rooms"   CARL SANDBURG   262

THE MANY METHODS OF SCIENCE

We Are All Scientists   THOMAS HENRY HUXLEY   263
Paradox   CLARENCE R. WYLIE, JR.   270

THE UNIQUE ACHIEVEMENT OF GREECE

    HERBERT J. MULLER   270
The Sacred Disease   HIPPOCRATES   273
Case History No. XV   HIPPOCRATES   274
The Training of Aristotle   ALFRED NOYES   275
"Here, Too, Are Gods"   ARISTOTLE   277
"See for Yourself"   HIPPOCRATIC COLLECTION   278
Eels and Embryo Chicks   ARISTOTLE   279
The Store of Matter   LUCRETIUS   281
The Study of Anatomy   GALEN   283

THE WEIGHT OF REASON: THE ART OF EXPERIMENT

Peter Peregrine as Experimentalist   ROGER BACON   286
Experimenting with Magnets   PETER PEREGRINE   287
A Plea for Experimentation   ROGER BACON   288
Natural Marvels — No Magic   ROGER BACON   290
"We Are Beholden to Experiments . . ."   THOMAS SPRAT   293

WHAT LANGUAGE FOR SCIENCE?

English for the English   GEOFFREY CHAUCER   294
Words and Matter   FRANCIS BACON   295
Marriage of the Faculties   FRANCIS BACON   297

MATHEMATICS AND THE LAWS OF NATURE

                                              HERMANN WEYL   300
"Bring Arguments and Proofs"   GALILEO GALILEI   304
A New Theory about Light and
    Colors   ISAAC NEWTON   307
Rules of Reasoning in Philosophy   ISAAC NEWTON   316
"I Frame No Hypotheses"   ISAAC NEWTON   318

NO HOLDS BARRED   PERCY W. BRIDGMAN   319
Benjamin Franklin: Electrician   CARL VAN DOREN   319
Incidental Discovery: What Is
    Heat?   BENJAMIN THOMPSON   325
Accidental Discovery: Galvani
    and Volta   JAMES B. CONANT   327
The Blunderbuss Method   PAUL DE KRUIF   332
Mechanisms of Discovery   RENÉ J. DUBOS   333
Planning Unplanned Research   IRVING LANGMUIR   336

NEW PATHWAYS
Yellow Jack   SIDNEY HOWARD   338
Chimpanzees as Servants of
    Science   ROBERT M. YERKES   372
The Story of the Electron
    Microscope   JAMES HILLIER   376
A Master Key: The Spectroscope   GEORGE R. HARRISON   379
The Idea of Chance in Science   JACOB BRONOWSKI   382
Parable of the Fishing Net   SIR ARTHUR EDDINGTON   387
Epilogue: New Pathways in
    Science   SIR ARTHUR EDDINGTON   388

4. Literary Naturalists

THE WONDER OF THE WORLD   SIR J. ARTHUR THOMSON
                                      AND PATRICK GEDDES   397

Brute Neighbors   HENRY DAVID THOREAU   400
A Descent into Perpetual Night   WILLIAM BEEBE   408
Fishes in Armor   MYRON GORDON   421

The Changing Year   RACHEL CARSON   430
The Sperm Whale's Head   HERMAN MELVILLE 436
The Intelligence of Birds   JULIAN HUXLEY   440
A Storm Is Born   GEORGE R. STEWART 449
The Plains of Patagonia   W. H. HUDSON   459
Polar Night   RICHARD E. BYRD 462
A Jaunt to the Limits of the
    Universe   LLOYD MOTZ   470

"THE PROPER STUDY OF MANKIND . . ."

The People of Tierra del Fuego   CHARLES DARWIN   478
Patterns of Culture: The Dance   RUTH BENEDICT   485
On Being the Right Size   J. B. S. HALDANE 490
The Neurosis Wears a Mask   LAWRENCE S. KUBIE 495
The Door   E. B. WHITE   503
The Colloid and the Crystal   JOSEPH WOOD KRUTCH 507

THE MIND REELS!

Common Sense and the Universe   STEPHEN LEACOCK 515
The Universe and Me
    or
How to Understand the Wonders   JACK GOODMAN AND
    of Science   ALAN GREEN   520
Lines in Dispraise of Dispraise   OGDEN NASH   527

5. The Gift of Prometheus

THE WORK OF HIS HANDS . . .

"Where Wast Thou When I Laid
    the Foundations of the Earth?"   THE BOOK OF JOB 531
"All Arts of Mortals from
    Prometheus Spring"   AESCHYLUS   537
"All Things Flow"   LUCRETIUS   539

SCIENCE: PROMETHEAN OR MEPHISTOPHELEAN

NATURE REHABILITATED   BASIL WILLEY   541
From Dr. Faustus   CHRISTOPHER MARLOWE   544
"Knowledge Infinite"   CHRISTOPHER MARLOWE   553
The Ordered Universe   WILLIAM SHAKESPEARE   554
"The New Philosophy Calls All in Doubt"   JOHN DONNE   555
Solomon's House   FRANCIS BACON   556
The Book of God   JOHN MILTON   564

SCIENCE ADORED: SCIENCE MOCKED
The Spacious Firmament   JOSEPH ADDISON   565
"Of God Above or Man Below . . ."   ALEXANDER POPE   566
The Proper Study of Mankind   ALEXANDER POPE   568
"And Don't Go Near the Water"   THOMAS SHADWELL   569
Laputan Projects   JONATHAN SWIFT   572

TWO WAYS OF SEEING

NEW MYTHS, NEW SYMBOLS   LEWIS MUMFORD   577
Three Rainbows   JAMES THOMSON   579
                                       WILLIAM WORDSWORTH   579
                                               JOHN KEATS   579

SEEING INTO THE LIFE OF THINGS
Mock On, Mock On!   WILLIAM BLAKE   580
A New Jerusalem   WILLIAM BLAKE   580
Lines Composed a Few Miles
    Above Tintern Abbey   WILLIAM WORDSWORTH   581
"Immortal Drink"   JOHN KEATS   584
Ode on a Grecian Urn   JOHN KEATS   585

SHELLEY: "A NEWTON AMONG POETS"
The Dance of Matter   SIR HUMPHRY DAVY   587
The Dance of Matter:
    The Motion of the Spheres   PERCY BYSSHE SHELLEY   588
The Dance of Light:
    The Cycle of the Waters   PERCY BYSSHE SHELLEY   589
The Dance of Mind: New Reading
    of Ancient Myth   PERCY BYSSHE SHELLEY   591

FAITH AND UNFAITH: ADVANCING SCIENCE CHALLENGES ESTABLISHED CREED

"CLASH BY NIGHT"

Dover Beach	MATTHEW ARNOLD	597
Ah, Yet Consider It Again	ARTHUR HUGH CLOUGH	598
With Whom Is No Variableness	ARTHUR HUGH CLOUGH	599
The Latest Decalogue	ARTHUR HUGH CLOUGH	599

"TRUTHS THAT NEVER CAN BE PROVED"

From In Memoriam A. H. H.	ALFRED, LORD TENNYSON	600
By an Evolutionist	ALFRED, LORD TENNYSON	604
Flower in the Crannied Wall	ALFRED, LORD TENNYSON	605
Crossing the Bar	ALFRED, LORD TENNYSON	606
Rubáiyát of Omar Khayyám	EDWARD FITZGERALD	606

"UNALTERABLE LAW"

Nature Without Check	WALT WHITMAN	608
When I Heard the Learn'd Astronomer	WALT WHITMAN	608
Miracles	WALT WHITMAN	609
Lucifer in Starlight	GEORGE MEREDITH	610
O World	GEORGE SANTAYANA	610
Each in His Own Tongue	WILLIAM HERBERT CARRUTH	611
The Far-Seeing Eye	TEMPLE RICE HOLLCROFT	611

"OUR PLACE AMONG THE INFINITIES"

PULVIS ET UMBRA	ROBERT LOUIS STEVENSON	613
MAN'S FATE	BERTRAND RUSSELL	618

VOICES OF PROPHECY

"What Is the Meaning of This City?"	T. S. ELIOT	619
Mother Goose's Garland	ARCHIBALD MACLEISH	622
Seafarer	ARCHIBALD MACLEISH	622
Lines for a Prologue	ARCHIBALD MACLEISH	623
You, Andrew Marvell	ARCHIBALD MACLEISH	624

Epistle to Be Left in the
  Earth   ARCHIBALD MACLEISH   625
Star Splitter   ROBERT FROST   626
Riders   ROBERT FROST   629
Desert Places   ROBERT FROST   630
Fire and Ice   ROBERT FROST   630
A Considerable Speck   ROBERT FROST   631
A Loose Mountain   ROBERT FROST   632

6. The World We Make

Evolution: At the Mind's Cinema   JULIAN HUXLEY   633

DREAMS AND PROMISES

Taming the Elements   THOMAS JEFFERSON   635
On the Advisableness of Improv-
  ing Natural Knowledge   THOMAS HENRY HUXLEY   636
The Encouragement of Science   J. ROBERT OPPENHEIMER   648

DREAM AND DISILLUSION

"I Dipt into the Future"   ALFRED, LORD TENNYSON 656
"Cosmos, Chaos!"   ALFRED, LORD TENNYSON 657

KNOWLEDGE COMES . . .

Science and Society   ALBERT EINSTEIN   663
THE PRACTICAL GIFTS OF SCIENCE
The Past Century — and the
  Next — in Science   WALDEMAR KAEMPFFERT   665
The Case of the Man from
  Mexico   BERTON ROUECHÉ   673
A Whole Heart for Ramona   GLADYS DENNY SHULTZ   686

THE ABOLITION OF SLAVERY
The Man with the Hoe   EDWIN MARKHAM   700
The Child-Slaves of England   BERTRAND RUSSELL   701
Machines To Do Our Work   EDWARD BELLAMY   709

THE CRY OF THE LAND
 The River   PARE LORENTZ 714
 Our Plundered Planet   FAIRFIELD OSBORN 722

. . . BUT WISDOM LINGERS
THE ATOM
 A First Reaction to the
  Atomic Bomb   JOHN W. CAMPBELL 736
 Able Day: Atomic Testing   DAVID BRADLEY 737
 The Equation   GERHARD FRIEDRICH 752
 A Message to Intellectuals ALBERT EINSTEIN 753

THE BATTLE FOR MEN'S MINDS
 "In Bondage to a Central Authority" ALDOUS HUXLEY 756
 The Machine Stops   E. M. FORSTER 763
 The Morning of the Day They
  Did It   E. B. WHITE 790

LOOKING FORWARD
 The Limitations of Science LAURENCE A. HAWKINS 804
 How to Get the Most Out of
  Science   I. BERNARD COHEN 807
 Toward a Greater America DAVID E. LILIENTHAL 817

FAITH IN SCIENCE   I. I. RABI 826

The
Armchair
SCIENCE
Reader

1

Science Sparks the Imagination

MAN AMONG THE STARS

◇◇

Invasion from Mars

HOWARD KOCH

*[The radio-script version of H. G. Wells's famous novel
The War of the Worlds, freely adapted by Howard Koch
and presented by Orson Welles and his Mercury Theater
of the Air over the Columbia Broadcasting System,
October 30, 1938.]*

NARRATOR: We know now that in the early years of the
twentieth century this world was being watched closely by in-
telligences greater than man's and yet as mortal as his own. We
know now that as human beings busied themselves about their
various concerns they were scrutinized and studied, perhaps almost
as narrowly as a man with a microscope might scrutinize the transient creatures that swarm and multiply in a drop of water. With
infinite complacence people went to and fro over the earth about
their little affairs, serene in the assurance of their dominion over
this small spinning fragment of solar driftwood which by chance
or design man has inherited out of the dark mystery of Time and
Space. Yet across an immense ethereal gulf, minds that are to our
minds as ours are to the beasts in the jungle, intellects vast, cool,
and unsympathetic, regarded this earth with envious eyes and
slowly and surely drew their plans against us. In the thirty-ninth
year of the twentieth century came the great disillusionment.

It was near the end of October. Business was better. The war
scare was over. More men were back at work. Sales were picking
up. On this particular evening, October 30, the Crossley service
estimated that thirty-two million people were listening in on radios.

ANNOUNCER CUE: . . . for the next twenty-four hours not
much change in temperature. A slight atmospheric disturbance
of undetermined origin is reported over Nova Scotia, causing a low-

pressure area to move down rather rapidly over the northeastern states, bringing a forecast of rain, accompanied by winds of light gale force. Maximum temperature 66; minimum 48. This weather report comes to you from the Government Weather Bureau.

ANNOUNCER TWO: We now take you to the Meridian Room in the Hotel Park Plaza in downtown New York, where you will be entertained by the music of Ramon Raquello and his orchestra.

(*Spanish theme song . . . Fades*)

ANNOUNCER THREE: Good evening, ladies and gentlemen. From the Meridian Room in the Park Plaza in New York City, we bring you the music of Ramon Raquello and his orchestra. With a touch of the Spanish, Ramon Raquello leads off with "La Cumparsita."

(*Piece starts playing*)

ANNOUNCER TWO: Ladies and gentlemen, we interrupt our program of dance music to bring you a special bulletin from the Intercontinental Radio News. At twenty minutes before eight, central time, Professor Farrell of the Mount Jennings Observatory, Chicago, Illinois, reports observing several explosions of incandescent gas, occurring at regular intervals on the planet Mars.

The spectroscope indicates the gas to be hydrogen and moving toward the earth with enormous velocity. Professor Pierson of the observatory at Princeton confirms Farrell's observation, and describes the phenomenon as (quote) like a jet of blue flame shot from a gun (unquote). We now return you to the music of Ramon Raquello, playing for you in the Meridian Room of the Park Plaza Hotel, situated in downtown New York.

(*Music plays for a few moments until piece ends . . . Sound of applause*)

Now a tune that never loses favor, the ever-popular "Star Dust." Ramon Raquello and his orchestra . . .

(*Music*)

ANNOUNCER TWO: Ladies and gentlemen, following on the news given in our bulletin a moment ago, the Government Meteorological Bureau has requested the large observatories of the country to keep an astronomical watch on any other disturbances occurring on the planet Mars. Due to the unusual nature of this occurrence, we have arranged an interview with the noted astronomer, Professor Pierson, who will give us his views on this event. In a few moments we will take you to the Princeton Observatory at Princeton, New Jersey. We return you until then to the music of Ramon Raquello and his orchestra.

(*Music*)

ANNOUNCER TWO: We are ready now to take you to the Princeton Observatory at Princeton, where Carl Phillips, our commentator, will interview Professor Richard Pierson, famous astronomer. We take you now to Princeton, New Jersey.

(*Echo chamber*)

PHILLIPS: Good evening, ladies and gentlemen. This is Carl Phillips, speaking to you from the observatory at Princeton. I am standing in a large semicircular room, pitch-black except for an oblong split in the ceiling. Through this opening I can see a sprinkling of stars that cast a kind of frosty glow over the intricate mechanism of the huge telescope. The ticking sound you hear is the vibration of the clockwork. Professor Pierson stands directly above me on a small platform, peering through the giant lens. I ask you to be patient, ladies and gentlemen, during any delay that may arise during our interview. Beside his ceaseless watch of the heavens, Professor Pierson may be interrupted by telephone or other communications. During this period he is in constant touch with the astronomical centers of the world — Professor, may I begin our questions?

PIERSON: At any time, Mr. Phillips.

PHILLIPS: Professor, would you please tell our radio audience exactly what you see as you observe the planet Mars through your telescope?

PIERSON: Nothing unusual at the moment, Mr. Phillips. A red disk swimming in a blue sea. Transverse stripes across the disk. Quite distinct now because Mars happens to be at the point nearest the earth — in opposition, as we call it.

PHILLIPS: In your opinion, what do these transverse stripes signify, Professor Pierson?

PIERSON: Not canals, I can assure you, Mr. Phillips, although that's the popular conjecture of those who imagine Mars to be inhabited. From a scientific viewpoint the stripes are merely the result of atmospheric conditions peculiar to the planet.

PHILLIPS: Then you're quite convinced as a scientist that living intelligence as we know it does not exist on Mars?

PIERSON: I should say the chances against it are a thousand to one.

PHILLIPS: And yet how do you account for these gas eruptions occurring on the surface of the planet at regular intervals?

PIERSON: Mr. Phillips, I cannot account for it.

PHILLIPS: By the way, Professor, for the benefit of our listeners, how far is Mars from the earth?

PIERSON: Approximately forty million miles.

PHILLIPS: Well, that seems a safe enough distance — Just a moment, ladies and gentlemen, someone has just handed Professor Pierson a message. While he reads it, let me remind you we are speaking to you from the observatory in Princeton, New Jersey, where we are interviewing the world-famous astronomer, Professor Pierson . . . One moment, please. Professor Pierson has passed me a message which he has just received. Professor, may I read the message to the listening audience?

PIERSON: Certainly, Mr. Phillips.

PHILLIPS: Ladies and gentlemen, I shall read you a wire addressed to Professor Pierson from Dr. Gray of the National History Museum, New York. "9:15 P.M. eastern standard time. Seismograph registered shock of almost earthquake intensity occurring within a radius of twenty miles of Princeton. Please investigate. Signed, Lloyd Gray, Chief of Astronomical Division." Professor Pierson, could this occurrence possibly have something to do with the disturbances observed on the planet Mars?

PIERSON: Hardly, Mr. Phillips. This is probably a meteorite of unusual size, and its arrival at this particular time is merely a coincidence. However, we shall conduct a search as soon as daylight permits.

PHILLIPS: Thank you, Professor. Ladies and gentlemen, for the past ten minutes we've been speaking to you from the observatory at Princeton, bringing you a special interview with Professor Pierson, noted astronomer. This is Carl Phillips speaking. We now return you to our New York studio.

(*Fade in piano playing*)

ANNOUNCER TWO: Ladies and gentlemen, here is the latest bulletin from the Intercontinental Radio News. Toronto, Canada: Professor Morse of Macmillan University reports observing a total of three explosions on the planet Mars, between the hours of 7:45 P.M. and 9:20 P.M., eastern standard time. This confirms earlier reports received from American observatories. Now, nearer home, comes a special announcement from Trenton, New Jersey. It is reported that at 8:50 P.M. a huge, flaming object, believed to be a meteorite, fell on a farm in the neighborhood of Grovers Mill, New Jersey, twenty-two miles from Trenton. The flash in the sky was visible within a radius of several hundred miles and the noise of the impact was heard as far north as Elizabeth.

We have dispatched a special mobile unit to the scene, and will have our commentator, Mr. Phillips, give you a word picture as soon as he can reach there from Princeton. In the meantime, we take you to the Hotel Martinet in Brooklyn, where Bobby Millette and his orchestra are offering a program of dance music.

(*Swing band for 20 seconds . . . Then cut*)

ANNOUNCER TWO: We take you now to Grovers Mill, New Jersey.

(*Crowd noises . . . Police sirens*)

PHILLIPS: Ladies and gentlemen, this is Carl Phillips again, at the Wilmuth farm, Grovers Mill, New Jersey. Professor Pierson and myself made the 11 miles from Princeton in ten minutes. Well, I — I hardly know where to begin, to paint for you a word picture of the strange scene before my eyes, like something out of a modern Arabian Nights. Well, I just got here. I haven't had a chance to look around yet. I guess that's it. Yes, I guess that's the — thing, directly in front of me, half buried in a vast pit. Must have struck with terrific force. The ground is covered with splinters of a tree it must have struck on its way down. What I can see of the — object itself doesn't look very much like a meteor, at least not the meteors I've seen. It looks more like a huge cylinder. It has a diameter of — what would you say, Professor Pierson?

PIERSON (*off*):   About thirty yards.

PHILLIPS: About thirty yards — The metal on the sheath is — well, I've never seen anything like it. The color is sort of yellowish-white. Curious spectators now are pressing close to the object in spite of the efforts of the police to keep them back. They're getting in front of my line of vision. Would you mind standing on one side, please?

POLICEMAN: One side, there, one side.

PHILLIPS: While the policemen are pushing the crowd back, here's Mr. Wilmuth, owner of the farm here. He may have some interesting facts to add. Mr. Wilmuth, would you please tell the radio audience as much as you remember of this rather unusual visitor that dropped in your backyard? Step closer, please. Ladies and gentlemen, this is Mr. Wilmuth.

WILMUTH: I was listenin' to the radio —

PHILLIPS: Closer and louder, please.

WILMUTH: Pardon me!

PHILLIPS: Louder, please, and closer.

WILMUTH: Yes, sir — while I was listening to the radio and

kinda drowsin', that Professor fellow was talkin' about Mars, so I
was half dozin' and half —

PHILLIPS: Yes, yes, Mr. Wilmuth. And then what happened?

WILMUTH: As I was sayin', I was listenin' to the radio
kinda halfways —

PHILLIPS: Yes, Mr. Wilmuth, and then you saw something?

WILMUTH: Not first off. I heard something.

PHILLIPS: And what did you hear?

WILMUTH: A hissing sound. Like this: sssssssss — kinda like
a fourt' of July rocket.

PHILLIPS: Then what?

WILMUTH: Turned my head out the window and would
have swore I was to sleep and dreamin'.

PHILLIPS: Yes?

WILMUTH: I seen a kinda greenish streak and then zingo!
Somethin' smacked the ground. Knocked me clear out of my chair!

PHILLIPS: Well, were you frightened, Mr. Wilmuth?

WILMUTH: Well, I — I ain't quite sure. I reckon I — I was
kinda riled.

PHILLIPS: Thank you, Mr. Wilmuth. Thank you.

WILMUTH: Want me to tell you some more?

PHILLIPS: No — that's quite all right, that's plenty — Ladies
and gentlemen, you've just heard Mr. Wilmuth, owner of the farm
where this thing has fallen. I wish I could convey the atmosphere —
the background of this — fantastic scene. Hundreds of cars are
parked in a field in back of us. Police are trying to rope off the
roadway leading into the farm. But it's no use. They're breaking
right through. Their headlights throw an enormous spot on the pit
where the object's half-buried. Some of the more daring souls are
venturing near the edge. Their silhouettes stand out against the
metal sheen.

(*Faint humming sound*)

One man wants to touch the thing — he's having an argument
with a policeman. The policeman wins — Now, ladies and gentlemen, there's something I haven't mentioned in all this excitement,
but it's becoming more distinct. Perhaps you've caught it already
on your radio. Listen (*Long pause*) . . . Do you hear it? It's a
curious humming sound that seems to come from inside the object.
I'll move the microphone nearer. Here. (*Pause*) Now we're not
more than twenty-five feet away. Can you hear it now? Oh, Professor Pierson!

PIERSON: Yes, Mr. Phillips?

PHILLIPS:　Can you tell us the meaning of that scraping noise inside the thing?

PIERSON:　Possibly the unequal cooling of its surface.

PHILLIPS:　Do you still think it's a meteor, Professor?

PIERSON:　I don't know what to think. The metal casing is definitely extra-terrestrial — not found on this earth. Friction with the earth's atmosphere usually tears holes in a meteorite. This thing is smooth and, as you can see, of cylindrical shape.

PHILLIPS:　Just a minute! Something's happening! Ladies and gentlemen, this is terrific! This end of the thing is beginning to flake off! The top is beginning to rotate like a screw! The thing must be hollow!

VOICES:　She's a movin'!

Look, the darn thing's unscrewing!

Keep back, there! Keep back, I tell you.

Maybe there's men in it trying to escape!

It's red-hot, they'll burn to a cinder!

Keep back there! Keep those idiots back!

(*Suddenly the clanking sound of a huge piece of falling metal*)

VOICES:　She's off! The top's loose!

Look out there! Stand back!

PHILLIPS:　Ladies and gentlemen, this is the most terrifying thing I have ever witnessed — Wait a minute! Something's crawling out of the hollow top. Someone or — something. I can see peering out of that black hole two luminous disks — are they eyes? It might be a face. It might be —

(*Shout of awe from the crowd*)

Good heavens, something's wriggling out of the shadow like a gray snake. Now it's another one, and another. They look like tentacles to me. There, I can see the thing's body. It's large as a bear and glistens like wet leather. But that face. It — it's indescribable. I can hardly force myself to keep looking at it. The eyes are black and gleam like a serpent's. The mouth is V-shaped with saliva dripping from its rimless lips that seem to quiver and pulsate. The monster or whatever it is can hardly move. It seems weighed down by — possibly gravity or something. The thing's raising up. The crowd falls back. They've seen enough. This is the most extraordinary experience. I can't find words — I'm pulling this microphone with me as I talk. I'll have to stop the description until I've taken a new position. Hold on, will you please, I'll be back in a minute.

(*Fade into piano*)

ANNOUNCER TWO: We are bringing you an eyewitness account of what's happening on the Wilmuth farm, Grovers Mill, New Jersey.

(*More piano*)

We now return you to Carl Phillips at Grovers Mill.

PHILLIPS: Ladies and gentlemen (Am I on?) — ladies and gentlemen, here I am, back of a stone wall that adjoins Mr. Wilmuth's garden. From here I get a sweep of the whole scene. I'll give you every detail as long as I can talk. As long as I can see. More state police have arrived. They're drawing up a cordon in front of the pit, about thirty of them. No need to push the crowd back now. They're willing to keep their distance. The captain is conferring with someone. We can't quite see who. Oh, yes, I believe it's Professor Pierson. Yes, it is. Now they've parted. The professor moves around one side, studying the object, while the captain and two policemen advance with something in their hands. I can see it now. It's a white handkerchief tied to a pole — a flag of truce. If those creatures know what that means — what anything means! . . . *Wait!* Something's happening!

(*Hissing sound followed by a humming that increases in intensity*)

A humped shape is rising out of the pit. I can make out a small beam of light against a mirror. What's that? There's a jet of flame springing from that mirror, and it leaps right at the advancing men. It strikes them head on! Good Lord, they're turning into flame!

(*Screams and unearthly shrieks*)

Now the whole field's caught fire. (*Explosion*) The woods — the barns — the gas tanks of automobiles — it's spreading everywhere. It's coming this way. About twenty yards to my right —

(*Crash of microphone . . . Then dead silence . . .*)

ANNOUNCER TWO: Ladies and gentlemen, due to circumstances beyond our control, we are unable to continue the broadcast from Grovers Mill. Evidently there's some difficulty with our field transmission. However, we will return to that point at the earliest opportunity. In the meantime, we have a late bulletin from San Diego, California. Professor Indellkoffer, speaking at a dinner of the California Astronomical Society, expressed the opinion that the explosions on Mars are undoubtedly nothing more than severe volcanic disturbances on the surface of the planet. We continue now with our piano interlude.

(*Piano . . . Then cut*)

Ladies and gentlemen, I have just been handed a message that came in from Grovers Mill by telephone. Just a moment. At least forty people, including six state troopers, lie dead in a field east of the village of Grovers Mill, their bodies burned and distorted beyond all possible recognition. The next voice you hear will be that of Brigadier General Montgomery Smith, commander of the State Militia at Trenton, New Jersey.

SMITH: I have been requested by the governor of New Jersey to place the counties of Mercer and Middlesex as far west as Princeton, and east to Jamesburg, under martial law. No one will be permited to enter this area except by special pass issued by state or military authorities. Four companies of State Militia are proceeding from Trenton to Grovers Mill, and will aid in the evacuation of homes within the range of military operations. Thank you.

ANNOUNCER: You have just been listening to General Montgomery Smith commanding the State Militia at Trenton. In the meantime, further details of the catastrophe at Grovers Mill are coming in. The strange creatures, after unleashing their deadly assault, crawled back in their pit and made no attempt to prevent the efforts of the firemen to recover the bodies and extinguish the fire. Combined fire departments of Mercer County are fighting the flames which menace the entire countryside.

We have been unable to establish any contact with our mobile unit at Grovers Mill, but we hope to be able to return you there at the earliest possible moment. In the meantime we take you — uh, just one moment, please.

(*Long pause . . . Whisper*)

Ladies and gentlemen, I have just been informed that we have finally established communication with an eyewitness of the tragedy. Professor Pierson has been located at a farmhouse near Grovers Mill where he has established an emergency observation post. As a scientist, he will give you his explanation of the calamity. The next voice you hear will be that of Professor Pierson, brought to you by direct wire. Professor Pierson.

PIERSON: Of the creatures in the rocket cylinder at Grovers Mill, I can give you no authoritative information — either as to their nature, their origin, or their purposes here on earth. Of their destructive instruments I might venture some conjectural explanation. For want of a better term, I shall refer to the mysterious weapon as a heat-ray. It's all too evident that these creatures have scientific knowledge far in advance of our own. It is my guess that in some way they are able to generate an intense heat in a chamber of practically absolute nonconductivity. This intense heat they project in a parallel beam against any object they choose, by means of a polished parabolic mirror of unknown composition, much as the mirror of a lighthouse projects a beam of light. That is my conjecture of the origin of the heat-ray.

ANNOUNCER TWO: Thank you, Professor Pierson. Ladies and gentlemen, here is a bulletin from Trenton. It is a brief statement informing us that the charred body of Carl Phillips, the radio commentator, has been identified in a Trenton hospital. Now here's another bulletin from Washington, D. C.

Office of the director of the National Red Cross reports ten units of Red Cross emergency workers have been assigned to the headquarters of the State Militia stationed outside of Grovers Mill, New Jersey. Here's a bulletin from State Police, Princeton Junction: The fires at Grovers Mill and vicinity now under control. Scouts reports all quiet in the pit, and no sign of life appearing from the mouth of the cylinder. And now, ladies and gentlemen, we have a special statement from Mr. Harry McDonald, vice-president in charge of operations.

MCDONALD: We have received a request from the militia at Trenton to place at their disposal our entire broadcasting facilities. In view of the gravity of the situation, and believing that radio has a definite responsibility to serve in the public interest at all times, we are turning over our facilities to the State Militia at Trenton.

ANNOUNCER: We take you now to the field headquarters of the State Militia near Grovers Mill, New Jersey.

CAPTAIN: This is Captain Lansing of the Signal Corps, attached to the State Militia now engaged in military operations in the vicinity of Grovers Mill. Situation arising from the reported presence of certain individuals of unidentified nature is now under complete control.

The cylindrical object which lies in a pit directly below our position is surrounded on all sides by eight battalions of infantry, without heavy fieldpieces, but adequately armed with rifles and machine guns. All cause for alarm, if such cause ever existed, is now entirely unjustified. The things, whatever they are, do not even venture to poke their heads above the pit. I can see their hiding-place plainly in the glare of the searchlights here. With all their reported resources, these creatures can scarcely stand up against heavy machine-gun fire. Anyway, it's an interesting outing for the troops. I can make out their khaki uniforms, crossing back and forth in front of the lights. It looks almost like a real war. There appears to be some slight smoke in the woods bordering the Millstone River. Probably fire started by campers. Well, we ought to see some action soon. One of the companies is deploying on the left flank. A quick thrust and it will all be over. Now wait a minute! I see something on top of the cylinder. No, it's nothing but a shadow. Now the troops are on the edge of the Wilmuth farm. Seven thousand armed men closing in on an old metal tube. Wait, that wasn't a shadow! It's something moving — solid metal — kind of a shieldlike affair rising up out of the cylinder — It's going higher and higher. Why, it's standing on legs — actually rearing up on a sort of metal framework. Now it's reaching above the trees and the searchlights are on it! Hold on!

(*Silence*)

ANNOUNCER TWO: Ladies and gentlemen, I have a grave announcement to make. Incredible as it may seem, both the observations of science and the evidence of our eyes lead to the inescapable assumption that those strange beings who landed in the Jersey farmlands tonight are the vanguard of an invading army from the planet Mars. The battle which took place tonight at Grovers Mill has ended in one of the most startling defeats ever suffered by an army in modern times; seven thousand men armed with rifles and machine guns pitted against a single fighting machine of the invaders from Mars. One hundred and twenty known survivors. The rest strewn over the battle area from Grovers Mill to Plainsboro crushed and trampled to death under the metal feet of the monster, or burned to cinders by its heat-ray. The monster is now in control of the middle section of New Jersey and has effectively cut the state through its center. Communication lines are down from Pennsylvania to the Atlantic Ocean. Railroad tracks are torn and service from New York to Philadelphia discontinued except routing some of the trains through Allentown and Phoenixville. Highways to the north, south, and west are clogged with frantic human traffic. Police and army reserves are unable to control the mad flight. By morning the fugitives will have swelled Philadelphia, Camden, and Trenton, it is estimated, to twice their normal population.

At this time martial law prevails throughout New Jersey and eastern Pennsylvania. We take you now to Washington for a special broadcast on the National Emergency. . . . The Secretary of the Interior —

SECRETARY: Citizens of the nation: I shall not try to conceal the gravity of the situation that confronts the country, nor the concern of your government in protecting the lives and property of its people. However, I wish to impress upon you — private citizens and public officials, all of you — the urgent need of calm and resourceful action. Fortunately, this formidable enemy is still confined to a comparatively small area, and we may place our faith in the military forces to keep them there. In the meantime, placing our faith in God, we must continue the performance of our duties each and every one of us, so that we may confront this destructive adversary with a nation united, courageous, and consecrated to the preservation of human supremacy on this earth. I thank you.

ANNOUNCER: You have just heard the Secretary of the Interior speaking from Washington. Bulletins too numerous to read are piling up in the studio here. We are informed that the central portion of New Jersey is blacked out from radio communication due to the effect of the heat-ray upon power lines and electrical equipment. Here is a special bulletin from New York. Cables received from English, French, German scientific bodies offering assistance. Astronomers report continued gas outbursts at regular intervals on planet Mars. Majority voice opinion that enemy will be reinforced by additional rocket machines. Attempts made to locate Professor Pierson of Princeton, who has observed Martians at close range. It is feared he was lost in recent battle. Langham Field, Virginia: Scouting planes report three Martian machines visible above treetops, moving north toward Somerville with population fleeing ahead of them. Heat-ray not in use; although advancing at express-train speed, invaders pick their way carefully. They seem to be making conscious effort to avoid destruction of cities and countryside. However, they stop to uproot power lines, bridges, and railroad tracks. Their apparent objective is to crush resistance, paralyze communication, and disorganize human society.

Here is a bulletin from Basking Ridge, New Jersey: Coon hunters have stumbled on a second cylinder similar to the first embedded in the great swamp twenty miles south of Morristown. U. S. Army fieldpieces are proceeding from Newark to blow up second invading unit before cylinder can be opened and the fighting machine rigged. They are taking up position in the foothills of Watchung Mountains. Another bulletin from Langham Field, Virginia: Scouting planes report enemy machines, now three in number, increasing speed northward kicking over houses and trees in their evident haste to form a conjunction with their allies south of Morristown. Machines also sighted by telephone operator east of Middlesex within ten miles of Plainfield. Here's a bulletin from Winston Field, Long Island: Fleet of army bombers carrying heavy explosives flying north in pursuit of enemy. Scouting planes act as

guides. They keep speeding enemy in sight. Just a moment, please.
Ladies and gentlemen, we've run special wires to the artillery line in
adjacent villages to give you direct reports in the zone of the advancing enemy. First we take you to the battery of the 22nd Field
Artillery, located in the Watchung Mountains.

OFFICER: Range thirty-two meters.
GUNNER: Thirty-two meters.
OFFICER: Projection, thirty-nine degrees.
GUNNER: Thirty-nine degrees.
OFFICER: Fire!

(*Boom of heavy gun . . . Pause*)

OBSERVER: One hundred and forty yards to the right, sir.
OFFICER: Shift range — thirty-one meters.
GUNNER: Thirty-one meters.
OFFICER: Projection — thirty-seven degrees.
GUNNER: Thirty-seven degrees.
OFFICER: Fire!

(*Boom of heavy gun . . . Pause*)

OBSERVER: A hit, sir! We got the tripod of one of them.
They've stopped. The others are trying to repair it.
OFFICER: Quick, get the range! Shift range thirty meters.
GUNNER: Thirty meters.
OFFICER: Projection — twenty-seven degrees.
GUNNER: Twenty-seven degrees.
OFFICER: Fire!

(*Boom of heavy gun . . . Pause*)

OBSERVER: Can't see the shell land, sir. They're letting off a
smoke.
OFFICER: What is it?
OBSERVER: A black smoke, sir. Moving this way. Lying close
to the ground. It's moving fast.
OFFICER: Put on gas masks. (*Pause*) Get ready to fire. Shift
to twenty-four meters.
GUNNER: Twenty-four meters.
OFFICER: Projection, twenty-four degrees.
GUNNER: Twenty-four degrees.
OFFICER: Fire! (*Boom*)
OBSERVER: I still can't see, sir. The smoke's coming nearer.
OFFICER: Get the range. (*Coughs*)
OBSERVER: Twenty-three meters. (*Coughs*)

OFFICER: Twenty-three meters. (*Coughs*)

OBSERVER: Projection twenty-two degrees. (*Coughing*)

OFFICER: Twenty-two degrees. (*Fade in coughing*)

(*Fading in . . . sound of airplane motor*)

COMMANDER: Army bombing plane, V-8-43 off Bayonne, New Jersey, Lieutenant Voght, commanding eight bombers. Reporting to Commander Fairfax, Langham Field — This is Voght, reporting to Commander Fairfax, Langham Field — Enemy tripod machines now in sight. Reinforced by three machines from the Morristown cylinder. Six altogether. One machine partially crippled. Believed hit by shell from army gun in Watchung Mountains. Guns now appear silent. A heavy black fog hanging close to the earth — of extreme density, nature unknown. No sign of heat-ray. Enemy now turns east, crossing Passaic River into Jersey marshes. Another straddles the Pulaski Skyway. Evident objective is New York City. They're pushing down a high-tension power station. The machines are close together now, and we're ready to attack. Planes circling, ready to strike. A thousand yards and we'll be over the first — eight hundred yards . . . six hundred . . . four hundred . . . two hundred . . . There they go! The giant arm raised — Green flash! They're spraying us with flame! Two thousand feet. Engines are giving out. No chance to release bombs. Only one thing left — drop on them, plane and all. We're diving on the first one. Now the engine's gone! Eight —

OPERATOR ONE: This is Bayonne, New Jersey, calling Langham Field — This is Bayonne, New Jersey, calling Langham Field — Come in, please — Come in, please —

OPERATOR TWO: This is Langham Field — go ahead —

OPERATOR ONE: Eight army bombers in engagement with enemy tripod machines over Jersey flats. Engines incapacitated by heat-ray. All crashed. One enemy machine destroyed. Enemy now discharging heavy black smoke in direction of —

OPERATOR THREE: This is Newark, New Jersey — This is Newark, New Jersey — Warning! Poisonous black smoke pouring in from Jersey marshes. Reaches South Street. Gas masks useless. Urge population to move into open spaces — automobiles use routes 7, 23, 24 — avoid congested areas. Smoke now spreading over Raymond Boulevard —

OPERATOR FOUR: 2X2L — calling CQ —   2X2L — calling CQ —   2X2L — calling 8X3R —

OPERATOR FIVE: This is 8X3R — coming back at 2X2L.

OPERATOR FOUR: How's reception? How's reception? K, please. Where are you, 8X3R? What's the matter? Where are you?

(*Bells ringing over city gradually diminishing*)

ANNOUNCER: I'm speaking from the roof of Broadcasting Building, New York City. The bells you hear are ringing to warn the people to evacuate the city as the Martians approach. Estimated in last two hours three million people have moved out along the roads to the north, Hutchison River Parkway still kept open for motor traffic. Avoid bridges to Long Island — hopelessly jammed. All communication with Jersey shore closed ten minutes ago. No more defenses. Our army wiped out — artillery, air force, everything wiped out. This may be the last broadcast. We'll stay here to the end. People are holding service below us — in the cathedral.

(*Voices singing hymn*)

Now I look down the harbor. All manner of boats, overloaded with fleeing population, pulling out from docks.

(*Sound of boat whistles*)

Streets are all jammed. Noise in crowds like New Year's Eve in city. Wait a minute — Enemy now in sight above the Palisades. Five great machines. First one is crossing river. I can see it from here, wading the Hudson like a man wading through a brook — A bulletin's handed me — Martian cylinders are falling all over the country. One outside Bufflalo, one in Chicago, St. Louis — seem to be timed and spaced — Now the first machine reaches the shore. He stands watching, looking over the city. His steel, cowlish head is even with the skyscrapers. He waits for the others. They rise like a line of new towers on the city's west side — Now they're lifting their metal hands. This is the end now. Smoke comes out — black smoke, drifting over the city. People in the streets see it now. They're running toward the East River — thousands of them, dropping in like rats. Now the smoke's spreading faster. It's reached Times Square. People trying to run away from it, but it's no use. They're falling like flies. Now the smoke's crossing Sixth Avenue — Fifth Avenue — a hundred yards away — it's fifty feet —

OPERATOR FOUR: 2X2L calling CQ — 2X2L calling CQ — 2X2L calling CQ — New York — Isn't there anyone on the air? Isn't there anyone — 2X2L —

II

PIERSON: As I set down these notes on paper, I'm obsessed by the thought that I may be the last living man on earth. I have been hiding in this empty house near Grovers Mill — a small island of daylight cut off by the black smoke from the rest of the world. All that happened before the arrival of these monstrous creatures in the world now seems part of another life — a life that has no continuity with the present furtive existence of the lonely derelict who pencils these words on the back of some astronomical notes bearing the signature of Richard Pierson. I look down at my blackened hands, my torn shoes, my tattered clothes, and I try to connect them with a professor who lives at Princeton, and who on the night of October 30 glimpsed through his telescope an orange splash of light on a distant planet. My wife, my colleagues, my students, my books, my observatory, my — my world — where are they? Did they ever exist? Am I Richard Pierson? What day is it? Do days exist without calendars? Does time pass when there are no human hands left to wind the clocks? In writing down my daily life I tell myself I shall preserve human history between the dark covers of this little book that was meant to record the movements of the stars. But to write I must live, and to live I must eat — I find moldy bread in the kitchen, and an orange not too spoiled to swallow. I keep watch at the window. From time to time I catch sight of a Martian above the black smoke.

The smoke still holds the house in its black coil — But at length there is a hissing sound and suddenly I see a Martian mounted on his machine, spraying the air with a jet of steam, as if to dissipate the smoke. I watch in a corner as his huge metal legs nearly brush against the house. Exhausted by terror, I fall asleep.

It's morning. Sun streams in the window. The black cloud of gas has lifted, and the scorched meadows to the north look as though a black snowstorm had passed over them. I venture from the house. I make my way to a road. No traffic. Here and there a wrecked car, baggage overturned, a blackened skeleton. I push on north. For some reason I feel safer trailing these monsters than running away from them. And I keep a careful watch. I have seen the Martians feed. Should one of their machines appear over the top of trees, I am ready to fling myself flat on the earth. I come to a chestnut tree. October, chestnuts are ripe. I fill my pockets. I must keep alive. Two days I wander in a vague northerly direction through a desolate world. Finally I notice a living creature — a small red squirrel in a beech tree. I stare at him and wonder. He stares back at me. I believe at that moment the animal and I shared the same emotion — the joy of finding another living being — I push on north. I find dead cows in a brackish field. Beyond, the charred ruins of a dairy. The silo remains standing guard over the wasteland like a lighthouse deserted by the sea. Astride the silo perches a weathercock. The arrow points north.

Next day I came to a city vaguely familiar in its contours, yet its buildings strangely dwarfed and leveled off as if a giant had sliced off its highest towers with a capricious sweep of his hand. I reached the outskirts. I found Newark, undemolished, but humbled by some whim of the advancing Martians. Presently, with an odd feeling of being watched, I caught sight of something crouching in a doorway. I made a step toward it, and it rose up and became a man — a man, armed with a large knife.

STRANGER: Stop — Where did you come from?

PIERSON: I come from — many places. A long time ago from Princeton.

STRANGER: Princeton, huh? That's near Grovers Mill!

PIERSON: Yes.

STRANGER: Grovers Mill — (*Laughs as at a great joke*) There's no food here. This is my country — all this end of town down to the river. There's only food for one — Which way are you going?

PIERSON: I don't know. I guess I'm looking for — for people.

STRANGER: (*nervously*) What was that? Did you hear something just then?

PIERSON: Only a bird — a live bird!

STRANGER: You get to know that birds have shadows these days — Say, we're in the open here. Let's crawl into this doorway and talk.

PIERSON: Have you seen any Martians?

STRANGER: They've gone over to New York. At night the sky is alive with their lights. Just as if people were still living in it. By daylight you can't see them. Five days ago a couple of them carried something big across the flats from the airport. I believe they're learning how to fly.

PIERSON: Fly!

STRANGER: Yeah, fly.

PIERSON: Then it's all over with humanity. Stranger, there's still you and I. Two of us left.

STRANGER: They got themselves in solid; they wrecked the greatest country in the world. Those green stars, they're probably falling somewhere every night. They've only lost one machine. There isn't anything to do. We're done. We're licked.

PIERSON: Where were you? You're in a uniform.

STRANGER: What's left of it. I was in the militia — National Guard. That's good! Wasn't any war any more than there's war between men and ants.

PIERSON: And we're eatable ants. I found that out. What will they do to us?

STRANGER: I've thought it all out. Right now we're caught

as we're wanted. The Martian only has to go a few miles to get a crowd on the run. But they won't keep doing that. They'll begin catching us systematic like — keeping the best and storing us in cages and things. They haven't begun on us yet!

PIERSON: Not begun!

STRANGER: Not begun. All that's happened so far is because we don't have sense enough to keep quiet — bothering them with guns and such stuff and losing our heads and rushing off in crowds. Now instead of our rushing around blind we've got to fix ourselves up according to the way things are now. Cities, nations, civilization, progress —

PIERSON: But if that's so, what is there to live for?

STRANGER: There won't be any more concerts for a million years or so, and no nice little dinners at restaurants. If it's amusement you're after, I guess the game's up.

PIERSON: And what is there left?

STRANGER: Life — that's what! I want to live. And so do you! We're not going to be exterminated. And I don't mean to be caught, either, and tamed, and fattened, and bred like an ox.

PIERSON: What are you going to do?

STRANGER: I'm going on — right under their feet. I gotta plan. We men, as men, are finished. We don't know enough. We gotta learn plenty before we've got a chance. And we've got to live and keep free while we learn. I've thought it all out, see.

PIERSON: Tell me the rest.

STRANGER: Well, it isn't all of us that are made for wild beasts, and that's what it's got to be. That's why I watched you. All these little office workers that used to live in these houses — they'd be no good. They haven't any stuff to 'em. They just used to run off to work. I've seen hundreds of 'em, running wild to catch their commuters' train in the morning for fear that they'd get canned if they didn't; running back at night afraid they won't be in time for dinner. Lives insured and a little invested in case of accidents. And on Sundays, worried about the hereafter. The Martians will be a godsend for those guys. Nice roomy cages, good food, careful breeding, no worries. After a week or so chasing about the fields on empty stomachs they'll come and be glad to be caught.

PIERSON: You've thought it all out, haven't you?

STRANGER: You bet I have! And that isn't all. These Martians will make pets of some of them, train 'em to do tricks. Who knows? Get sentimental over the pet boy who grew up and had to be killed. And some, maybe, they'll train to hunt us.

PIERSON: No, that's impossible. No human being —

STRANGER: Yes, they will. There's men who'll do it gladly. If one of them ever comes after me —

PIERSON: In the meantime, you and I and others like us — where are we to live when the Martians own the earth?

STRANGER: I've got it all figured out. We'll live underground. I've been thinking about the sewers. Under New York are miles and miles of 'em. The main ones are big enough for anybody. Then there's cellars, vaults, underground storerooms, railway tunnels, subways. You begin to see, eh? And we'll get a bunch of strong men together. No weak ones. That rubbish, out.

PIERSON: And you meant me to go?

STRANGER: Well, I gave you a chance, didn't I?

PIERSON: We won't quarrel about that. Go on.

STRANGER: And we've got to make safe places for us to stay in, see, and get all the books we can — science books. That's where men like you come in, see? We'll raid the museums, we'll even spy on the Martians. It may not be so much we have to learn before — just imagine this: Four or five of their own fighting machines suddenly start off — heat-rays right and left and not a Martian in 'em. Not a Martian in 'em! But men — men who have learned the way how. It may even be in our time. Gee! Imagine having one of them lovely things with its heat-ray wide and free! We'd turn it on Martians, we'd turn it on men. We'd bring everybody down to their knees.

PIERSON: That's your plan?

STRANGER: You and me and a few more of us, we'd own the world.

PIERSON: I see.

STRANGER: Say, what's the matter? Where are you going?

PIERSON: Not to *your* world. Good-by, stranger. . . .

PIERSON: After parting with the artilleryman, I came at last to the Holland Tunnel. I entered that silent tube anxious to know the fate of the great city on the other side of the Hudson. Cautiously I came out of the tunnel and made my way up Canal Street.

I reached Fourteenth Street, and there again were black powder and several bodies, and an evil ominous smell from the gratings of the cellars of some of the houses. I wandered up through the Thirties and Forties; I stood alone on Times Square. I caught sight of a lean dog running down Seventh Avenue with a piece of dark brown meat in his jaws, and a pack of starving mongrels at his heels. He made a wide circle around me, as though he feared I might prove a fresh competitor. I walked up Broadway in the direction of that strange power — past silent shop windows, displaying their mute wares to empty sidewalks — past the Capitol Theater, silent, dark — past a shooting-gallery, where a row of empty guns faced an arrested line of wooden ducks. Near Columbus Circle I noticed models of 1939 motor cars in the show rooms facing empty streets. From over the top of the General Motors Building I watched a flock of black birds circling in the sky. I hurried on. Suddenly I caught sight of the hood of a Martian machine, standing somewhere in Central Park, gleaming in the late afternoon sun. An insane idea! I rushed recklessly across Columbus Circle and into the Park. I climbed a small hill above the pond at Sixtieth Street. From there I could see, standing in a silent row along the Mall, nineteen of those great metal Titans, their cowls empty, their steel arms hanging listlessly by their sides. I looked in vain for the monsters that inhabit those machines.

Suddenly, my eyes were attracted to the immense flock of black birds that hovered directly below me. They circled to the ground, and there before my eyes, stark and silent, lay the Martians, with the hungry birds pecking and tearing brown shreds of flesh from their dead bodies. Later when their bodies were examined in laboratories, it was found that they were killed by the putrefactive and disease bacteria against which their systems were unprepared — slain after all man's defenses had failed, by the humblest thing that God in His wisdom put upon this earth.

Before the cylinder fell there was a general persuasion that through all the deep of space no life existed beyond the petty surface of our minute sphere. Now we see farther. Dim and wonderful is the vision I have conjured up in my mind of life spreading slowly from this little seed-bed of the solar system throughout the inanimate vastness of sidereal space. But that is a remote dream. It may be that the destruction of the Martians is only a reprieve. To them, and not to us, is the future ordained perhaps.

Strange it now seems to sit in my peaceful study at Princeton writing down this last chapter of the record begun at a deserted farm in Grovers Mill. Strange to see from my window the university spires dim and blue through an April haze. Strange to watch children playing in the streets. Strange to see young people strolling on the green, where the new spring grass heals the last black scars of a bruised earth. Strange to watch the sight-seers enter the museum where the disassembled parts of a Martian machine are kept on public view. Strange when I recall the time I first saw it, bright and clean-cut, hard and silent, under the dawn of that last great day.

Flight to Malacandra

C. S. LEWIS

WHEN RANSOM came to his senses he seemed to be in bed in a
dark room. He had a pretty severe headache, and this, combined
with a general lassitude, discouraged him at first from attempting to
rise or to take stock of his surroundings. He noticed, drawing his
hand across his forehead, that he was sweating freely, and this directed his attention to the fact that the room (if it was a room) was
remarkably warm. Moving his arms to fling off the bedclothes, he
touched a wall at the right side of the bed: it was not only warm,
but hot. He moved his left hand to and fro in the emptiness on the
other side and noticed that there the air was cooler — apparently
the heat was coming from the wall. He felt his face and found a
bruise over the left eye. This recalled to his mind the struggle with
Weston and Devine, and he instantly concluded that they had put
him in an outhouse behind their furnace. At the same time, he
looked up and recognized the source of the dim light in which,
without noticing it, he had all along been able to see the movements
of his own hands. There was some kind of skylight immediately over
his head — a square of night sky filled with stars. It seemed to
Ransom that he had never looked out on such a frosty night. Pulsing
with brightness as with some unbearable pain or pleasure, clustered
in pathless and countless multitudes, dreamlike in clarity, blazing
in perfect blackness, the stars seized all his attention, troubled him,
excited him, and drew him up to a sitting position. At the same time
they quickened the throb of his headache, and this reminded him
that he had been drugged. He was just formulating to himself the
theory that the stuff they had given him might have some effect on
the pupil and that this would explain the unnatural splendor and
fullness of the sky, when a disturbance of silver light, almost a pale
and miniature sunrise, at one corner of the skylight, drew his eyes
upward again. Some minutes later the orb of the full moon was pushing its way into the field of vision. Ransom sat still and watched. He
had never seen such a moon — so white, so blinding and so large.
"Like a great football just outside the glass," he thought, and then, a
moment later, "No — it's bigger than that." By this time he was quite
certain that something was seriously wrong with his eyes: no moon
could possibly be the size of the thing he was seeing.

From Lewis, C. S., *Out of the Silent Planet.* New York: The Macmillan Company, 1934, and The Bodley Head Limited.

The light of the huge moon — if it was a moon — had by now illuminated his surroundings almost as clearly as if it were day. It was a very strange room. The floor was so small that the bed and a table beside it occupied the whole width of it: the ceiling seemed to be nearly twice as wide and the walls sloped outward as they rose, so that Ransom had the impression of lying at the bottom of a deep and narrow wheelbarrow. This confirmed his belief that his sight was either temporarily or permanently injured. In other respects, however, he was recovering rapidly and even beginning to feel an unnatural lightness of heart and a not disagreeable excitement. The heat was still oppressive, and he stripped off everything but his shirt and trousers before rising to explore. His rising was disastrous and raised graver apprehensions in his mind about the effects of being drugged. Although he had been conscious of no unusual muscular effort, he found himself leaping from the bed with an energy which brought his head into sharp contact with the skylight and flung him down again in a heap on the floor. He found himself on the other side against the wall — the wall that ought to have sloped outward like the side of a wheelbarrow, according to his previous reconnaissance. But it didn't. He felt it and looked at it: it was unmistakably at right angles to the floor. More cautiously this time, he rose again to his feet. He felt an extraordinary lightness of body: it was with difficulty that he kept his feet on the floor. For the first time a suspicion that he might be dead and already in the ghost-life crossed his mind. He was trembling, but a hundred mental habits forbade him to consider this possibility. Instead, he explored his prison. The result was beyond doubt: all the walls looked as if they sloped outward so as to make the room wider at the ceiling than it was at the floor, but each wall as you stood beside it turned out to be perfectly perpendicular — not only to sight but to touch also if one stooped down and examined with one's fingers the angle between it and the floor. The same examination revealed two other curious facts. The room was walled and floored with metal, and was in a state of continuous faint vibration — a silent vibration with a strangely lifelike and unmechanical quality about it — but if the vibration was silent, there was plenty of noise going on — a series of musical raps or percussions at quite irregular intervals which seemed to come from the ceiling. It was as if the metal chamber in which he found himself was being bombarded with small, tinkling missiles. Ransom was by now thoroughly frightened — not with the prosaic fright that a man suffers in a war, but with a heady, bounding kind of fear that was hardly distinguishable from his general excitement: he was poised on a sort of emotional watershed from which, he felt, he might at any moment pass either into delirious terror or into an ecstasy of joy.

He knew now that he was not in a house, but in some moving vessel. It was clearly not a submarine: and the infinitesimal quivering of the metal did not suggest the motion of any wheeled vehicle. A ship then, he supposed, or some kind of airship . . . but there was an oddity in all his sensations for which neither supposition accounted. Puzzled, he sat down again on the bed, and stared at the portentous moon.

An airship, some kind of flying-machine . . . but why did the moon look so big? It was larger than he had thought at first. No moon could really be that size; and he realized now that he had known this from the first but had repressed the knowledge through terror. At the same moment a thought came into his head which stopped his breath — there could be no full moon at all that night. He remembered distinctly that he had walked from Nadderby in a moonless night. Even if the thin crescent of a new moon had escaped his notice, it could not have grown to this in a few hours. It could not have grown to this at all — this megalomaniac disk, far larger than the football he had at first compared it to, larger than a child's hoop, filling almost half the sky. And where was the old "man in the moon" — the familiar face that had looked down on all the generations of men? The thing wasn't the moon at all; and he felt his hair move on his scalp.

At that moment the sound of an opening door made him turn his head. An oblong of dazzling light appeared behind him and instantly vanished as the door closed again, having admitted the bulky form of a naked man whom Ransom recognized as Weston. No reproach, no demand for an explanation, rose to Ransom's lips or even to his mind; not with that monstrous orb above them. The mere presence of a human being, with its offer of at least some companionship, broke down the tension in which his nerves had long been resisting a bottomless dismay. He found, when he spoke, that he was sobbing.

"Weston! Weston!" he gasped. "What is it? It's not the moon, not that size. It can't be, can it?"

"No," replied Weston, "it's the Earth."

Ransom's legs failed him, and he must have sunk back upon his bed, but he only became aware of this many minutes later. At the moment he was unconscious of everything except his fear. He did not even know what he was afraid of: the fear itself possessed his whole mind, a formless, infinite misgiving. He did not lose consciousness, though he greatly wished that he might do so. Any change — death or sleep, or, best of all, a waking which should show all this for a dream — would have been inexpressibly welcome. None

came. Instead, the lifelong self-control of social man, the virtues
which are half hypocrisy or the hypocrisy which is half a virtue,
came back to him and soon he found himself answering Weston in a
voice not shamefully tremulous.

"Do you mean that?" he asked.

"Certainly."

"Then where are we?"

"Standing out from Earth about eighty-five thousand miles."

"You mean we're — in space." Ransom uttered the word with difficulty as a frightened child speaks of ghosts or a frightened man of
cancer.

Weston nodded.

"What for?" said Ransom. "And what on earth have you kid-
naped me for? And how have you done it?"

For a moment Weston seemed disposed to give no answer; then,
as if on a second thought, he sat down on the bed beside Ransom
and spoke as follows:

"I suppose it will save trouble if I deal with these questions at
once, instead of leaving you to pester us with them every hour for
the next month. As to how we do it — I suppose you mean how the
space-ship works — there's no good your asking that. Unless you
were one of the four or five real physicists now living, you couldn't
understand: and if there were any chance of your understanding
you certainly wouldn't be told. If it makes you happy to repeat
words that don't mean anything — which is, in fact, what unscien-
tific people want when they ask for an explanation — you may say
we work by exploiting the less observed properties of solar radiation.
As to why we are here, we are on our way to Malacandra. . . ."

"Do you mean a star called Malacandra?"

"Even you can hardly suppose we are going out of the solar system. Malacandra is much nearer than that: we shall make it in
about twenty-eight days."

"There isn't a planet called Malacandra," objected Ransom.

"I am giving it its real name, not the name invented by terrestrial astronomers," said Weston.

"But surely this is nonsense," said Ransom. "How the deuce
did you find out its real name, as you call it?"

"From the inhabitants."

It took Ransom some time to digest this statement. "Do you
mean to tell me you claim to have been to this star before, or this
planet, or whatever it is?"

"Yes."

"You can't really ask me to believe that," said Ransom. "Damn it all, it's not an everyday affair. Why has no one heard of it? Why has it not been in all the papers?"

"Because we are not perfect idiots," said Weston gruffly.

After a few moments' silence Ransom began again. "Which planet is it in our terminology?" he asked.

"Once and for all," said Weston, "I am not going to tell you. If you know how to find out when we get there, you are welcome to do so: I don't think we have much to fear from your scientific attainments. In the meantime, there is no reason for you to know."

"And you say this place is inhabited?" said Ransom.

Weston gave him a peculiar look and then nodded. The uneasiness which this produced in Ransom rapidly merged in an anger which he had almost lost sight of amidst the conflicting emotions that beset him.

"And what has all this to do with me?" he broke out. "You have assaulted me, drugged me, and are apparently carrying me off as a prisoner in this infernal thing. What have I done to you? What do you say for yourself?"

"I might reply by asking you why you crept into my back yard like a thief. If you had minded your own business you would not be here. As it is, I admit that we have had to infringe your rights. My only defense is that small claims must give way to great. As far as we know, we are doing what has never been done in the history of man, perhaps never in the history of the universe. We have learned how to jump off the speck of matter on which our species began; infinity, and therefore perhaps eternity, is being put into the hands of the human race. You cannot be so small-minded as to think that the rights or the life of an individual or of a million individuals are of the slightest importance in comparison with this."

"I happen to disagree," said Ransom, "and I always have disagreed, even about vivisection. But you haven't answered my question. What do you want me for? What good am I to do you on this — on Malacandra?"

"That I don't know," said Weston. "It was no idea of ours. We are only obeying orders."

"Whose?"

There was another pause. "Come," said Weston at last, "there is really no use in continuing this cross-examination. You keep on asking me questions I can't answer: in some cases because I don't know the answers, in others because you wouldn't understand them. It will make things very much pleasanter during the voyage if you can only resign your mind to your fate and stop bothering yourself and us. It would be easier if your philosophy of life were not so insufferably narrow and individualistic. I had thought no one could fail to be inspired by the role you are being asked to play: that even a worm, if it could understand, would rise to the sacrifice. I mean, of course, the sacrifice of time and liberty, and some little risk. Don't misunderstand me."

"Well," said Ransom, "you hold all the cards, and I must make the best of it. I consider *your* philosophy of life raving lunacy. I suppose all that stuff about infinity and eternity means that you think you are justified in doing anything — absolutely anything — here and now, on the off chance that some creature or other descended from man as we know him may crawl about a few centuries longer in some part of the universe."

"Yes — anything whatever," returned the scientist sternly, "and all educated opinion — for I do not call classics and history and such trash education — is entirely on my side. I am glad you raised the point, and I advise you to remember my answer. In the meantime, if you will follow me into the next room, we will have breakfast. Be careful how you get up: your weight here is hardly appreciable compared with your weight on Earth."

Ransom rose and his captor opened the door. Instantly the room was flooded with a dazzling golden light which completely eclipsed the pale earthlight behind him.

"I will give you darkened glasses in a moment," said Weston as he preceded him into the chamber whence the radiance was pouring. It seemed to Ransom that Weston went up a hill toward the doorway and disappeared suddenly downward when he had passed it. When he followed — which he did with caution — he had the curious impression that he was walking up to the edge of a precipice: the new room beyond the doorway seemed to be built on its side so that its farther wall lay almost in the same plane as the floor of the room he was leaving. When, however, he ventured to put forward his foot, he found that the floor continued flush and as he entered the second room the walls suddenly righted themselves and the rounded ceiling was over his head. Looking back, he perceived that the bedroom in its turn was now heeling over — its roof a wall and one of its walls a roof.

"You will soon get used to it," said Weston, following his gaze. "The ship is roughly spherical, and now that we are outside the gravitational field of the Earth 'down' means — and feels — toward the center of our own little metal world. This, of course, was foreseen and we built her accordingly. The core of the ship is a hollow globe — we keep our stores inside it — and the surface of that globe is the floor we are walking on. The cabins are arranged all round this, their walls supporting an outer globe which from our point of

view is the roof. As the center is always 'down,' the piece of floor
you are standing on always feels flat or horizontal and the wall you
are standing against always seems vertical. On the other hand, the
globe of floor is so small that you can always see over the edge of it
— over what would be the horizon if you were a flea — and then
you see the floors and wall of the next cabin in a different plane. It
is just the same on Earth, of course, only we are not big enough to
see it."

After this explanation he made arrangements in his precise, un-
gracious way for the comfort of his guest or prisoner. Ransom, at
his advice, removed all his clothes and substituted a little metal
girdle hung with enormous weights to reduce, as far as possible, the
unmanageable lightness of his body. He also assumed tinted glasses,
and soon found himself seated opposite Weston at a small table laid
for breakfast. He was both hungry and thirsty and eagerly attacked
the meal which consisted of tinned meat, biscuit, butter and coffee.

But all these actions he had performed mechanically. Stripping,
eating and drinking passed almost unnoticed, and all he ever remembered of his first meal in the space-ship was the tyranny of
heat and light. Both were present in a degree which would have
been intolerable on Earth, but each had a new quality. The light
was paler than any light of comparable intensity that he had ever
seen; it was not pure white but the palest of all imaginable golds,
and it cast shadows as sharp as a floodlight. The heat, utterly free
from moisture, seemed to knead and stroke the skin like a gigantic
masseur: it produced no tendency to drowsiness: rather intense
alacrity. His headache was gone: he felt vigilant, courageous and
magnanimous as he had seldom felt on Earth. Gradually he dared to
raise his eyes to the skylight. Steel shutters were drawn across all
but a chink of the glass, and that chink was covered with blinds of
some heavy and dark material; but still it was too bright to look at.

"I always thought space was dark and cold," he remarked
vaguely.

"Forgotten the sun?" said Weston contemptuously.

Ransom went on eating for some time. Then he began, "If it's like
this in the early morning," and stopped, warned by the expression
on Weston's face. Awe fell upon him: there were no mornings here,
no evenings, and no night — nothing but the changeless noon which
had filled for centuries beyond history so many millions of cubic
miles. He glanced at Weston again, but the latter held up his hand.

"Don't talk," he said. "We have discussed all that is necessary.
The ship does not carry oxygen enough for any unnecessary exertion; not even for talking."

Shortly afterward he rose, without inviting the other to follow him, and left the room by one of the many doors which Ransom had not yet seen opened. . . .

There was an endless night on one side of the ship and an endless day on the other: each was marvelous and he moved from the one to the other at his will, delighted. In the nights, which he could create by turning the handle of a door, he lay for hours in contemplation of the skylight. The Earth's disk was nowhere to be seen; the stars, thick as daisies on an uncut lawn, reigned perpetually with no cloud, no moon, no sunrise to dispute their sway. There were planets of unbelievable majesty, and constellations undreamed of: there were celestial sapphires, rubies, emeralds and pinpricks of burning gold; far out on the left of the picture hung a comet, tiny and remote: and between all and behind all, far more emphatic and palpable than it showed on Earth, the undimensioned, enigmatic blackness. The lights trembled: they seemed to grow brighter as he looked. Stretched naked on his bed, a second Danaë, he found it night by night more difficult to disbelieve in old astrology: almost he felt, wholly he imagined, "sweet influence" pouring or even stabbing into his surrendered body. All was silence but for the irregular tinkling noises. He knew now that these were made by meteorites, small, drifting particles of the world-stuff that smote continually on their hollow drum of steel; and he guessed that at any moment they might meet something large enough to make meteorites of ship and all. But he could not fear. He now felt that Weston had justly called him little-minded in the moment of his first panic. The adventure was too high, its circumstance too solemn, for any emotion save a severe delight. But the days — that is, the hours spent in the sunward hemisphere of their microcosm — were the best of all. Often he rose after only a few hours' sleep to return, drawn by an irresistible attraction, to the regions of light; he could not cease to wonder at the noon which always awaited you however early you went to seek it. There, totally immersed in a bath of pure ethereal color and of unrelenting though unwounding brightness, stretched his full length and with eyes half closed in the strange chariot that bore them, faintly quivering, through depth after depth of tranquillity far above the reach of night, he felt his body and mind daily rubbed and scoured and filled with new vitality. Weston, in one of his brief, reluctant answers, admitted a scientific basis for these sensations: they were receiving, he said, many rays that never penetrated the terrestrial atmosphere.

But Ransom, as time wore on, became aware of another and more spiritual cause for his progressive lightening and exultation of heart. A nightmare, long engendered in the modern mind by the mythology that follows in the wake of science, was falling off him.

He had read of "Space": at the back of his thinking for years had lurked the dismal fancy of the black, cold vacuity, the utter deadness, which was supposed to separate the worlds. He had not known how much it affected him till now — now that the very name "Space" seemed a blasphemous libel for this empyrean ocean of radiance in which they swam. He could not call it "dead"; he felt life pouring into him from it every moment. How indeed should it be otherwise, since out of this ocean the worlds and all their life had come? He had thought it barren: he saw now that it was the womb of worlds, whose blazing and innumerable offspring looked down nightly even upon the earth with so many eyes — and here, with how many more! No: Space was the wrong name. Older thinkers had been wiser when they named it simply the heavens — the heavens which declared the glory — the

> "happy climes that ly
> Where day never shuts his eye
> Up in the broad fields of the sky."

He quoted Milton's words to himself lovingly, at this time and often.

Our Distant Cousins

LORD DUNSANY

I WAS ELECTED a member of the club to which Jorkens belongs. The Billiards Club it is called, though they don't play much billiards there. I went there many days before I met Jorkens again; and heard many tales after lunch, when we sat round the fire; but somehow there seemed something missing in all of them, to one who was waiting for one of Jorkens'. One heard tales of many lands and of many people, some of them strange enough; and yet, just when the story promised to grip one, there was something that was not there. Or perhaps there was too much; too many facts, too impartial a love of truth, that led so many of them to throw everything into their tales, apart from its interests, merely because it was true. I do

Reprinted by the kind permission of the Dowager Lady Dunsany.

not mean that Jorkens' tales were not true, as to some extent his biographer I should be the last to suggest that; it would be unfair to a man from whom I have had so much entertainment. I give the words as they fell from his lips, so far as I can remember them, and leave the reader to judge.

Well, about the fifth time I came in, to my great delight there was Jorkens. He was not very talkative at lunch, nor for some time after; and it was not till he had been awhile in his usual armchair, with his whisky and soda at hand on a little table, that he began to mutter. I, who had made a point of sitting beside him, was one of the few that heard him. "There's a lot of loose talk," he was saying, "goes on in clubs. People say things. They don't mean them. But they say things. A lot of loose talk."

"Yes," I said, "I suppose there is rather. There oughtn't to be."

"Of course there oughtn't," said Jorkens. "Now I'll give you an instance. Only today; before you came in; but only today I heard a man saying to another (they've both gone out now, so never mind who they were), I heard him saying, 'There's no one tells taller tales than Jorkens.' Merely because he hasn't traveled, or, if he has, has kept all the time to roads and paths and railways, merely because he has never been off a good wide path he thinks that things that I may have seen hundreds of times merely weren't there."

"Oh, he can't really have meant it," I said.

"No," said Jorkens, "but he shouldn't have said it. Now, just to prove to you, as I happen to be able to do, that his remark is definitely inaccurate, I can show you a man not a mile from here who tells very much taller stories than I do; and they happen to be perfectly true."

"Oh, I'm sure they are," I said, for Jorkens was distinctly annoyed.

"Care to come and see him?" said Jorkens.

"Well, I'd just as soon hear one of your own stories of things you've seen," I said, "if you'd care to tell me one."

"Not till I've cleared myself," said Jorkens, "of that loose assertion."

"Yes, I'll come," I said.

So we left the club together.

"I'd take a taxi," said Jorkens, "only I happen to have run out of change."

Though Jorkens was once a great traveler, I was not sure what training he was in to walk a mile just then. So I hailed a taxi, Jorkens insisting that he must owe me the money, as it was he who was taking me. We went eastward, and soon arrived at our destination, Jorkens generously placing himself in debt to me for the fare.

It was a small lodging house beyond Charing Cross Road, and we were shown upstairs by a maid to a carpetless room; and there was Jorkens' friend Terner, a man probably still in the thirties, though he obviously smoked too much, and that made him look a bit older; and besides that he had pure-white hair, which gave a queer venerable appearance to a face that seemed somehow unsuited to it.

They greeted each other, and I was introduced.

"He has come to hear your story," said Jorkens.

"You know I never tell it," answered Terner.

"I know," said Jorkens; "not to sneering fools. But he's not one of those. He can tell when a man's speaking the truth."

They looked at each other, but Terner still seemed uncertain, still seemed to cling to the reticence of a man that has often been doubted.

"It's all right," said Jorkens. "I've told him lots of my tales. He's not one of those sneering fools."

"Told him about the Abu Laheeb?" asked Terner suddenly.

"Oh, yes," said Jorkens.

Terner looked at me.

"A very interesting experience," I said.

"Well," said Terner, taking another cigarette in his stained fingers, "I don't mind telling you. Take a chair."

He lit his cigarette and began.

"It was in 1924; when Mars was about its nearest to the earth. I took off from Ketling aërodrome, and was away two months. Where did they think I was? I certainly hadn't enough petrol to fly about in our atmosphere for two months. If I came down, where did I come down? It was their business to find out and to prove it; and, if not, to believe my story."

1924, and Ketling aërodrome. I did remember now. Yes, a man had claimed to have flown to Mars; had been reluctant to say much at first, because of some horror that he had seen, would not give cheery interviews, was too grimly solemn about it, and so encouraged doubts that might otherwise not have been, and was soured by them, and overwhelmed by a rush of them.

"Why, yes, I remember, of course," I said. "You flew to . . ."

"A thousand letters by one post, calling me a liar," said Terner. "So after that I refused to tell my story. They wouldn't have believed it in any case. Mars isn't quite what we think it.

"Well, this is what happened. I'd thought of it ever since I realized that aëroplanes could do it. But about 1920, with Mars coming nearer and nearer, and 1924 the only year that would be possible, I began my calculations. I worked at them steadily for three years;

I have the figures still: I will not ask you to read them, but the whole point of my work was this, that there was only one motive power that could possibly get me to Mars before all my provisions gave out, and that power was the pace of the world. An aëroplane can do over two hundred miles an hour, and mine got up to nearly three hundred by means of the propeller alone; and in addition to that I had a rocket attachment that gradually increased my pace to an enormous extent; but the world, which is ninety-three million miles from the sun, goes right round it in a year; and nothing we know on its surface has any pace like that. My petrol and my rocket were merely to pull clear of the earth's attraction, but my journey was made by the force that is moving you in that chair at this moment at something like a thousand miles a minute. One doesn't lose that pace merely by leaving the earth; it remains with one. But my calculations were to direct it; and I found that the pace of the earth would only carry me to Mars when Mars was a bit ahead of us. Unfortunately Mars is never straight ahead, but a bit out to the right, and I had to calculate at what angle I was to aim my plane away to the right of our orbit, in order that the combined pull of my little plane and my rockets, and the vast pace of the earth, should give me the right direction. It had to be as precise as aiming a rifle, with this slight advantage on my side, to make up for all the forces that grudged my journey, that the target would attract any missile that was going a little too wide.

"But how to get back? That doubled the complexity of my calculations. If the pace of the world sent me forward, so would the pace of Mars. Mars would be ahead of the world when I started. Where would the pace of Mars send me?"

I saw a flash of doubt even on Jorkens' face at that.

"But it was fairly simple," continued Terner. "Our world has the inside berth, a much shorter journey round the sun at ninety-three million miles than Mars at an average of a hundred and thirty-nine million. It consequently soon passes its neighbor, and I found that just as I was to shoot forward from earth to Mars, so, by leaving at the right hour, I could shoot forward from Mars to earth. As I said, these calculations took me three years, and of course my life depended on them.

"There was no difficulty in taking food for two months. Water was more cumbersome; so I took the great risk of carrying water for only a month, and trusting to find it in Mars. After all, we have seen it there. It seemed a certainty, and yet it was an anxiety all the while, and I drank so sparingly that, as it turned out, I had ten full days' supply when I got to Mars. A far more complicated matter was my supply of compressed air in cylinders, my method of releasing it for use, and my utilization of exhaled air to the utmost that it could be utilized."

I was about to ask some questions about those cylinders when Jorkens interrupted. "You know my theory about Jules Verne and the men in the moon?" he said.

"No," I replied.

"So many things he describes have been done since, and have become commonplace," said Jorkens; "Zeppelins, submarines, and one thing and another; and are described so minutely and vividly; that 'tis my theory, I don't know what you think, that he actually experienced these, especially the trip to the moon, and then told them as fiction."

"No, I never heard that theory," I said.

"Why not?" said Jorkens. "Why shouldn't he? There are innumerable ways of recording events. There's history, journalism, ballads, and many more. People don't believe any of them very devoutly. They may disbelieve fiction too, now and then. But look how often you hear it said 'That's Little Dorrit's home, that's where Sam Weller lived, that's Bleak House,' and so on and so on. That shows you they believe fiction more than most things; so why shouldn't he have left his record in that form? But I am interrupting you. I beg your pardon."

"Never mind," said Terner. "Another thing that perplexed me greatly, and gave rise to immense discomfort, was the loss of the pressure of the atmosphere, to which we are accustomed. I shall always regard this as the greatest of all the handicaps that anyone has to face on a journey from earth. Indeed without the most careful and thorough binding with bandages, one's body would be crushed by the pressure within it working outward when the weight of the air was gone. I should have published details of all these things if it hadn't been for that outbreak of disbelief, which would not have occurred if I had a publicity agent."

"Most annoying," said Jorkens.

Terner got up and paced about the room, still smoking as always.

There certainly had been an outbreak of disbelief. It was just one of those things that the public had turned against, like Epstein's Rima, only far more so. Some men are unlucky. It was largely his own fault. It was as he had said; if he had had a good publicity agent, the outbreak would not have occurred. They would have believed him without his troubling to make the journey at all.

He paced up and down, a few long strides, in silence.

"I spent every penny I'd got," he went on, "on the aëroplane and the outfit. I had no dependents. And if my calculations were wrong and I missed the red planet, I shouldn't want the cash. If I found it and got safely back to earth, I imagined it wouldn't be hard to earn all I needed. I was mistaken there. Well, one never knows. Achievement by itself is not enough. The necessary thing is for people to admit your achievement. I had not thought of that. And the bigger the achievement, the less ready people may be to admit it. Lear was recognized much quicker than Keats."

He lit another cigarette, as he did throughout his story as soon as he had finished one.

"Well, the planet came nearer and nearer. It was quite large now every night, distinctly colored. Orange perhaps, rather than red. I used to go out and look at it at night. The awful thought occurred to me more than once that that orange glow might well come from a waste of deserts, yellow sand without a drop of water for me; but I was consoled by the thought of those vast canals that had been seen with our telescopes, for I believed like everyone else that they were canals.

"I had finished all my calculations by then, by the winter of 1923; and Mars, as I said, was coming nearer and nearer. I grew pretty calm about it as the time approached. All my calculations were done, and it seemed to me that any peril that threatened me was all decided months ago, one way or the other. The dangers seemed all behind me; they were in my calculations. If they were right, they would take me through; if they were wrong, I was doomed two or three years ago. The same way with those tawny deserts that I used to think I saw. I gave up worrying about them too. I had decided that the telescope could see better than I could, so that was the end of them. I wouldn't tell anyone I was going; I hate to talk about things I am *going* to do. Apparently one has to on a stunt like that. Anyway I didn't. There was a girl I used to see a good deal of in those days. Amely her name was. I didn't even tell her. It would have soon got out if I had. And there would I have been, the silly hero of an adventure that as yet I was only talking about. I told her I was going in my plane on a long journey. She thought I meant to America. I said I would be away two months; and that puzzled her; but I wouldn't say more.

"Every night I took a look at Mars. He was large and ruddy now, so that everyone noticed him. Just think of the different interests with which they were looking at Mars; admiration of his beauty glowing with that bright color, casual curiosity, apathy, scientists waiting the chance that would not come round again for years, witch doctors making spells, astrologers working out portents, reporters making their articles, and I alone looking at that distant neighbor with lonely thoughts unshared by anyone on our planet. For, as I told you, not even Amely had the very slightest idea.

"Mars was not at his nearest on the night that I started; still over forty million miles away. The reason of this I told you: I had to shoot forward while Mars was ahead of us. He came within thirty-five million in 1924. But I set off before that.

"I started, naturally, from the night side of the earth, as Mars was lying beyond us away from the sun, and this enabled me to aim accurately at my target. It was a far trickier job coming back. When I say I aimed at my target, I aimed of course far in front of it. That will be understood by anyone who has ever done any shooting. Well, I went to Ketling aërodrome on the night in question, where my plane was. There were one or two fellows there that I knew, and of course my rig-out astonished them.

" 'Going to keep warm,' I remembered one of them said.

"Well, I was. Because in addition to my system of bandages to hold me in when I lost the pressure of our atmosphere, I had to wrap up against the absolute cold of Space. I should have that inconceivable cold in my face, while on my back I should need all the clothes I could wear, to protect me from the blaze of the sun; for those clothes would be the only protection there was, when our fifty miles of air were behind me. Sunstroke and frostbite could very easily have overcome me at the same moment. Well, they are very keen at Ketling about nobody going up if he's in the least bit biffed. You know: a bit the better for his dinner. So they started asking me questions with that in view. I wouldn't tell them where I was going. It wasn't till I actually got the plane out that I told two of the mechanics, so as to have my start recorded. One of them merely thought I was making a joke, and laughed, not at me exactly, but in order to show that he appreciated my having a joke with him. He merely thought it was funny in some way that he couldn't see. The other laughed too, but at least he knew what I was talking about. 'How much juice are you taking, sir?' he said.

" 'Fifteen gallons,' I said, which as a matter of fact he knew. It's good for three hundred miles, which gave me plenty to spare if I wanted to cruise a bit over Mars.

" 'Going there and back in three hours, sir?' he said.

"He was quite right. That's as long as you can fly on fifteen gallons.

" 'I'm going there,' I said.

" 'Well, good night, sir,' he answered. I told a third man too.

" 'To Mars are you, sir,' he said. He was annoyed that I should, as he thought, play a joke on him.

"Then we were off. I had a system of sights that gave me a perfect aim all the time that I was in the darkness of earth and within its atmosphere, and could still see Mars and still steer. Before I left our atmosphere I accelerated with my system of rockets, and broke away by a dozen explosions from the pull of our planet. Then I shut off my engines and fired no more rockets, and a most enormous stillness wrapped us about. The sun shone, and Mars and all the stars went out, and there we were perfectly still in that most absolute stillness. Yet I was moving, as you are now, at a thousand miles a minute. The soundlessness was amazing, the discomforts beyond description; the difficulties of eating alone, without being frostbitten, and without being crushed by the awful emptiness of Space, which we are not built to inhabit, were enough to make the most resolute man turn back, except that you can neither turn nor steer without air to turn in.

"I was sure of my aim: it was accurate enough according to my calculations, the last I saw of Mars: I was pretty sure of arriving: but I soon began to doubt my capacity to hold out for a month of it. Days and nights can go by pretty slowly sometimes even on earth, but this was one interminable day.

"The compressed air worked all right: of course I had practiced it on earth. But the machinery for letting out continually the exactly right quantities into a kind of metal helmet, from which I breathed it, was so complicated, that I could never sleep for more than two hours on end, without having to wake and attend to it. For this purpose I had to have an alarm clock quite close to my ear. My discomforts would, I think, be no more interesting than a record of a long and tedious illness. But, to put it briefly, a little after halfway they got the better of me and I was going to give up and die, when suddenly I saw Mars. In the broad glare of the daylight I saw a pale white circle, like the very littlest of moons, nearly ahead of me and a bit to the right. It was this that saved me. I gazed at it and forgot my great discomforts.

"It was no more visible than a small bird's feather, high in the air, in sunlight. But it was Mars unmistakably, and just where it ought to be if I was to reach it. With nothing else to look at through that endless day, I gazed too much at Mars. That brought it no nearer; and I found that if I was to get any comfort from it in my weariness I must look away from it for a bit. That wasn't easy with nothing else to look at, but when I did look away from it for an hour or so, and looked again, I could see a change. I noticed now that it was not entirely lit, being dark on the right hand side, and illuminated about as much as the moon on its eleventh day, three days from full. I looked away again and then looked back at it, and so I passed about two hundred hours of that long weary day. Gradually the canals, as we call them, came in view, gradually the seas. It grew to the size of our moon, and then grew larger, exhibiting a spectacle the like of which no human eye had even seen before. From then on I forgot my discomforts. Now I saw mountains clearly, and presently rivers, and the flashing panorama widened before me, giving up secrets at which our astronomers have guessed for over a century. There came the time when after a spell of sleep I looked at Mars again, and found that it had lost the look of a planet, or any celestial body, and appeared now like a landscape. Soon after that I got the feeling that, though my course was quite unchanged, Mars was no longer ahead of me but underneath. And then I began to feel the pull of the planet. Things rocked in my plane: kegs, tins and such; and began to shift, as far as their lashings would let them. I felt the pull too where I sat. Then I got ready for entering the atmosphere of Mars."

"What did you have to do?" said Jorkens.

"Had to be very careful," said Terner. "Or I'd have burned up like a meteorite. Of course I was overtaking it, not meeting it, so that our two speeds largely neutralized each other; and luckily the atmosphere is only thin at first, like ours, so you don't strike it bang. But the plane took some handling for all that. Once I'd steadied her, flying is much the same there as it is here. Of course I'd turned on my engines as soon as I struck Mars' atmosphere. I came down pretty straight, not wishing to show over too wide an area, so as not to excite too much curiosity amongst whatever might be there. I may say that I expected to find men there, not through any knowledge I had or researches I'd made, but because most people do. I don't mean that I was persuaded by that, but what vaguely persuaded them had vaguely persuaded me. I came down over a country that was considerably covered with forests, though with plenty of clearings for a landing. The spot I chose was a clearing down in a valley, as it gave the best cover for my aëroplane, and I didn't want to show too much. I expected human beings, but thought it just as well to keep out of sight if I could: they're not always as friendly as all that even here. In a little over ten minutes from the time I turned on my engines, I landed in this valley. I had been away from earth a month, just as I'd calculated. It wasn't so very unlike earth when I stepped out. All the trees were different, and of course twigs of these were the first things I had meant to bring back. I actually picked a bunch from five different ones and laid them down in my aëroplane. But the very first thing I did was to replenish my water supply, and to have a good drink, at a stream that I had spotted before I came down, running out of the forest and down that valley. The water was all right. I had had some fear that it might be full of salt, or some wholly unknown chemical; but it was all right. And the next thing I did was to take off those infernal bandages and my breathing helmet, and to have a bath in the stream, the first I had had for a month. I didn't put them on again, but left them in the plane, and dressed decently, as I wanted to show the inhabitants something human. After all, I would be the first one they had seen from here, and I didn't want them to think we were like caterpillars in a cocoon. I took a .450 revolver with me too. Well, you have to do that here sometimes. Then I started off to look for these remote neighbors of ours. I passed wonderful flowers but did not stop to pick one: I was only looking for man. I had seen no sign of buildings as I came down. Yet I had not walked a mile through the wood when I came to open land, and there by the very edge of the trees, quite close to me, I saw what was clearly a building made by some intelligent being: and a very odd building it was.

"It was a long rectangle, barely fifteen feet high, and about ten yards wide. At one end of it four windowless walls and a flat roof shut out all light for about twenty yards, but the rest of it was a stretch of quite fifty yards guarded by roof and walls of open metalwork, a stout mesh of the same material of which the whole building was made.

"And at once I saw that our scientists' dreams were true, for walking in that enclosure so carefully protected by metal, I saw a large party of the human race."

"Human!" I exclaimed.

"Yes," said Terner, "human. Folk like ourselves. And not only that, but, as I had often gathered from books was likely to be the case on account of the smaller planet cooling sooner than ours and so starting life earlier, rather more refined than the best of our people. I never saw anything more graceful; ages had given them a refinement that has not yet come to us. I never saw anything more delicate than their women's beauty. There was a stately simplicity in their walk alone that was lovelier to see than our dances."

Then he strode on, up and down the room, in silence awhile, smoking furiously.

"Oh, it is an accursed planet," he said once, and went on with his rapid smoking. I was going to say something to get him back to his story; but Jorkens saw me and held up his hand. He evidently knew this point of the story, and the strong effect that it had upon Terner. So we left him awhile to his pacing and to his cigarettes.

And after a bit he continued calmly, as though there had been no pause: "When I saw that mesh I got my revolver ready, for it seemed to me a pretty obvious protection against some powerful animal. Otherwise, I thought, why not walk about in the open instead of in that narrow inclosure?

"There were about thirty of them there, dressed simply and gracefully, though their dress was a bit oriental from our point of view. Everything about them was graceful except that dingy-looking flat house. I came up to the mesh and greeted them. I knew that taking my hat off would probably have no meaning to them, but I took it off with a wide sweep and bowed. It was the best I could do, and I hoped that it might convey my feelings. And it did too. They were sympathetic and quick, and every sign that I made to them, except when too utterly clumsy, they understood at once. And when they didn't understand they seemed to laugh at themselves, not me. They were like that. Here was I utterly crude and uncouth, half savage, compared to them; and they treated me with every courtesy that they could get my poor wits to understand. How I'd like to go back with a thousand more of us . . . but it's no good, they won't believe me. Well, I stood there with my hands on the mesh, and found it was good stout metal though much less than half an inch wide: I could easily get my thumb through the round apertures, so that we could see each other quite clearly. Well, I stood there talking to them, or whatever you call it, as well as I could, and remembering all the time that there must be something pretty bad in those forests for all that thick wire to be necessary. I never guessed what.

"I pointed to the sky, in the direction in which they would have seen earth shining at night; and they understood me. Fancy understanding a thing like that just from my uncouth gestures. And they obviously did. But they won't believe me here. And then they tried to tell me all about their world, and of course I understood nothing. And it wasn't just being ignorant of their language that I felt as my greatest handicap: it was my awful lack of every kind of refinement, in comparison with those gracious gentle creatures, that weighed on me the most heavily all the time I was there. One thing I was able to understand from them. Would you like to hear about those canals?"

"Yes, very much," I said.

"Well, they aren't canals at all," he replied. "There was one in sight of where we stood, a huge expanse of water with a straight edge to it, going through flat plains. I pointed and asked them about it. And they all pointed up, and there I saw a little moon of Mars, lit up and shining like ours. Well, that conveyed nothing to me. I knew Mars had two moons, but I saw no connection with canals. So I pointed to the water again, and again they all pointed up. This still conveyed absolutely nothing, so they pointed then to the far end of the great canal out in the plains; and at length after a great while I was able to see that the water was moving, which is what they were trying to explain by signs to me. Then they pointed up to their moon again. And in the end I was able to understand them. That moon passes so close over plains of mud that its attraction drags the mud along after it, and the water pours in behind. Once I had seen it, it seemed simple enough. No one would dig a canal fifty miles wide, and they are at least that. Whereas pulling water along is just the job for a moon."

"But are the canals as wide as that?" I said.

"You'd never see them from earth if they weren't," said Terner. I'd never thought of that.

"There was one girl there that was extraordinarily lovely," said Terner. "But to describe any of them you'd need the language of a lover, and then turn that into poetry. No one will believe me. Not a soul will believe me. I talked to her, though of course my words meant nothing; I trusted so much to her bright intelligence that I almost expected her to understand every word; and so she often did. Strange bright birds flew often over us going to and from the forest, and she told me the names of them in the queer Martial language. Mpah and Nto are two that I can remember, as far as I can spell it; and then there was Ingu, bright orange and black, with a long tail like our magpie. She was trying to tell me something about Ingu who was just then flying over us, squawking, away from the trees; when suddenly she pointed. I looked, and sure enough something was coming out of the forest."

For a while he puffed rapidly in silence.

"I can't describe it to you. We have nothing like it here. At any rate not on land. An octopus has some slight resemblance to it in its obese body and thin long legs, though this had only two, and two long thin arms. But the head and the huge mouth were like nothing one knows. I have never seen anything so horrible. It came straight to the wire netting. I slipped away at once before it saw me, as that lovely girl was warning me to do. I had no idea that the thick wire had not been woven as a protection against this very beast. I hid amongst some sort of flowering scrub. I can smell the scent of it to this day; a sweet aroma unlike any on earth. I had no idea that they were not perfectly safe from it. And then it came straight toward them, and up to the wire. I saw it close, all nude and flabby, except for those wiry limbs. It lifted a lid in the roof before I knew what it was doing, and put in it a long horrible arm. It groped about with extraordinary rapidity, and seized a girl and drew her up through the lid. I was on the far side of the wire from it and couldn't shoot. It wrung her neck in a moment and threw her down, and slipped in that arm again. I ran out from my covert, but before I got near, it had caught a young man and drawn him up, and was wringing his neck as I came round the corner. They had made little effort to avoid that gruesome hand, just dodging as it swept by them; though when it singled one out there was little chance to dodge, as they seemed to know. And they were all standing together now in the corner as I came by them, with a dignified resignation in their faces."

"Couldn't they have done *anything?*" I asked. For the idea of a branch of the human race quite helpless before such a horror was too new for me to accept it. But he had seen it, and understood.

"It was nothing more than a chicken-run," he said. "What could they do? They belonged to this beast."

"Belonged to it!" I exclaimed.

"You see," said Jorkens, "you don't understand. Man isn't top dog there."

"What!" I gasped.

"No," said Terner, "that's it."

"Another race, you see," said Jorkens.

"Yes," said Terner. "It's an older planet, you know. And somehow in all that time it's got ahead of them."

"What did you do?" I asked.

"Ran up to the beast," he answered. "I somehow thought he wouldn't be afraid of a man, from the way he treated them, so I didn't trouble to stalk him, but just ran after him as he was moving off and swinging those two young bodies by their ankles. Then he turned round on me and reached out an arm and I let him have one from the .450. He spun around and dropped the bodies and stumbled away, waving his arms above him and bleating out of his great mouth. He was evidently not accustomed to being hurt. He went bleating away and I went after him and gave him two or three more, and left him dead or dying. I didn't care which.

"At the sound of my shots the whole wood had awoken. Birds soared up piping and whistling, and animals I had not seen began to hoot in the shadows. And amongst the general clamor I thought I detected some sounds that might have come from mouths like that of the beast I had killed. It was clearly time to go.

"I turned back to the cage, and there they were all gazing at the dead creature in silence and curiosity. I went up to them but they continued to gaze at it. None of them spoke to me. I saw then that I had done the wrong thing. It seemed that one did not kill these beasts. Only the girl I had spoken with about the birds turned to me, and she pointed swiftly up to the sky, toward earth. The clamor was increasing in the forest. She was right; it was time to go. I said farewell to her. I wonder what my eyes told her. I said farewell more sadly than I have ever said it before. I nearly stayed.

If it hadn't been for what I had to tell our own people, I would have stayed, and shared out my two dozen cartridges amongst those hideous beasts; but I thought I owed it to earth to bring home the news. And in the end they never believed me!

"I heaved a rock at that horrible body as I went by, not liking to spare another cartridge, on account of the clamor in the forest. But those poor people in the chicken-run didn't approve. One could see that in a moment. To be eaten by that beast was their fate, and no interference with that seemed right to them.

"I got back to my plane as fast as I could. Nothing had found it. It was still safe in the valley. Perhaps I felt a moment of regret when I found my retreat to earth was not cut off. It would have made things so simple. And yet it would never have done. Well, there was my plane, and I jumped in and began to wrap on those bindings, without which it is impossible to keep together in the bleak emptiness between our atmosphere and theirs. Something peered out of the wood at me as it heard me get into the plane. It looked to me like some sort of a fox, and I went on with my wrappings. All the noises in the wood seemed coming nearer. Then all of a sudden I thought: what if it was a dog, and not a fox at all! Whose side would a dog be on in Mars? I could hardly imagine a dog on anyone's side but man's. But I had seen such horrible things, that I wondered. What if it belonged to those beasts! As man did, for that matter. It would go and tell them I was here. I hurried with my wrappings. But the brushwood was being trodden quite close. Then I saw branches waving. And a lot of them came pouring out of the forest, hurrying toward their chicken-run. They were not a hundred yards away, and they all saw me. Then the filthy things turned to their left and came toward me. I gave them one shot, and started my engines. One seemed hit, but I couldn't hear its noises on account of the sound of my engines. They seemed puzzled by the shot for a moment, then came toward me, with a queer look on their hideous faces, hands stretched out. I only just cleared them. With their great height they could almost have gripped my plane as I went over them. And away I went with all my bindings flapping. Of course I couldn't face Space like that. And I couldn't dress myself and steer at the same time, with such steering as I had to do. One degree out and I should have missed earth. I hadn't much petrol either. It is petrol that I had economized on. Obviously. As it was of no use to me except for about one millionth part of my journey at each end. You can't churn up Space. Well, I went about twenty miles, and lit down in the wide plain through which that moon was dragging its fifty-mile groove of mud, for us to look at through telescopes. And I had to fly up and down a good deal before I was sure of a landing in which I wouldn't be bogged; as happened to me later. Well, I lit down and got on with my dressing. And all the while I had the idea that Mars knew a lot more about my presence there than I had hoped for. Birds seemed ill at ease, and there seemed too much scurrying. At any rate I was in the open and could see what was coming. Yet I should have liked to have gone a hundred miles or so further, except for the uneasy feeling it gave me to be left without any reserve of petrol beyond what I knew I should want. So I stayed there and saved up my petrol; and it was lucky I did. Well, I got my bandages on, but I still had my observations to make from the sun in order to find my way home, when I saw some of those foul creatures a long way off. Whether they were coming after me or not I never knew, but they hurried my calculations, and did not encourage me to go gathering Martial rocks and flora, which of course would have made all this vehement disbelief impossible. And the samples from five different trees that I had got in the wood were of course all blown away when I went off in a hurry the first time."

"And you brought back nothing at all?" I asked. For there was the ring of truth in his story and I was hoping it could be proved.

"Nothing except an old matchbox broken in a very peculiar way. And, if you can't see what broke it, that will prove nothing to you either. I'll show it to you later."

"What broke it?" I asked.

"When we come to it," he said, "you shall tell me. I'll show it you and you shall see for yourself."

Jorkens nodded his head.

"Well, I didn't go gathering flowers or anything else, except for those twigs that I lost. I ought to have, I know. And perhaps I was in too much of a hurry to get away when I saw that second lot in the distance. But I had seen the faces of the beasts, and they were all I was thinking of. I had a large camera, and took a few shots at the landscape, which ought to have been conclusive. But I didn't get it home. I'll tell you what happened to that afterward.

"Well, all that incredulity here was the last thing that I thought of; and the mounds of those loathsome beasts were filling all my imagination. I hurried my calculations and was off, homeward towards the sun. I saw several more of those chicken-runs as I went; but little else besides forest, and plains of mud. I might have seen more if the sun had not been in my eyes. Very soon Mars turned a lovely cobalt blue, and the beauty of it made me even sadder.

"Then began again that long weary day, with sun and plane apparently motionless. Engines shut off, no sound, no movement, no weather; and the weeks dragging by with no sign that time was passing at all. It is an awful place; time seems dead there.

"Again I began to despair, nearly to death; when suddenly I saw ahead of me, like a swan's feather all alone in Space, the familiar curved shape of a world, a quarter lit by the sun. There is no mistaking a planet. And yet, rejoiced as I was to be nearing home, one thing strangely perplexed me: I seemed to be ten days ahead of my time. What amazing luck, I thought, that part of my calculations must have been wrong, and yet I had not missed earth.

"I had not seen it as soon as I had seen Mars, on account of its being so near to the line of the sun. Consequently it was large when I did see it. As it grew larger and larger, I tried to work out what continent I was approaching, not that it greatly mattered, as I had petrol enough to make a good landing unless I was very unlucky. Though it couldn't be where I had expected to land, as I was so much ahead of my time. Well, I couldn't make out anything, as most of the orb was in darkness. And when I got into that darkness it was a blessed thing, after the glare of the sun in that endless lonely day. For there is no light there really, only glare. In that awful loneliness there is nowhere for light to fall; it just goes by you in a glare. I got into the darkness at last and switched on my engines, and flew till I came to the very first edge of twilight that gave light enough for me to land, for I was tired of staring at the sun. And that was how I came to make a bad landing, with my wheels deep down in a marsh. It was not that that whitened my hair. I felt my scalp go cold, and my hair whitened; but it was not being stuck in a marsh that whitened it. It was the knowledge I had, the very moment I landed, that I was on the wrong planet. I should have seen it before, coming down, although in the dark: the whole thing was much too small. But I saw it now: I was on the wrong planet and didn't even know which. The awful concentrated loneliness of the accident at first froze my thoughts. And, when I did begin to think, all was bewilderment. What lay inside of Mars? Only earth, Venus and Mercury. The size pointed at Mercury. But I was ahead of my time, not behind it. Or was my chronometer all wrong? But the sun had appeared no larger, five minutes ago than it appears from earth. In fact rather smaller. Perhaps, I thought, it was Venus in spite of this; though it was too small even for Venus. And the asteroids were behind me, outside Mars.

"What I did not know then was how Eros (and perhaps others too), on account of the tilt of the planes of some of the asteroids, comes at certain times within fourteen million miles of us. So that though his path round the sun lies outside Mars, whose nearest is thirty-five million, Eros at certain times is earth's nearest neighbor. Of this I knew nothing; and yet, when I began to think reasonably, the facts at last spoke for themselves: I was on a strayed or an unknown asteroid. It should be easier to examine such a body when one is actually on it, with its continents all spread round one, than when it appears no more than a small pin's head in a telescope. But the calm, the safety, above all that feeling of Home, which lie about the astronomer, are aids to accurate thought which cannot be estimated.

"I saw that I had blundered when leaving Mars, making some wrong calculation in my hurry, and was very lucky to have got anywhere. Who can say when he thinks of all the things he might have become, who can say as I can that I nearly became a comet?"

"Very true," said Jorkens.

Terner said this with the utmost seriousness. The danger had evidently been near to him.

"When I realized where I must be," continued Terner, "I set to work to pull my plane out of the marsh, standing up to my knees in it. It was easier than I thought. And, when I had got it up I lifted it over my head and carried it about nine miles on to good dry land."

"But an aëroplane?" I said. "What does it weigh?"

"Over a ton," said Terner.

"And you carried it?"

"With one hand," he said. "The pull of those asteroids is a weak and puny thing to anyone accustomed to earth. I felt pretty strong on Mars, but that's nothing to what one could do here, in Eros, or whichever it was.

"I got out at the edge of a forest of minute scrub oak, the size of the ones that are dwarfed by the Japanese. I looked out for any disgusting beasts such as those foul things on Mars, but saw nothing of any sort. A few small moths, as I thought them, flew by me out of the trees; though, looking back on it, I think they were birds. Well, then I settled down to work out my new calculations. I was so near earth now, that I might get it if I could pull away from the asteroid, and if only I was close in my guess (and it could be no more) at the pace that the asteroid was doing. More than a guess I could not make, for I did not even know on what little planet I was, and guesses are bad things for calculations. But you must use them when you've got nothing else. I knew at least where the path of these asteroids lay, so I knew how far they had to go, but the time that they took to do it I could only guess from the time that I knew their neighbors took. Had I been further from earth these guesses would have ruined my calculations, and I should never have found my way home.

"Well, I sat there undisturbed by anything except my own rapid breathing, and worked out those calculations as near as I could. I had to breathe three or four times as fast as one does on earth, for there didn't seem as much air as there is here. And of course there wouldn't be in a little place like Eros. What troubled me far more than the breathing was the thought that I had only my engines to pull me clear of the planet, having used the last of my rockets in leaving Mars, and never guessing I should need them again. Imagine a passenger from Southampton to New York being suddenly landed at an island in the Atlantic. He would be far less surprised than I was at landing here, and I was not prepared for it. The pull of Eros, or whatever small world it was, was not much to get away from; but the amount of atmosphere I should have in which to pull away from it was bound to be diminutive also, like the planet round which it was wrapped. I knew I could get up enough speed to pull clear of Eros, if only I had long enough to do it, if only the air went far enough. I knew roughly how far it went, as I had felt it in the wings of my plane on the way down. But would it go far enough? That was the thought that was troubling me as I worked at my figures, and breathed as men breathe in high fevers. I wouldn't use my compressed air while I had air of any kind to breathe outside. For the hours that I could live before I reached earth were numbered by my supply of compressed air. Well, I made my plans, and arranged my aim at the earth, in leisure, such as I had not had on Mars, while the little planet spun toward the sun, and its day was dawning where I had landed in twilight. Then I had time to look round at the oak forest, whose billowy tops were rolling away below me. Take a look now at this matchbox. Handle it gently. Now what would you say made that hole in it?"

I took from his hand a Bryant and May's matchbox, considerably shattered; shattered from the inside; leaving a hole large enough for a mouse to run through.

"It looks as if something had gone through it pretty hard," I said.

"Not through it," he answered. "There's only a hole on one side."

"Well, into it," I said.

"Nor into it. Look again," said Terner.

Sure enough it was all burst outward. But what had done it was more than I could see. And so I told Terner.

Then he took it over to the mantelpiece, where he had two little cottages made of china, and put it between the two, and put a little thatch over the matchbox, that he had made to fit it. The little cottages on each side of it were just about the same size.

"Now what do you make of it?" he asked.

I didn't know, and I had told him so, but I had to say something.
"It looks as if an elephant had broken out of a cottage," I said.

Terner looked round at Jorkens, who was nodding an approving
head, almost benevolent except for a certain slyness.

I didn't understand this vehement exchange of glances.

"What?" I said.

"The very thing," said Terner.

"An elephant?" I said.

"There were herds of them in the oak forest," said Terner. "I was
stooping down to pick a branch of a tree to bring back, when I suddenly saw them in the dawn. They stampeded and I caught one, a
magnificent tusker, and none of them bigger than mice. This I knew
must be absolute proof. I threw away the branch; after all, they
were only small oak leaves; and I put the elephant into that matchbox and put an elastic band round it to keep it shut. The matchbox
I threw into a haversack that I wore over my bandages.

"Well, I might have collected lots more things; but, as I said,
I had absolute proof, and I had hanging over me all the while, and
oppressing me with its weight, that feeling that I was on the wrong
planet. It is a feeling that no one who experiences it can shake off
for a single moment. You, Jorkens, you have traveled a good deal
too; you've been in deserts and queer places."

"Yes, the papyrus marshes," muttered Jorkens.

"But," continued Terner, "not even there, nor far out with the
Sahara all round you, can you have had so irresistibly, so unremit-
tingly, that feeling I spoke of. It is no mere homesickness, it is an al-
ways-present overwhelming knowledge that you are in the wrong
place, so strong that it amounts to a menacing warning that your
very spirit repeats to you with every beat of the pulse. It is a thing I
cannot explain to anyone who has not been lost outside earth, an
emotion I can share with no one."

"Very natural," said Jorkens.

"Well, so I got everything ready," Terner went on, "not only for
myself but for the little elephant. I had a tin into which I meant to
drop him before we left the atmosphere of Eros, and I had found a
way of renewing the air in it from my own breathing supply often
enough to keep the little beast alive. I had a handful of green stuff,
branches of oak trees, just as one does with a caterpillar. And water
and all for him. Then I threw over everything that I could do without, in order to lighten the plane for the dash away from Eros. My
revolver and cartridges I threw into the marsh, and that is where
my camera went too. Then I started off and flew back into night, to
the one part of Eros from which I could just see earth, hanging low

above her little neighbor's horizon. It shone in the night of Eros like a small moon, like a cricket ball of pale turquoise set in silver. I aimed exactly, with all the allowances that I had calculated, and shot homeward flying low where the air of Eros was densest. At that low level I merely got my speed. Then came the crucial moment when I tilted upward to my aim. Would the air be heavy enough for my wings to work on? It was: I was heading in exactly the right direction, just as I got clear of night and earth paled away. Now would the speed I had last? I couldn't make much more in that thin air. I wondered if someone from earth would ever find my bones, if Eros pulled me back, and my plane beside them. But I did not forget my elephant, and reached for the matchbox to drop it into the tin; when I found what I've shown you."

"Gone?" I said.

"Charged out, as an elephant would," said Terner. "He must have gone before I left Eros. You see for yourself, now that you get the proper proportions, that that matchbox would be to him no more than a hut of laths to one of our own elephants. And he had magnificent tusks. You wouldn't try to shut up an elephant here in a hut of the very thinnest boards. But I never thought of that. You saw it at once. But then I had put those cottages just beside it so as to give you the right scale. Well, I didn't grudge him his liberty at the time. I had no idea of the bitter incredulity that I should have to face. I was thinking more of the tug-of-war on which my life depended, the speed of my plane against the pull of Eros.

"And all of a sudden we did it. There was a slight rocking of all my kegs and tins as Eros let go. Then the long day started once more. I spent it mostly thinking over all the things that I was to tell our learned societies about Mars, and that asteroid which I believe to have been Eros. But they were too busy with their learning to look at a new truth. Their ears were turned to the past; they were deaf to the present. Well, well." And he smoked in silence.

"Your aim was all right," said Jorkens.

"Good enough," said Terner. "Of course the pull of the earth helped me. I suddenly saw it shining in the day, and I didn't seem much out. Oh, what a feeling it is to be coming home. Earth pale at first, then slowly turning to silver; and growing larger and larger. Then it takes a faint touch of gold, an enormous pale-gold crescent in the sky; to the mere eye a sight of the utmost beauty, but saying something more to the whole being, which the understanding fails to grip. Perhaps one does take it in after all, but if one does one can never pass it on, never tell a soul of all that golden beauty. Words cannot do it. Music might, but I can't play. I'd like to make a tune, you know, about earth calling one home with all that changing light; only it would be so damned unpopular, because it is nothing like what they experience every day.

"Well, I hit it. With the help of that great pull that earth flings out so far, I got home again. The Atlantic was the only thing I was afraid of, and I missed that by a good deal. I came down in the Sahara, which might have been little better than the Atlantic. But I got out and walked about, and hadn't been looking round for five minutes when I came on a copper coin the size of a sixpence, and on it the head of Constantine. I had recognized the Sahara at once, but I knew then that I was in the north of it, where the old Roman Empire had been, and knew I had petrol enough to get to the towns. I started off again northward, and flew till I saw some Arabs with a flock of sheep or goats: you can't tell which till you are quite close. I landed near them and said I had come from England. I had no vulgar wish to astonish, as the bare truth would have done, so I said I had flown from England. And I saw that they did not believe me. I had a foretaste then of the world's incredulity.

"Well, I got home, and I told my tale. The Press weren't hostile at first. They interviewed me. But they wanted cheery interviews. They wanted a photograph of me waving my handkerchief up toward Mars, to friends I had left there. But how could I be cheery after seeing what I had seen? My blood grows colder even now when I think of it. And I think of it always. How could I wave my handkerchief toward those poor people, when I knew that one by one they were being eaten by a beast more foul than our imaginations can picture? I would not even smile when they photographed me. I insisted on deleting little jokes from the interviews. I became irritated. Morose, they said. Well, I was. And after that they turned against me. Bitterest of all, Amely would not believe me. When I think what we were to each other! She might have."

"In common politeness," said Jorkens.

"Oh, she was polite enough," said Terner. "I asked her straight out if she believed me; and she said, 'I believe you absolutely.'"

"Well, there you are," said Jorkens cheerfully. "Of course she believes you."

"No, no," said Terner, smoking harder than ever. "No, she didn't. When I told her about that lovely girl in Mars, she never asked me a single question. That wasn't like Amely. Never a word about her."

For a long time then he went up and down that room smoking with rapid puffs. For so long he was silent and quite unobservant of us that Jorkens caught my eye, and we left him alone and walked away from the house.

◇◇◇◇◇◇◇◇◇◇◇◇◇◇◇◇◇◇◇◇◇◇◇◇◇◇◇◇◇◇◇◇◇◇

The *Nautilus* Reaches the Pole

JULES VERNE

THE *Nautilus* was steadily pursuing its southerly course, following the fiftieth meridian with considerable speed. Did Captain Nemo wish to reach the pole? I did not think so, for every attempt to reach that point had hitherto failed. Again the season was far advanced, for in the antarctic regions, the 13th of March corresponds with the 13th of September of northern regions, as the beginning of the equinoctial season. On the 14th of March I saw floating ice at latitude 55°, merely pale bits of debris from twenty to twenty-five feet long, forming banks over which the sea curled. The *Nautilus* remained on the surface of the ocean. Ned Land, who had fished in the Arctic seas, was familiar with their icebergs; but Conseil and I were admiring them for the first time. In the atmosphere toward the southern horizon stretched a white dazzling band. English whalers have given it the name of "ice blink." However thick the clouds may be, it is always visible, and announces the presence of an ice pack or bank. As we expected, larger blocks soon appeared, whose brilliancy changed with the caprices of the fog. Some of these masses showed green veins, as if long undulating lines had been traced with sulphate of copper; others resembled enormous amethysts with the light shining through them. Some reflected the light of day upon a thousand crystal facets. Others shaded with vivid calcareous reflections resembled a perfect town of marble. The more we neared the south, the more these floating islands increased both in number and importance.

At the sixtieth degree of latitude, every pass had disappeared. But seeking carefully, Captain Nemo soon found a narrow opening, through which he boldly slipped, knowing, however, that it would close behind him. Thus, guided by this clever hand, the *Nautilus* passed through all the ice with a precision which quite charmed Conseil: icebergs or mountains, ice fields or smooth plains, seeming to have no limits, drift ice or floating ice packs, or plains broken up,

From *Twenty Thousand Leagues Under the Sea.*

called *palchs* when they are circular, and streams when they are
made up of long strips. The temperature was very low; the thermometer exposed to the air marked two or three degrees below
zero, but we were warmly clad with fur, at the expense of the sea
bear and seal. The interior of the *Nautilus,* warmed regularly by its
electric apparatus, defied the most intense cold. Besides, it would
only have been necessary to go some yards beneath the waves to
find a more bearable temperature. Two months earlier we should
have had perpetual daylight in these latitudes; but already we had
three or four hours night, and by and by there would be six months
of darkness in these circumpolar regions. On the 15th of March we
were in the latitude of New Shetland and South Orkney. The Captain told me that formerly numerous tribes of seals inhabited them;
but that English and American whalers, in their rage for destruction,
massacred both old and young; thus where there was once life and
animation, they had left silence and death.

About eight o'clock on the morning of the 16th of March, the
Nautilus, following the fifty-fifth meridian, cut the Antarctic polar
circle. Ice surrounded us on all sides, and closed the horizon. But
Captain Nemo went from one opening to another, still going higher.
I cannot express my astonishment at the beauties of these new regions. The ice took most surprising forms. Here the grouping
formed an oriental town, with innumerable mosques and minarets;
there a fallen city thrown to the earth, as it were, by some convulsion of nature. The whole aspect was constantly changed by the oblique rays of the sun, or lost in the grayish fog amidst hurricanes of
snow. Detonations and falls were heard on all sides, great over-
throws of icebergs, which altered the whole landscape like a dio-
rama.

When the *Nautilus* was immersed at the moment the icebergs lost
their equilibrium, the sound was propagated under the water with a
frightening intensity. And the falling of the masses of ice created
dreadful eddies even in the profound ocean depths. Then the *Nautilus* rolled and pitched like a vessel abandoned to the fury of the
elements. Often, seeing no exit, I thought we were definitely prisoners; but instinct guiding him at the slightest indication, Captain
Nemo would discover a new pass. He was never mistaken when he
saw the thin threads of bluish water trickling along the ice fields;
and I had no doubt that he had already ventured into the midst of
these Antarctic seas before. On the 16th of March, however, the ice
fields absolutely blocked our path. It was not the ice shelf itself, as
yet, but vast fields cemented by the cold. But this obstacle could not
stop Captain Nemo; he hurled himself against it with frightful violence. The *Nautilus* entered the brittle mass like a wedge, and split

it with frightful cracklings. It was the battering ram of the ancients hurled by infinite strength. The ice, thrown high in the air, fell like hail around us. By its own power of impulsion our apparatus made a canal for itself; sometimes carried away by its own impetus it lodged on the ice field, crushing it with its weight; and sometimes buried beneath it, dividing it by a simple pitching movement, producing large rents in it. Violent gales assailed us at this time, accompanied by thick fogs, through which, from one end of the platform to the other, we could see nothing. The wind blew sharply from all points of the compass, and the snow lay in such hard heaps that we had to break it with blows of a pickax. The temperature was steady at five degrees below zero; every outward part of the *Nautilus* was covered with ice. A rigged vessel could never have worked its way there, for all the rigging would have been entangled in the blocked-up gorges. A vessel without sails, with electricity for its motive power, and wanting no coal, could alone brave such high latitudes. At length, on the 18th of March, after many futile assaults, the *Nautilus* was positively blocked. It was no longer either streams, packs, or ice fields, but an interminable and immovable barrier, formed by mountains soldered together.

"An ice shelf!" said the Canadian to me.

I knew that to Ned Land, as well as to all other navigators who had preceded us, this was an inevitable obstacle. The sun appearing for an instant at noon, Captain Nemo took an observation as near as possible, which gave our situation at 51° 30′ longitude and 67° 39′ of south latitude. We had advanced one degree more in this Antarctic region. Of the liquid surface of the sea there was no longer a glimpse. Under the spur of the *Nautilus* lay stretched a vast plain, studded with confused blocks. Here and there sharp points, and slender needles rising to a height of 200 feet; further on, a steep shore, hewn as it were with an ax, and clothed with grayish tints; huge mirrors reflecting a few rays of sunshine, half drowned in the fog. And over this desolate face of Nature a stern silence reigned, scarcely broken by the flapping of wings of petrels and puffins. Everything was frozen — even the noise. The *Nautilus* was then obliged to stop in its adventurous course amid these fields of ice. In spite of our efforts, in spite of the powerful means employed to break up the ice, the *Nautilus* remained immovable.

"Sir," Ned Land said to me that day, "your captain will not go further."

"What do you mean?"

"Even a clever man must stop here."

"Why, Ned?"

"Because one cannot leap over an ice shelf. Your captain is powerful; but, confound it! he is not more powerful than Nature, and here is where she has put her boundary; here we stop, willing or not."

"To be sure, Ned Land, and yet I would like to know what is behind this ice shelf. A wall is what irritates me most."

"Master is right," said Conseil. "Walls were invented to set the teeth of savants on edge. They simply refuse to have walls at all."

"Good," put in the Canadian. "We know well enough what we would find behind this ice shelf."

"What's that?" I demanded.

"Ice and still more ice."

"You are certain of that, Ned," I replied, "but I am not. That's why I want to go and see."

"Very well, professor, give up that idea. You have arrived at the ice shelf — even that is an accomplishment — and you will not go farther, nor will Captain Nemo or his *Nautilus*. And whether he wants to or not, we'll have to go back toward the North, that is to say, toward the lands of decent people."

I had to admit that Ned Land was right, and that, as long as ships were not made to sail on ice fields, they would be forced to stop before the icecap.

Generally, when we can proceed no further, we have return still open to us; but here return was as impossible as advance, for every pass had closed behind us; and for the few moments when we were stationary, we were likely to be entirely blocked. This did, indeed, happen about two o'clock in the afternoon, the fresh ice forming around the ship's sides with astonishing rapidity. I was obliged to admit that Captain Nemo was more than imprudent. I was on the platform at that moment. The Captain had been observing our situation for some time, when he said to me: "Well, sir, what do you think of this?"

"I think that we are caught, Captain."

"So, M. Aronnax, you really think that the *Nautilus* cannot disengage itself?"

"That it will be hard, Captain; for the season is already too far advanced for you to count on the breaking up of the ice."

"Ah! sir," said Captain Nemo, in an ironical tone, "you will always be the same. You see nothing but difficulties and obstacles. I affirm that not only can the *Nautilus* disengage itself, but also that it can go further still."

"Further to the south?" I asked, looking at the Captain.

"Yes, sir; it shall go to the pole."

"To the pole!" I exclaimed, unable to repress a gesture of incredulity.

"Yes," replied the Captain, coldly, "to the Antarctic pole — to that unknown point from whence springs every meridian of the globe. *You* know whether I can do what I please with the *Nautilus!*"

Yes, I knew that. I knew that this man was bold even to rashness. But to conquer those obstacles which bristled round the south pole, rendering it more inaccessible than the north, which had not yet been reached by the boldest navigators — was it not a mad enterprise, one which only a maniac would have conceived? It then came into my head to ask Captain Nemo if he had ever discovered that pole which had never yet been trodden by a human creature.

"No, sir," he replied; "but we will discover it together. Where others have failed, *I* will not fail. I have never yet led my *Nautilus* so far into southern seas; but, I repeat, it shall go further yet."

"I can well believe you, Captain," said I, in a slightly ironical tone. "I believe you! Let us go ahead! There are no obstacles for us! Let us smash this ice sheet! Let us blow it up; and if it resists, let us give the *Nautilus* wings to fly over it!"

"Over it, sir!" said Captain Nemo, quietly; "no, not *over* it, but *under* it!"

"Under it!" I exclaimed, a sudden idea of the Captain's projects flashing upon my mind. I understood; the wonderful qualities of the *Nautilus* were going to serve us in this superhuman enterprise.

"I see we are beginning to understand one another, sir," said the Captain, half smiling. "You begin to see the possibility — I should say the success — of this attempt. What is impossible for an ordinary vessel, is easy to the *Nautilus*. If a continent lies before the pole, it must stop before the continent; but if, on the contrary, the pole is washed by open sea, it will go even to the pole."

"Certainly," said I, carried away by the Captain's reasoning; "if the surface of the sea is solidified by the ice, the lower depths are free by the providential law which has placed the maximum of density of the waters of the ocean one degree higher than freezing point; and, if I am not mistaken, the portion of this ice sheet which is above the water, is as four to one to that which is below."

"Very nearly, sir; for each foot of iceberg above the sea there are three below it. If these ice mountains are not more than 300 feet above the surface, they are not more than 900 beneath. And what are 900 feet to the *Nautilus?*"

"Nothing, sir."

"It could even seek at greater depths that uniform temperature of sea water, and there brave with impunity the thirty or forty degrees of surface cold."

"Just so, sir — just so," I replied, more and more excited.

"The only difficulty," continued Captain Nemo, "is that of remaining several days without renewing our provision of air."

"Is that all? The *Nautilus* has vast reservoirs; we can fill them, and they will supply us with all the oxygen we want."

"Well thought of, M. Aronnax," replied the Captain, smiling. "But not wishing you to accuse me of rashness, I will first give you all my objections."

"Have you any more to make?"

"Only one. It is possible, if the sea exists at the south pole, that it may be covered; and, consequently, we shall be unable to come to the surface."

"Good, sir! but do you forget that the *Nautilus* is armed with a powerful spur? Could we not send it diagonally against these fields of ice, which would open at the shock?"

"Ah! sir, you are full of ideas today."

"Besides, Captain," I added, enthusiastically, "why should we not find the sea open at the south pole as well as at the north? The frozen poles and the poles of the earth do not coincide, either in the southern or in the northern regions; and, until it is proved to the contrary, we may suppose either a continent or an ocean free from ice at these two points of the globe."

"I think so, too, M. Aronnax," replied Captain Nemo. "I only wish you to observe that, after having made so many objections to my project, you are now crushing me with arguments in its favor!"

Captain Nemo spoke the truth. I had come to adopt his method of conquering by boldness. It was I who dragged him to the Pole. I preceded him, I outdistanced him — No, that was not so. Captain Nemo knew the pros and cons of the question well, and was amusing himself by seeing me carried away in reveries of the impossible.

Meanwhile, he did not lose an instant. At a signal, the second in command appeared. The two men conversed rapidly in their incomprehensible language; whether the second had been forewarned, or whether he at once found the project practicable, he showed no surprise.

But, impassive as he was, he did not now attain a more complete impassivity than Conseil, when I announced to that good fellow our intention of pushing even to the South Pole. My communication received an "If Master wishes," and I had to be content with it. As for Ned Land, if ever shoulders were shrugged, those of the Canadian were.

"Go, sir," he said to me, "you and your Captain Nemo. I pity you."

"But we are going to the Pole, Master Ned."

"Possibly, but you will not return." And Ned Land re-entered his cabin, "in order not to cause harm," he said to me in leaving.

The preparations for this audacious attempt now began. The powerful pumps of the *Nautilus* were working air into the reservoirs and storing it at high pressure. About four o'clock Captain Nemo announced the closing of the panels on the platform. I threw one last look at the massive ice shelf which we were going to cross. The weather was clear, the atmosphere pure enough, the cold very great, being twelve degrees below zero; but the wind having gone down, this temperature was not so unbearable. About ten men mounted the sides of the *Nautilus,* armed with pickaxes to break the ice around the vessel, which was soon free. The operation was quickly performed, for the fresh ice was still very thin. We all went below. The usual reservoirs were filled with the newly liberated water, and the *Nautilus* soon descended. I had taken my place with Conseil in the saloon; through the open window we could see the lower beds of the Southern Ocean. The thermometer went up, the needle of the compass deviated on the dial. At about nine hundred feet, as Captain Nemo had foreseen, we were floating beneath the undulating bottom of the icecap. But the *Nautilus* went lower still — it went to the depth of four hundred fathoms. The temperature of the water at the surface showed twelve degrees, it was now only eleven; we had gained two. I need not say the temperature of the *Nautilus* was raised by its heating apparatus to a much higher degree; every maneuver was accomplished with wonderful precision.

"We shall pass it, if you please, sir," said Conseil.

"I believe we shall," I said, in a tone of firm conviction.

In this open sea, the *Nautilus* had taken its course direct to the pole, without leaving the fifty-second meridian. From 67° 30' to 90°, twenty-two degrees and a half of latitude remained to travel; that is, about five hundred leagues. The *Nautilus* kept up a mean speed of twenty-six miles an hour — the speed of an express train. If we kept that up, in forty hours we should reach the pole.

For a part of the night the novelty of the situation kept us at the window. The sea was lit with the electric lantern; but it was deserted; fishes did not sojourn in these imprisoned waters: they only found there a passage to take them from the Antarctic Ocean to the open polar sea. Our pace was rapid; we could feel it by the quivering of the long steel body. About two in the morning, I took some hours' repose, and Conseil did the same. In crossing the waist I did not meet Captain Nemo: I supposed him to

be in the pilot's cage. The next morning, the 19th of March, I
took my post once more in the saloon. The electric log told me
that the speed of the *Nautilus* had been slackened. It was then
going toward the surface; but prudently emptying its reservoirs
very slowly. My heart beat fast. Were we going to emerge and
regain the open polar atmosphere? No! A shock told me that the
Nautilus had struck the bottom of the ice sheet, still very thick,
judging from the deadened sound. We had indeed "struck," to use a
sea expression, but in an inverse sense, and at a thousand feet deep.
This would give three thousand feet of ice above us; one thousand
being above the watermark. The ice shelf was then higher than at
its borders — not a very reassuring fact. Several times that day the
Nautilus tried again, and every time it struck the wall which lay like
a ceiling above it. Sometimes it met with but 900 yards, only 200
of which rose above the surface. It was twice the height it was
when the *Nautilus* had gone under the waves. I carefully noted the
different depths, and thus obtained a submarine profile of the chain
as it was developed under water. That night no change had taken
place in our situation. Still ice between four and five hundred
yards in depth! It was evidently diminishing, but still what a thickness between us and the surface of the ocean! It was then eight. According to the daily custom on board the *Nautilus*, its air should have
been renewed four hours ago; but I did not suffer much, although
Captain Nemo had not yet made any demand upon his reserve of
oxygen. My sleep was painful that night; hope and fear besieged
me by turns: I woke several times. The groping of the *Nautilus* continued. About three in the morning, I noticed that the lower surface
of the icecap was only about fifty feet deep. One hundred and fifty
feet now separated us from the surface of the waters. The ice range
was by degrees becoming an ice field, the mountain, a plain. My
eyes never left the manometer. We were still rising diagonally to the
surface, which sparkled under the electric rays. The ice sheet was
stretching both above and beneath into lengthening slopes; mile
after mile it was getting thinner. At length, at six in the morning of
that memorable day, the 19th of March, the door of the saloon
opened, and Captain Nemo appeared.

"The sea is open!" was all he said.

I rushed on to the platform. Yes! the open sea, with but a few
scattered pieces of ice and moving icebergs — a long stretch of sea;
a world of birds in the air, and myriads of fishes under those waters,
which varied from intense blue to olive green, according to the bottom. The thermometer marked three degrees centigrade above zero.

It was comparatively spring, shut up as we were behind this iceberg, whose lengthened mass was dimly seen on our northern horizon.

"Are we at the pole?" I asked the Captain, with a beating heart.

"I do not know," he replied. "At noon I will take our bearings."

"But will the sun show itself through this fog?" said I, looking at the leaden sky.

"However little it shows, it will be enough," replied the Captain.

About ten miles south, a solitary island rose to a height of one hundred and four yards. We made for it, but carefully, for the sea might be strewn with banks. One hour afterward we had reached it; two hours later we had made the round of it. It measured four or five miles in circumference. A narrow canal separated it from a considerable stretch of land, perhaps a continent, for we could not see its limits. The existence of this land seemed to give some color to Maury's hypothesis. The ingenious American has remarked, that between the South Pole and the sixtieth parallel, the sea is covered with floating ice of enormous size, which is never met with in the North Atlantic. From this fact he has drawn the conclusion that the Antarctic Circle encloses considerable continents, as icebergs cannot form in open sea, but only on the coasts. According to these calculations, the mass of ice surrounding the southern pole forms a vast cap, the circumference of which must be, at least, 2500 miles. But the *Nautilus*, for fear of running aground, had stopped about three cables' length from a strand over which reared a superb heap of rocks. The boat was launched; the Captain, two of his men bearing instruments, Conseil, and myself, were in it. It was ten in the morning. I had not seen Ned Land. Doubtless the Canadian did not wish to admit the presence of the South Pole. A few strokes of the oar brought us to the sand, where we ran ashore. Conseil was going to jump on to the land, when I held him back.

"Sir," said I to Captain Nemo, "to you belongs the honor of first setting foot on this land."

"Yes, sir," said the Captain; "and if I do not hesitate to tread this South Pole, it is because, up to this time, no human being has left a trace there."

Saying this, he jumped lightly on to the sand. His heart beat with emotion. He climbed a rock, sloping to a little promontory, and there, with his arms crossed, mute and motionless, and with an eager look, he seemed to take possession of these southern regions. After five minutes passed in this ecstasy, he turned to us.

"When you like, sir."

I landed, followed by Conseil, leaving the two men in the boat. For a long way the soil was composed of a reddish, sandy stone, something like crushed brick, scoriæ, streams of lava, and pumice stones. One could not mistake its volcanic origin. In some parts, slight curls of smoke emitted a sulphurous smell, proving that the internal fires had lost nothing of their expansive powers, though, having climbed a high acclivity, I could see no volcano for a radius of several miles. We know that in those antarctic countries, James Ross found two craters, the Erebus and Terror, in full activity, on the 167th meridian, latitude 77° 32'. The vegetation of this desolate continent seemed to me much restricted. Some lichens of the species unsnea melanoxantha lay upon the black rocks; some microscopic plants, rudimentary diatomas, a kind of cell, placed between two quartz shells; long purple and scarlet fucus, supported on little swimming bladders, which the breaking of the waves brought to the shore. These constituted the meager flora of this region. . . . Albatrosses passed in the air (the expanse of their wings being at least four yards and a half); they are justly called the vultures of the ocean; there were some gigantic petrels, and some damiers, a kind of small duck, the under part of whose body is black and white; then there were a whole series of petrels, some whitish, with brown-bordered wings, others blue, peculiar to the Antarctic seas, and so oily, as I told Conseil, that the inhabitants of the Ferroe Islands had nothing to do before lighting them, but to put a wick in.

"A little more," said Conseil, "and they would be perfect lamps! After all, we cannot expect Nature to have furnished them with wicks!"

About half a mile further on, the soil was riddled with ruffs' nests, a sort of laying ground, out of which many birds were issuing. Captain Nemo had some hundreds hunted. They uttered a cry like the braying of an ass, were about the size of a goose, slate color on the body, white beneath, with a yellow line round their throats; they allowed themselves to be killed with a stone, never trying to escape. But the fog did not lift, and at eleven the sun had not yet shown itself. Its absence made me uneasy. Without it no observations were possible. How, then, could we decide whether we had reached the pole? When I rejoined Captain Nemo, I found him leaning on a piece of rock, silently watching the sky. He seemed impatient and vexed. But what was to be done? This rash and powerful man could not command the sun as he did the sea. Noon arrived without the orb of day showing itself for an instant. We could not even tell its position behind the curtain of fog; and soon the fog turned to snow.

"Till tomorrow," said the Captain, quietly, and we returned to the *Nautilus* amid these atmospheric disturbances.

The tempest of snow continued till the next day. It was impossible to remain on the platform. From the saloon, where I was taking notes of the incidents of this excursion to the polar continent, I could hear the cries of petrels and albatrosses sporting in the midst of this violent storm. The *Nautilus* did not remain motionless, but skirted the coast, advancing ten miles more to the south in the half light left by the sun as it skirted the edge of the horizon. The next day, the 20th of March, the snow had ceased. The cold was a little greater, the thermometer showing two degrees below zero. The fog was rising, and I hoped that that day our observations might be taken. Captain Nemo not having yet appeared, the boat took Conseil and myself to land. The soil was still of the same volcanic nature; everywhere were traces of lava, scoriæ, and basalt; but the crater which had vomited them I could not see. Here, as lower down, this continent was alive with myriads of birds. But their rule was now divided with large troops of sea mammals, looking at us with their soft eyes. There were several kinds of seals, some stretched on the earth, some on flakes of ice, many going in and out of the sea. They did not flee at our approach, never having had anything to do with man; and I reckoned that there were provisions there for hundreds of vessels. . . .

At nine we landed; the sky was brightening, the clouds were flying to the south, and the fog seemed to be leaving the cold surface of the waters. Captain Nemo went toward the peak, which he doubtless meant to be his observatory. It was a painful ascent over the sharp lava and the pumice stones, in an atmosphere often impregnated with a sulphurous smell from the smoking cracks. For a man unaccustomed to walk on land, the Captain climbed the steep slopes with an agility I never saw equaled, and which a hunter would have envied. We were two hours getting to the summit of this peak, which was half porphyry and half basalt. From thence we looked upon a vast sea, which, toward the north, distinctly traced its boundary line upon the sky. At our feet lay fields of dazzling whiteness. Over our heads a pale azure, free from fog. To the north the disc of the sun seemed like a ball of fire, already horned by the cutting of the horizon. From the bosom of the water rose sheaves of liquid jets by hundreds. In the distance lay the *Nautilus* like a whale asleep on the water.

Behind us, to the south and east, an immense country, and a chaotic heap of rocks and ice, the limits of which were not visible. On arriving at the summit, Captain Nemo carefully took the mean height of the barometer, for he would have to consider that in taking his observations. At a quarter to twelve, the sun, then seen only by reflection, looked like a golden disc shedding its last rays upon this deserted continent, and seas which never man had yet ploughed. Captain Nemo, furnished with a glass lens which, by means of a mirror, corrected the refraction, watched the orb sinking below the horizon by degrees, following a lengthened diagonal. I held the chronometer. My heart beat fast. If the disappearance of the half-disc of the sun coincided with twelve o'clock on the chronometer, we were at the pole itself.

"Twelve!" I exclaimed.

"The South Pole!" replied Captain Nemo, in a grave voice, handing me the glass, which showed the orb cut in exactly equal parts by the horizon.

I looked at the last rays crowning the peak, and the shadows mounting by degrees up its slopes. At that moment Captain Nemo, resting with his hand on my shoulder, said: "I, Captain Nemo, on this 21st day of March, 1868, have reached the South Pole on the ninetieth degree; and I take possession of this part of the globe, equal to one-sixth of the known continents."

"In whose name, Captain?"

"In my own, sir!"

Saying which, Captain Nemo unfurled a black banner, bearing an N in gold quartered on its bunting. Then turning toward the orb of day, whose last rays lapped the horizon of the sea, he exclaimed: "Adieu, sun! Disappear, thou radiant orb! rest beneath this open sea, and let a night of six months spread its shadows over my new domains!"

A Descent into the Maelström

EDGAR ALLAN POE

WE HAD NOW REACHED the summit of the loftiest crag. For some minutes the old man seemed too much exhausted to speak.

"Not long ago," said he at length, "and I could have guided you on this route as well as the youngest of my sons; but, about three years past, there happened to me an event such as never happened before to mortal man — or at least such as no man ever survived to tell of — and the six hours of deadly terror which I then endured have broken me up body and soul. You suppose me a *very* old man — but I am not. It took less than a single day to change these hairs from a jetty black to white, to weaken my limbs, and to unstring my nerves, so that I tremble at the least exertion, and am frightened at a shadow. Do you know I can scarcely look over this little cliff without getting giddy?"

The "little cliff," upon whose edge he had so carelessly thrown himself down to rest that the weightier portion of his body hung over it, while he was only kept from falling by the tenure of his elbow on its extreme and slippery edge — this "little cliff" arose, a sheer unobstructed precipice of black shining rock, some fifteen or sixteen hundred feet from the world of crags beneath us. Nothing would have tempted me to within half a dozen yards of its brink. In truth so deeply was I excited by the perilous position of my companion, that I fell at full length upon the ground, clung to the shrubs around me, and dared not even glance upward at the sky — while I struggled in vain to divest myself of the idea that the very foundations of the mountain were in danger from the fury of the winds. It was long before I could reason myself into sufficient courage to sit up and look out into the distance.

"You must get over these fancies," said the guide, "for I have brought you here that you might have the best possible view of the scene of that event I mentioned — and to tell you the whole story with the spot just under your eye."

"We are now," he continued, in that particularizing manner which distinguished him, "we are now close upon the Norwegian coast — in the sixty-eighth degree of latitude — in the great province of Nordland — and in the dreary district of Lofoden. The mountain upon whose top we sit is Helseggen, the Cloudy. Now raise yourself up a little higher — hold on to the grass if you feel giddy — so — and look out, beyond the belt of vapor beneath us, into the sea."

I looked dizzily, and beheld a wide expanse of ocean, whose waters wore so inky a hue as to bring at once to my mind the Nubian geographer's account of the *Mare Tenebrarum*. A panorama more deplorably desolate no human imagination can conceive. To the right and left, as far as the eye could reach, there lay outstretched, like ramparts of the world, lines of horridly black and beetling cliff, whose character of gloom was but the more forcibly illustrated by the surf which reared high up against it its white and ghastly crest, howling and shrieking forever. Just opposite the promontory upon whose apex we were placed, and at a distance of some five or six miles out at sea, there was visible a small, bleak-looking island; or, more properly, its position was discernible through the wilderness

of surge in which it was enveloped. About two miles nearer the
land, arose another of smaller size, hideously craggy and barren,
and encompassed at various intervals by a cluster of dark rocks.

The appearance of the ocean, in the space between the more
distant island and the shore, had something very unusual about it.
Although, at the time, so strong a gale was blowing landward that
a brig in the remote offing lay to under a double-reefed trysail, and
constantly plunged her whole hull out of sight, still there was here
nothing like a regular swell, but only a short, quick, angry cross
dashing of water in every direction — as well in the teeth of the
wind as otherwise. Of foam there was little except in the immediate
vicinity of the rocks.

"The island in the distance," resumed the old man, "is called by
the Norwegians Vurrgh. The one midway is Moskoe. That a mile to
the northward is Ambaaren. Yonder are Iflesen, Hoeyholm, Kield-
holm, Suarven, and Buckholm. Farther off — between Moskoe and
Vurrgh — are Otterholm, Flimen, Sandflesen, and Skarholm. These
are the true names of the places — but why it has been thought necessary to name them at all, is more than either you or I can understand. Do you hear anything? Do you see any change in the water?"

We had now been about ten minutes upon the top of Helseggen, to which we had ascended from the interior of Lofoden, so
that we had caught no glimpse of the sea until it had burst upon us
from the summit. As the old man spoke, I became aware of a loud
and gradually increasing sound, like the moaning of a vast herd of
buffaloes upon an American prairie; and at the same moment I perceived that what seamen term the *chopping* character of the ocean
beneath us, was rapidly changing into a current which set to the
eastward. Even while I gazed, this current acquired a monstrous
velocity. Each moment added to its speed — to its headlong impetuosity. In five minutes the whole sea, as far as Vurrgh, was
lashed into ungovernable fury; but it was between Moskoe and the
coast that the main uproar held its sway. Here the vast bed of the
waters, seamed and scarred into a thousand conflicting channels,
burst suddenly into frenzied convulsion — heaving, boiling, hissing
— gyrating in gigantic and innumerable vortices, and all whirling
and plunging on to the eastward with a rapidity which water never
elsewhere assumes except in precipitous descents.

In a few minutes more, there came over the scene another radical alteration. The general surface grew somewhat more smooth,
and the whirlpools, one by one, disappeared, while prodigious streaks
of foam became apparent where none had been seen before. These
streaks, at length, spreading out to a great distance, and entering
into combination, took unto themselves the gyratory motion of the

subsided vortices, and seemed to form the germ of another more vast. Suddenly — very suddenly — this assumed a distinct and definite existence, in a circle of more than half a mile in diameter. The edge of the whirl was represented by a broad belt of gleaming spray; but no particle of this slipped into the mouth of the terrific funnel, whose interior, as far as the eye could fathom it, was a smooth, shining, and jet-black wall of water, inclined to the horizon at an angle of some forty-five degrees, speeding dizzily round and round with a swaying and sweltering motion, and sending forth to the winds an appalling voice, half shriek, half roar, such as not even the mighty cataract of Niagara ever lifts up in its agony to Heaven.

The mountain trembled to its very base, and the rock rocked. I threw myself upon my face, and clung to the scant herbage in an excess of nervous agitation.

"This," said I at length, to the old man, "this *can* be nothing else than the great whirlpool of the Maelström."

"So it is sometimes termed," said he. "We Norwegians call it the Moskoe-ström, from the island of Moskoe in the midway."

The ordinary accounts of this vortex had by no means prepared me for what I saw. That of Jonas Ramus, which is perhaps the most circumstantial of any, cannot impart the faintest conception either of the magnificence, or of the horror of the scene — or of the wild bewildering sense of *the novel* which confounds the beholder. I am not sure from what point of view the writer in question surveyed it, nor at what time; but it could neither have been from the summit of Helseggen, nor during a storm. There are some passages of his description, nevertheless, which may be quoted for their details, although their effect is exceedingly feeble in conveying an impression of the spectacle.

"Between Lofoden and Moskoe," he says, "the depth of the water is between thirty-six and forty fathoms; but on the other side, toward Ver (Vurrgh) this depth decreases so as not to afford a convenient passage for a vessel, without the risk of splitting on the rocks, which happens even in the calmest weather. When it is flood, the stream runs up the country between Lofoden and Moskoe with a boisterous rapidity; but the roar of its impetuous ebb to the sea is scarce equaled by the loudest and most dreadful cataracts; the noise being heard several leagues off, and the vortices or pits are of such an extent and depth, that if a ship comes within its attraction, it is inevitably absorbed and carried down to the bottom, and there beat to pieces against the rocks; and when the water relaxes, the fragments thereof are thrown up again. But these intervals of tranquillity are only at the turn of the ebb and flood, and in calm weather, and last but a quarter of an hour, its violence gradually returning.

When the stream is most boisterous, and its fury heightened by a storm, it is dangerous to come within a Norway mile of it. Boats, yachts, and ships have been carried away by not guarding against it before they were within its reach. It likewise happens frequently, that whales come too near the stream, and are overpowered by its violence; and then it is impossible to describe their howlings and bellowings in their fruitless struggles to disengage themselves. A bear once, attempting to swim from Lofoden to Moskoe, was caught by the stream and borne down, while he roared terribly, so as to be heard on shore. Large stocks of firs and pine trees, after being absorbed by the current, rise again broken and torn to such a degree as if bristles grew upon them. This plainly shows the bottom to consist of craggy rocks, among which they are whirled to and fro. This stream is regulated by the flux and reflux of the sea — it being constantly high and low water every six hours. In the year 1645, early in the morning of Sexagesima Sunday, it raged with such noise and impetuosity that the very stones of the houses on the coast fell to the ground."

In regard to the depth of the water, I could not see how this could have been ascertained at all in the immediate vicinity of the vortex. The "forty fathoms" must have reference only to portions of the channel close upon the shore either of Moskoe or Lofoden. The depth in the center of the Moskoe-ström must be immeasurably greater; and no better proof of this fact is necessary than can be obtained from even the sidelong glance into the abyss of the whirl which may be had from the highest crag of Helseggen. Looking down from this pinnacle upon the howling Phlegethon below, I could not help smiling at the simplicity with which the honest Jonas Ramus records, as a matter difficult of belief, the anecdotes of the whales and the bears; for it appeared to me, in fact, a self-evident thing, that the largest ships of the line in existence, coming within the influence of that deadly attraction, could resist it as little as a feather the hurricane, and must disappear bodily and at once.

The attempts to account for the phenomenon — some of which, I remember, seemed to me sufficiently plausible in perusal — now wore a very different and unsatisfactory aspect. The idea generally received is that this, as well as three smaller vortices among the Feroe islands, "have no other cause than the collision of waves rising and falling, at flux and reflux, against a ridge of rocks and shelves, which confines the water so that it precipitates itself like a cataract; and thus the higher the flood rises, the deeper must the fall be, and the natural result of all is a whirlpool or vortex, the prodigious suction of which is sufficiently known by lesser experiments." — These are the words of the Encyclopædia Britannica.

Kircher and others imagine that in the center of the channel of the Maelström is an abyss penetrating the globe, and issuing in some very remote part — the Gulf of Bothnia being somewhat decidedly named in one instance. This opinion, idle in itself, was the one to which, as I gazed, my imagination most readily assented; and, mentioning it to the guide, I was rather surprised to hear him say that, although it was the view almost universally entertained of the subject by the Norwegians, it nevertheless was not his own. As to the former notion he confessed his inability to comprehend it; and here I agreed with him — for, however conclusive on paper, it becomes altogether unintelligible, and even absurd, amid the thunder of the abyss.

"You have had a good look at the whirl now," said the old man, "and if you will creep round this crag, so as to get in its lee, and deaden the roar of the water, I will tell you a story that will convince you I ought to know something of the Moskoe-ström."

I placed myself as desired, and he proceeded.

"Myself and my two brothers once owned a schooner-rigged smack of about seventy tons burthen, with which we were in the habit of fishing among the islands beyond Moskoe, nearly to Vurrgh. In all violent eddies at sea there is good fishing, at proper opportunities, if one has only the courage to attempt it; but among the whole of the Lofoden coastmen, we three were the only ones who made a regular business of going out to the islands, as I tell you. The usual grounds are a great way lower down to the southward. There fish can be got at all hours, without much risk, and therefore these places are preferred. The choice spots over here among the rocks, however, not only yield the finest variety, but in far greater abundance; so that we often got in a single day, what the more timid of the craft could not scrape together in a week. In fact, we made it a matter of desperate speculation — the risk of life standing instead of labor, and courage answering for capital.

"We kept the smack in a cove about five miles higher up the coast than this; and it was our practice, in fine weather, to take advantage of the fifteen minutes' slack to push across the main channel of the Moskoe-ström, far above the pool, and then drop down upon anchorage somewhere near Otterholm, or Sandflesen, where the eddies are not so violent as elsewhere. Here we used to remain until nearly time for slack water again, when we weighed and made for home. We never set out upon this expedition without a steady side wind for going and coming — one that we felt sure would not fail us before our return — and we seldom made a miscalculation upon this point. Twice, during six years, we were forced to stay all night at anchor on account of a dead calm, which is a rare thing indeed just about here; and once we had to remain on the grounds nearly a week, starving to death, owing to a gale which blew up shortly after our arrival, and made the channel too boisterous to be thought of. Upon this occasion we should have been driven out to sea in spite of everything (for the whirlpools threw us round and round so violently, that, at length, we fouled our anchor and dragged it), if it had not been that we drifted into one of the innumerable cross currents — here today and gone tomorrow — which drove us under the lee of Flimen, where, by good luck, we brought up.

"I could not tell you the twentieth part of the difficulties we encountered 'on the ground' — it is a bad spot to be in, even in good weather — but we made shift always to run the gauntlet of the Moskoe-ström itself without accident; although at times my heart has been in my mouth when we happened to be a minute or so behind or before the slack. The wind sometimes was not as strong as we thought it at starting, and then we made rather less way than we could wish, while the current rendered the smack unmanageable. My eldest brother had a son eighteen years old, and I had two stout boys of my own. These would have been of great assistance at such times, in using the sweeps, as well as afterward in fishing — but, somehow, although we ran the risk ourselves, we had not the heart to let the young ones get into the danger — for, after all said and done, it *was* a horrible danger, and that is the truth.

"It is now within a few days of three years since what I am going to tell you occurred. It was on the tenth of July, 18 —, a day which the people of this part of the world will never forget — for it was one in which blew the most terrible hurricane that ever came out of the heavens. And yet all the morning, and indeed until late in the afternoon, there was a gentle and steady breeze from the southwest, while the sun shone brightly, so that the oldest seaman among us could not have foreseen what was to follow.

"The three of us — my two brothers and myself — had crossed over to the islands about two o'clock P.M., and soon nearly loaded the smack with fine fish, which, we all remarked, were more plenty that day than we had ever known them. It was just seven, *by my watch*, when we weighed and started for home, so as to make the worst of the Ström at slack water, which we knew would be at eight.

"We set out with a fresh wind on our starboard quarter, and for some time spanked along at a great rate, never dreaming of danger, for indeed we saw not the slightest reason to apprehend it. All at once we were taken aback by a breeze from over Helseggen. This was most unusual — something that had never happened to us

before — and I began to feel a little uneasy, without exactly knowing why. We put the boat on the wind, but could make no head-
way at all for the eddies, and I was upon the point of proposing to
return to the anchorage, when, looking astern, we saw the whole
horizon covered with a singular copper-colored cloud that rose with
the most amazing velocity.

"In the meantime the breeze that had headed us off fell away,
and we were dead becalmed, drifting about in every direction. This
state of things, however, did not last long enough to give us time to
think about it. In less than a minute the storm was upon us — in
less than two the sky was entirely overcast — and what with this
and the driving spray, it became suddenly so dark that we could
not see each other in the smack.

"Such a hurricane as then blew it is folly to attempt describing.
The oldest seaman in Norway never experienced anything like it.
We had let our sails go by the run before it cleverly took us; but, at
the first puff, both our masts went by the board as if they had been
sawed off — the mainmast taking with it my youngest brother, who
had lashed himself to it for safety.

"Our boat was the lightest feather of a thing that ever sat upon
water. It had a complete flush deck, with only a small hatch near
the bow, and this hatch it had always been our custom to batten
down when about to cross the Ström, by way of precaution against
the chopping seas. But for this circumstance we should have foun-
dered at once — for we lay entirely buried for some moments. How
my elder brother escaped destruction I cannot say, for I never had
an opportunity of ascertaining. For my part, as soon as I had let
the foresail run, I threw myself flat on deck, with my feet against
the narrow gunwale of the bow, and with my hands grasping a ring-
bolt near the foot of the foremast. It was mere instinct that
prompted me to do this — which was undoubtedly the very best
thing I could have done — for I was too much flurried to think.

"For some moments we were completely deluged, as I say, and
all this time I held my breath, and clung to the bolt. When I could
stand it no longer, I raised myself upon my knees, still keeping hold
with my hands, and thus got my head clear. Presently our little
boat gave herself a shake, just as a dog does in coming out of the
water, and thus rid herself, in some measure, of the seas. I was now
trying to get the better of the stupor that had come over me, and to
collect my senses so as to see what was to be done, when I felt somebody grasp my arm. It was my elder brother, and my heart leaped
for joy, for I had made sure that he was overboard — but the next
moment all this joy was turned into horror — for he put his mouth
close to my ear, and screamed out the word 'Moskoe-ström!'

"No one ever will know what my feelings were at that moment. I shook from head to foot as if I had had the most violent fit of the ague. I knew what he meant by that one word well enough — I knew what he wished to make me understand. With the wind that now drove us on, we were bound for the whirl of the Ström, and nothing could save us!

"You perceive that in crossing the Ström *channel*, we always went a long way up above the whirl, even in the calmest weather, and then had to wait and watch carefully for the slack — but now we were driving right upon the pool itself, and in such a hurricane as this! 'To be sure,' I thought, 'we shall get there just about the slack — there is some little hope in that'; but in the next moment I cursed myself for being so great a fool as to dream of hope at all. I knew very well that we were doomed, had we been ten times a ninety-gun ship.

"By this time the first fury of the tempest had spent itself, or perhaps we did not feel it so much, as we scudded before it, but at all events the seas, which at first had been kept down by the wind, and lay flat and frothing, now got up into absolute mountains. A singular change, too, had come over the heavens. Around in every direction it was still as black as pitch, but nearly overhead there burst out, all at once, a circular rift of clear sky — as clear as I ever saw — and of a deep bright blue — and through it there blazed forth the full moon with a luster that I never before knew her to wear. She lit up everything about us with the greatest distinctness — but, oh God, what a scene it was to light up!

"I now made one or two attempts to speak to my brother — but in some manner which I could not understand, the din had so increased that I could not make him hear a single word, although I screamed at the top of my voice in his ear. Presently he shook his head, looking as pale as death, and held up one of his fingers, as if to say '*listen!*'

"At first I could not make out what he meant — but soon a hideous thought flashed upon me. I dragged my watch from its fob. It was not going. I glanced at its face by the moonlight, and then burst into tears as I flung it far away into the ocean. *It had run down at seven o'clock! We were behind the time of the slack, and the whirl of the Ström was in full fury!*

"When a boat is well built, properly trimmed, and not deep laden, the waves in a strong gale, when she is going large, seem always to slip from beneath her — which appears very strange to a landsman — and this is what is called *riding*, in sea phrase.

"Well, so far we had ridden the swells very cleverly; but presently a gigantic sea happened to take us right under the counter.

and bore us with it as it rose — up — up — as if into the sky. I would
not have believed that any wave could rise so high. And then down
we came with a sweep, a slide, and a plunge, that made me feel
sick and dizzy, as if I was falling from some lofty mountaintop in a
dream. But while we were up I had thrown a quick glance around
— and that one glance was all sufficient. I saw our exact position in
an instant. The Moskoe-ström whirlpool was about a quarter of a
mile dead ahead — but no more like the everyday Moskoe-ström,
than the whirl as you now see it, is like a mill-race. If I had not
known where we were, and what we had to expect, I should not
have recognized the place at all. As it was, I voluntarily closed my
eyes in horror. The lids clenched themselves together as if in a
spasm.

"It could not have been more than two minutes afterward until
we suddenly felt the waves subside, and were enveloped in foam.
The boat made a sharp half turn to larboard, and then shot off in
its new direction like a thunderbolt. At the same moment the roaring
noise of the water was completely drowned in a kind of shrill shriek
— such a sound as you might imagine given out by the water pipes
of many thousand steam vessels, letting off their steam all together.
We were now in the belt of surf that always surrounds the whirl;
and I thought, of course, that another moment would plunge us into
the abyss — down which we could only see indistinctly on account
of the amazing velocity with which we were borne along. The boat
did not seem to sink into the water at all, but to skim like an air-bub-
ble upon the surface of the surge. Her starboard side was next the
whirl, and on the larboard arose the world of ocean we had left. It
stood like a huge writhing wall between us and the horizon.

"It may appear strange, but now, when we were in the very
jaws of the gulf, I felt more composed than when we were only approaching it. Having made up my mind to hope no more, I got
rid of a great deal of that terror which unmanned me at first. I suppose it was despair that strung my nerves.

"It may look like boasting — but what I tell you is truth — I
began to reflect how magnificent a thing it was to die in such a manner, and how foolish it was in me to think of so paltry a consideration as my own individual life, in view of so wonderful a manifestation of God's power. I do believe that I blushed with shame when
this idea crossed my mind. After a little while I became possessed
with the keenest curiosity about the whirl itself. I positively felt a
wish to explore its depths, even at the sacrifice I was going to make;
and my principal grief was that I should never be able to tell my
old companions on shore about the mysteries I should see. These, no
doubt, were singular fancies to occupy a man's mind in such ex-

tremity — and I have often thought since, that the revolutions of the boat around the pool might have rendered me a little light-headed.

"There was another circumstance which tended to restore my self-possession; and this was the cessation of the wind, which could not reach us in our present situation — for, as you saw yourself, the belt of surf is considerably lower than the general bed of the ocean, and this latter now towered above us, a high, black, mountainous ridge. If you have never been at sea in a heavy gale, you can form no idea of the confusion of mind occasioned by the wind and spray together. They blind, deafen and strangle you, and take away all power of action or reflection. But we were now, in a great measure, rid of these annoyances — just as death-condemned felons in prison are allowed petty indulgences, forbidden them while their doom is yet uncertain.

"How often we made the circuit of the belt it is impossible to say. We careered round and round for perhaps an hour, flying rather than floating, getting gradually more and more into the middle of the surge, and then nearer and nearer to its horrible inner edge. All this time I had never let go of the ring-bolt. My brother was at the stern, holding on to a large empty water cask which had been securely lashed under the coop of the counter, and was the only thing on deck that had not been swept overboard when the gale first took us. As we approached the brink of the pit he let go his hold upon this, and made for the ring, from which, in the agony of his terror, he endeavored to force my hands, as it was not large enough to afford us both a secure grasp. I never felt deeper grief than when I saw him attempt this act — although I knew he was a madman when he did it — a raving maniac through sheer fright. I did not care, however, to contest the point with him. I thought it could make no difference whether either of us held on at all; so I let him have the bolt, and went astern to the cask. This there was no great difficulty in doing; for the smack flew round steadily enough, and upon an even keel — only swaying to and fro, with the immense sweeps and swelters of the whirl. Scarcely had I secured myself in my new position, when we gave a wild lurch to starboard, and rushed headlong into the abyss. I muttered a hurried prayer to God, and thought all was over.

"As I felt the sickening sweep of the descent, I had instinctively tightened my hold upon the barrel, and closed my eyes. For some seconds I dared not open them — while I expected instant destruction, and wondered that I was not already in my death struggles with the water. But moment after moment elapsed. I still lived. The sense of falling had ceased; and the motion of the vessel seemed much as it had been before while in the belt of foam, with the exception that she now lay more along. I took courage and looked once again upon the scene.

"Never shall I forget the sensations of awe, horror, and admiration with which I gazed about me. The boat appeared to be hanging, as if by magic, midway down, upon the interior surface of a funnel vast in circumference, prodigious in depth, and whose perfectly smooth sides might have been mistaken for ebony, but for the bewildering rapidity with which they spun around, and for the gleaming and ghastly radiance they shot forth, as the rays of the full moon, from that circular rift amid the clouds which I have already described, streamed in a flood of golden glory along the black walls, and far away down into the inmost recesses of the abyss.

"At first I was too much confused to observe anything accurately. The general burst of terrific grandeur was all that I beheld. When I recovered myself a little, however, my gaze fell instinctively downward. In this direction I was able to obtain an unobstructed view, from the manner in which the smack hung on the inclined surface of the pool. She was quite upon an even keel — that is to say, her deck lay in a plane parallel with that of the water — but this latter sloped at an angle of more than forty-five degrees, so that we seemed to be lying upon our beam ends. I could not help observing, nevertheless, that I had scarcely more difficulty in maintaining my hold and footing in this situation, than if we had been upon a dead level; and this, I suppose, was owing to the speed at which we revolved.

"The rays of the moon seemed to search the very bottom of the profound gulf; but still I could make out nothing distinctly, on account of a thick mist in which everything there was enveloped, and over which there hung a magnificent rainbow, like that narrow and tottering bridge which Mussulmen say is the only pathway between Time and Eternity. This mist, or spray, was no doubt occasioned by the clashing of the great walls of the funnel, as they all met together at the bottom — but the yell that went up to the Heavens from out of that mist, I dare not attempt to describe.

"Our first slide into the abyss itself, from the belt of foam above, had carried us to a great distance down the slope; but our farther descent was by no means proportionate. Round and round we swept — not with any uniform movement — but in dizzying swings and jerks, that sent us sometimes only a few hundred feet — sometimes nearly the complete circuit of the whirl. Our progress downward, at each revolution, was slow, but very perceptible.

"Looking about me upon the wide waste of liquid ebony on which we were thus borne, I perceived that our boat was not the only object in the embrace of the whirl. Both above and below us were visible fragments of vessels, large masses of building timber and trunks of trees, with many smaller articles, such as pieces of house furniture, broken boxes, barrels and staves. I have already described the unnatural curiosity which had taken the place of my original terrors. It appeared to grow upon me as I drew nearer and nearer to my dreadful doom. I now began to watch, with a strange interest, the numerous things that floated in our company. I *must* have been delirious — for I even sought *amusement* in speculating upon the relative velocities of their several descents toward the foam below. 'This fir tree,' I found myself at one time saying, 'will certainly be the next thing that takes the awful plunge and disappears,' — and then I was disappointed to find that the wreck of a Dutch merchant ship overtook it and went down before. At length, after making several guesses of this nature, and being deceived in all — this fact — the fact of my invariable miscalculation, set me upon a train of reflection that made my limbs again tremble, and my heart beat heavily once more.

"It was not a new terror that thus affected me, but the dawn of a more exciting *hope*. This hope arose partly from memory, and partly from present observation. I called to mind the great variety of buoyant matter that strewed the coast of Lofoden, having been absorbed and then thrown forth by the Moskoe-ström. By far the greater number of the articles were shattered in the most extraordinary way — so chafed and roughened as to have the appearance of being stuck full of splinters — but then I distinctly recollected that there were *some* of them which were not disfigured at all. Now I could not account for this difference except by supposing that the roughened fragments were the only ones which had been *completely absorbed* — that the others had entered the whirl at so late a period of the tide, or, for some reason, had descended so slowly after entering, that they did not reach the bottom before the turn of the flood came, or of the ebb, as the case might be. I conceived it possible, in either instance, that they might thus be whirled up again to the level of the ocean, without undergoing the fate of those which had been drawn in more early or absorbed more rapidly. I made, also, three important observations. The first was, that as a general rule, the larger the bodies were, the more rapid their descent; the second, that, between two masses of equal extent, the one spherical, and the other *of any other shape*, the superiority in speed of descent was with the sphere; the third, that, between two masses of equal size, the one cylindrical, and the other of any other shape, the cylinder was absorbed the more slowly.

"Since my escape, I have had several conversations on this subject with an old schoolmaster of the district; and it was from him that I learned the use of the words 'cylinder' and 'sphere.' He explained to me — although I have forgotten the explanation — how what I observed was, in fact, the natural consequence of the forms of the floating fragments — and showed me how it happened that a cylinder, swimming in a vortex, offered more resistance to its suction and was drawn in with greater difficulty than an equally bulky body, of any form whatever.

"There was one startling circumstance which went a great way in enforcing these observations, and rendering me anxious to turn them to account, and this was that, at every revolution, we passed something like a barrel, or else the broken yard or the mast of a vessel, while many of these things, which had been on our level when I first opened my eyes upon the wonders of the whirlpool, were now high up above us, and seemed to have moved but little from their original station.

"I no longer hesitated what to do. I resolved to lash myself securely to the water cask upon which I now held, to cut it loose from the counter, and to throw myself with it into the water. I attracted my brother's attention by signs, pointed to the floating barrels that came near us, and did everything in my power to make him understand what I was about to do. I thought at length that he comprehended my design — but, whether this was the case or not, he shook his head despairingly, and refused to move from his station by the ring-bolt. It was impossible to force him; the emergency admitted no delay; and so, with a bitter struggle, I resigned him to his fate, fastened myself to the cask by means of the lashings which secured it to the counter, and precipitated myself with it into the sea, without another moment's hesitation.

"The result was precisely what I had hoped it might be. As it is myself who now tell you this tale — as you see that I *did* escape — and as you are already in possession of the mode in which this escape was effected, and must therefore anticipate all that I have farther to say — I will bring my story quickly to conclusion. It might have been an hour, or thereabout, after my quitting the smack, when, having descended to a vast distance beneath me, it made three or four wild gyrations in rapid succession, and, bearing my loved brother with it, plunged headlong, at once and forever, into the chaos of foam below. The barrel to which I was attached sunk very little farther than half the distance between the bottom of the gulf and the spot at which I leaped overboard, before a great change took place in the character of the whirlpool. The slope of the sides of the vast funnel became momently less and less steep. The gyrations of the whirl grew, gradually, less and less violent. By degrees, the froth and the rainbow disappeared, and the bottom of the gulf seemed slowly to uprise. The sky was clear, the winds had gone down, and the full moon was setting radiantly in the west, when I found myself on the surface of the ocean, in full view of the shores of Lofoden, and above the spot where the pool of the Moskoe-ström *had been*. It was the hour of the slack — but the sea still heaved in mountainous waves from the effects of the hurricane. I was borne violently into the channel of the Ström, and in a few minutes, was hurried down the coast into the 'grounds' of the fishermen. A boat picked me up — exhausted from fatigue, and (now that the danger was removed) speechless from the memory of its horror. Those who drew me on board were my old mates and daily companions — but they knew me no more than they would have known a traveler from the spirit land. My hair, which had been raven-black the day before, was as white as you see it now. They say too that the whole expression of my countenance had changed. I told them my story — they did not believe it. I now tell it to *you* — and I can scarcely expect you to put more faith in it than did the merry fishermen of Lofoden."

MAN AND HIS EARTH

◇◇◇◇◇◇◇◇◇◇◇◇◇◇◇◇◇◇◇◇◇◇◇◇◇◇◇◇◇◇◇◇◇

John Thomas's Cube

JOHN LEIMERT

JOHN THOMAS THOMPSON, aged eight years and nine months, lived in a house with an old, warped, but extremely large and fruitful apple tree in the back yard. Beneath this tree, leaning with his back against the trunk, or in it, wedged between forking limbs, John Thomas often took refuge. Here he came to escape the turmoil of his expanding world and to dream the dreams and think the thoughts important to a boy aged eight years and nine months.

John Thomas went out to visit this tree at seven-thirty o'clock of the morning of September 30. He didn't even wait for his breakfast. He just tumbled out of bed, threw his clothes on, and dashed out. He wasn't much more than past the door when he set up a clamor for his mother to come and see what he had found. His mother, however, was busy making toast, and frying bacon, and pouring John's father's coffee. She called to him to hurry back into the house and eat his breakfast, and to be sure his hands and face were clean, or else he would be late for school.

John Thomas ordinarily was an obedient boy, but on this morning he ignored his mother's summons. "But, Mother," he said, "it's the queerest thing I've found. A little block of metal so heavy I can't lift it. Come and see. Please, Mother."

"You might just as well," John Thomas's father said.

When his mother came to where John Thomas was standing under the apple tree, she at first could see nothing. But the boy pointed to a bare spot and there on the ground was a perfect cube about one inch each way.

"It appears to be made of highly polished steel," Mrs. Thompson said, and stooped to pick it up. To her surprise, she could not lift it. "That's the strangest thing I ever saw," she said as her fingers slipped on the gleaming surfaces.

By this time Mr. Thompson had come out to see what was going on, and he, too, tried to lift the cube, without success. "John

Thomas," he said, "did you bury a steel rod in the ground just to see what would happen?"

"No, Father," the boy said, "I didn't. Honest. I found it that way."

"Why don't you get a shovel and see whether it's buried?" Mrs. Thompson asked reasonably.

"I believe I will," Mr. Thompson said. He got a garden spade from the garage and shoved it into the ground at an angle under the metal cube. The spade cut easily into the soft earth without striking an obstruction.

"You see," Mrs. Thompson said, "it isn't buried."

Mr. Thompson grasped the spade firmly and tried to lift the dirt with the cube resting on top. He couldn't do it. He then shifted both hands to the end of the spade handle and tried to pry with it. The handle bent slightly with his effort, but the metal cube remained immovable.

Mr. Thompson now pulled the spade out of the ground, bringing a quantity of loose dirt from beneath the cube as he did so. John Thomas squatted to inspect the cube more narrowly. "Look, Father," he said. "The block isn't even touching the ground."

"That," Mr. Thompson said, "is impossible." Nevertheless, he stooped to look, and after looking returned to his spade. He began to dig a hole around the cube, and before long he was able to take a spadeful from directly beneath it. The weight of the small cube had been astonishing enough, but what now occurred dumfounded them.

When the supporting column of earth was removed, the cube, contrary to all the laws with which the Thompsons were familiar, remained suspended a good two inches in the air. As they stared at the perverse, shiny object, a few grains of dirt fell free from its under surface, as though to demonstrate that for dirt, at least, the law of gravitational attraction still held firm.

"Perhaps the hole isn't deep enough to make it fall," Mrs. Thompson said, and her husband, anxious for an explanation, excavated another six inches of dirt from beneath the cube. Nothing happened.

Mr. Thompson now thought of another force. "Stand back," he said to his wife and son. "I'll fix this thing's clock for it." He raised the spade above his head, took careful aim, and then swung down at the cube with all his strength. He was rewarded with a terrific clang. The spade bounced into the air again, almost wrenching itself out of his hands, but the cube continued serenely to occupy the precise sections of time and space as before.

Five minutes later, when the city editor of the largest daily heard an excited account of these events from Mr. Thompson, he was understandably skeptical. Nevertheless, he sent a reporter out to have a look. The reporter, who was a cynical and degraded person, cynical without conviction and degraded without villainy, because his station in life required it of him, also was skeptical. He stopped along the way for two or three quick ones and when he finally arrived, looking bored and smelling of strong liquor, he found not only the Thompsons but most of their near neighbors impatiently awaiting him.

The hole had been enlarged by succeeding workers, who had the same idea as John Thomas's father, to a diameter of four feet and a depth of two. The reporter surveyed the hole, the block of metal suspended above it, and a branch of the apple tree directly above the cube. Then he said knowingly, "Which is the kid who found it?"

"I am," John Thomas said.

"Quite a magician, ain't you?" the reporter said, and taking off his hat, he swung it vigorously above the cube. The hat met nothing more resistant than air, and therewith the reporter became the first of a series of professional gentlemen who came to scoff and stayed to wonder.

The news spread rapidly and the mayor was among the earliest of the dignitaries to arrive. He was followed by a committee of inquiry from the university, consisting of its president, the head of the physics department, the head of the chemistry department, an associate professor who was an expert metallurgist, the professor of astronomy, and their respective assistants bearing scientific instruments of all kinds.

"Here, gentlemen," the mayor greeted them, "is an incredible situation. This block of metal arrived in the Thompsons' yard, no one knows precisely when nor from where. There it remains, suspended in mid-air. Where did it come from? Why doesn't it fall? Will there be more like it? When will it go?"

"One question at a time, if you please, Mr. Mayor," the president of the university said. "Let us first have the facts so far known, and then proceed with an orderly inquiry. Mr. Thompson, would you mind telling us whatever you know about this cube?"

John Thomas's father obliged with a recital of the events of the morning, suppressing, however, the episode of hitting the cube with the spade. He did not want these people to know that he could lose his temper at an inanimate object.

When Mr. Thompson had finished, the president of the university went on. "I have formed a hypothesis that I am confident will explain all the puzzling questions that here confront us. There was a shower of meteors last night, a fact that my astronomical colleague will confirm, and this object arrived in the place it now is, in the form it now has, from the limitless distance of outer space.

"Why does it neither fall nor fly away again? We all know that there are two opposite but unequal forces that act upon every body at the earth's surface. One of these is the centrifugal force that results from the spinning of the earth upon its axis, a force that tends to hurl objects away. The other and stronger force is that of gravity tending to pull objects towards the earth's center.

"This particular object, moving freely at tremendous velocity through space, entered into the gravitational field of the earth and was pulled from its course. As it hurtled through the atmosphere that envelops us, it became increasingly hot from friction, with the result that its molecular activity was distorted in such a way as to set up within the structure of the cube itself a force that neutralizes the force of gravity.

"The result we all see. The cube is at rest in a perfect state of equilibrium. Centrifugal force plus the gravity-resistant force within the material itself exactly equals the force of gravity. In a moment I shall prove my contention by lifting upward against the cube, thus giving it an impetus that will destroy its present perfect balance and send it flying back into the void from whence it came. Before I do so, does anyone question the accuracy of my hypothesis?"

The various scientists present remained silent, but John Thomas said, "I don't think it will fly away."

"Well, well," the president of the university said. "And why not, my little man?"

"Because my father hit it with a spade and it didn't budge."

The president reversed his field with a mental agility that no doubt had contributed to his reputation as an administrator. "Exactly," he said. "What this boy has said exactly proves the point I was trying to make. When confronted with the unknown, it is idle to speculate, however rationally, without having first erected a sound foundation of fact. I shall now retire in favor of my colleagues of the physics and chemistry departments. When they have examined this object from every scientific aspect, we shall consult together and, in the light of known mathematical formulae, arrive at the correct description."

The chemists and physicists now came forward with acids and bases, with agents and reagents, with spectroscopes and microscopes, with cyclotrons and atom smashers, with electric fur-

naces and vacuum machines — in fact with every known instrument by means of which man projects his senses into the infinite.
The results were disappointing.

Viewed under the most powerful microscope, the surface of the
cube looked no different than when viewed with the naked eye.
No slightest fissure was revealed, no clue obtained as to the
structure of the block. After finishing this part of the examination,
the metallurgist said, "All I can say is that the surface is absolutely
smooth, so that no part of it reflects more or less light than any
other part. It is amazing."

The use of various chemicals proved equally ineffective. The
block was impervious to every test and shed the most vitriolic
concoctions like water off a duck's back. When it was exposed to
intense heat, it not only remained cool, but it refused to expand or
contract. No matter what they did to it, its dimensions remained
constant.

It proved to be a nonconductor of electricity and had neither a
positive nor a negative pole; yet when someone touched the base
of an electric light bulb to it, the bulb lit. When this phenomenon
occurred, the scientists retired to a corner of the yard for consultation.

Their places were taken by a delegation from the principal
churches of the town headed by the president of the local theological seminary. "Mr. Mayor," this gentleman said, "we believe
that further scientific inquiry into the nature of this object will
prove fruitless. It belongs not to man but to God. What we witness
is a veritable and unquestionable miracle.

"No material description of this block is possible, since it is not
material, but spiritual. Science, in its search for a purely mech-
anistic explanation of reality, sooner or later comes up against an
irreducible minimum which remains as unfathomable and mysterious as the larger conglomerate it was intended to explain.

"What we now have before us is a corporeal representation
of this irreducible minimum. God in His wisdom has chosen to
send us a reminder made manifest that, though men can tinker
with the building blocks of nature, they cannot explain them."

At this stage of the proceedings a Mr. Heartly, chief engineer
for a firm of tool and die makers in the town, stepped forward and
asked to be heard. "I am neither a pure scientist," he said, "nor
am I trained in theology and metaphysics, and therefore I am
unqualified to make any statements concerning the nature of this
block. But I am a toolmaker, and if I cannot account for the unusual behavior of this cube of metal, at least I can name it.

"In our business we use similar cubes machined with nearly

perfect precision so that each face forms exactly a 90-degree angle with every adjacent face, and so smooth that when two blocks are placed together, the pressure of the surrounding atmosphere holds them firmly in place. Gentlemen, this mysterious object is a Johanssen Block, and with your permission I will now prove it."

With these words Mr. Heartly took a second block of metal from his pocket exactly like the suspended cube in every respect except that it was larger, and placed two faces of the cubes together. He then stepped back for all to see that they firmly adhered — so firmly that he was forced to strike his own cube a sharp blow to release it. "Only Johanssen Blocks," he said, "are machined perfectly enough to hold together in this fashion."

It would be pleasant to report that Mr. Heartly's solution proved satisfactory to all concerned. The scientists, however, while they thanked Mr. Heartly for identifying the object and demonstrating some of its properties, felt that to name a thing is not necessarily to have it. They advanced the proposition that no Johanssen Block could be expected to remain suspended in midair, equally resisting all forces exerted upon it, and to this Mr. Heartly agreed.

They stated that since the metal cube had been shown in certain respects to possess perfectly natural qualities and quantities, it must be assumed that its apparently unnatural qualities were capable of a natural and materialistic explanation. All that was needed was a patient application of the scientific method until the truth was made known.

To this the churchmen dissented. They did not deny that the block was a Johanssen Block if Mr. Heartly said it was, nor that it possessed some of the attributes of a Johanssen Block. But it did not possess all of those attributes, and the Divine purpose was to make the basic contradiction more clear. The shiny cube was sent to demonstrate that the fundamental mystery can never be discovered with man-made measuring sticks, not even that incorporeal measuring stick, the higher mathematics.

By now it was past noon and John Thomas suddenly realized that he was hungry. Not only that, but most of the discussions he had been hearing were totally without meaning for him. He recognized a word here and there, but that was all. It is true that the general feeling of excitement and wonder had communicated itself to him and he had enjoyed being the center, directly and indirectly, of so much attention. But at last he was bored and wanted his lunch.

His mother took him into the house and made him a peanut butter and jelly sandwich and gave him a glass of milk. While he was eating, he said to her, "Mother, do you like having that funny block in our back yard and all those queer people?"

"No," she said, "I don't. I'll never get any work done, and all that talk makes my head swim. I don't know who's right and who's wrong, but I do know that your father will want to stay around to superintend things, and the people he works for won't like that. I wish that block would take itself off to whatever place it came from."

"So do I," John Thomas said. "I'm tired of it."

At that precise moment there was a shout from the yard. "It's gone. The block has gone."

So it had. The mayor noted this fact with relief, since he believed that once the object that had caused so much discord and disquiet no longer existed, the problems it had raised were no longer of any importance. He stated this point of view and found that the majority of those present agreed with him, which, of course, is why he had been elected mayor.

The crowd dispersed at his direction, peaceably, except for the scientists and the churchmen, who could be seen contending for their respective positions as they walked off down the street.

As for John Thomas, he heard no more of the affair until that night at supper, but what he didn't know was that his father and mother had been holding a conference about him. His father approached the problem obliquely, as is the custom with parents.

"John Thomas," he said, "your mother tells me that the moment you said you were tired of the block, it disappeared. Is that right?"

"What block, Father?" John Thomas said.

"You know very well what block. The block in our back yard that caused all the trouble and excitement this morning."

Actually, being only eight years old, John Thomas had forgotten about the block. "Oh," he said, "that block."

"Yes, that block," his father said. "I know you had something to do with its being there. You were the first to see it, and when you said you were tired of it, it was gone. Did you have some reason why you didn't want to go to school today? Did you play during study hour yesterday and fail to prepare your lessons?"

When confronted with this partly right guess, John Thomas supposed that everything was known and that the best thing was to confess his crime in detail.

"It wasn't my fault," he said. "Billy Dixon kept whispering to me and writing notes and I couldn't get my work done. When I woke up this morning, I thought wouldn't it be swell if I didn't have to go to school. And then I thought that if there was a shiny little cube in the back yard that nobody could lift or move, maybe everyone would get so interested that I wouldn't have to. Then I got to thinking there was such a cube, and when I went out to see, it was there."

The next morning John Thomas's father and mother took him to Dr. Emanuel Klein, the famous psychiatrist with offices in the Rookery Building. Like nearly everyone else in town, Dr. Klein was familiar with the facts in the case, and indeed had spent the previous evening discussing it with members of the committee of inquiry from the university. However, he was devoted to his profession and conscientious in the practice of it, and therefore first listened to a detailed account of the events as described by the Thompsons, and then proceeded with a careful examination of the boy himself.

John Thomas spent nearly an hour having his reflexes tested, starting at sudden noises, arranging blocks, sorting colors, identifying qualities of tone, and finding his way through labyrinths with pencil on paper. He then answered questions as politely and accurately as he could about the food he ate, how he liked his school, what his favorite games were, and the content of any dreams he could remember. When the examination at last was finished, Dr. Klein with great solemnity pronounced the opinion he had formed the night before.

In every respect save one, he said, John Thomas was perfectly normal for a boy of his age. He was above average in intelligence, had an excellent emotional balance, and was on the whole happy and content with his life. For this his parents were to be congratulated.

Nevertheless, he did have an unusually vivid imagination and was subject to hallucinations, auditory, visual, and tactual. Further, through the operation of a kind of mass hypnosis, he had the rare faculty of making the creation of his imagination as real to others as to himself. Hallucinations, however, are likely to become antisocial, as witness the perverse characteristics of John Thomas's cube, and dangerous, therefore, to the subject and his family. For this reason, Dr. Klein recommended a series of treatments designed to teach John Thomas to distinguish between the fabrications of his subconscious mind and the hearty, solid world outside of him.

Mr. and Mrs. Thompson, relieved that it was no worse, agreed to this program. They took the boy home confident that he soon would be able to tell the false from the true, the imagined from the

real, as easily as the next one. As for John Thomas, he determined
never again to admit adults to his own special world. The fuss they
stirred up, he decided, wasn't worth it.

In Hiding

WILMAR H. SHIRAS

*I have sometimes amused myself by endeavoring to
fancy what would be the fate of any individual gifted, or
rather accursed, with an intellect very far superior to
that of his race. Of course, he would be conscious of his
superiority; nor could he (if otherwise constituted as
man is) help manifesting his consciousness. Thus he
would make himself enemies at all points. And since his
opinions and speculations would widely differ from those
of all mankind — that he would be considered a madman,
is evident. How horribly painful such a condition! Hell
could invent no greater torture than that of being
charged with abnormal weakness on account of being
abnormally strong.*

— EDGAR ALLAN POE: "Marginalia"
Southern Literary Messenger, June 1849

PETER WELLES, psychiatrist, eyed the boy thoughtfully. Why
had Timothy Paul's teacher sent him for examination?

"I don't know, myself, that there's really anything wrong with
Tim," Miss Page had told Dr. Welles. "He seems perfectly normal.
He's rather quiet as a rule, doesn't volunteer answers in class or
anything of that sort. He gets along well enough with other
boys and seems reasonably popular, although he has no special
friends. His grades are satisfactory — he gets B faithfully in all his
work. But when you've been teaching as long as I have, Peter, you

get a feeling about certain ones. There is a tension about him — a look in his eyes sometimes — and he is very absent-minded."

"What would your guess be?" Welles had asked. Sometimes these hunches were very valuable. Miss Page had taught school for thirty-odd years; she had been Peter's teacher in the past, and he thought highly of her opinion.

"I ought not to say," she answered. "There's nothing to go on — yet. But he might be starting something, and if it could be headed off —"

"Physicians are often called before the symptoms are sufficiently marked for the doctor to be able to see them," said Welles. "A patient, or the mother of a child, or any practiced observer, can often see that something is going to be wrong. But it's hard for the doctor in such cases. Tell me what you think I should look for."

"You won't pay too much attention to me? It's just what occurred to me, Peter; I know I'm not a trained psychiatrist. But it could be delusions of grandeur. Or it could be a withdrawing from the society of others. I always have to speak to him twice to get his attention in class — and he has no real chums."

Welles had agreed to see what he could find, and promised not to be too much influenced by what Miss Page herself called "an old woman's notions."

Timothy, when he presented himself for examination, seemed like an ordinary boy. He was perhaps a little small for his age, he had big dark eyes and close-cropped dark curls, thin sensitive fingers and — yes, a decided air of tension. But many boys were nervous on their first visit to the — psychiatrist. Peter often wished that he was able to concentrate on one or two schools, and spend a day a week or so getting acquainted with all the youngsters.

In response to Welles's preliminary questioning, Tim replied in a clear, low voice, politely and without wasting words. He was thirteen years old, and lived with his grandparents. His mother and father had died when he was a baby, and he did not remember them. He said that he was happy at home, that he liked school "pretty well," that he liked to play with other boys. He named several boys when asked who his friends were.

"What lessons do you like at school?"

Tim hesitated, then said: "English, and arithmetic . . . and history . . . and geography," he finished thoughtfully. Then he looked up, and there was something odd in the glance.

"What do you like to do for fun?"

"Read, and play games."

"What games?"

"Ball games . . . and marbles . . . and things like that. I like to play with other boys," he added, after a barely perceptible pause, "anything they play."

"Do they play at your house?"

"No; we play on the school grounds. My grandmother doesn't like noise."

Was that the reason? When a quiet boy offers explanations, they may not be the right ones.

"What do you like to read?"

But about his reading Timothy was vague. He liked, he said, to read "boys' books," but could not name any.

Welles gave the boy the usual intelligence tests. Tim seemed willing, but his replies were slow in coming. *Perhaps*, Welles thought, *I'm imagining this, but he is too careful — too cautious.* Without taking time to figure exactly, Welles knew what Tim's I.Q. would be — about 120.

"What do you do outside of school?" asked the psychiatrist.

"I play with the other boys. After supper, I study my lessons."

"What did you do yesterday?"

"We played ball on the school playground."

Welles waited a while to see whether Tim would say anything of his own accord. The seconds stretched into minutes.

"Is that all?" said the boy finally. "May I go now?"

"No; there's one more test I'd like to give you today. A game, really. How's your imagination?"

"I don't know."

"Cracks on the ceiling — like those over there — do they look like anything to you? Faces, animals, or anything?"

Tim looked.

"Sometimes. And clouds, too. Bob saw a cloud last week that was like a hippo." Again the last sentence sounded like something tacked on at the last moment, a careful addition made for a reason.

Welles got out the Rorschach cards. But at the sight of them, his patient's tension increased, his wariness became unmistakably evident. The first time they went through the cards, the boy could scarcely be persuaded to say anything but "I don't know."

"You can do better than this," said Welles. "We're going through them again. If you don't see anything in these pictures, I have to mark you a failure," he explained. "That won't do. You did all right on the other things. And maybe next time we'll do a game you'll like better."

"I don't feel like playing this game now. Can't we do it again next time?"

"May as well get it done now. It's not only a game, you know, Tim; it's a test. Try harder, and be a good sport."

So Tim, this time, told what he saw in the ink blots. They went through the cards slowly, and the test showed Tim's fear, and that there was something he was hiding; it showed his caution, a lack of trust, and an unnaturally high emotional self-control.

Miss Page had been right; the boy needed help.

"Now," said Welles cheerfully, "that's all over. We'll just run through them again quickly and I'll tell you what other people have seen in them."

A flash of genuine interest appeared on the boy's face for a moment.

Welles went through the cards slowly, seeing that Tim was attentive to every word. When he first said, "And some see what you saw here," the boy's relief was evident. Tim began to relax, and even to volunteer some remarks. When they had finished he ventured to ask a question.

"Dr. Welles, could you tell me the name of this test?"

"It's sometimes called the Rorschach test, after the man who worked it out."

"Would you mind spelling that?"

Welles spelled it, and added: "Sometimes it's called the ink-blot test."

Tim gave a start of surprise, and then relaxed again with a visible effort.

"What's the matter? You jumped."

"Nothing."

"Oh, come on! Let's have it," and Welles waited.

"Only that I thought about the ink-pool in the Kipling stories," said Tim, after a minute's reflection. "This is different."

"Yes, very different," laughed Welles. "I've never tried that. Would you like to?"

"Oh, no, sir," cried Tim earnestly.

"You're a little jumpy today," said Welles. "We've time for some more talk, if you are not too tired."

"No, I'm not very tired," said the boy warily.

Welles went to a drawer and chose a hypodermic needle. It wasn't usual, but perhaps — "I'll just give you a little shot to relax your nerves, shall I? Then we'd get on better."

When he turned around, the stark terror on the child's face stopped Welles in his tracks.

"Oh, no! Don't! Please, please, don't!"

Welles replaced the needle and shut the drawer before he said a word.

"I won't," he said, quietly. "I didn't know you didn't like shots. I won't give you any, Tim."

The boy, fighting for self-control, gulped and said nothing.

"It'll all right," said Welles, lighting a cigarette and pretending to watch the smoke rise. Anything rather than appear to be watching the badly shaken small boy shivering in the chair opposite him. "Sorry. You didn't tell me about the things you don't like, the things you're afraid of."

The words hung in the silence.

"Yes," said Timothy slowly. "I'm afraid of shots. I hate needles. It's just one of those things." He tried to smile.

"We'll do without them, then. You've passed all the tests, Tim, and I'd like to walk home with you and tell your grandmother about it. Is that all right with you?"

"Yes, sir."

"We'll stop for something to eat," Welles went on, opening the door for his patient. "Ice cream, or a hot dog."

They went out together.

Timothy Paul's grandparents, Mr. and Mrs. Herbert Davis, lived in a large old-fashioned house that spelled money and position. The grounds were large, fenced, and bordered with shrubbery. Inside the house there was little that was new; everything was well-kept. Timothy led the psychiatrist to Mr. Davis's library, and then went in search of his grandmother.

When Welles saw Mrs. Davis, he thought he had some of the explanation. Some grandmothers are easygoing, jolly, comparatively young. This grandmother was, as soon became apparent, quite different.

"Yes, Timothy is a pretty good boy," she said, smiling on her grandson. "We have always been strict with him, Dr. Welles, but I believe it pays. Even when he was a mere baby, we tried to teach him right ways. For example, when he was barely three I read him some little stories. And a few days later he was trying to tell us, if you will believe it, that he could read! Perhaps he was too young to know the nature of a lie, but I felt it my duty to make him understand. When he insisted, I spanked him. The child had a remarkable memory, and perhaps he thought that was all there was to reading. Well! I don't mean to brag of my brutality," said Mrs. Davis, with a charming smile. "I assure you, Dr. Welles, it was a painful experience for me. We've had very little occasion for punishments. Timothy is a good boy."

Welles murmured that he was sure of it.

"Timothy, you may deliver your papers now," said Mrs. Davis.

"I am sure Dr. Welles will excuse you." And she settled herself for a good long talk about her grandson.

Timothy, it seemed, was the apple of her eye. He was a quiet boy, an obedient boy, and a bright boy.

"We have our rules, of course. I have never allowed Timothy to forget that children should be seen and not heard, as the good old-fashioned saying is. When he first learned to turn somersaults, when he was three or four years old, he kept coming to me and saying, 'Grandmother, see me!' I simply had to be firm with him. 'Timothy,' I said, 'let us have no more of this! It is simply showing off. If it amuses you to turn somersaults, well and good. But it doesn't amuse me to watch you endlessly doing it. Play if you like, but do not demand admiration.'"

"Did you never play with him?"

"Certainly I played with him. And it was a pleasure to me also. We — Mr. Davis and I — taught him a great many games, and many kinds of handcraft. We read stories to him and taught him rhymes and songs. I took a special course in kindergarten craft, to amuse the child — and I must admit that it amused me also!" added Tim's grandmother, smiling reminiscently. "We made houses of toothpicks, with balls of clay at the corners. His grandfather took him for walks and drives. We no longer have a car, since my husband's sight has begun to fail him slightly, so now the garage is Timothy's workshop. We had windows cut in it, and a door, and nailed the large doors shut."

It soon became clear that Tim's life was not all strictures by any means. He had a workshop of his own, and upstairs beside his bedroom was his own library and study.

"He keeps his books and treasures there," said his grandmother, "his own little radio, and his schoolbooks, and his typewriter. When he was only seven years old, he asked us for a typewriter. But he is a careful child, Dr. Welles, not at all destructive, and I had read that in many schools they make use of typewriters in teaching young children to read and write and to spell. The words look the same as in printed books, you see; and less muscular effort is involved. So his grandfather got him a very nice noiseless typewriter, and he loved it dearly. I often hear it purring away as I pass through the hall. Timothy keeps his own rooms in good order, and his shop also. It is his own wish. You know how boys are — they do not wish others to meddle with their belongings. 'Very well, Timothy,' I told him, 'if a glance shows me that you can do it yourself properly, nobody will go into your rooms; but they must be kept neat.' And he has done so for several years. A very neat boy, Timothy."

"Timothy didn't mention his paper route," remarked Welles. "He said only that he plays with other boys after school."

"Oh, but he does," said Mrs. Davis. "He plays until five o'clock, and then he delivers his papers. If he is late, his grandfather walks down and calls him. The school is not very far from here, and Mr. Davis frequently walks down and watches the boys at their play. The paper route is Timothy's way of earning money to feed his cats. Do you care for cats, Dr. Welles?"

"Yes, I like cats very much," said the psychiatrist. "Many boys like dogs better."

"Timothy had a dog when he was a baby — a collie." Her eyes grew moist. "We all loved Ruff dearly. But I am no longer young, and the care and training of a dog is difficult. Timothy is at school or at the Boy Scout camp or something of the sort a great part of the time, and I thought it best that he should not have another dog. But you wanted to know about our cats, Dr. Welles. I raise Siamese cats."

"Interesting pets," said Welles cordially. "My aunt raised them at one time."

"Timothy is very fond of them. But three years ago he asked me if he could have a pair of black Persians. At first I thought not; but we like to please the child, and he promised to build their cages himself. He had taken a course in carpentry at vacation school. So he was allowed to have a pair of beautiful black Persians. But the very first litter turned out to be short-haired, and Timothy confessed that he had mated his queen to my Siamese tom, to see what would happen. Worse yet, he had mated his tom to one of my Siamese queens. I really was tempted to punish him. But, after all, I could see that he was curious as to the outcome of such crossbreeding. Of course I said the kittens must be destroyed. The second litter was exactly like the first — all black, with short hair. But you know what children are. Timothy begged me to let them live, and they were his first kittens. Three in one litter, two in the other. He might keep them, I said, if he would take full care of them and be responsible for all the expense. He mowed lawns and ran errands and made little footstools and bookcases to sell, and did all sorts of things, and probably used his allowance, too. But he kept the kittens and has a whole row of cages in the yard beside his workshop."

"And their offspring?" inquired Welles, who could not see what all this had to do with the main question, but was willing to listen to anything that might lead to information.

"Some of the kittens appear to be pure Persian, and others pure Siamese. These he insisted on keeping, although, as I have explained to him, it would be dishonest to sell them, since they are not pure-bred. A good many of the kittens are black short-haired and these we destroy. But enough of cats, Dr. Welles. And I am afraid I am talking too much about my grandson."

"I can understand that you are very proud of him," said Welles.

"I must confess that we are. And he is a bright boy. When he and his grandfather talk together, and with me also, he asks very intelligent questions. We do not encourage him to voice his opinions — I detest the smart-Aleck type of small boy — and yet I believe they would be quite good opinions for a child of his age."

"Has his health always been good?" asked Welles.

"On the whole, very good. I have taught him the value of exercise, play, wholesome food and suitable rest. He has had a few of the usual childish ailments, not seriously. And he never has colds. But, of course, he takes his cold shots twice a year when we do."

"Does he mind the shots?" asked Welles, as casually as he could.

"Not at all. I always say that he, though so young, sets an example I find hard to follow. I still flinch, and really rather dread the ordeal."

Welles looked toward the door at a sudden, slight sound.

Timothy stood there, and he had heard. Again, fear was stamped on his face and terror looked out of his eyes.

"Timothy," said his grandmother, "don't stare."

"Sorry, sir," the boy managed to say.

"Are your papers all delivered? I did not realize we had been talking for an hour, Dr. Welles. Would you like to see Timothy's cats?" Mrs. Davis inquired graciously. "Timothy, take Dr. Welles to see your pets. We have had quite a talk about them."

Welles got Tim out of the room as fast as he could. The boy led the way around the house and into the side yard where the former garage stood.

There the man stopped.

"Tim," he said, "you don't have to show me the cats if you don't want to."

"Oh, that's all right."

"Is that part of what you are hiding? If it is, I don't want to see it until you are ready to show me."

Tim looked up at him then.

"Thanks," he said. "I don't mind about the cats. Not if you like cats really."

"I really do. But, Tim, this I would like to know: You're not afraid of the needle. Could you tell me why you were afraid . . . why you said you were afraid . . . of my shot? The one I promised not to give you after all?"

Their eyes met.

"You won't tell?" asked Tim.

"I won't tell."

"Because it was pentothal. Wasn't it?"

Welles gave himself a slight pinch. Yes, he was awake. Yes, this was a little boy asking him about pentothal. A boy who — Yes, certainly, a boy who knew about it.

"Yes, it was," said Welles. "A very small dose. You know what it is?"

"Yes, sir. I . . . I read about it somewhere. In the papers."

"Never mind that. You have a secret — something you want to hide. That's what you are afraid about, isn't it?"

The boy nodded dumbly.

"If it's anything wrong, or that might be wrong, perhaps I could help you. You'll want to know me better, first. You'll want to be sure you can trust me. But I'll be glad to help, any time you say the word, Tim. Or I might stumble on to things the way I did just now. One thing though — I never tell secrets."

"Never?"

"Never. Doctors and priests don't betray secrets. Doctors seldom, priests never. I guess I am more like a priest, because of the kind of doctoring I do."

He looked down at the boy's bowed head.

"Helping fellows who are scared sick," said the psychiatrist very gently. "Helping fellows in trouble, getting things straight again, fixing things up, unsnarling tangles. When I can, that's what I do. And I don't tell anything to anybody. It's just between that one fellow and me."

But, he added to himself, *I'll have to find out. I'll have to find out what ails this child. Miss Page is right* — *he needs me.*

They went to see the cats.

There were the Siamese in their cages, and the Persians in their cages, and there, in several small cages, the short-haired black cats and their hybrid offspring. "We take them into the house, or let them into this big cage, for exercise," explained Tim. "I take mine into my shop sometimes. These are all mine. Grandmother keeps hers on the sun porch."

"You'd never know these were not all pure-bred," observed Welles. "Which did you say were the full Persians? Any of their kittens here?"

"No; I sold them."

"I'd like to buy one. But these look just the same — it wouldn't make any difference to me. I want a pet, and wouldn't use it for breeding stock. Would you sell me one of these?"

Timothy shook his head.

"I'm sorry. I never sell any but the pure-breds."

It was then that Welles began to see what problem he faced. Very dimly he saw it, with joy, relief, hope and wild enthusiasm.

"Why not?" urged Welles. "I can wait for a pure-bred, if you'd rather, but why not one of these? They look just the same. Perhaps they'd be more interesting."

Tim looked at Welles for a long, long minute.

"I'll show you," he said. "Promise to wait here? No, I'll let you come into the workroom. Wait a minute, please."

The boy drew a key from under his blouse, where it had hung suspended from a chain, and unlocked the door of his shop. He went inside, closed the door, and Welles could hear him moving about for a few moments. Then he came to the door and beckoned.

"Don't tell Grandmother," said Tim. "I haven't told her yet. If it lives, I'll tell her next week."

In the corner of the shop under a table there was a box, and in the box there was a Siamese cat. When she saw a stranger she tried to hide her kittens; but Tim lifted her gently, and then Welles saw. Two of the kittens looked like little white rats with stringy tails and smudgy paws, ears and noses. But the third — yes, it was going to be a different sight. It was going to be a beautiful cat if it lived. It had long, silky white hair like the finest Persian, and the Siamese markings were showing up plainly.

Welles caught his breath.

"Congratulations, old man! Haven't you told anyone yet?"

"She's not ready to show. She's not a month old."

"But you're going to show her?"

"Oh, yes, Grandmother will be thrilled. She'll love her. Maybe there'll be more."

"You knew this would happen. You made it happen. You planned it all from the start," accused Welles.

"Yes," admitted the boy.

"How did you know?"

The boy turned away.

"I read it somewhere," said Tim.

The cat jumped back into the box and began to nurse her babies. Welles felt as if he could endure no more. Without a glance at anything else in the room — and everything else was hidden under tarpaulins and newspapers — he went to the door.

"Thanks for showing me, Tim," he said. "And when you have any to sell, remember me. I'll wait. I want one like that."

The boy followed him out and locked the door carefully.

"But, Tim," said the psychiatrist, "that's not what you were afraid I'd find out. I wouldn't need a drug to get you to tell me this, would I?"

Tim replied carefully, "I didn't want to tell this until I was ready. Grandmother really ought to know first. But you made me tell you."

"Tim," said Peter Welles earnestly, "I'll see you again. Whatever you are afraid of, don't be afraid of me. I often guess secrets. I'm on the way to guessing yours already. But nobody else need ever know."

He walked rapidly home, whistling to himself from time to time. Perhaps he, Peter Welles, was the luckiest man in the world.

He had scarcely begun to talk to Timothy on the boy's next appearance at the office, when the phone in the hall rang. On his return, when he opened the door he saw a book in Tim's hands. The boy made a move as if to hide it, and thought better of it.

Welles took the book and looked at it.

"Want to know more about Rorschach, eh?" he asked.

"I saw it on the shelf. I —"

"Oh, that's all right," said Welles, who had purposely left the book near the chair Tim would occupy. "But what's the matter with the library?"

"They've got some books about it, but they're on the closed shelves. I couldn't get them." Tim spoke without thinking first, and then caught his breath.

But Welles replied calmly: "I'll get it out for you. I'll have it next time you come. Take this one along today when you go. Tim, I mean it — you can trust me."

"I can't tell you anything," said the boy. "You've found out some things. I wish . . . oh, I don't know what I wish! But I'd rather be let alone. I don't need help. Maybe I never will. If I do, can't I come to you then?"

Welles pulled out his chair and sat down slowly.

"Perhaps that would be the best way, Tim. But why wait for the ax to fall? I might be able to help you ward it off — what you're afraid of. You can kid people along about the cats; tell them you were fooling around to see what would happen. But you can't fool all of the people all of the time, they tell me. Maybe with me to help, you could. Or with me to back you up, the blowup would be easier. Easier on your grandparents, too."

"I haven't done anything wrong!"

"I'm beginning to be sure of that. But things you try to keep hidden may come to light. The kitten — you could hide it, but you don't want to. You've got to risk something to show it."

"I'll tell them I read it somewhere."

"That wasn't true, then. I thought not. You figured it out."

There was silence.

Then Timothy Paul said: "Yes. I figured it out. But that's my secret."

"It's safe with me."

But the boy did not trust him yet. Welles soon learned that he had been tested. Tim took the book home, and returned it, took the library books which Welles got for him, and in due course returned them also. But he talked little and was still wary. Welles could talk all he liked, but he got little or nothing out of Tim. Tim had told all he was going to tell. He would talk about nothing except what any boy would talk about.

After two months of this, during which Welles saw Tim officially once a week and unofficially several times — showing up at the school playground to watch games, or meeting Tim on the paper route and treating him to a soda after it was finished — Welles had learned very little more. He tried again. He had probed no more during the two months, respected the boy's silence, trying to give him time to get to know and trust him.

But one day he asked: "What are you going to do when you grow up, Tim? Breed cats?"

Tim laughed a denial.

"I don't know what, yet. Sometimes I think one thing, sometimes another."

This was a typical boy answer. Welles disregarded it.

"What would you like to do best of all?" he asked.

Tim leaned forward eagerly. "What you do!" he cried.

"You've been reading up on it, I suppose," said Welles, as casually as he could. "Then you know, perhaps, that before anyone can do what I do, he must go through it himself, like a patient. He must also study medicine and be a full-fledged doctor, of course. You can't do that yet. But you can have the works now, like a patient."

"Why? For the experience?"

"Yes. And for the cure. You'll have to face that fear and lick it. You'll have to straighten out a lot of other things, or at least face them."

"My fear will be gone when I'm grown up," said Timothy. "I think it will. I hope it will."

"Can you be sure?"

"No," admitted the boy. "I don't know exactly why I'm afraid. I just know I *must* hide things. Is that bad, too?"

"Dangerous, perhaps."

Timothy thought a while in silence. Welles smoked three cigarettes and yearned to pace the floor, but dared not move.

"What would it be like?" asked Tim finally.

"You'd tell me about yourself. What you remember. Your childhood — the way your grandmother runs on when she talks about you."

"She sent me out of the room. I'm not supposed to think I'm bright," said Tim, with one of his rare grins.

"And you're not supposed to know how well she reared you?"

"She did fine," said Tim. "She taught me all the wisest things I ever knew."

"Such as what?"

"Such as shutting up. Not telling all you know. Not showing off."

"I see what you mean," said Welles. "Have you heard the story of St. Thomas Aquinas?"

"No."

"When he was a student in Paris, he never spoke out in class, and the others thought him stupid. One of them kindly offered to help him, and went over all the work very patiently to make him understand it. And then one day they came to a place where the other student got all mixed up and had to admit he didn't understand. Then Thomas suggested a solution and it was the right one. He knew more than any of the others all the time; but they called him the Dumb Ox."

Tim nodded gravely.

"And when he grew up?" asked the boy.

"He was the greatest thinker of all time," said Welles. "A fourteenth-century super-brain. He did more original work than any other ten great men; and he died young."

After that, it was easier.

"How do I begin?" asked Timothy.

"You'd better begin at the beginning. Tell me all you can remember about your early childhood, before you went to school."

Tim gave this his consideration.

"I'll have to go forward and backward a lot," he said. "I couldn't put it all in order."

"That's all right. Just tell me today all you can remember about that time of your life. By next week you'll have remembered more. As we go on to later periods of your life, you may remember things that belonged to an earlier time; tell them then. We'll make some sort of order out of it."

Welles listened to the boy's revelations with growing excitement. He found it difficult to keep outwardly calm.

"When did you begin to read?" Welles asked.

"I don't know when it was. My grandmother read me some stories, and somehow I got the idea about the words. But when I tried to tell her I could read, she spanked me. She kept saying I couldn't, and I kept saying I could, until she spanked me. For a while I had a dreadful time, because I didn't know any word she hadn't read to me — I guess I sat beside her and watched, or else I remembered and then went over it by myself right after. I must have learned as soon as I got the idea that each group of letters on the page was a word."

"The word-unit method," Welles commented. "Most self-taught readers learned like that."

"Yes. I have read about it since. And Macaulay could read when he was three, but only upside-down, because of standing opposite when his father read the Bible to the family."

"There are many cases of children who learned to read as you did, and surprised their parents. Well? How did you get on?"

"One day I noticed that two words looked almost alike and sounded almost alike. They were 'can' and 'man.' I remember staring at them and then it was like something beautiful boiling up in me. I began to look carefully at the words, but in a crazy excitement. I was a long while at it, because when I put down the book and tried to stand up I was stiff all over. But I had the idea, and after that it wasn't hard to figure out almost any words. The really hard words are the common ones that you get all the time in easy books. Other words are pronounced the way they are spelled."

"And nobody knew you could read?"

"No. Grandmother told me not to say I could, so I didn't. She read to me often, and that helped. We had a great many books, of course, I liked those with pictures. Once or twice they caught me with a book that had no pictures, and then they'd take it away and say, 'I'll find a book for a little boy.'"

"Do you remember what books you liked then?"

"Books about animals, I remember. And geographies. It was funny about animals —"

Once you got Timothy started, thought Welles, it wasn't hard to get him to go on talking.

"One day I was at the zoo," said Tim, "and by the cages alone.

Grandmother was resting on a bench and she let me walk along by myself. People were talking about the animals and I began to tell them all I knew. It must have been funny in a way, because I had read a lot of words I couldn't pronounce correctly, words I had never heard spoken. They listened and asked me questions and I thought I was just like grandfather, teaching them the way he sometimes taught me. And then they called another man to come, and said, 'Listen to this kid; he's a scream!' and I saw they were all laughing at me."

Timothy's face was redder than usual, but he tried to smile as he added, "I can see now how it must have sounded funny. And unexpected, too; that's a big point in humor. But my little feelings were so dreadfully hurt that I ran back to my grandmother crying, and she couldn't find out why. But it served me right for disobeying her. She always told me not to tell people things; she said a child had nothing to teach its elders."

"Not in that way, perhaps — at that age."

"But, honestly, some grown people don't know very much," said Tim. "When we went on the train last year, a woman came up and sat beside me and started to tell me things a little boy should know about California. I told her I'd lived here all my life, but I guess she didn't even know we are taught things in school, and she tried to tell me things, and almost everything was wrong."

"Such as what?" asked Welles, who had also suffered from tourists.

"We . . . she said so many things . . . but I thought this was the funniest: She said all the Missions were so old and interesting, and I said yes, and she said, 'You know, they were all built long before Columbus discovered America,' and I thought she meant it for a joke, so I laughed. She looked very serious and said, 'Yes, those people all came here from Mexico.' I suppose she thought they were Aztec temples."

Welles, shaking with laughter, could not but agree that many adults were sadly lacking in the rudiments of knowledge.

"After that zoo experience, and a few others like it, I began to get wise to myself," continued Tim. "People who knew things didn't want to hear me repeating them, and people who didn't know, wouldn't be taught by a four-year-old baby. I guess I was four when I began to write."

"How?"

"Oh, I just thought if I couldn't say anything to anybody at any time, I'd burst. So I began to put it down — in printing, like in books. Then I found out about writing, and we had some old-fashioned schoolbooks that taught how to write. I'm left-handed. When I went to school, I had to use my right hand. But by then I had learned how to pretend that I didn't know things. I watched the others and did as they did. My grandmother told me to do that."

"I wonder why she said that," marveled Welles.

"She knew I wasn't used to other children, she said, and it was the first time she had left me to anyone else's care. So she told me to do what the others did and what my teacher said," explained Tim simply, "and I followed her advice literally. I pretended I didn't know anything, until the others began to know it, too. Lucky I was so shy. But there were things to learn, all right. Do you know, when I first went to school, I was disappointed because the teacher dressed like other women. The only picture of teachers I had noticed were those in an old Mother Goose book, and I thought that all teachers wore hoop skirts. But as soon as I saw her, after the little shock of surprise, I knew it was silly, and I never told."

The psychiatrist and the boy laughed together.

"We played games. I had to learn to play with children, and not be surprised when they slapped or pushed me. I just couldn't figure out why they'd do that, or what good it did them. But if it was to surprise me, I'd say 'Boo' and surprise them some time later; and if they were mad because I had taken a ball or something they wanted, I'd play with them."

"Anybody ever try to beat you up?"

"Oh, yes. But I had a book about boxing — with pictures. You can't learn much from pictures, but I got some practice too, and that helped. I didn't want to win, anyway. That's what I like about games of strength or skill — I'm fairly matched, and I don't have to be always watching in case I might show off or try to boss somebody around."

"You must have tried bossing sometimes."

"In books, they all cluster around the boy who can teach new games and think up things to play. But I found out that doesn't work. They just want to do the same thing all the time — like hide and seek. It's no fun if the first one to be caught is 'it' next time. The rest just walk in any old way and don't try to hide or even to run, because it doesn't matter whether they are caught. But you can't get the boys to see that, and play right, so the last one caught is 'it.' "

Timothy looked at his watch.

"Time to go," he said. "I've enjoyed talking to you, Dr. Welles. I hope I haven't bored you too much."

Welles recognized the echo and smiled appreciatively at the small boy.

"You didn't tell me about the writing. Did you start to keep a diary?"

"No. It was a newspaper. One page a day, no more and no less. I still keep it," confided Tim. "But I get more on the page now. I type it."

"And you write with either hand now?"

"My left hand is my own secret writing. For school and things like that I use my right hand."

When Timothy had left, Welles congratulated himself. But for the next month he got no more. Tim would not reveal a single significant fact. He talked about ball playing, he described his grandmother's astonished delight over the beautiful kitten, he told of its growth and the tricks it played. He gravely related such enthralling facts as that he liked to ride on trains, that his favorite wild animal was the lion, and that he greatly desired to see snow falling. But not a word of what Welles wanted to hear. The psychiatrist, knowing that he was again being tested, waited patiently.

Then one afternoon when Welles, fortunately unoccupied with a patient, was smoking a pipe on his front porch, Timothy Paul strode into the yard.

"Yesterday Miss Page asked me if I was seeing you and I said yes. She said she hoped my grandparents didn't find it too expensive, because you had told her I was all right and didn't need to have her worrying about me. And then I said to Grandma, was it expensive for you to talk to me, and she said, 'Oh no, dear; the school pays for that. It was your teacher's idea that you have a few talks with Dr. Welles.'"

"I'm glad you came to me, Tim, and I'm sure you didn't give me away to either of them. Nobody's paying me. The school pays for my services if a child is in a bad way and his parents are poor. It's a new service, since 1956. Many maladjusted children can be helped — much more cheaply to the State than the cost of having them go crazy or become criminals or something. You understand all that. But — sit down, Tim — I can't charge the State for you, and I can't charge your grandparents. You're adjusted marvelously well in every way, as far as I can see; and when I see the rest, I'll be even more sure of it."

"Well — gosh! I wouldn't have come —" Tim was stammering in confusion. "You ought to be paid. I take up so much of your time. Maybe I'd better not come any more."

"I think you'd better. Don't you?"

"Why are you doing it for nothing, Dr. Welles?"

"I think you know why."

The boy sat down in the glider and pushed himself meditatively back and forth. The glider squeaked.

"You're interested. You're curious," he said.

"That's not all, Tim."

Squeak-squeak. Squeak-squeak.

"I know," said Timothy. "I believe it. Look, is it all right if I call you Peter? Since we're friends."

At their next meeting, Timothy went into details about his newspaper. He had kept all the copies, from the first smudged, awkwardly printed pencil issues to the very latest neatly typed ones. But he would not show Welles any of them.

"I just put down every day the things I most wanted to say, the news or information or opinion I had to swallow unsaid. So it's a wild medley. The earlier copies are awfully funny. Sometimes I guess what they were all about, what made me write them. Sometimes I remember. I put down the books I read too, and mark them like school grades, on two points — how I liked the book, and whether it was good. And whether I had read it before, too."

"How many books do you read? What's your reading speed?"

It proved that Timothy's reading speed on new books of adult level varied from eight hundred to nine hundred fifty words a minute. The average murder mystery — he loved them — took him less than half an hour. A year's homework in history, Tim performed easily by reading his textbook through three or four times during the year. He apologized for that, but explained that he had to know what was in the book so as not to reveal in examinations too much that he had learned from other sources. Evenings, when his grandparents believed him to be doing homework, he spent reading other books, or writing his newspaper, "or something." As Welles had already guessed, Tim had read everything in his grandfather's library, everything in the public library that was not on the closed shelves, and everything he could order from the state library.

"What do the librarians say?"

"They think the books are for my grandfather. I tell them that, if they ask what a little boy wants with such a big book. Peter, telling so many lies is what gets me down. I have to do it, don't I?"

"As far as I can see, you do," agreed Welles. "But here's material for a while in my library. There'll have to be a closed shelf here, too, though, Tim."

"Could you tell me why? I know about the library books. Some of them might scare people, and some are —"

"Some of my books might scare you too, Tim. I'll tell you a little about abnormal psychology if you like, one of these days, and then I think you'll see that until you're actually training to deal with such cases, you'd be better off not knowing too much about them."

"I don't want to be morbid," agreed Tim. "All right. I'll read only what you give me. And from now on I'll tell you things. There was more than the newspaper, you know."

"I thought as much. Do you want to go on with your tale?"

"It started when I first wrote a letter to a newspaper — of course, under a pen name. They printed it. For a while I had a high old time of it — a letter almost every day, using all sorts of pen names. Then I branched out to magazines, letters to the editor again. And stories — I tried stories."

He looked a little doubtfully at Welles, who said only: "How old were you when you sold the first story?"

"Eight," said Timothy. "And when the check came, with my name on it, 'T. Paul,' I didn't know what in the world to do."

"That's a thought. What did you do?"

"There was a sign in the window of the bank. I always read signs, and that one came back to my mind. 'Banking by Mail.' You can see I was pretty desperate. So I got the name of a bank across the Bay and I wrote them — on my typewriter — and said I wanted to start an account, and here was a check to start it with. Oh, I was scared stiff, and had to keep saying to myself that, after all, nobody could do much to me. It was my own money. But you don't know what it's like to be only a small boy! They sent the check back to me and I died ten deaths when I saw it. But the letter explained. I hadn't endorsed it. They sent me a blank to fill out about myself. I didn't know how many lies I dared to tell. But it was my money and I had to get it. If I could get it into the bank, then some day I could get it out. I gave my business as 'author' and I gave my age as twenty-four. I thought that was awfully old."

"I'd like to see the story. Do you have a copy of the magazine around?"

"Yes," said Tim. "But nobody noticed it — I mean, 'T. Paul' could be anybody. And when I saw magazines for writers on the newsstands, and bought them I got on to the way to use a pen name on the story and my own name and address up in the corner. Before that I used a pen name and sometimes never got the things back or heard about them. Sometimes I did, though."

"What then?"

"Oh, then I'd endorse the check payable to me and sign the pen name, and then sign my own name under it. Was I scared to do that! But it was my money."

"Only stories?"

"Articles, too. And things. That's enough of that for today. Only — I just wanted to say — a while ago, T. Paul told the bank he wanted to switch some of the money over to a checking account. To buy books by mail, and such. So, I could pay you, Dr. Welles —" with sudden formality.

"No, Tim," said Peter Welles firmly. "The pleasure is all mine. What I want is to see the story that was published when you were eight. And some of the other things that made T. Paul rich enough to keep a consulting psychiatrist on the payroll. And, for the love of Pete, will you tell me how all this goes on without your grandparents' knowing a thing about it?"

"Grandmother thinks I send in box tops and fill out coupons," said Tim. "She doesn't bring in the mail. She says her little boy gets such a big bang out of that little chore. Anyway that's what she said when I was eight. I played mailman. And there were box tops — I showed them to her, until she said, about the third time, that really she wasn't greatly interested in such matters. By now she has the habit of waiting for me to bring in the mail."

Peter Welles thought that was quite a day of revelation. He spent a quiet evening at home, holding his head and groaning, trying to take it all in.

And that I.Q. — 120, nonsense! The boy had been holding out on him. Tim's reading had obviously included enough about I.Q. tests, enough puzzles and oddments in magazines and such, to enable him to stall successfully. What could he do if he would co-operate?

Welles made up his mind to find out.

He didn't find out. Timothy Paul went swiftly through the whole range of Superior Adult tests without a failure of any sort. There were no tests yet devised that could measure his intelligence. While he was still writing his age with one figure, Timothy Paul had faced alone, and solved alone, problems that would have baffled the average adult. He had adjusted to the hardest task of all — that of appearing to be a fairly normal, B-average small boy.

And it must be that there was more to find out about him. What did he write? And what did he do besides read and write, learn carpentry and breed cats and magnificently fool his whole world?

When Peter Welles had read some of Tim's writings, he was surprised to find that the stories the boy had written were vividly human, the product of close observation of human nature. The articles, on the other hand, were closely reasoned and showed thorough study and research. Apparently Tim read every word of several newspapers and a score or more of periodicals.

"Oh, sure," said Tim, when questioned. "I read everything. I go back once in a while and review old ones, too."

"If you can write like this," demanded Welles, indicating a magazine in which a staid and scholarly article had appeared, "and this —" this was a man-to-man political article giving the arguments for and against a change in the whole Congressional system — "then why do you always talk to me in the language of an ordinary stupid schoolboy?"

"Because I'm only a little boy," replied Timothy. "What would happen if I went around talking like that?"

"You might risk it with me. You've showed me these things."

"I'd never dare to risk talking like that. I might forget and do it again before others. Besides, I can't pronounce half the words."

"What!"

"I never look up a pronunciation," explained Timothy. "In case I do slip and use a word beyond the average, I can anyway hope I didn't say it right."

Welles shouted with laughter, but was sober again as he realized the implications back of that thoughtfulness.

"You're just like an explorer living among savages," said the psychiatrist. "You have studied the savages carefully and tried to imitate them so they won't know there are differences."

"Something like that," acknowledged Tim.

"That's why your stories are so human," said Welles. "That one about the awful little girl —"

They both chuckled.

"Yes, that was my first story," said Tim. "I was almost eight, and there was a boy in my class who had a brother, and the boy next door was the other one, the one who was picked on."

"How much of the story was true?"

"The first part. I used to see, when I went over there, how that girl picked on Bill's brother's friend Steve. She wanted to play with Steve all the time herself and whenever he had boys over, she'd do something awful. And Steve's folks were just like I said — they wouldn't let Steve do anything to a girl. When she threw all the watermelon rinds over the fence into his yard, he just had to pick them all up and say nothing back; and she'd laugh at him over the fence. She got him blamed for things he never did, and when he had work to do in the yard she'd hang out of her window and scream at him and make fun. I thought first, what made her act like that, and then I made up a way for him to get even with her, and wrote it out the way it might have happened."

"Didn't you pass the idea on to Steve and let him try it?"

"Gosh, no! I was only a little boy. Kids seven don't give ideas to kids ten. That's the first thing I had to learn — to be always the one that kept quiet, especially if there was any older boy or girl around, even only a year or two older. I had to learn to look blank and let my mouth hang open and say, 'I don't get it,' to almost everything."

"And Miss Page thought it was odd that you had no close friends of your own age," said Welles. "You must be the loneliest boy that ever walked this earth, Tim. You're living in hiding like a criminal. But tell me, what are you afraid of?"

"I'm afraid of being found out, of course. The only way I can live in this world is in disguise — until I'm grown up, at any rate. At first, it was just my grandparents scolding me and telling me not to show off, and the way people laughed if I tried to talk to them. Then I saw how people hate anyone who is better or brighter or luckier. Some people sort of trade off; if you're bad at one thing you're good at another, but they'll forgive you for being good at some things, because you're not good at others and they can balance that off. They can beat you at something. You have to strike a balance. A child has no chance at all. No grownup can stand it to have a child know anything he doesn't. Oh, a little thing, if it amuses them. But not much of anything. There's an old story about a man who found himself in a country where everyone else was blind. I'm like that — but they shan't put out my eyes. I'll never let them know I can see anything."

"Do you see things that no grown person can see?"

Tim waved his hand towards the magazines.

"Only like that, I meant. I hear people talking in street cars and stores, and while they work, and around. I read about the way they act — in the news. I'm like them, just like them, only I seem about a hundred years older — more matured."

"Do you mean that none of them have much sense?"

"I don't mean that exactly. I mean that so few of them have any, or show it if they do have. They don't even seem to want to. They're good people in their way, but what could they make of me? Even when I was seven, I could understand their motives, but they couldn't understand their own motives. And they're so lazy — they don't seem to want to know or to understand. When I first went to the library for books, the books I learned from were seldom touched by any of the grown people. But they were meant for ordinary grown people. But the grown people didn't want to know things — they only wanted to fool around. I feel about most people the way my grandmother feels about babies and puppies. Only she doesn't have to pretend to be a puppy all the time," Tim added, with a little bitterness.

"You have a friend now, in me."

"Yes, Peter," said Tim, brightening up. "And I have pen friends, too. People like what I write, because they can't see I'm only a little boy. When I grow up —"

Tim did not finish that sentence. Welles understood, now, some of the fears that Tim had not dared to put into words at all. When he grew up, would he be as far beyond all other grown-ups as he had, all his life, been above his contemporaries? The adult friends whom he now met on fairly equal terms — would they then, too, seem like babies or puppies?

Peter did not dare to voice the thought, either. Still less did he venture to hint at another thought. Tim, so far, had no great interest in girls; they existed for him as part of the human race, but there would come a time when Tim would be a grown man and would wish to marry. And where among the puppies could he find a mate?

"When you're grown up, we'll still be friends," said Peter. "And who are the others?"

It turned out that Tim had pen friends all over the world. He played chess by correspondence — a game he never dared to play in person, except when he forced himself to move the pieces about idly and let his opponent win at least half the time. He had, also, many friends who had read something he had written, and had written to him about it, thus starting a correspondence-friendship. After the first two or three of these, he had started some on his own account, always with people who lived at a great distance. To most of these he gave a name which, although not false, looked it. That was Paul T. Lawrence. Lawrence was his middle name; and with a comma after the Paul, it was actually his own name. He had a post office box under that name, for which T. Paul of the large bank account was his reference.

"Pen friends abroad? Do you know languages?"

Yes, Tim did. He had studied by correspondence, also; many universities gave extension courses in that manner, and lent the student records to play so that he could learn the correct pronunciation. Tim had taken several such courses, and learned other languages from books. He kept all these languages in practice by means of the letters to other lands and the replies which came to him.

"I'd buy a dictionary, and then I'd write to the mayors of some towns, or to a foreign newspaper, and ask them to advertise for some pen friends to help me learn the language. We'd exchange souvenirs and things."

Nor was Welles in the least surprised to find that Timothy had also taken other courses by correspondence. He had completed, within three years, more than half the subjects offered by four separate universities, and several other courses, the most recent being architecture. The boy, not yet fourteen, had completed a full course in that subject and, had he been able to disguise himself as a full-grown man, could have gone out at once and built almost anything you'd like to name, for he also knew much of the trades involved.

"It always said how long an average student took, and I'd take that long," said Tim, "so, of course, I had to be working several schools at the same time."

"And carpentry at the playground summer school?"

"Oh, yes. But there I couldn't do too much, because people could see me. But I learned how, and it made a good cover-up, so I could make cages for the cats, and all that sort of thing. And many boys are good with their hands. I like to work with my hands. I built my own radio too — it gets all the foreign stations, and that helps me with my languages."

"How did you figure it about the cats?" asked Welles.

"Oh, there had to be recessives, that's all. The Siamese coloring was a recessive, and it had to be mated with another recessive. Black was one possibility, and white was another, but I started with black because I liked it better. I might try white too, but I have so much else on my mind —"

He broke off suddenly and would say no more.

Their next meeting was by prearrangement at Tim's workshop. Welles met the boy after school and they walked to Tim's home together; there the boy unlocked his door and snapped on the lights.

Welles looked around with interest. There was a bench, a tool chest. Cabinets, padlocked. A radio, clearly not store-purchased. A file cabinet, locked. Something on a table, covered with a cloth. A box in the corner — no, two boxes in two corners. In each of them was a mother cat with kittens. Both mothers were black Persians.

"This one must be all black Persian," Tim explained. "Her third litter and never a Siamese marking. But this one carries both recessives in her. Last time she had a Siamese short-haired kitten. This morning — I had to go to school. Let's see."

They bent over the box where the newborn kittens lay. One kitten was like the mother. The other two were Siamese-Persian; a male and a female.

"You've done it again, Tim!" shouted Welles. "Congratulations!"

They shook hands in jubilation.

"I'll write it in the record," said the boy blissfully.

In a nickel book marked "Compositions" Tim's left hand added the entries. He had used the correct symbols — F_1, F_2, F_3; Ss, Bl.

"The dominants in capitals," he explained, "B for black, and S for short hair; the recessives in small letters — s for Siamese, l for long hair. Wonderful to write ll over ss again, Peter! Twice more. And the other kitten is carrying the Siamese markings as a recessive."

He closed the book in triumph.

"Now," and he marched to the covered thing on the table, "my latest big secret."

Tim lifted the cloth carefully and displayed a beautifully built dollhouse. No, a model house — Welles corrected himself swiftly. A beautiful model, and — yes, built to scale.

"The roof comes off. See, it has a big storage room and a room for a playroom or a maid or something. Then I lift off the attic —"

"Good heavens!" cried Peter Welles. "Any little girl would give her soul for this!"

"I used fancy wrapping papers for the wallpapers. I wove the rugs on a little hand loom," gloated Timothy. "The furniture's just like real, isn't it? Some I bought; that's plastic. Some I made of construction paper and things. The curtains were the hardest; but I couldn't ask my grandmother to sew them —"

"Why not?" the amazed doctor managed to ask.

"She might recognize this afterward," said Tim, and he lifted off the upstairs floor.

"Recognize it? You haven't showed it to her? Then when would she see it?"

"She might not," admitted Tim. "But I have to take some risks."

"That's a very livable floor plan you've used," said Welles, bending closer to examine the house in detail.

"Yes, I thought so. It's awful how many house plans leave no clear wall space for books or pictures. Some of them have doors placed so you have to detour around the dining room table every time you go from the living room to the kitchen, or so that a whole corner of a room is good for nothing, with doors at all angles. Now, I designed this house to —"

"You designed it, Tim!"

"Why, sure. Oh, I see — you thought I built it from blueprints I'd bought. My first model home, I did, but the architecture courses gave me so many ideas that I wanted to see how they would look. Now, the cellar and game room —"

Welles came to himself an hour later, and gasped when he looked at his watch.

"It's too late. My patient has gone home again by this time. I may as well stay — how about the paper route?"

"I gave that up. Grandmother offered to feed the cats as soon as I gave her the kitten. And I wanted the time for this. Here are the pictures of the house."

The color prints were very good.

"I'm sending them and an article to the magazines," said Tim. "This time I'm T. L. Paul. Sometimes I used to pretend all the different people I am were talking together — but now I talk to you instead, Peter."

"Will it bother the cats if I smoke? Thanks. Nothing I'm likely to set on fire, I hope? Put the house together and let me sit here and look at it. I want to look in through the windows. Put its little lights on. There."

The young architect beamed, and snapped on the little lights.

"Nobody can see in here. I got Venetian blinds; and when I work in here, I even shut them sometimes."

"If I'm to know all about you, I'll have to go through the alphabet from A to Z," said Peter Welles. "This is Architecture. What else in the A's?"

"Astronomy. I showed you those articles. My calculations proved correct. Astrophysics — I got A in the course, but haven't done anything original so far. Art, no, I can't paint or draw very well, except mechanical drawing. I've done all the Merit Badge work in scouting, all through the alphabet."

"Darned if I can see you as a Boy Scout," protested Welles.

"I'm a very good Scout. I have almost as many badges as any other boy my age in the troop. And at camp I do as well as most city boys."

"Do you do a good turn every day?"

"Yes," said Timothy. "Started that when I first read about Scouting — I was a Scout at heart before I was old enough to be a Cub. You know, Peter, when you're very young you take all that seriously, about the good deed every day, and the good habits and ideals and all that. And then you get older and it begins to seem funny and childish and posed and artificial, and you smile in a superior way and make jokes. But there is a third step, too, when you take it

all seriously again. People who make fun of the Scout Law are doing the boys a lot of harm; but those who believe in things like that
don't know how to say so, without sounding priggish and platitu-
dinous. I'm going to do an article on it before long."

"Is the Scout Law your religion — if I may put it that way?"

"No," said Timothy. "But 'a Scout is Reverent.' Once I tried to
study the churches and find out what was the truth. I wrote letters
to pastors of all denominations — all those in the phone book and
the newspaper — when I was on a vacation in the East, I got the
names, and then wrote after I got back. I couldn't write to people
here in the city. I said I wanted to know which church was true,
and expected them to write to me and tell me about theirs, and
argue with me, you know. I could read library books, and all they
had to do was recommend some, I told them, and then correspond
with me a little about them."

"Did they?"

"Some of them answered," said Tim, "but nearly all of them
told me to go to somebody near me. Several said they were very
busy men. Some gave me the name of a few books, but none of
them told me to write again, and . . . and I was only a little boy.
Nine years old, so I couldn't talk to anybody. When I thought it
over, I knew that I couldn't very well join any church so young, unless it was my grandparents' church. I keep on going there — it is
a good church and it teaches a great deal of truth, I am sure. I'm
reading all I can find, so when I am old enough I'll know what I
must do. How old would you say I should be, Peter?"

"College age," replied Welles. "You are going to college? By
then, any of the pastors would talk to you — except those that are
too busy!"

"It's a moral problem, really. Have I the right to wait? But I
have to wait. It's like telling lies — I have to tell some lies, but I
hate to. If I have a moral obligation to join the true church as soon
as I find it, well, what then? I can't, until I'm eighteen or twenty?"

"If you can't, you can't. I should think that settles it. You are
legally a minor, under the control of your grandparents, and while
you might claim the right to go where your conscience leads you,
it would be impossible to justify and explain your choice without
giving yourself away entirely — just as you are obliged to go to
school until you are at least eighteen, even though you know more
than most Ph.D.'s. It's all part of the game, and He who made you
must understand that."

"I'll never tell you any lies," said Tim. "I was getting so desperately lonely — my pen pals didn't know anything about me really.
I told them only what was right for them to know. Little kids are

satisfied to be with other people but when you get a little older you have to make friends, really."

"Yes, that's a part of growing up. You have to reach out to others and share thoughts with them. You've kept to yourself too long as it is."

"It wasn't that I wanted to. But without a real friend, it was only pretense, and I never could let my playmates know anything about me. I studied them and wrote stories about them and it was all of them, but it was only a tiny part of me."

"I'm proud to be your friend, Tim. Every man needs a friend. I'm proud that you trust me."

Tim patted the cat a moment in silence and then looked up with a grin.

"How would you like to hear my favorite joke?" he asked.

"Very much," said the psychiatrist, bracing himself for almost any major shock.

"It's records. I recorded this from a radio program."

Welles listened. He knew little of music, but the symphony which he heard pleased him. The announcer praised it highly in little speeches before and after each movement. Timothy giggled.

"Like it?"

"Very much. I don't see the joke."

"I wrote it."

"Tim, you're beyond me! But I still don't get the joke."

"The joke is that I did it by mathematics. I calculated what ought to sound like joy, grief, hope, triumph, and all the rest, and — it was just after I had studied harmony; you know how mathematical that is."

Speechless, Welles nodded.

"I worked out the rhythms from different metabolisms — the way you function when under the influences of these emotions; the way your metabolic rate varies, your heartbeats and respiration and things. I sent it to the director of that orchestra, and he didn't get the idea that it was a joke — of course I didn't explain — he produced the music. I get nice royalties from it, too."

"You'll be the death of me yet," said Welles in deep sincerity. "Don't tell me anything more today; I couldn't take it. I'm going home. Maybe by tomorrow I'll see the joke and come back to laugh. Tim, did you ever fail at anything?"

"There are two cabinets full of articles and stories that didn't sell. Some of them I feel bad about. There was a chess story. You know, in 'Through the Looking Glass,' it wasn't a very good game, and you couldn't see the relation of the moves to the story very well."

"I never could see it at all."

"I thought it would be fun to take a championship game and write a fantasy about it, as if it were a war between two little old countries, with knights and foot soldiers, and fortified walls in charge of captains, and the bishops couldn't fight like warriors, and, of course, the queens were women — people don't kill them, not in hand-to-hand fighting and . . . well, you see? I wanted to make up the attacks and captures, and keep the people alive, a fairy-tale war you see, and make the strategy of the game and the strategy of the war coincide, and have everything fit. It took me ever so long to work it out and write it. To understand the game as a chess game and then to translate it into human actions and motives, and put speeches to it to fit different kinds of people. I'll show it to you. I loved it. But nobody would print it. Chess players don't like fantasy, and nobody else likes chess. You have to have a very special kind of mind to like both. But it was a disappointment. I hoped it would be published, because the few people who like that sort of thing would like it *very* much."

"I'm sure I'll like it."

"Well, if you do like that sort of thing, it's what you've been waiting all your life in vain for. Nobody else has done it." Tim stopped, and blushed as red as a beet. "I see what grandmother means. Once you get started bragging, there's no end to it. I'm sorry, Peter."

"Give me the story. I don't mind, Tim — brag all you like to me; I understand. You might blow up if you never express any of your legitimate pride and pleasure in such achievements. What I don't understand is how you have kept it all under for so long."

"I had to," said Tim.

The story was all its young author had claimed. Welles chuckled as he read it, that evening. He read it again, and checked all the moves and the strategy of them. It was really a fine piece of work. Then he thought of the symphony, and this time he was able to laugh. He sat up until after midnight, thinking about the boy. Then he took a sleeping pill and went to bed.

The next day he went to see Tim's grandmother. Mrs. Davis received him graciously.

"Your grandson is a very interesting boy," said Peter Welles carefully. "I'm asking a favor of you. I am making a study of various boys and girls in this district, their abilities and backgrounds and environment and character traits and things like that. No names will ever be mentioned, of course, but a statistical report will be kept, for ten years or longer, and some case histories might later be published. Could Timothy be included?"

"Timothy is such a good, normal little boy, I fail to see what would be the purpose of including him in such a survey."

"That is just the point. We are not interested in maladjusted persons in this study. We eliminate all psychotic boys and girls. We are interested in boys and girls who succeed in facing their youthful problems and making satisfactory adjustments to life. If we could study a selected group of such children, and follow their progress for the next ten years at least — and then publish a summary of the findings, with no names used —"

"In that case, I see no objection," said Mrs. Davis.

"If you'd tell me, then, something about Timothy's parents — their history?"

Mrs. Davis settled herself for a good long talk.

"Timothy's mother, my only daughter, Emily," she began, "was a lovely girl. So talented. She played the violin charmingly. Timothy is like her, in the face, but has his father's dark hair and eyes. Edwin had very fine eyes."

"Edwin was Timothy's father?"

"Yes. The young people met while Emily was at college in the East. Edwin was studying atomics there."

"Your daughter was studying music?"

"No; Emily was taking the regular liberal arts course. I can tell you little about Edwin's work, but after their marriage he returned to it and . . . you understand, it is painful for me to recall this, but their deaths were such a blow to me. They were so young."

Welles held his pencil ready to write.

"Timothy has never been told. After all, he must grow up in this world, and how dreadfully the world has changed in the past thirty years, Dr. Welles! But you would not remember the days before 1945. You have heard, no doubt, of the terrible explosion in the atomic plant, when they were trying to make a new type of bomb? At the time, none of the workers seemed to be injured. They believed the protection was adequate. But two years later they were all dead or dying."

Mrs. Davis shook her head, sadly. Welles held his breath, bent his head, scribbled.

"Tim was born just fourteen months after the explosion, fourteen months to the day. Everyone still thought that no harm had been done. But the radiation had some effect which was very slow — I do not understand such things — Edwin died, and then Emily came home to us with the boy. In a few months, she, too, was gone.

"Oh, but we do not sorrow as those who have no hope. It is hard to have lost her, Dr. Welles, but Mr. Davis and I have reached the time of life when we can look forward to seeing her again. Our hope is to live until Timothy is old enough to fend for himself. We were so anxious about him; but you see he is perfectly normal in every way."

"Yes."

"The specialists made all sorts of tests. But nothing is wrong with Timothy."

The psychiatrist stayed a little longer, took a few more notes, and made his escape as soon as he could. Going straight to the school, he had a few words with Miss Page and then took Tim to his office, where he told him what he had learned.

"You mean — I'm a mutation?"

"A mutant. Yes, very likely you are. I don't know. But I had to tell you at once."

"Must be a dominant, too," said Tim, "coming out this way in the first generation. You mean — there may be more? I'm not the only one?" he added in great excitement. "Oh, Peter, even if I grow up past you I won't have to be lonely?"

There. He had said it.

"It could be, Tim. There's nothing else in your family that could account for you."

"But I have never found anyone at all like me. I would have known. Another boy or girl my age — like me — I would have known."

"You came West with your mother. Where did the others go, if they existed? The parents must have scattered everywhere, back to their homes all over the country, all over the world. We can trace them, though. And, Tim, haven't you thought it's just a little bit strange that with all your pen names and various contacts, people don't insist more on meeting you? People don't ask about you? Everything gets done by mail? It's almost as if the editors are used to people who hide. It's almost as if people are used to architects and astronomers and composers whom nobody ever sees, who are only names in care of other names at post office boxes. There's a chance — just a chance, mind you — that there are others. If there are we'll find them."

"I'll work out a code they will understand," said Tim, his face screwed up in concentration. "In articles — I'll do it — several magazines and in letters I can inclose copies — some of my pen friends may be the ones —"

"I'll hunt up the records — they must be on file somewhere —

psychologists and psychiatrists know all kinds of tricks — we can make some excuse to trace them all — the birth records —"

Both of them were talking at once, but all the while Peter Welles was thinking sadly, perhaps he had lost Tim now. If they did find those others, those to whom Tim rightfully belonged, where would poor Peter be? Outside, among the puppies —

Timothy Paul looked up and saw Peter Welles' eyes on him. He smiled.

"You were my first friend, Peter, and you shall be forever," said Tim. "No matter what, no matter who."

"But we must look for the others," said Peter.

"I'll never forget who helped me," said Tim.

An ordinary boy of thirteen may say such a thing sincerely, and a week later have forgotten all about it. But Peter Welles was content. Tim would never forget, Tim would be his friend always. Even when Timothy Paul and those like him should unite in a maturity undreamed of, to control the world if they chose, Peter Welles would be Tim's friend — not a puppy, but a beloved friend — as a loyal dog, loved by a good master, is never cast out.

"Creative Evolution —"

GEORGE BERNARD SHAW

[*FROM THE* PREFACE *TO* BACK TO METHUSELAH.]

. . . THE TIME BEING thus ripe, the genius appeared; and his name was Charles Darwin. And now, what did Darwin really discover?

Here, I am afraid, I shall require once more the assistance of the giraffe, or, as he was called in the days of the celebrated Buffon, the camelopard (by children, cammyleopard). I do not remember

From *Back to Methuselah* by George Bernard Shaw. Reprinted by permission of the Public Trustee and The Society of Authors.

how this animal imposed himself illustratively on the Evolution controversy; but there was no getting away from him then; and I am old-fashioned enough to be unable to get away from him now. How did he come by his long neck? Lamarck would have said, by wanting to get at the tender leaves high up on the tree, and trying until he succeeded in wishing the necessary length of neck into existence. Another answer was also possible: namely, that some prehistoric stockbreeder, wishing to produce a natural curiosity, selected the longest-necked animals he could find, and bred from them until at last an animal with an abnormally long neck was evolved by intentional selection, just as the race-horse or the fantail pigeon has been evolved. Both these explanations, you will observe, involve consciousness, will, design, purpose, either on the part of the animal itself or on the part of a superior intelligence controlling its destiny. Darwin pointed out — and this and no more was Darwin's famous discovery — that a third explanation, involving neither will nor purpose nor design either in the animal or anyone else, was on the cards. If your neck is too short to reach your food, you die. That may be the simple explanation of the fact that all the surviving animals that feed on foliage have necks or trunks long enough to reach it. So bang goes your belief that the necks must have been designed to reach the food. But Lamarck did not believe that the necks were so designed in the beginning: he believed that the long necks were evolved by wanting and trying. Not necessarily, said Darwin. Consider the effect on the giraffes of the natural multiplication of their numbers, as insisted on by Malthus. Suppose the average height of the foliage-eating animals is four feet, and that they increase in numbers until a time comes when all the trees are eaten away to within four feet of the ground. Then the animals who happen to be an inch or two short of the average will die of starvation. All the animals who happen to be an inch or so above the average will be better fed and stronger than the others. They will secure the strongest and tallest mates; and their progeny will survive whilst the average ones and the sub-average ones will die out. This process, by which the specific gains, say, an inch in reach, will repeat itself until the giraffe's neck is so long that he can always find food enough within his reach, at which point, of course, the selective process stops and the length of the giraffe's neck stops with it. Otherwise, he would grow until he could browse off the trees in the moon. And this, mark you, without the intervention of any stock-breeder, human or divine, and without will, purpose, design, or even consciousness beyond the blind will to satisfy hunger. It is true that this blind will, being in effect a will to live, gives away the whole case; but still, as compared to the open-eyed intelligent wanting and trying of Lamarck, the Darwinian process may be described as a chapter of accidents. As such, it seems simple, because you do not at first realize all that it involves. But when its whole significance dawns on you, your heart sinks into a heap of sand within you. There is a hideous fatalism about it, a ghastly and damnable reduction of beauty and intelligence, of strength and purpose, of honor and aspiration, to such casually picturesque changes as an avalanche may make in a mountain landscape, or a railway accident in a human figure. To call this Natural Selection is a blasphemy, possible to many for whom Nature is nothing but a casual aggregation of inert and dead matter, but eternally impossible to the spirits and souls of the righteous. If it be no blasphemy, but a truth of science, then the stars of heaven, the showers and dew, the winter and summer, the fire and heat, the mountains and hills, may no longer be called to exalt the Lord with us by praise: their work is to modify all things by blindly starving and murdering everything that is not lucky enough to survive in the universal struggle for hogwash. . . .

Thus did the neck of the giraffe reach out across the whole heavens and make men believe that what they saw there was a gloaming of the gods. For if this sort of selection could turn an antelope into a giraffe, it could conceivably turn a pond full of amoebas into the French Academy. Though Lamarck's way, the way of life, will, aspiration, and achievement, remained still possible, this newly shown way of hunger, death, stupidity, delusion, chance and bare survival was also possible: was indeed most certainly the way in which many apparently intelligently designed transformations had actually come to pass. . . .

I now find myself inspired to make a second legend of Creative Evolution without distractions and embellishments. . . .

PART II: GOSPEL OF THE BROTHERS BARNABAS

LUBIN (*still immovably skeptical*): And what does Science say to this fairy tale, Doctor Barnabas? Surely Science knows nothing of Genesis, or of Adam and Eve.

CONRAD: Then it isn't Science: that's all. Science has to account for everything; and everything includes the Bible.

FRANKLYN: The Book of Genesis is a part of nature like any other part of nature. The fact that the tale of the Garden of Eden has survived and held the imagination of men spellbound for centuries, whilst hundreds of much more plausible and amusing stories have gone out of fashion and perished like last year's popular song, is a scientific fact; and Science is bound to explain it. You tell me that Science knows nothing of it. Then Science is more ignorant than the children at any village school.

CONRAD: Of course if you think it more scientific to say that what we are discussing is not Adam and Eve and Eden, but the phylogeny of the blastoderm —

SAVVY: You needn't swear, Nunk.

CONRAD: Shut up, *you:* I am not swearing. (*To Lubin*) If you want the professional humbug of rewriting the Bible in words of four syllables, and pretending it's something new, I can humbug you to your heart's content. I can call it Genesis Phylogenesis. Let the Creator say, if you like, "I will establish an antipathetic symbiosis between thee and the female, and between thy blastoderm and her blastoderm." Nobody will understand you; and Savvy will think you are swearing. The meaning is the same.

HASLAM: Priceless. But it's quite simple. The one version is poetry; the other is science.

FRANKLYN: The one is classroom jargon: the other is inspired human language.

LUBIN (*calmly reminiscent*):   One of the few modern authors into whom I have occasionally glanced is Rousseau, who was a sort of Deist like Burge —

BURGE (*interrupting him forcibly*):   Lubin, has this stupendously important communication which Professor Barnabas has just made to us: a communication for which I shall be indebted to him all my life long: has this, I say, no deeper effect on you than to set you pulling my leg by trying to make out that I am an infidel?

LUBIN: It's very interesting and amusing, Burge; and I think I see a case in it. I think I could undertake to argue it in an ecclesiastical court. But important is hardly a word I should attach to it.

BURGE: Good God! Here is this professor: a man utterly removed from the turmoil of our political life: devoted to pure learning in its most abstract phases; and I solemnly declare he is the greatest politician, the most inspired party leader, in the kingdom. I take off my hat to him. I, Joyce Burge, give him best. And you sit there purring like an Angora cat, and can see nothing in it!

CONRAD (*opening his eyes widely*):   Hallo! What have I done to deserve this tribute?

BURGE: Done! You have put the Liberal Party into power for the next thirty years, Doctor: that's what you've done.

CONRAD: God forbid!

BURGE: It's all up with the Church now. Thanks to you, we go to the country with one cry and one only: Back to the Bible. Think of the effect on the Nonconformist vote. You gather that in

with one hand and you gather in the modern scientific skeptical professional vote with the other. The village atheist and the first cornet
in the local Salvation Army band meet on the village green and
shake hands. You take your schoolchildren, your Bible class under
the Cowper-Temple clause, into the museum. You show the kids
the Piltdown skull; and you say, "That's Adam. That's Eve's husband." You take the spectacled science student from the laboratory
in Owens College; and when he asks you for a truly scientific history
of Evolution, you put into his hand *The Pilgrim's Progress*. You —
(*Savvy and Haslam explode into shrieks of merriment.*) What are
you two laughing at?

    SAVOY: Oh, go on, Mr. Burge. Don't stop.

    HASLAM: Priceless!

    FRANKLYN: Would thirty years of office for the Liberal Party
seem so important to you, Mr. Burge, if you had another two and
a half centuries to live?

    BURGE (*decisively*):   No. You will have to drop that part of
it. The constituencies won't swallow it.

    LUBIN (*seriously*):   I am not so sure of that, Burge. I am
not so sure that it may not prove the only point they *will* swallow.

    BURGE: It will be of no use to us even if they do. It's not a
party point. It's as good for the other side as for us.

    LUBIN: Not necessarily. If we get in first with it, it will be
associated in the public mind with our party. Suppose I put it forward as a plank in our program that we advocate the extension of
human life to three hundred years! Dunreen, as leader of the opposite party, will be bound to oppose me; to denounce me as a vision-
ary and so forth. By doing so he will place himself in the position
of wanting to rob the people of two hundred and thirty years of their
natural life. The Unionists will become the party of premature
Death; and we shall become the Longevity party.

    BURGE (*shaken*):   You really think the electorate would swal-
low it?

    LUBIN: My dear Burge: is there anything the electorate will
not swallow if it is judiciously put to them? But we must make sure
of our ground. We must have the support of the men of science. Is
there serious agreement among them, Doctor, as to the possibility
of such an evolution as you have described?

    CONRAD: Yes. Ever since the reaction against Darwin set in
at the beginning of the present century, all scientific opinion worth
counting has been converging rapidly upon Creative Evolution.

    FRANKLYN: Poetry has been converging on it: philosophy
has been converging on it: religion has been converging on it. It
is going to be the religion of the twentieth century: a religion that

has its intellectual roots in philosophy and science, just as medieval Christianity had its intellectual roots in Aristotle.

LUBIN: But surely any change would be so extremely gradual that —

CONRAD: Don't deceive yourself. It's only the politicians who improve the world so gradually that nobody can see the improvement. The notion that Nature does not proceed by jumps is only one of the budget of plausible lies that we call classical education. Nature always proceeds by jumps. She may spend twenty thousand years making up her mind to jump; but when she makes it up at last, the jump is big enough to take us into a new age.

LUBIN (*impressed*):   Fancy my being leader of the party for the next three hundred years!

BURGE: What!

LUBIN: Perhaps hard on some of the younger men. I think in fairness I shall have to step aside to make room after another century or so: that is, if Mimi can be persuaded to give up Downing Street.

BURGE: This is too much. Your colossal conceit blinds you to the most obvious necessity of the political situation.

LUBIN: You mean my retirement. I really cannot see that it is a necessity. I could not see it when I was almost an old man — or at least an elderly one. Now that it appears I am a young man, the case for it breaks down completely. (*To Conrad*) May I ask are there any alternative theories? Is there a scientific Opposition?

CONRAD: Well, some authorities held that the human race is a failure, and that a new form of life, better adapted to high civilization, will supersede us as we have superseded the ape and the elephant.

BURGE: The superman: eh?

CONRAD: No. Some being quite different from us.

LUBIN: Is that altogether desirable?

FRANKLYN: I fear so. However that may be, we may be quite sure of one thing. We shall not be let alone. The force behind evolution, call it what you will, is determined to solve the problem of civilization; and if it cannot do it through us, it will produce some more capable agents. Man is not God's last word: God can still create. If you cannot do His work He will produce some being who can.

BURGE (*with zealous reverence*):   What do we know about Him, Barnabas? What does anyone know about Him?

CONRAD: We know this about Him with absolute certainty. The power my brother calls God proceeds by the method of Trial and Error; and if we turn out to be one of the errors, we shall go

the way of the mastodon and the megatherium and all the other
scrapped experiments.

Split Cherry Tree

JESSE STUART

"I DON'T MIND staying after school," I says to Professor Herbert, "but I'd rather you'd whip me with a switch and let me go
home early. Pa will whip me anyway for getting home two
hours late."

"You are too big to whip," says Professor Herbert, "and I have
to punish you for climbing up in that cherry tree. You boys knew
better than that! The other five boys have paid their dollar each.
You have been the only one who has not helped pay for the tree.
Can't you borrow a dollar?"

"I can't," I says. "I'll have to take the punishment. I wish it
would be quicker punishment. I wouldn't mind."

Professor Herbert stood and looked at me. He was a big man.
He wore a gray suit of clothes. The suit matched his gray hair.

"You don't know my father," I says to Professor Herbert. "He
might be called a little old-fashioned. He makes us mind him
until we're twenty-one years old. He believes: 'If you spare the
rod you spoil the child.' I'll never be able to make him understand
about the cherry tree. I'm the first of my people to go to high
school."

"You must take the punishment," says Professor Herbert. "You
must stay two hours after school today and two hours after school
tomorrow. I am allowing you twenty-five cents an hour. That is
good money for a high-school student. You can sweep the schoolhouse floor, wash the blackboards, and clean windows. I'll pay the
dollar for you."

I couldn't ask Professor Herbert to loan me a dollar. He never
offered to loan it to me. I had to stay and help the janitor and
work out my fine at a quarter an hour.

I thought as I swept the floor, "What will Pa do to me? What lie can I tell him when I go home? Why did we ever climb that cherry tree and break it down for anyway? Why did we run crazy over the hills away from the crowd? Why did we do all of this? Six of us climbed up in a little cherry tree after one little lizard! Why did the tree split and fall with us? It should have been a stronger tree! Why did Eif Crabtree just happen to be below us plowing and catch us in his cherry tree? Why wasn't he a better man than to charge us six dollars for the tree?"

It was six o'clock when I left the schoolhouse. I had six miles to walk home. It would be after seven when I got home. I had all my work to do when I got home. It took Pa and me both to do the work. Seven cows to milk. Nineteen head of cattle to feed, four mules, twenty-five hogs, firewood and stovewood to cut, and water to draw from the well. He would be doing it when I got home. He would be mad and wondering what was keeping me!

I hurried home. I would run under the dark, leafless trees. I would walk fast uphill. I would run down the hill. The ground was freezing. I had to hurry. I had to run. I reached the long ridge that led to our cow pasture. I ran along this ridge. The wind dried the sweat on my face. I ran across the pasture to the house.

I threw down my books in the chipyard. I ran to the barn to spread fodder on the ground for the cattle. I didn't take time to change my clean school clothes for my old work clothes. I ran out to the barn. I saw Pa spreading fodder on the ground to the cattle. That was my job. I ran up to the fence. I says, "Leave that for me, Pa. I'll do it. I'm just a little late."

"I see you are," says Pa. He turned and looked at me. His eyes danced fire. "What in th' world has kept you so? Why ain't you been here to help me with this work? Make a gentleman out'n one boy in th' family and this is what you get! Send you to high school and you get too onery fer th' buzzards to smell!"

I never said anything. I didn't want to tell why I was late from school. Pa stopped scattering the bundles of fodder. He looked at me. He says, "Why are you gettin' in here this time o' night? You tell me or I'll take a hickory withe to you right here on th' spot!"

I says, "I had to stay after school." I couldn't lie to Pa. He'd go to school and find out why I had to stay. If I lied to him it would be too bad for me.

"Why did you haf to stay atter school?" says Pa.

I says, "Our biology class went on a field trip today. Six of us boys broke down a cherry tree. We had to give a dollar apiece to pay for the tree. I didn't have the dollar. Professor Herbert is making me work out my dollar. He gives me twenty-five cents an hour. I had to stay in this afternoon. I'll have to stay in tomorrow afternoon!"

"Are you telling me th' truth?" says Pa.

"I'm telling you the truth," I says. "Go and see for yourself."

"That's jist what I'll do in th' mornin'," says Pa. "Jist whose cherry tree did you break down?"

"Eif Crabtree's cherry tree!"

"What was you doin' clear out in Eif Crabtree's place?" says Pa. "He lives four miles from th' county high school. Don't they teach you no books at that high school? Do they jist let you get out and gad over th' hillsides? If that's all they do I'll keep you at home, Dave. I've got work here fer you to do!"

"Pa," I says, "spring is just getting here. We take a subject in school where we have to have bugs, snakes, flowers, lizards, frogs, and plants. It is biology. It was a pretty day today. We went out to find a few of these. Six of us boys saw a lizard at the same time sunning on a cherry tree. We all went up the tree to get it. We broke the tree down. It split at the forks. Eif Crabtree was plowing down below us. He ran up the hill and got our names. The other boys gave their dollar apiece. I didn't have mine. Professor Herbert put mine in for me. I have to work it out at school."

"Poor man's son, huh," says Pa. "I'll attend to that myself in th' mornin'. I'll take keer o' 'im. He ain't from this county nohow. I'll go down there in th' mornin' and see 'im. Lettin' you leave your books and galavant all over th' hills. What kind of a school is it nohow! Didn't do that, my son, when I's a little shaver in school. All fared alike too."

"Pa, please don't go down there," I says, "just let me have fifty cents and pay the rest of my fine! I don't want you to go down there! I don't want you to start anything with Professor Herbert!"

"Ashamed of your old Pap are you, Dave," says Pa, "atter th' way I've worked to raise you! Tryin' to send you to school so you can make a better livin' than I've made.

"I'll straighten this thing out myself! I'll take keer o' Professor Herbert myself! He ain't got no right to keep you in and let the other boys off jist because they've got th' money! I'm a poor man. A bullet will go in a professor same as it will any man. It will go in a rich man same as it will a poor man. Now you get into this work before I take one o' these withes and cut the shirt off'n your back!"

I thought once I'd run through the woods above the barn just as hard as I could go. I thought I'd leave high school and home forever! Pa could not catch me! I'd get away! I couldn't go back to school with him. He'd have a gun and maybe he'd shoot Professor Herbert. It was hard to tell what he would do. I could tell Pa that school had changed in the hills from the way it was when he was a boy, but he wouldn't understand. I could tell him we studied frogs, birds, snakes, lizards, flowers, insects. But Pa wouldn't understand. If I did run away from home it wouldn't matter to Pa. He would see Professor Herbert anyway. He would think that high school and Professor Herbert had run me away from home. There was no need to run away. I'd just have to stay, finish foddering the cattle, and go to school with Pa the next morning.

I would take a bundle of fodder, remove the hickory witheband from around it, and scatter it on rocks, clumps of green briers, and brush so the cattle wouldn't tramp it under their feet. I would lean it up against the oak trees and the rocks in the pasture just above our pigpen on the hill. The fodder was cold and frosty where it had set out in the stacks. I would carry bundles of the fodder from the stack until I had spread out a bundle for each steer. Pa went to the barn to feed the mules and throw corn in the pen to the hogs.

The moon shone bright in the cold March sky. I finished my work by moonlight. Professor Herbert really didn't know how much work I had to do at home. If he had known he would not have kept me after school. He would have loaned me a dollar to have paid my part on the cherry tree. He had never lived in the hills. He didn't know the way the hill boys had to work so that they could go to school. Now he was teaching in a county high school where all the boys who attended were from hill farms.

After I'd finished doing my work I went to the house and ate my supper. Pa and Mom had eaten. My supper was getting cold. I heard Pa and Mom talking in the front room. Pa was telling Mom about me staying in after school.

"I had to do all th' milkin' tonight, chop th' wood myself. It's too hard on me atter I've turned ground all day. I'm goin' to take a day off tomorrow and see if I can't remedy things a little. I'll go down to that high school tomorrow. I won't be a very good scholar fer Professor Herbert nohow. He won't keep me in atter school. I'll take a different kind of lesson down there and make 'im acquainted with it."

"Now, Luster," says Mom, "you jist stay away from there. Don't cause a lot o' trouble. You can be jailed fer a trick like that. You'll get th' Law atter you. You'll jist go down there and show off and plague your own boy Dave to death in front o' all th' scholars!"

"Plague or no plague," says Pa, "he don't take into consideration what all I haf to do here, does he? I'll show 'im it ain't right to keep one boy in and let the rest go scot free. My boy is good as th' rest, ain't he? A bullet will make a hole in a schoolteacher same as it will anybody else. He can't do me that way and get by with it. I'll plug 'im first. I aim to go down there bright and early in the mornin' and get all this straight! I aim to see about bug larnin' and this runnin' all over God's creation huntin' snakes, lizards, and frogs. Ransackin' the country and goin' through cherry orchards and breakin' th' trees down atter lizards! Old Eif Crabtree ought to a-poured th' hot lead to 'em instead o' chargin' six dollars fer th' tree! He ought to a-got old Herbert th' first one!"

I ate my supper. I slipped upstairs and lit the lamp. I tried to forget the whole thing. I studied plane geometry. Then I studied my biology lesson. I could hardly study for thinking about Pa. "He'll go to school with me in the morning. He'll take a gun for Professor Herbert! What will Professor Herbert think of me! I'll tell him when Pa leaves that I couldn't help it. But Pa might shoot him. I hate to go with Pa. Maybe he'll cool off about it tonight and not go in the morning."

Pa got up at four o'clock. He built a fire in the stove. Then he built a fire in the fireplace. He got Mom up to get breakfast. Then he got me up to help feed and milk. By the time we had our work done at the barn, Mom had breakfast ready for us. We ate our breakfast. Daylight came and we could see the bare oak trees covered white with frost. The hills were white with frost. A cold wind was blowing. The sky was clear. The sun would soon come out and melt the frost. The afternoon would be warm with sunshine and the frozen ground with thaw. There would be mud on the hills again. Muddy water would then run down the little ditches on the hills.

"Now, Dave," says Pa, "let's get ready fer school. I aim to go with you this mornin' and look into bug larnin', frog larnin', lizard and snake larnin', and breakin' down cherry trees! I don't like no sicha foolish way o' larnin' myself!"

Pa hadn't forgot. I'd have to take him to school with me. He would take me to school with him. We were going early. I was glad we were going early. If Pa pulled a gun on Professor Herbert there wouldn't be so many of my classmates there to see him.

I knew that Pa wouldn't be at home in the high school. He wore overalls, big boots, a blue shirt and a sheepskin coat and a slouched black hat gone to seed at the top. He put his gun in its holster. We started trudging toward the high school across the hill.

It was early when we got to the county high school. Professor Herbert had just got there. I just thought as we walked up the steps into the schoolhouse, "Maybe Pa will find out Professor Herbert is a good man. He just doesn't know him. Just like I felt toward the Lambert boys across the hill. I didn't like them until I'd seen them and talked to them. After I went to school with them and talked to them, I liked them and we were friends. It's a lot in knowing the other fellow."

"You're th' Professor here, ain't you?" says Pa.

"Yes," says Professor Herbert, "and you are Dave's father."

"Yes," says Pa, pulling out his gun and laying it on the seat in Professor Herbert's office. Professor Herbert's eyes got big behind his black-rimmed glasses when he saw Pa's gun. Color came into his pale cheeks.

"Jist a few things about this school I want to know," says Pa. "I'm tryin' to make a scholar out'n Dave. He's the only one out'n eleven youngins I've sent to high school. Here he comes in late and leaves me all th' work to do! He said you's all out bug huntin' yesterday and broke a cherry tree down. He had to stay two hours atter school yesterday and work out money to pay on that cherry tree! Is that right?"

"Wwwwy," says Professor Herbert, "I guess it is."

He looked at Pa's gun.

"Well," says Pa, "this ain't no high school. It's a bug school, a lizard school, a snake school! It ain't no school nohow!"

"Why did you bring that gun?" says Professor Herbert to Pa.

"You see that little hole," says Pa as he picked up the long blue forty-four and put his finger on the end of the barrel, "a bullet can come out'n that hole that will kill a schoolteacher same as it will any other man. It will kill a rich man same as a poor man. It will kill a man. But atter I come in and saw you, I know'd I wouldn't need it. This maul o' mine could do you up in a few minutes."

Pa stood there, big, hard, brown-skinned, and mighty beside of Professor Herbert. I didn't know Pa was so much bigger and harder. I'd never seen Pa in a schoolhouse before. I'd seen Professor Herbert. He'd always looked big before to me. He didn't look big standing beside of Pa.

"I was only doing my duty," says Professor Herbert, "Mr. Sexton, and following the course of study the state provided us with."

"Course o' study," says Pa, "what study, bug study? Varmint study? Takin' youngins to th' woods and their poor old Ma's and Pa's at home a-slavin' to keep 'em in school and give 'em a education! You know that's dangerous, too, puttin' a lot o' boys and girls out together like that!"

Students were coming into the schoolhouse now.

Professor Herbert says, "Close the door, Dave, so others won't hear."

I walked over and closed the door. I was shaking like a leaf in the wind. I thought Pa was going to hit Professor Herbert every minute. He was doing all the talking. His face was getting red. The red color was coming through the brown, weatherbeaten skin on Pa's face.

"I was right with these students," says Professor Herbert. "I know what they got into and what they didn't. I didn't send one of the other teachers with them on this field trip. I went myself. Yes, I took the boys and girls together. Why not?"

"It jist don't look good to me," says Pa, "a-takin' all this swarm of youngins out to pillage th' whole deestrict. Breakin' down cherry trees. Keepin' boys in atter school."

"What else could I have done with Dave, Mr. Sexton?" says Professor Herbert. "The boys didn't have any business all climbing that cherry tree after one lizard. One boy could have gone up in the tree and got it. The farmer charged us six dollars. It was a little steep, I think, but we had it to pay. Must I make five boys pay and let your boy off? He said he didn't have the dollar and couldn't get it. So I put it in for him. I'm letting him work it out. He's not working for me. He's working for the school!"

"I jist don't know what you could a-done with 'im," says Pa, "only a-larruped 'im with a withe! That's what he needed!"

"He's too big to whip," says Professor Herbert, pointing at me. "He's a man in size."

"He's not too big fer me to whip," says Pa. "They ain't too big until they're over twenty-one! It jist didn't look fair to me! Work one and let th' rest out because they got th' money. I don't see what bugs has got to do with a high school! It don't look good to me no-how!"

Pa picked up his gun and put it back in its holster. The red color left Professor Herbert's face. He talked more to Pa. Pa softened a little. It looked funny to see Pa in the high-school building. It was the first time he'd ever been there.

"We were not only hunting snakes, toads, flowers, butterflies, lizards," says Professor Herbert, "but, Mr. Sexton, I was hunting dry timothy grass to put in an incubator and raise some protozoa."

"I don't know what that is," says Pa. "Th' incubator is th' new-fangled way o' cheatin' th' hens and raisin' chickens. I ain't so sure about th' breed o' chickens you mentioned."

"You've heard of germs, Mr. Sexton, haven't you?" says Professor Herbert.

"Jist call me Luster, if you don't mind," says Pa, very casual-like.

"All right, Luster, you've heard of germs, haven't you?"

"Yes," says Pa, "but I don't believe in germs. I'm sixty-five years old and I ain't seen one yet!"

"You can't see them with your naked eye," says Professor Herbert. "Just keep that gun in the holster and stay with me in the high school today. I have a few things I want to show you. That scum on your teeth has germs in it."

"What," says Pa, "you mean to tell me I've got germs on my teeth!"

"Yes," says Professor Herbert. "The same kind as we might be able to find in a living black snake if we dissect it!"

"I don't mean to dispute your word," says Pa, "but I don't believe it. I don't believe I have germs on my teeth!"

"Stay with me today and I'll show you. I want to take you through the school anyway! School has changed a lot in the hills since you went to school. I don't guess we had high schools in this county when you went to school!"

"No," says Pa, "jist readin', writin', and cipherin'. We didn't have all this bug larnin', frog larnin', and findin' germs on your teeth and in the middle o' black snakes! Th' world's changin'."

"It is," says Professor Herbert, "and we hope all for the better. Boys like your own there are going to help change it. He's your boy. He knows all of what I've told you. You stay with me today."

"I'll shore stay with you," says Pa. "I want to see th' germs off'n my teeth. I jist want to see a germ. I've never seen one in my life. 'Seein' is believin',' Pap allus told me."

Pa walks out of the office with Professor Herbert. I just hoped Professor Herbert didn't have Pa arrested for pulling his gun. Pa's gun has always been a friend to him when he goes to settle disputes.

The bell rang. School took up. I saw the students when they marched in the schoolhouse look at Pa. They would grin and punch each other. Pa just stood and watched them pass in at the schoolhouse door. Two long lines marched in the house. The boys and girls were clean and well dressed. Pa stood over in the schoolyard under a leafless elm, in his sheepskin coat, his big boots laced in front with buckskin, and his heavy socks stuck above his boot tops. Pa's overall legs were baggy and wrinkled between his coat and boot tops. His blue work shirt showed at the collar. His big black hat showed his gray-streaked black hair. His face was hard and weather-tanned to the color of a ripe fodder blade. His hands were big and gnarled like the roots of the elm tree he stood beside.

When I went to my first class I saw Pa and Professor Herbert going around over the schoolhouse. I was in my geometry class when Pa and Professor Herbert came in the room. We were explaining our propositions on the blackboard. Professor Herbert and Pa just quietly came in and sat down for a while. I heard Fred Wurts whisper to Glenn Armstrong, "Who is that old man? Lord, he's a rough-look-ing scamp." Glenn whispered back, "I think he's Dave's Pap." The students in geometry looked at Pa. They must have wondered what he was doing in school. Before the class was over, Pa and Professor Herbert got up and went out. I saw them together down on the playground. Professor Herbert was explaining to Pa. I could see the prints of Pa's gun under his coat when he'd walk around.

At noon in the high-school cafeteria Pa and Professor Herbert sat together at the little table where Professor Herbert always ate by himself. They ate together. The students watched the way Pa ate. He ate with his knife instead of his fork. A lot of the students felt sorry for me after they found out he was my father. They didn't have to feel sorry for me. I wasn't ashamed of Pa after I found out he wasn't going to shoot Professor Herbert. I was glad they had made friends. I wasn't ashamed of Pa. I wouldn't be as long as he behaved. He would find out about the high school as I had found out about the Lambert boys across the hill.

In the afternoon when we went to biology Pa was in the class. He was sitting on one of the high stools beside the microscope. We went ahead with our work just as if Pa wasn't in the class. I saw Pa take his knife and scrape tartar from one of his teeth. Professor Herbert put it on the lens and adjusted the microscope for Pa. He adjusted it and worked awhile. Then he says: "Now Luster, look! Put your eye right down to the light. Squint the other eye!"

Pa put his head down and did as Professor Herbert said. "I see 'im," says Pa. "Who'd a ever thought that? Right on a body's teeth! Right in a body's mouth. You're right certain they ain't no fake to this, Professor Herbert?"

"No, Luster," says Professor Herbert. "It's there. That's the germ. Germs live in a world we cannot see with the naked eye. We must use the microscope. There are millions of them in our bodies. Some are harmful. Others are helpful."

Pa holds his face down and looks through the microscope. We stop and watch Pa. He sits upon the tall stool. His knees are against the table. His legs are long. His coat slips up behind when he bends over. The handle of his gun shows. Professor Herbert pulls his coat down quickly.

"Oh, yes," says Pa. He gets up and pulls his coat down. Pa's face gets a little red. He knows about his gun and he knows he doesn't have any use for it in high school.

"We have a big black snake over here we caught yesterday," says Professor Herbert. "We'll chloroform him and dissect him and show you he has germs in his body, too."

"Don't do it," says Pa. "I believe you. I jist don't want to see you kill the black snake. I never kill one. They are good mousers and a lot o' help to us on the farm. I like black snakes. I jist hate to see people kill 'em. I don't allow 'em killed on my place."

The students look at Pa. They seem to like him better after he said that. Pa with a gun in his pocket but a tender heart beneath his ribs for snakes, but not for man! Pa won't whip a mule at home. He won't whip his cattle.

"Man can defend hisself," says Pa, "but cattle and mules can't. We have the drop on 'em. Ain't nothin' to a man that'll beat a good pullin' mule. He ain't got th' right kind o' a heart!"

Professor Herbert took Pa through the laboratory. He showed him the different kinds of work we were doing. He showed him our equipment. They stood and talked while we worked. Then they walked out together. They talked louder when they got out in the hall.

When our biology class was over I walked out of the room. It was our last class for the day. I would have to take my broom and sweep two hours to finish paying for the split cherry tree. I just wondered if Pa would want me to stay. He was standing in the hallway watching the students march out. He looked lost among us. He looked like a leaf turned brown on the tree among the treetop filled with growing leaves.

I got my broom and started to sweep. Professor Herbert walked up and says, "I'm going to let you do that some other time. You can go home with your father. He is waiting out there."

I laid my broom down, got my books, and went down the steps.

Pa says, "Ain't you got two hours o' sweepin' yet to do?"

I says, "Professor Herbert said I could do it some other time. He said for me to go home with you."

"No," says Pa. "You are goin' to do as he says. He's a good man. School has changed from my day and time. I'm a dead leaf, Dave. I'm behind. I don't belong here. If he'll let me I'll get a broom and we'll both sweep one hour. That pays your debt. I'll hep you pay it. I'll ast 'im and see if he won't let me hep you."

"I'm going to cancel the debt," says Professor Herbert. "I just wanted you to understand, Luster."

"I understand," says Pa, "and since I understand, he must pay his debt fer th' tree and I'm goin' to hep 'im."

"Don't do that," says Professor Herbert. "It's all on me."

"We don't do things like that," says Pa, "we're just and honest people. We don't want somethin' fer nothin'. Professor Herbert, you're wrong now and I'm right. You'll haf to listen to me. I've larned a lot from you. My boy must go on. Th' world has left me. It changed while I've raised my family and plowed th' hills. I'm a just and honest man. I don't skip debts. I ain't larned 'em to do that. I ain't got much larnin' myself but I do know right from wrong atter I see through a thing."

Professor Herbert went home. Pa and I stayed and swept one hour. It looked funny to see Pa use a broom. He never used one at home. Mom used the broom. Pa used the plow. Pa did hard work. Pa says, "I can't sweep. Durned if I can. Look at th' streaks o' dirt I leave on th' floor! Seems like no work a-tall fer me. Brooms is too light 'r somethin'. I'll jist do th' best I can, Dave. I've been wrong about th' school."

I says, "Did you know Professor Herbert can get a warrant out for you for bringing your pistol to school and showing it in his office! They can railroad you for that!"

"That's all made right," says Pa. "I've made that right. Professor Herbert ain't goin' to take it to court. He likes me. I like 'im. We jist had to get together. He had the remedies. He showed me. You must go on to school. I am as strong a man as ever come out'n th' hills fer my years and th' hard work I've done. But I'm behind, Dave. I'm a little man. Your hands will be softer than mine. Your clothes will be better. You'll allus look cleaner than your old Pap. Jist remember, Dave, to pay your debts and be honest. Jist be kind to animals and don't bother th' snakes. That's all I got agin th' school. Puttin' black snakes to sleep and cuttin' 'em open."

It was late when we got home. Stars were in the sky. The moon was up. The ground was frozen. Pa took his time going home. I couldn't run like I did the night before. It was ten o'clock before we got the work finished, our suppers eaten. Pa sat before the fire and told Mom he was going to take her and show her a germ sometime. Mom hadn't seen one either. Pa told her about the high school and the fine man Professor Herbert was. He told Mom about the strange school across the hill and how different it was from the school in their day and time.

"Cabinet Decision"

NIGEL BALCHIN

SEWELL ACCEPTED the big armchair, but he sat upright in it with his back very straight. The sun on his silver hair made a sort of halo.

Gatling said, "Do smoke if you'd care to. I'm going to." He had a reputation as the rudest and most short-tempered of men on the public platform. It was of great value to him in personal contacts. His quiet friendliness was always such a pleasant surprise.

Sewell inclined his head politely, but his hands stayed in his lap. The Minister fumbled in his pocket and took out his pipe.

"You know, Professor Sewell, I've always wanted to meet you — and for a reason you'll never guess." He started to load his pipe. "I hadn't much chance of ordinary education — not as much as I wanted, anyhow. So I had to educate myself as best I could." He smiled. "The good thing about that is that you can work on what you like. One of the things I wanted to know about was biology. And one of the first books I bought was called *Elements for Biological Students*. Remember it?"

Sewell said, "That little book? . . . That was written thirty years ago."

"*Sewell's Elements for Biological Students*," said Gatling, smiling. "I remember it well."

Sewell smiled slightly. "You remember the photographs. They were rather fine."

The Minister frowned. "I don't think there were any photographs in my edition," he said doubtfully.

"No, no. There weren't. I was thinking of another book," said Sewell expressionlessly.

The Minister glanced at him sharply and then smiled. "I'm sorry to find you a cynic, Professor," he said gently. "I really did work from that book, you know."

"I'm very gratified to know that," said Sewell coldly.

Gatling put a match to his pipe and said between puffs, "Well, now . . . though I read your book . . . I don't know much about these things nowadays. . . . But the people who do tell me that you're just finishing a . . . wonderful piece of work."

"I should prefer to say that I was just beginning it," said Sewell.

From *Who Is My Neighbor*, copyright 1950 by Nigel Balchin.

He was saying all his words very carefully, sounding all the consonants fully.

"In fact," said Gatling, flicking his match away, "the trouble from
our point of view is that it's a damned sight too good. You've scared
my people out of their wits."

"In what way, Minister? I see no reason why any man should
be alarmed at the prospect of not having typhoid fever or bubonic
plague." Sewell rolled the words out in his best prize-reader manner.

Gatling's lips tightened slightly. "Well, I think they've told you
that, haven't they? I thought I saw a letter to you setting out our
point of view?"

"Yes," said Sewell briefly. "I was sent a letter."

"Then we needn't spend time going all over it again. The point
is that here's something that everybody agrees is a fine piece of
work but which is felt to be too mixed up with defense matters to
broadcast in the present state of the world. So we're asking you not
to publish for the time being. We don't like the position any more
than you do, but there it is. Now then — if you want to ask me
about that decision, fire ahead."

Sewell hesitated. "You wish me to be frank, sir?"

"Of course. Say what you like, ask what you like. I want you to
go away from here happy. Or at least, not happy, because I'm not
happy about it myself. But convinced."

There was a long pause. Then Sewell lifted his head and said,
"By whom was this decision made?"

"By the Cabinet. Advised by its committee on scientific developments."

"Which in turn was advised by you?"

"Up to a point — yes."

Sewell nodded. "But you, sir, despite your early reading,
wouldn't claim to be a scientist. You were therefore advised by — ?"

"Sir Guthrie Brewer is my scientific adviser."

"Quite. But Sir Guthrie Brewer is, or was, a physicist. This matter is quite outside his field."

"The Government employs quite a few biologists, you know."

"Exactly. And Sir Guthrie Brewer was advised by them?"

"Yes."

Sewell smiled faintly. "Then the fact is that, though this is a
Cabinet decision, the Cabinet is only the mouthpiece for some comparatively junior man in a government department?"

Gatling frowned at the bowl of his pipe. "That's a very nice
piece of debating, Professor. But you can see the hole in it as well
as I can. The Cabinet wasn't considering the scientific side of your

work. The Cabinet aren't experts on science or any other technical
subject — and I can tell you that if you ever do get a technical expert in the Cabinet he's a damned nuisance. On the technical facts
we have to rely on our advisers. But on the *policy* arising out of
those facts we have to make up our own minds. The advice we got
— quite unanimously — was that your work, directly or indirectly,
could be used by a potential enemy against this country. Now —
do you dispute that?"

Sewell hesitated. "I don't dispute that it is possible. But I dispute
whether it is at all likely."

"But that's nothing to do with you, is it? That's not a scientific
matter but a matter of judgment. And matters of judgment are *our*
business."

"But can you divorce knowledge and judgment quite as easily
as that?" said Sewell. "Are men who admittedly have no technical
knowledge the best judges of the reaction of other technicians in
other countries?"

"I don't know," said Gatling bluntly. "But that happens to be the
way government's carried on."

Sewell nodded. "Now, supposing," he said reflectively, "that,
thinking that decision to be wrong, I refuse to accept it? I mean,
supposing I just disobey your orders and publish my work?"

"Need we go into that?" said Gatling, peering up under his
heavy eyebrows with a smile.

"I should prefer to go into it," said Sewell coldly.

"All right. Then the answer is that you would bring the full force
of the law against you. The Government, however inadequately,
represents society, and if you defy the Government you defy society."

"But I might easily feel that since an ignorant government was
acting against the interests of an even more ignorant society it was
my duty to defy both."

"Then we should just have to put you in jail as a public menace,"
said Gatling curtly. "And that goes however good your intentions
might be. All the worst public menaces have good intentions."

"Oh, yes. I quite realize that. If I defy you, you have the power
of revenge. But how does it help you? You can't arrest me and keep
me locked up for the rest of my life because I *might* prefer my judgment to yours. And if I once do so, and communicate my work
abroad, the harm, from your point of view, is done."

Gatling's small eyes were very bright. He smiled broadly and
said, "Look Professor — this is a very interesting theoretical discussion, but where can it get us? You're not the sort of man who com-
mits treason just to have his own way."

Sewell had gone very pale. He said, "Treason . . ."

"Yes," said Gatling, misunderstanding. "It's a nasty word. But that's what it would amount to, you know."

Sewell threw up his great head. "You don't seem to realize, sir," he said very quietly, "that you are placing me in a position in which treason is unavoidable."

Gatling frowned. "I don't . . . ?"

"I am not a patriot," said Sewell in a low voice, staring straight ahead of him. "I have never felt that because I happened to be born in this country, it was the only country that mattered. I have tried to give it a fair return for what it has given me. But after that my loyalty is to the world. I seem to remember a time, sir, when you and some of your present colleagues in the Government felt the same in your sphere. You seem to have changed your minds. I haven't."

Gatling said quickly, "Don't answer this if you don't want to. But are you a member of — of any political party?"

"No," said Sewell savagely, "I'm not a Communist nor a Socialist nor a Fascist nor any of your precious 'ists,' except a scientist. But more particularly I'm not a nationalist. You tell me that I mustn't publish my work because there's an outside chance that some vague enemy might use the stuff to kill Englishmen. But I *know* that that stuff, properly developed, can save half a million lives a year all over the world. You say it will be treason to publish it. I say it will be treason to those half a million people if I don't."

There was a moment's pause. Then Gatling said quietly, "Professor Sewell — do you realize the present state of the world?"

"No, sir," said Sewell bitterly, "I don't. Except that I assume it's in its usual mess. But who made it in that mess? People who took my line or people who took yours? We're told every day that what's wrong with the world is fear and suspicion and lack of goodwill. You all go round deploring it. And then you do things like this just to make sure that everybody's got something to be frightened and suspicious about." He paused for a moment and closed his eyes. Then very quietly and politely he said, "What I am asking, sir, is why I or any other scientist should allow our work to be hindered and suppressed and wasted by what we know to be criminal folly. You asked me to speak frankly."

He opened his eyes. Gatling was staring at him with the bright little eyes, but he was not smiling now. He said slowly, "That's right. I'm glad you *have* spoken frankly. Mind if I do the same?"

Sewell bowed his head with conscious dignity.

"Right," said Gatling briskly. The Scots accent had disappeared and was replaced by the merest trace of Cockney. "Professor, if I came to your laboratory and admitted I knew nothing about biology and then lectured you about it, you'd be angry. And quite right. But you come here and tell me you're not interested in politics — sounding proud of it, mind you — and then tell me my job." He raised his hand as Sewell was about to speak. "Wait a minute — let me finish. The trouble with all you experts is that you want it both ways. You spend a lifetime learning to do your particular sort of trick or crossword puzzle and at the end you're very good at it — much better than any of the rest of us. But you don't feel that that makes you any less qualified to do other things. In fact, you think it makes you *better* qualified. After forty years in a laboratory, you feel quite capable of coming out and telling the politician his business — though he may have spent those forty years learning it."

Sewell said, "If the scientist has spent forty years learning to think properly and logically . . ."

"I know. I know. I read an article by Professor Booth the other day. He was saying it too — only scientists know how to think and it's high time they took over the running of the world. . . ."

"I really can't take responsibility for Booth," said Sewell with a slight smile.

"Maybe not. But his argument is the same as yours. You may not agree on any other single damn thing — scientists hardly ever do as far as I can see — except that scientists know all the answers better than anyone else."

"On the contrary — I have no faith in scientists as such."

"Haven't you? Well, I have. I think they know a lot about science. And if they'd stick to that it would be fine. But when they start talking about the 'scientific mind' and 'logical thinking' as though they were the only people with minds above the two-plus-two-equals-four level then I get angry. And it makes me rude."

Gatling leaned forward with his hard, bulldog grin. "Everything you've told me," he said, "I'd thought about and talked about and argued at street corners by the time I was twenty. For the last thirty years, while you've been studying biology, I've been learning what's wrong with that point of view — by studying people. Let me tell you what I've learnt. . . ." He leaned back in his chair and stared at his blotting paper with the bushy eyebrows puckered.

"You think," he said slowly, "that people are fundamentally decent and just and peaceful and that they want decency and justice and peace. You're right. They do. But what you forget is that they they want them on their own terms. And their own terms don't add up. They want decency and justice without interference with their liberty to do as they like. They want peace without risks — and so on. You think the politician makes opinion — that he twists the people round his little finger by exploiting their simple ignorance. Well, there are a lot of politicians about who think that too. You'll find them losing their deposits at elections, or hanging from lamp-posts all over Europe. The men who survive — the 'leaders,' as they like to call themselves — are the chaps who've spent a lifetime learning to compromise between a set of demands that are all very reasonable in themselves but that don't add up. How to do less work and have more money. How to spend more, reduce taxation, and balance the budget. How to be strong if there's a war but not to prepare for it, mention it, or even think about it beforehand. You talk to me about logical thinking, Professor — give me a logical problem — give me something in which two and two are allowed to equal four and haven't somehow got to equal five — and I'll agree with you. But until then — it isn't so easy."

Sewell hesitated. "I don't quite see the application. . . ."

"You say," said Gatling moodily, "that you'd be prepared to take the chance that this stuff of yours might be used against us, in order to give it to the world. Fine. So would I. So let's do it and feel really big and bold and generous. Then there's a war and it comes back at us and kills us. That's all right. We took a gamble and it didn't come off. But it also kills Mrs. Jones of Tooting, and her cousin Harold. They didn't feel big and bold and generous. They just got killed."

"But surely if government is going to be any good it must take responsibility for doing the right thing," said Sewell. "You've got to explain to Mrs. Jones and Harold what you're doing and why you're doing it."

Gatling sighed. "D'you know what they'd say?" he said wearily. "They'd say — 'Go ahead. That's fine. We're all in favor of generosity and boldness.' And then, just as you were going out of the door, they'd say, 'But of course, mind you, if you take the slightest risk with our safety, you're a scoundrel.'" He spread out his hands. "Look, Professor. You're an idealist and an internationalist and all the nice, admirable things that make you feel good inside. And tomorrow you can go back to your laboratory feeling that you've stuck to your principles and that if only the bloody politicians would follow them everything would be fine. I used to feel just like that. But like a fool I never arranged to have a laboratory to go to. I stuck around in politics. And after a while they got tired of my telling them what to do and said, 'All right. You know so much, you have a go.' And here I am."

He shook his head. "Now I don't mind your thinking that I'm wrong about this. I may well be. But what I mind is your thinking that you and people like you can be right just by some sort of instinct. Every man's got a right to his own view of how to run the world — and even to try it, if anybody'll let him. But what he hasn't got a right to do is to think himself so superior that he can do it with one hand — without knowledge — without experience — without any damn thing except plenty of confidence."

"I have no such illusions," said Sewell coldly.

"Or," said Gatling gently, "that he can suddenly wash out the Government, the law of the land, and anything else he likes just because they don't fit in with his theory, and act as a pure individualist answerable to nobody but himself."

Sewell hesitated. "Frankly, I can't say I'm prepared to abandon my own judgment in favor . . ."

"I'm not talking about your judgment," said Gatling sharply. "Everybody's entitled to his own judgment. I'm talking about your actions." He peered up at Sewell from under the heavy brows. "We're talking frankly, so I'll tell you something. Before I saw you I was advised by two lots of people. One lot suggested that you should be offered the K.B.E. and the other that you should be threatened with the Official Secrets Act. Both quite reasonable suggestions in their way — for some people." He paused. "But for you I'd rather just say this — what you'd like to do is what *I'd* like to do — as an individual. But as a Minister of the Crown, knowing what I do about the international situation, I can't do it without betraying a trust. I ask you to accept that as my honest verdict — as the verdict of a man doing his best with a difficult job." He paused and then added, "It's one of those cases where people like ourselves have to accept that the world's very imperfect and get on and improve it, instead of acting as though it was perfect already."

"The world will never be perfect enough, sir, to make it unnecessary to take risks."

The spotlight of the sun was full on the silver halo. Gatling hesitated for a moment and then shook his head.

"That might be a good thing to say in debate, Professor. It doesn't mean anything, and it sounds as though it means a lot. But this isn't a debate."

Sewell flushed. "I would remind you, sir, that to you this matter is a small administrative point. To me it is the fate of twelve years' work and twenty years of thought. It is unlikely to be I who am doing the debating." He threw out a hand. "I simply disagree with you about the nature of your responsibilities. Surely I am entitled to do that without being charged with insincerity?"

"Of course you are," said Gatling curtly. "It's a free country. Anybody's allowed to disagree with anybody. But if you want to *do* anything about it I'm afraid you'll have to go and ask the electorate to put itself in your hands instead of in the Government's. And until you do that your opinion's just — an opinion." He passed a hand over his eyes. "Come on, Professor," he said wearily. "The system's all wrong. The world's all wrong. The politicians are all wrong. But they're all *there* and we've got to do the best we can with them *now*. Forty years in a laboratory learning to face the facts. Help me face this one."

Sewell made no reply. His face, turned toward the window, was slightly sullen. The sunlight emphasized his wrinkles, making him look very worn and old. After a short silence he made a helpless gesture. "You criticize me," he said, "for trusting my own judgment when I don't know the facts. But you expect me to trust yours still not knowing them."

"What facts do you want to know?"

"What's the reason for your alarm? Is it based on anything specific or just on vague suspicion? Whom do you fear, and why? Are you just worrying on principle or have you got something to worry about?"

Gatling hesitated. "All right," he said. "That's fair enough. If we want you to co-operate we've got to convince you. I know you'll understand that this is in the strictest confidence, but here are the facts as we see them."

Myers came silently in and stood waiting. For some minutes the Lord President did not look up. Then he said, "Not so good, Percy."

Myers said, "He was difficult?"

"Bloody difficult."

"In what way, Minister?"

"He's a spoiled old man who's used to having his own way. He's given plenty of orders, but I doubt he's been given one in twenty years. I tried being nice and I tried being tough, but neither really helped. He just doesn't see why he should take anybody's word for anything."

"You told him what would happen if he doesn't?"

"Oh, yes. I mixed up knighthoods and jails very nicely. But I didn't really sell him."

"You don't think he'll do — anything silly?"

Gatling thought for a moment. "No, I don't think so. But he isn't convinced, and as long as he isn't convinced he's a risk." He shifted restlessly in his chair. "He's one of those damned people with a mind like a bright boy of eighteen. And it's very difficult to show a famous old man that he's all up in the air and immature."

There was a short silence. Myers said, "You think we should put the dogs on him?"

"We must put them on the place, anyhow." Gatling frowned. "I don't want him to come to any harm," he said thoughtfully. "He's bogus all through, but he doesn't know it."

"Bogus?"

"As bogus as hell. He can't even sit down sincerely. And all this stuff about humanity. He wouldn't know humanity if he met it in the street. . . ." He reflected. "Maybe it was me. Maybe he'd be all right if he was talking to someone else in his own line. I expect that's it. He just thought that I was a politician and played up to me. Otherwise I don't see how he could ever do any good in his job, play-acting like that." He got up and flicked a paper clip irritably off his desk. "Why did it have to be him? Why couldn't it have been some nice respectful little bloke instead of that old prima donna? We'll have to get somebody to talk to him . . . somebody he'll listen to."

"Brewer?"

"No. He may be a nuisance, but he hasn't deserved to be talked to by Brewer. Besides, he'd act Brewer off the stage. No. Somebody he can talk to without thinking about the audience all the time." He knocked his pipe out into the ash tray. "Have a think about it, Percy, will you? We don't want any trouble."

Dr. Southport Vulpes's Nightmare

BERTRAND RUSSELL

DR. SOUTHPORT VULPES had had a long, tiring day at the Ministry of Mechanical Production. He had been trying to persuade the officials that there was no longer need of human beings in factories except for one to each building to act as caretaker and turn the switch on or off. He was an enthusiast, and was merely puzzled by the slow and traditional mentality of the bureaucrats. They pointed out that his schemes would require a vast capital outlay in the way of robot factories, and that, before their output had become adequate, they might be wrecked by rioting wage-earners or stopped dead by the fiat of indignant trade unions. Such fears seemed to him paltry and unimaginative. He was amazed that the splendid visions by which he was fired did not at once kindle like hopes in those to whom he endeavored to communicate them. Coming out of the cold March drizzle, discouraged and exhausted, he sank into a chair and, in the welcome warmth, he fell asleep. In sleep he experienced all the triumph that had eluded him in his waking hours. He dreamed; and the dream was sweet:

The Third World War, like the Siege of Troy, was in its tenth year. In a military sense, its course had been inconclusive. Sometimes victory seemed to incline to the one side, sometimes to the other, but never decisively or for any long period to either. But from the technical point of view, which alone concerned Dr. Vulpes, its progress had been all that could be wished.

During the first two years of the war, robots had been substituted for live workers in all factories on both sides, thereby releasing immense reserves of manpower for the armies. But this advance, which governments at first welcomed enthusiastically, proved less satisfactory than had been hoped. The casualties, caused largely by bacteriological warfare, were enormous. In some parts of the vast fronts, after destructive pestilences, the survivors mutinied and clamored for peace. For a time, the rival governments despaired of keeping the war alive, but Dr. Vulpes and his opposite number Phinnichovski Stukinmudovich, found a way of surmounting the crisis.

During the third and fourth years of the war they manufactured military robots who took the place of privates in the infantry of both sides. In the fifth and sixth years, they extended this process to all officers below the rank of general. They discovered also that the work of education — or of indoctrination, as it was now officially called — could be performed with far more certainty and exactness by machines than by live teachers and professors. It had been found very difficult to eliminate personal idiosyncrasies completely from live educators, whereas the mass-produced indoctrinators, manufactured by Dr. Vulpes and Comrade Stukinmudovich, all said exactly the same thing and all made precisely the same speeches about the importance of victory. The consequent improvement in morale was truly remarkable. By the eighth year of the war, none of the young people who were trained for the higher command over the vast robot armies shrank from the almost complete certainty of death in the plague-stricken areas where the fighting took place. But step by step, as they died, increased mechanical ingenuity found means of rendering them superfluous.

At last almost everything was done by robots. Some human beings, so far, had proved indispensable: geological experts to direct the mining robots into suitable areas, governments to decide great matters of policy, and, of course, Dr. Vulpes and Comrade Stukinmudovich to devote their great brains to new heights of ingenuity.

These two men were both wholehearted enthusiasts. Both were above the battle in the sense that they cared nothing for the issues on which politicians wasted their eloquence, but only for the perfecting of their machines. Both liked the war because it induced the politicians to give them scope. Neither wished the war to end, since they feared that with its ending men would fall back into traditional ways and would insist upon again doing, by means of human muscles and brains, things that robots could do without fatigue and with far more precision. Their objects being identical, they were close friends — though this had to be kept as a secret from their politician employers. They had used some portion of their armies of robots to make a great tunnel through the mountains of the Caucasus. One mouth of the tunnel was held by the forces of the West, the other by the forces of the East. Nobody except Dr. Vulpes and Comrade Stukinmudovich knew that the tunnel had two mouths, for, except for themselves, they allowed only robots into the tunnel. They had employed the robots to heat the tunnel, and to light it brilliantly, and to fill it with great stores of food in capsules scientifically calculated to promote life and health, though not to delight the palate, for both lived only in the life of the mind and were indifferent to the joys of sense.

Dr. Vulpes, as he was about to enter the tunnel, permitted himself some unprofessional reflections upon the world of sunlight that he was temporarily abandoning for one of his periodical conferences with Comrade Stukinmudovich. Gazing upon the sea below and the snowy peaks above, dim recollections floated into his mind of the classical education upon which, at the bidding of old-fashioned parents, some of his early years had been reluctantly wasted. "It was here," so he reflected, "that Prometheus was chained by Zeus, Prometheus who took the first step in that glorious progress of science which has led to the present splendid consummation. Zeus, like the governments of my youth, preferred the ancient ways. But Prometheus, unlike me and my friend Stukinmudovich, had not discovered how to outwit the reactionaries of his day. It is fitting that I should triumph on the spot where he suffered, and that Zeus with his paltry lightnings should be put in his place by our atomic skill." With these thoughts he bade farewell to the daylight and advanced to meet his friend.

They had had during the course of the war many secret conferences. In perfect mutual confidence they had communicated to each other whatever inventions might make the war more ingenious and more lasting.

In the middle of the tunnel he was met by his friend Stukinmudovich advancing from the East. They clasped hands and gazed into each other's eyes with warm affection. For a little moment before they became engulfed in technicalities they allowed themselves to rejoice in their joint work. "How beautiful," they said, "is the world that we are creating! Human beings were unpredictable, often mad, often cowardly, sometimes afflicted with anti-governmental ideals. How different are our robots! On them propaganda always has the intended effect."

"What," said the two sages to each other, "what could the most ardent moralist desire that we have not provided? Man was liable to sin; robots are not. Man was often foolish; robots never are. Man was liable to sexual aberrations; robots are not. You and I," they said to each other, "have long ago decided that the only thing that counts in a man is his behavior — i.e., what may be viewed from without. The behavior of our robots is in all respects better than that of the accidental biological product which has hitherto puffed itself up with foolish pride. How ingenious are their devices! How masterly their strategy! How bold their tactics, and how intrepid their conduct in battle! Who that is not the victim of obsolete superstition could desire more?"

Dr. Vulpes and Comrade Stukinmudovich had discovered means of making their robots sensitive to eloquence. The best speeches of the statesmen on the two sides were recorded, and at the sound of their soul-stirring words the wheels of the robots began to whirr and they behaved, though with more precision, as politicians had hoped that living crowds would behave. Only slight differences were needed to make the robots of one side respond to one kind of propaganda and those of the other to a different kind. Dr. Vulpes's robots responded to the noble words of our great Western statesman: "Can we hesitate, when we see vast hordes determined to extirpate belief in God, and to wipe out in our hearts that faith in a beneficent Creator which sustains us through all ardors, difficulties and dangers? Can we endure to think that we are nothing but ingenious mechanisms as our soulless enemies pretend? Can we forgo that immortal heritage of freedom for which our ancestors fought, and in defense of which we have been compelled to inflict upon thousands the rigors of incarceration? Can any of us hesitate at such a moment? Can any of us hold back? Can any of us think for one moment that the sacrifice of our mere individual life, of our petty personal existence is to be weighed against the preservation in the

world of those ideals for which our ancestors fought and bled? No!
A thousand times, No! Onward, fellow citizens! And in the knowledge of right be assured of the ultimate triumph of our Cause!"

All Dr. Vulpes's robots were so constructed that, when a gramophone recited these noble words in their presence, they set themselves to perform, without hesitation or doubt, their allotted task, of
which the ultimate purpose was to prove that the world is not gov-
erned by mere mechanism.

Comrade Stukinmudovich's robots were equally efficient and
responded with equal readiness to the gramophone records of the
Generalissimo's inspired utterances: "Comrades, are you prepared
to be forever the slaves of soulless capitalist exploiters? Are you prepared to deny the great destiny which dialectical materialism has
prepared for those who are emancipated from the chains imposed
by base exploiters? Can anything so dead, so lifeless, so cruel, so base
as the foul philosophy of Wall Street subdue the human race forever? No! A thousand times, No! Freedom is yours if you will work
for it now with that ardor with which your precursors worked to
create the Great State that is now your champion. Onward to victory! Onward to freedom! Onward to life and joy!" These words
on the gramophone equally activated Stukinmudovich's robots.

The rival armies met in their millions. The rival planes, guided
by robots, darkened the sky. Never once did a robot fail in its duty.
Never once did it flee from the field of battle. Never once did its
machinery whirr in response to enemy propaganda.

Until this meeting in the tenth year of the war, the happiness of
Dr. Vulpes and Comrade Stukinmudovich had had its limitations.
There were still human beings in governments, and human beings
were still necessary as geological experts to direct the robots to new
sources of raw material as the old sources became exhausted. There
was a danger that governments might decide upon peace. There
was another danger even more difficult to avert, that, if geological
experts were eliminated, the activities of robots might some day be
brought to an end by the exhaustion of mines. The first of these dangers was not unavoidable. When they met on this occasion they confided to each other that they had plans for the mutual extermina-
tion of the governments on each side. But the need of geological
experts remained to trouble them. It was to the solution of this problem that they devoted their joint intelligence on this occasion. At
last, after a month of arduous thought, they arrived at the solution.
They invented pathfinder robots capable of guiding others to the
right mines. There were robots that could find iron, robots that
could find oil, robots that could find copper, robots that could find
uranium, and so on through all the materials of scientific warfare.

Now at last they had no fear that when existing mines were no longer productive the war would have to stop, and so much ingenuity would cease to function.

When they had completed the manufacture of these pathfinding robots they decided to stay in their tunnel and await calmly the extinction of the rest of the human race. They were no longer young and they had the philosophic calm of men whose work was completed. The two sages, fed and tended by hordes of subservient robots, lived to a great age and died at the same moment. They died happy, knowing that, while the planet lasted, the war would continue, with no diplomats to call it off, no cynics to doubt the holiness of rival slogans, no skeptics to ask the purpose of unending ingenious activity.

Filled with enthusiasm, Dr. Vulpes awoke. As he woke, he heard himself exclaiming: "No more risk of victory! War forever!" Unfortunately, the words were overheard, and he was sent to jail.

The Portable Phonograph

WALTER VAN TILBURG CLARK

THE RED SUNSET, with narrow, black cloud strips like threats across it, lay on the curved horizon of the prairie. The air was still and cold, and in it settled the mute darkness and greater cold of night. High in the air there was wind, for through the veil of the dusk the clouds could be seen gliding rapidly south and changing shapes. A queer sensation of torment, of two-sided, unpredictable nature, arose from the stillness of the earth air beneath the violence of the upper air. Out of the sunset, through the dead, matted grass and isolated weed stalks of the prairie, crept the narrow and deeply rutted remains of a road. In the road, in places, there were crusts of shallow, brittle ice. There were little islands of an old oiled pavement in the road, too, but most of it was mud, now frozen rigid. The frozen mud still bore the toothed impress of great tanks, and a

From *The Watchful Gods and Other Stories* by Walter Van Tilburg Clark. Copyright 1941 by Walter Van Tilburg Clark. Reprinted by permission of Random House, Inc.

wanderer on the neighboring undulations might have stumbled, in this light, into large, partially filled-in and weed-grown cavities, their banks channeled and beginning to spread into badlands. These pits were such as might have been made by falling meteors, but they were not. They were the scars of gigantic bombs, their rawness already made a little natural by rain, seed, and time. Along the road, there were rakish remnants of fence. There was also, just visible, one portion of tangled and multiple barbed wire still erect, behind which was a shelving ditch with small caves, now very quiet and empty, at intervals in its back wall. Otherwise there was no structure or remnant of a structure visible over the dome of the darkling earth, but only, in sheltered hollows, the darker shadows of young trees trying again.

Under the wuthering arch of the high wind a V of wild geese fled south. The rush of their pinions sounded briefly, and the faint, plaintive notes of their expeditionary talk. Then they left a still greater vacancy. There was the smell and expectation of snow, as there is likely to be when the wild geese fly south. From the remote distance, towards the red sky, came faintly the protracted howl and quick yap-yap of a prairie wolf.

North of the road perhaps a hundred yards, lay the parallel and deeply intrenched course of a small creek, lined with leafless alders and willows. The creek was already silent under ice. In the bank above it was dug a sort of cell, with a single opening, like the mouth of a mine tunnel. Within the cell there was a little red of fire, which showed dully through the opening, like a reflection or a deception of the imagination. The light came from the chary burning of four blocks of poorly aged peat, which gave off a petty warmth and much acrid smoke. But the precious remnants of wood, old fence posts and timbers from the long-deserted dugouts, had to be saved for the real cold, for the time when a man's breath blew white, the moisture in his nostrils stiffened at once when he stepped out, and the expansive blizzards paraded for days over the vast open, swirling and settling and thickening, till the dawn of the cleared day when the sky was thin blue-green and the terrible cold, in which a man could not live for three hours unwarmed, lay over the uniformly drifted swell of the plain.

Around the smoldering peat, four men were seated cross-legged. Behind them, traversed by their shadows, was the earth bench, with two old and dirty army blankets, where the owner of the cell slept. In a niche in the opposite wall were a few tin utensils which caught the glint of the coals. The host was rewrapping in a piece of daubed burlap four fine, leather-bound books. He worked slowly and very carefully, and at last tied the bundle securely with a piece of grass-woven cord. The other three looked intently upon the process, as if a great significance lay in it. As the host tied the cord, he spoke. He was an old man, his long, matted beard and hair gray to nearly white. The shadows made his brows and cheekbones appear gnarled, his eyes and cheeks deeply sunken. His big hands, rough with frost and swollen by rheumatism, were awkward but gentle at their task. He was like a prehistoric priest performing a fateful ceremonial rite. Also his voice had in it a suitable quality of deep, reverent despair, yet perhaps at the moment, a sharpness of selfish satisfaction.

"When I perceived what was happening," he said, "I told myself, 'It is the end. I cannot take much; I will take these.'

"Perhaps I was impractical," he continued. "But for myself, I do not regret, and what do we know of those who will come after us? We are the doddering remnant of a race of mechanical fools. I have saved what I love; the soul of what was good in us is here; perhaps the new ones will make a strong enough beginning not to fall behind when they become clever."

He rose with slow pain and placed the wrapped volumes in the niche with his utensils. The others watched him with the same ritualistic gaze.

"Shakespeare, the Bible, *Moby Dick*, the *Divine Comedy*," one of them said softly. "You might have done worse, much worse."

"You will have a little soul left until you die," said another harshly. "That is more than is true of us. My brain becomes thick, like my hands." He held the big, battered hands, with their black nails, in the glow to be seen.

"I want paper to write on," he said. "And there is none."

The fourth man said nothing. He sat in the shadow farthest from the fire, and sometimes his body jerked in its rags from the cold. Although he was still young, he was sick and coughed often. Writing implied a greater future than he now felt able to consider.

The old man seated himself laboriously, and reached out, groaning at the movement, to put another block of peat on the fire. With bowed heads and averted eyes, his three guests acknowledged his magnanimity.

"We thank you, Dr. Jenkins, for the reading," said the man who had named the books.

They seemed then to be waiting for something. Dr. Jenkins understood, but was loath to comply. In an ordinary moment he would have said nothing. But the words of *The Tempest* which he had been reading, and the religious attention of the three, made this an unusual occasion.

"You wish to hear the phonograph," he said grudgingly.

The two middle-aged men stared into the fire, unable to formulate and expose the enormity of their desire.

The young man, however, said anxiously, between suppressed coughs, "Oh, please," like an excited child.

The old man rose again in his difficult way, and went to the back of the cell. He returned and placed tenderly upon the packed floor, where the firelight might fall upon it, an old portable phonograph in a black case. He smoothed the top with his hand, and then opened it. The lovely green-felt-covered disk became visible.

"I have been using thorns as needles," he said. "But tonight, because we have a musician among us," he bent his head to the young man, almost invisible in the shadow, "I will use a steel needle. There are only three left."

The two middle-aged men stared at him in speechless adoration. The one with the big hands, who wanted to write, moved his lips, but the whisper was not audible.

"Oh, don't!" cried the young man, as if he were hurt. "The thorns will do beautifully."

"No," the old man said. "I have become accustomed to the thorns, but they are not really good. For you, my young friend, we will have good music tonight.

"After all," he added generously, and beginning to wind the phonograph, which creaked, "they can't last forever."

"No, nor we," the man who needed to write said harshly. "The needle, by all means."

"Oh, thanks," said the young man. "Thanks," he said again in a low, excited voice, and then stifled his coughing with a bowed head.

"The records, though," said the old man when he had finished winding, "are a different matter. Already they are very worn. I do not play them more than once a week. One, once a week, that is what I allow myself.

"More than a week I cannot stand it; not to hear them," he apologized.

"No, how could you?" cried the young man. "And with them here like this."

"A man can stand anything," said the man who wanted to write, in his harsh, antagonistic voice.

"Please, the music," said the young man.

"Only the one," said the old man. "In the long run, we will remember more that way."

He had a dozen records with luxuriant gold and red seals. Even in that light the others could see that the threads of the records were becoming worn. Slowly he read out the titles, and the tremendous, dead names of the composers and the artists and the orchestras. The three worked upon the names in their minds, carefully. It was difficult to select from such a wealth what they would at once most like to remember. Finally, the man who wanted to write named Gershwin's "New York."

"Oh, no!" cried the sick young man, and then could say nothing more because he had to cough. The others understood him, and the harsh man withdrew his selection and waited for the musician to choose.

The musician begged Dr. Jenkins to read the titles again, very slowly, so that he could remember the sounds. While they were read, he lay back against the wall, his eyes closed, his thin, horny hand pulling at his light beard, and listened to the voices and the orchestras and the single instruments in his mind.

When the reading was done he spoke despairingly. "I have forgotten," he complained; "I cannot hear them clearly.

"There are things missing," he explained.

"I know," said Dr. Jenkins. "I thought that I knew all of Shelley by heart. I should have brought Shelley."

"That's more soul than we can use," said the harsh man. "*Moby Dick* is better.

"By God, we can understand that," he emphasized.

The Doctor nodded.

"Still," said the man who had admired the books, "we need the absolute if we are to keep a grasp on anything.

"Anything but these sticks and peat clods and rabbit snares," he said bitterly.

"Shelley desired an ultimate absolute," said the harsh man. "It's too much," he said. "It's no good; no earthly good."

The musician selected a Debussy nocturne. The others considered and approved. They rose to their knees to watch the Doctor prepare for the playing, so that they appeared to be actually in an attitude of worship. The peat glow showed the thinness of their bearded faces, and the deep lines in them, and revealed the condition of their garments. The other two continued to kneel as the old man carefully lowered the needle onto the spinning disk, but the musician suddenly drew back against the wall again, with his knees up, and buried his face in his hands.

At the first notes of the piano the listeners were startled. They stared at each other. Even the musician lifted his head in amazement, but then quickly bowed it again, strainingly, as if he were suffering from a pain he might not be able to endure. They were all listening deeply, without movement. The wet, blue-green notes tinkled forth from the old machine, and were individual, delectable presences in the cell. The individual, delectable presences swept into a sudden tide of unbearably beautiful dissonance, and then continued fully the swelling and ebbing of that tide, the dissonant inpourings, and the resolutions, and the diminishings, and the little, quiet wavelets of interlude lapping between. Every sound was piercing and singularly sweet. In all the men except the musician, there occurred rapid sequences of tragically heightened recollection. He heard nothing but what was there. At the final, whispering disappearance, but moving quietly so that the others would not hear him and look at him, he let his head fall back in agony, as if it were drawn there by the hair, and clenched the fingers of one hand over his teeth. He sat that way while the others were silent, and until they began to breathe again normally. His drawn-up legs were trembling violently.

Quickly Dr. Jenkins lifted the needle off, to save it and not to spoil the recollection with scraping. When he had stopped the whirling of the sacred disk, he courteously left the phonograph open and by the fire, in sight.

The others, however, understood. The musician rose last, but then abruptly, and went quickly out at the door without saying anything. The others stopped at the door and gave their thanks in low voices. The Doctor nodded magnificently.

"Come again," he invited, "in a week. We will have the 'New York.'"

When the two had gone together, out towards the rimed road, he stood in the entrance, peering and listening. At first, there was only the resonant boom of the wind overhead, and then far over the dome of the dead, dark plain, the wolf cry lamenting. In the rifts of clouds the Doctor saw four stars flying. It impressed the Doctor that one of them had just been obscured by the beginning of a flying cloud at the very moment he heard what he had been listening for, a sound of suppressed coughing. It was not nearby, however. He believed that down against the pale alders he could see the moving shadow.

With nervous hands he lowered the piece of canvas which served as a door, and pegged it at the bottom. Then quickly and quietly, looking at the piece of canvas frequently, he slipped the records into the case, snapped the lid shut, and carried the phonograph to his couch. There, pausing often to stare at the canvas and listen, he dug earth from the wall and disclosed a piece of board. Behind this there was a deep hole in the wall, into which he put the phonograph. After a moment's consideration, he went over and reached down his bundle of books and inserted it also. Then, guardedly, he once more sealed up the hole with the board and the earth. He also changed his blankets, and the grass-stuffed sack which served as a pillow, so that he could lie facing the entrance. After carefully placing two more blocks of peat upon the fire, he stood for a long time watching the stretched canvas, but it seemed to billow naturally with the first gusts of a lowering wind. At last he prayed, and got in under his blankets, and closed his smoke-smarting eyes. On the inside of the bed, next the wall, he could feel with his hands, the comfortable piece of lead pipe.

By the Waters of Babylon

STEPHEN VINCENT BENÉT

THE NORTH and the west and the south are good hunting ground, but it is forbidden to go east. It is forbidden to go to any of the Dead Places except to search for metal and then he who touches the metal must be a priest or the son of a priest. Afterwards, both the man and the metal must be purified. These are the rules and the laws; they are well made. It is forbidden to cross the great river and look upon the place that was the Place of the Gods — this is most strictly forbidden. We do not even say its name though we know its name. It is there that spirits live, and demons — it is there that there are the ashes of the Great Burning. These things are forbidden — they have been forbidden since the beginning of time.

My father is a priest; I am the son of a priest. I have been in the Dead Places near us, with my father — at first, I was afraid. When my father went into the house to search for the metal, I stood by the door and my heart felt small and weak. It was a dead man's house, a spirit house. It did not have the smell of man, though there were old bones in a corner. But it is not fitting that a priest's son should show fear. I looked at the bones in the shadow and kept my voice still.

Then my father came out with the metal — a good, strong piece. He looked at me with both eyes but I had not run away. He gave me the metal to hold — I took it and did not die. So he knew that I was truly his son and would be a priest in my time. That was when

I was very young — nevertheless my brothers would not have done it, though they are good hunters. After that, they gave me the good piece of meat and the warm corner by the fire. My father watched over me — he was glad that I should be a priest. But when I boasted or wept without a reason, he punished me more strictly than my brothers. That was right.

After a time, I myself was allowed to go into the dead houses and search for metal. So I learned the ways of those houses — and if I saw bones, I was no longer afraid. The bones are light and old — sometimes they will fall into dust if you touch them. But that is a great sin.

I was taught the chants and the spells — I was taught how to stop the running of blood from a wound and many secrets. A priest must know many secrets — that was what my father said. If the hunters think we do all things by chants and spells, they may believe so — it does not hurt them. I was taught how to read in the old books and how to make the old writings — that was hard and took a long time. My knowledge made me happy — it was like a fire in my heart. Most of all, I liked to hear of the Old Days and the stories of the gods. I asked myself many questions that I could not answer, but it was good to ask them. At night, I would lie awake and listen to the wind — it seemed to me that it was the voice of the gods as they flew through the air.

We are not ignorant like the Forest People — our women spin wool on the wheel, our priests wear a white robe. We do not eat grubs from the tree, we have not forgotten the old writings, although they are hard to understand. Nevertheless, my knowledge and my lack of knowledge burned in me — I wished to know more. When I was a man at last, I came to my father and said, "It is time for me to go on my journey. Give me your leave."

He looked at me for a long time, stroking his beard, then he said at last, "Yes. It is time." That night, in the house of the priesthood, I asked for and received purification. My body hurt but my spirit was a cool stone. It was my father himself who questioned me about my dreams.

He bade me look into the smoke of the fire and see — I saw and told what I saw. It was what I have always seen — a river, and, beyond it, a great Dead Place and in it the gods walking. I have always thought about that. His eyes were stern when I told him — he was no longer my father but a priest. He said, "This is a strong dream."

"It is mine," I said, while the smoke waved and my head felt light. They were singing the Star song in the outer chamber and it was like the buzzing of bees in my head.

He asked me how the gods were dressed and I told him how they were dressed. We know how they were dressed from the book, but I saw them as if they were before me. When I had finished, he threw the sticks three times and studied them as they fell.

"This is a very strong dream," he said. "It may eat you up."

"I am not afraid," I said and looked at him with both eyes. My voice sounded thin in my ears but that was because of the smoke.

He touched me on the breast and the forehead. He gave me the bow and the three arrows.

"Take them," he said. "It is forbidden to travel east. It is forbidden to cross the river. It is forbidden to go to the Place of the Gods. All these things are forbidden."

"All these things are forbidden," I said, but it was my voice that spoke and not my spirit. He looked at me again.

"My son," he said. "Once I had young dreams. If your dreams do not eat you up, you may be a great priest. If they eat you, you are still my son. Now go on your journey."

I went fasting, as is the law. My body hurt but not my heart. When the dawn came, I was out of sight of the village. I prayed and purified myself, waiting for a sign. The sign was an eagle. It flew east.

Sometimes signs are sent by bad spirits. I waited again on the flat rock, fasting, taking no food. I was very still — I could feel the sky above me and the earth beneath. I waited till the sun was beginning to sink. Then three deer passed in the valley, going east — they did not wind me or see me. There was a white fawn with them — a very great sign.

I followed them, at a distance, waiting for what would happen. My heart was troubled about going east, yet I knew that I must go. My head hummed with my fasting — I did not even see the panther spring upon the white fawn. But, before I knew it, the bow was in my hand. I shouted and the panther lifted his head from the fawn. It is not easy to kill a panther with one arrow but the arrow went through his eye and into his brain. He died as he tried to spring — he rolled over, tearing at the ground. Then I knew I was meant to go east — I knew that was my journey. When the night came, I made my fire and roasted meat.

It is eight suns' journey to the east and a man passes by many Dead Places. The Forest People are afraid of them but I am not. Once I made my fire on the edge of a Dead Place at night and, next morning, in the dead house, I found a good knife, little rusted. That was small to what came afterward but it made my heart feel big. Always when I looked for game, it was in front of my arrow, and twice I passed hunting parties of the Forest People without their knowing. So I knew my magic was strong and my journey clean, in spite of the law.

Toward the setting of the eighth sun, I came to the banks of the great river. It was half-a-day's journey after I had left the god-road — we do not use the god-roads now for they are falling apart into great blocks of stone, and the forest is safer going. A long way off, I had seen the water through trees but the trees were thick. At last, I came out upon an open place at the top of a cliff. There was the great river below, like a giant in the sun. It is very long, very wide. It could eat all the streams we know and still be thirsty. Its name is Ou-dis-sun, the Sacred, the Long. No man of my tribe had seen it, not even my father, the priest. It was magic and I prayed.

Then I raised my eyes and looked south. It was there, the Place of the Gods.

How can I tell what it was like — you do not know. It was there, in the red light, and they were too big to be houses. It was there with the red light upon it, mighty and ruined. I knew that in another moment the gods would see me. I covered my eyes with my hands and crept back into the forest.

Surely, that was enough to do, and live. Surely it was enough to spend the night upon the cliff. The Forest People themselves do not come near. Yet, all through the night, I knew that I should have to cross the river and walk in the places of the gods, although the gods ate me up. My magic did not help me at all and yet there was a fire in my bowels, a fire in my mind. When the sun rose, I thought, "My journey has been clean. Now I will go home from my journey." But, even as I thought so, I knew I could not. If I went to the place of the gods, I would surely die, but, if I did not go, I could never be at peace with my spirit again. It is better to lose one's life than one's spirit, if one is a priest and the son of a priest.

Nevertheless, as I made the raft, the tears ran out of my eyes. The Forest People could have killed me without fight, if they had come upon me then, but they did not come. When the raft was made, I said the sayings for the dead and painted myself for death. My heart was cold as a frog and my knees like water, but the burning in my mind would not let me have peace. As I pushed the raft from the shore, I began my death song — I had the right. It was a fine song.

"I am John, son of John," I sang. "My people are the Hill People. They are the men.
I go into the Dead Places but I am not slain.

I take the metal from the Dead Places but I am not blasted.
I travel upon the god-roads and am not afraid. E-yah! I have
 killed the panther, I have killed the fawn!
E-yah! I have come to the great river. No man has come there
 before.
It is forbidden to go east, but I have gone, forbidden to go on the
 great river, but I am there.
Open your hearts, you spirits, and hear my song.
Now I go to the place of the gods, I shall not return.
My body is painted for death and my limbs weak, but my heart
 is big as I go to the place of the gods!"

All the same, when I came to the Place of the Gods, I was afraid,
afraid. The current of the great river is very strong — it gripped
my raft with its hands. That was magic, for the river itself is wide
and calm. I could feel evil spirits about me, in the bright morning;
I could feel their breath on my neck as I was swept down the
stream. Never have I been so much alone — I tried to think of my
knowledge, but it was a squirrels' heap of winter nuts. There was
no strength in my knowledge any more and I felt small and naked
as a new-hatched bird — alone upon the great river, the servant of
the gods.

Yet, after a while, my eyes were opened and I saw. I saw both
banks of the river — I saw that once there had been god-roads
across it, though now they were broken and fallen like broken
vines. Very great they were, and wonderful and broken — broken
in the time of the Great Burning when the fire fell out of the sky.
And always the current took me nearer to the Place of the Gods,
and the huge ruins rose before my eyes.

I do not know the customs of rivers — we are the People of the
Hills. I tried to guide my raft with the pole but it spun around. I
thought the river meant to take me past the Place of the Gods and
out into the Bitter Water of the legends. I grew angry then — my
heart felt strong. I said aloud, "I am a priest and the son of a priest!"
The gods heard me — they showed me how to paddle with the
pole on one side of the raft. The current changed itself — I drew
near to the Place of the Gods.

When I was very near, my raft struck and turned over. I can
swim in our lakes — I swam to the shore. There was a great spike
of rusted metal sticking out into the river — I hauled myself up
upon it and sat there, panting. I had saved my bow and two arrows
and the knife I found in the Dead Place but that was all. My raft
went whirling downstream toward the Bitter Water. I looked after
it, and thought if it had trod me under, at least I would be safely

dead. Nevertheless, when I had dried my bow-string and restrung it, I walked forward to the Place of the Gods.

It felt like ground underfoot; it did not burn me. It is not true what some of the tales say, that the ground there burns forever, for I have been there. Here and there were the marks and stains of the Great Burning, on the ruins, that is true. But they were old marks, and old stains. It is not true either, what some of our priests say, that it is an island covered with fogs and enchantments. It is not. It is a great Dead Place — greater than any Dead Place we know. Everywhere in it there are god-roads, though most are cracked and broken. Everywhere there are the ruins of the high towers of the gods.

How shall I tell what I saw? I went carefully, my strung bow in my hand, my skin ready for danger. There should have been the wailings of spirits and the shrieks of demons, but there were not. It was very silent and sunny where I had landed — the wind and the rain and the birds that drop seeds had done their work — the grass grew in the cracks of the broken stone. It is a fair island — no wonder the gods built there. If I had come there, a god, I also would have built.

How shall I tell what I saw? The towers are not all broken — here and there one still stands, like a great tree in a forest, and the birds nest high. But the towers themselves look blind, for the gods are gone. I saw a fish-hawk, catching fish in the river. I saw a little dance of white butterflies over a great heap of broken stones and columns. I went there and looked about me — there was a carved stone with cut-letters, broken in half. I can read letters but I could not understand these. They said UBTREAS. There was also the shattered image of a man or a god. It had been made of white stone and he wore his hair tied back like a woman's. His name was ASHING, as I read on the cracked half of a stone. I thought it wise to pray to ASHING, though I do not know that god.

How shall I tell what I saw? There was no smell of man left, on stone or metal. Nor were there many trees in that wilderness of stone. There are many pigeons, nesting and dropping in the towers — the gods must have loved them, or, perhaps, they used them for sacrifices. There are wild cats that roam the god-roads, green-eyed, unafraid of man. At night they wail like demons but they are not demons. The wild dogs are more dangerous, for they hunt in a pack, but them I did not meet till later. Everywhere there are the carved stones, carved with magical numbers or words.

I went North — I did not try to hide myself. When a god or a demon saw me, then I would die, but meanwhile I was no longer afraid. My hunger for knowledge burned in me — there was so much that I could not understand. After awhile, I knew that my belly was hungry. I could have hunted for my meat, but I did not hunt. It is known that the gods did not hunt as we do — they got their food from enchanted boxes and jars. Sometimes these are still found in the Dead Places — once, when I was a child and foolish, I opened such a jar and tasted it and found the food sweet. But my father found out and punished me for it strictly, for, often, that food is death. Now, though, I had long gone past what was forbidden, and I entered the likeliest towers, looking for the food of the gods.

I found it at last in the ruins of a great temple in the mid-city. A mighty temple it must have been, for the roof was painted like the sky at night with its stars — that much I could see, though the colors were faint and dim. It went down into great caves and tunnels — perhaps they kept their slaves there. But when I started to climb down, I heard the squeaking of rats, so I did not go — rats are unclean, and there must have been many tribes of them, from the squeaking. But near there, I found food, in the heart of a ruin, behind a door that still opened. I ate only the fruits from the jars — they had a very sweet taste. There was drink, too, in bottles of glass — the drink of the gods was strong and made my head swim. After I had eaten and drunk, I slept on the top of a stone, my bow at my side.

When I woke, the sun was low. Looking down from where I lay, I saw a dog sitting on his haunches. His tongue was hanging out of his mouth; he looked as if he were laughing. He was a big dog, with a gray-brown coat, as big as a wolf. I sprang up and shouted at him but he did not move — he just sat there as if he were laughing. I did not like that. When I reached for a stone to throw, he moved swiftly out of the way of the stone. He was not afraid of me; he looked at me as if I were meat. No doubt I could have killed him with an arrow, but I did not know if there were others. Moreover, night was falling.

I looked about me — not far away there was a great, broken god-road, leading North. The towers were high enough, but not so high, and while many of the dead-houses were wrecked, there were some that stood. I went toward this god-road, keeping to heights of the ruins, while the dog followed. When I had reached the god-road, I saw that there were others behind him. If I had slept later, they would have come upon me asleep and torn out my throat. As it was, they were sure enough of me; they did not hurry. When I went into the dead-house, they kept watch at the entrance

— doubtless they thought they would have a fine hunt. But a dog cannot open a door and I knew, from the books, that the gods did not like to live on the ground but on high.

I had just found a door I could open when the dogs decided to rush. Ha! They were surprised when I shut the door in their faces — it was a good door, of strong metal. I could hear their foolish baying beyond it but I did not stop to answer them. I was in darkness — I found stairs and climbed. There were many stairs, turning around till my head was dizzy. At the top was another door — I found the knob and opened it. I was in a long small chamber — on one side of it was a bronze door that could not be opened, for it had no handle. Perhaps there was a magic word to open it but I did not have the word. I turned to the door in the opposite side of the wall. The lock of it was broken and I opened it and went in.

Within, there was a place of great riches. The god who lived there must have been a powerful god. The first room was a small ante-room — I waited there for some time, telling the spirits of the place that I came in peace and not as a robber. When it seemed to me that they had had time to hear me, I went on. Ah, what riches! Few, even, of the windows had been broken — it was all as it had been. The great windows that looked over the city had not been broken at all though they were dusty and streaked with many years. There were coverings on the floors, the colors not greatly faded, and the chairs were soft and deep. There were pictures upon the walls, very strange, very wonderful — I remember one of a bunch of flowers in a jar — if you came close to it, you could see nothing but bits of color, but if you stood away from it, the flowers might have been picked yesterday. It made my heart feel strange to look at this picture — and to look at the figure of a bird, in some hard clay, on a table and see it so like our birds. Everywhere there were books and writings, many in tongues that I could not read. The god who lived there must have been a wise god and full of knowledge. I felt I had right there, as I sought knowledge also.

Nevertheless, it was strange. There was a washing-place but no water — perhaps the gods washed in air. There was a cooking-place but no wood, and though there was a machine to cook food, there was no place to put fire in it. Nor were there candles or lamps — there were things that looked like lamps but they had neither oil nor wick. All these things were magic, but I touched them and lived — the magic had gone out of them. Let me tell one thing to show. In the washing-place, a thing said "Hot" but it was not hot to the touch — another thing said "Cold" but it was not cold. This must have been a strong magic but the magic was gone. I do not understand — they had ways — I wish that I knew.

It was close and dry and dusty in their house of the gods. I have said the magic was gone but that is not true — it had gone from the magic things but it had not gone from the place. I felt the spirits about me, weighing upon me. Nor had I ever slept in a Dead Place before — and yet, tonight, I must sleep there. When I thought of it, my tongue felt dry in my throat, in spite of my wish for knowledge. Almost I would have gone down again and faced the dogs, but I did not.

I had not gone through all the rooms when the darkness fell. When it fell, I went back to the big room looking over the city and made fire. There was a place to make fire and a box with wood in it, though I do not think they cooked there. I wrapped myself in a floor-covering and slept in front of the fire — I was very tired.

Now I tell what is very strong magic. I woke in the midst of the night. When I woke, the fire had gone out and I was cold. It seemed to me that all around me there were whisperings and voices. I closed my eyes to shut them out. Some will say that I slept again, but I do not think that I slept. I could feel the spirits drawing my spirit out of my body as a fish is drawn on a line.

Why should I lie about it? I am a priest and the son of a priest. If there are spirits, as they say, in the small Dead Places near us, what spirits must there not be in that great Place of the Gods? And would not they wish to speak? After such long years? I know that I felt myself drawn as a fish is drawn on a line. I had stepped out of my body — I could see my body asleep in front of the cold fire, but it was not I. I was drawn to look out upon the city of the gods.

It should have been dark, for it was night, but it was not dark. Everywhere there were lights — lines of light — circles and blurs of light — ten thousand torches would not have been the same. The sky itself was alight — you could barely see the stars for the glow in the sky. I thought to myself "This is strong magic" and trembled. There was a roaring in my ears like the rushing of rivers. Then my eyes grew used to the light and my ears to the sound. I knew that I was seeing the city as it had been when the gods were alive.

That was a sight indeed — yes, that was a sight: I could not have seen it in the body — my body would have died. Everywhere went the gods, on foot and in chariots — there were gods beyond number and counting and their chariots blocked the streets. They had turned night to day for their pleasure — they did not sleep with the sun. The noise of their coming and going was the noise of many waters. It was magic what they could do — it was magic what they did.

I looked out of another window — the great vines of their

bridges were mended and the god-roads went East and West. Restless, restless, were the gods and always in motion! They burrowed tunnels under rivers — they flew in the air. With unbelievable tools they did giant works — no part of the earth was safe from them, for, if they wished for a thing, they summoned it from the other side of the world. And always, as they labored and rested, as they feasted and made love, there was a drum in their ears — the pulse of the giant city, beating and beating like a man's heart.

Were they happy? What is happiness to the gods? They were great, they were mighty, they were wonderful and terrible. As I looked upon them and their magic, I felt like a child — but a little more, it seemed to me, and they would pull down the moon from the sky. I saw them with wisdom beyond wisdom and knowledge beyond knowledge. And yet not all they did was well done — even I could see that — and yet their wisdom could not but grow until all was peace.

Then I saw their fate come upon them and that was terrible past speech. It came upon them as they walked the streets of their city. I have been in the fights with the Forest People — I have seen men die. But this was not like that. When gods war with gods, they use weapons we do not know. It was fire falling out of the sky and a mist that poisoned. It was the time of the Great Burning and the Destruction. They ran about like ants in the streets of their city — poor gods, poor gods! Then the towers began to fall. A few escaped — yes, a few. The legends tell it. But, even after the city had become a Dead Place, for many years the poison was still in the ground. I saw it happen, I saw the last of them die. It was darkness over the broken city and I wept.

All this, I saw. I saw it as I have told it, though not in the body. When I woke in the morning, I was hungry, but I did not think first of my hunger for my heart was perplexed and confused. I knew the reason for the Dead Places but I did not see why it had happened. It seemed to me it should not have happened, with all the magic they had. I went through the house looking for an answer. There was so much in the house I could not understand — and yet I am a priest and the son of a priest. It was like being on one side of the great river, at night, with no light to show the way.

Then I saw the dead god. He was sitting in his chair, by the window, in a room I had not entered before and, for the first moment, I thought that he was alive. Then I saw the skin on the back of his hand — it was like dry leather. The room was shut, hot and dry — no doubt that had kept him as he was. At first I was afraid to approach him — then the fear left me. He was sitting looking out over the city — he was dressed in the clothes of the gods. His age was neither young nor old — I could not tell his age. But there was wisdom in his face and great sadness. You could see that he would have not run away. He had sat at his window, watching his city die — then he himself had died. But it is better to lose one's life than one's spirit — and you could see from the face that his spirit had not been lost. I knew, that, if I touched him, he would fall into dust — and yet, there was something unconquered in the face.

That is all of my story, for then I knew he was a man — I knew then that they had been men, neither gods nor demons. It is a great knowledge, hard to tell and believe. They were men — they went a dark road, but they were men. I had no fear after that — I had no fear going home, though twice I fought off the dogs and once I was hunted for two days by the Forest People. When I saw my father again, I prayed and was purified. He touched my lips and my breast, he said, "You went away a boy. You come back a man and a priest." I said, "Father, they were men! I have been in the Place of the Gods and seen it! Now slay me, if it is the law — but still I know they were men."

He looked at me out of both eyes. He said, "The law is not always the same shape — you have done what you have done. I could not have done it in my time, but you come after me. Tell!"

I told and he listened. After that, I wished to tell all the people but he showed me otherwise. He said, "Truth is a hard deer to hunt. If you eat too much truth at once, you may die of the truth. It was not idly that our fathers forbade the Dead Places." He was right — it is better the truth should come little by little. I have learned that, being a priest. Perhaps, in the old days, they ate knowledge too fast.

Nevertheless, we make a beginning. It is not for the metal alone we go to the Dead Places now — there are the books and the writings. They are hard to learn. And the magic tools are broken — but we can look at them and wonder. At least, we make a beginning. And, when I am chief priest we shall go beyond the great river. We shall go to the Place of the Gods — the place new-york — not one man but a company. We shall look for the images of the gods and find the god ASHING and the others — the gods Lincoln and Biltmore and Moses. But they were men who built the city, not gods or demons. They were men. I remember the dead man's face. They were men who were here before us. We must build again.

2

Eureka!

SOME GENERAL OBSERVATIONS

◇◇

On Sharing in the Conquests of Science

HARLOW SHAPLEY

IT'S A WONDER I can stand it! Tramping for hours through the damp woods back of Walden Pond with Henry Thoreau, checking up on the food preferences of the marsh hawk, and the spread of sumach and goldenrod in old abandoned clearings. It requires stamina to match his stride as he plunges through swamps and philosophy, through underbrush, poetry, and natural history; it takes agility of body and mind if one does a full share of the day's measuring and speculation.

But no sooner have I left the Walden Woods than I am scrambling up the fossil-rich Scottish cliffs with Hugh Miller, preparing the groundwork of the immortal history of The Old Red Sandstone. With the wonderment of pioneers we gaze at the petrified ripple-marks that some shallow receding sea, in ancient times, has left as its fluted memorial — its monument built on the sand and of the sand, but nevertheless enduring. We break open a stony ball — this Scottish stonemason and I — a nodular mass of blue limestone, and expose beautiful traces of an extinct world of animals and plants; we find fossilized tree ferns, giant growths from the Carboniferous Period of two hundred and fifty million years ago — and forthwith we lose ourselves in conjecture.

And then I am off on another high adventure, higher than the moon this time; I am entering the study of the Frauenburg Cathedral to help Nicholas Copernicus do calculations on the hypothetical motions of the planets. He is, of course, deeply bemused with that rather queer notion that it might be the Sun that stands still — not the Earth. Perhaps he can demonstrate that the planets go around the Sun, each in its own course. Fascinated, I peer over his shoulder at the archaic geometry, watch his laborious penning of the great book, and listen to his troubled murmuring about the inaccuracies

From Harlow Shapley's Introduction to *A Treasury of Science* edited by Harlow Shapley, Samuel Rapport and Helen Wright. Copyright 1943 by Harper and Brothers.

of the measured co-ordinates of Saturn. "There are, you know, two other big ones further out," I put in; "and a system of many moons around Jupiter, which makes it all very clear and obvious." It must startle him no end to have me interrupt in such a confident way. But he does nothing about it. More planets? An incredible idea! Difficulties enough in trying to explain the visible, without complicating the complexities further by introducing invisible planets. My assistance ignored, I experience, nevertheless, a carefree exhilaration; for I have, as it were, matched my wits with the wisdom of the greatest of revolutionaries, and come off not too badly!

Now that I am fully launched in this career of working with the great explorers, and of co-operating in their attacks on the mysteries of the universe, I undertake further heroic assignments. I labor in the laboratories of the world; I maintain fatiguing vigils in the mountains and on the sea, try dangerous experiments, and make strenuous expeditions to Arctic shores and to torrid jungles — all without moving from the deep fireside chair.

Benjamin Franklin has a tempting idea, and I am right there to lend him a hand. We are having a lot of trouble in keeping that cantankerous kite in the thunder-cloud, from which the electric fluid should flow to charge and animate the house key. "Before long, Sir, we shall run printing presses with this fluid, and light our houses, and talk around the world" — but he does not put it in the *Autobiography*. I am clearly a century ahead of my time!

Youthful Charles Darwin is in the Galapagos. The good brig *Beagle* stands offshore. He has with him the collecting kit, the notebooks, and his curiosity. He is making records of the slight variations among closely similar species of plants and animals. He is pondering the origin of these differences, and the origin of species, and the whole confounding business of the origin of plants and animals. I sit facing him, on the rocks beside the tide pool, admiring the penetration and grasp of this young dreamer. The goal of his prolonged researches is a revolution in man's conception of life; he is assembling the facts and thoughts, and in this work I am a participant! Nothing could be more exciting. Also I have an advantage. I know about Mendel and Mendelian laws, and genes and chromosomes. I know that X rays (unknown to Darwin), and other agents, can produce mutations and suddenly create living forms that Nature has not attained. This posterior knowledge of mine enhances the pleasure of my collaboration with the great naturalist; and I need have no fear that my information, or my ethereal presence, might bother him.

There is so much scientific work of this sort for me to do before some tormenting duty draws me out of my strategic chair. The possibilities are nearly endless. Like a benign gremlin, I sit on the brim of a test tube in Marie Curie's laboratory and excitedly speculate with her on that radioactive ingredient in the pitchblende; I help name it radium. With Stefansson and the Eskimos I live for months on a scanty menu, and worry with him about the evils of civilization. And when young Evariste Galois, during his beautiful, brief, perturbed life in Paris, sits down to devise sensationally new ideas and techniques in pure mathematics, I am right there with applause and sympathy.

Whenever I pause to appreciate how simple it is for me to take an active part in unraveling the home life of primitive man, or observing the voracity of a vampire bat; how simple for me, in company with the highest authorities, to reason on the theory of relativity or explore with a cyclotron the insides of atoms, it is then that I call for additional blessings on those artisans who invented printing. They have provided me with guide lines to remote wonders — highly conductive threads that lead me, with a velocity faster than that of light itself, into times long past and into minds that biologically are long extinct. Through the simple process of learning how to interpret symbols, such as those that make this sentence, I can take part in most of the great triumphs of the human intellect. Blessings and praises, laurel wreaths and myrtle, are due those noble spirits who made writing and reading easily accessible, and thus opened to us all the romance of scientific discovery. . . .

To more than the art of printing, however, do we owe the successes and pleasures of our vicarious adventures in science. We are also greatly indebted to those who can write and will write in terms of our limited comprehension. Not all the scientists have the facility. Sometimes the talk is too tough for us, or too curt. They have not the time to be lucid on our level and within our vocabulary, or perhaps their mental intensity has stunted the faculty of sympathetic explanation. When such technical barriers shut us from the scientific workshop, it is then we like to consult with a clear-spoken and understanding interpreter. We sit on the back porch of the laboratory, while he, as middleman, goes inside to the obscurities and mysteries, to return occasionally with comprehensible reports. In listening to him we hear not only his voice, but the overtones of the master he interprets. I like these men of understanding who play Boswell to the specialist. They often have a gift greater than that of the concentrated workers whom they soften up for us. For they have breadth and perspective, which help us to get at the essence of a problem more objectively than we could even if we were fully equipped with the language and knowledge of the

fact-bent explorer and analyst. The scientific interpreters frequently enhance our enjoyment in that they give us of themselves,
as well as of the discoverers whose exploits they recount.

Science and the Imagination

WALDEMAR KAEMPFFERT

"OF ALL THE DEFINITIONS mouthed by a certain branch of the
critical fraternity that which has to do with creation in literary fields
is the most completely bogus," Charles Angoff quotes George Jean
Nathan as saying in a recently published biographical appraisal of
that iconoclast. "It is the persistent theory of the branch in point
that the phrase creative writing must be reserved for novelists,
poets and writers of a kind, however bad, and that it cannot be
truthfully visited upon any others, however good."

The pronouncement will be greeted with cheers from the bleach-
ers where sit the critics (for whom Nathan has kind words), but it
does not define creative writing. So far as this reader of novels,
poetry, plays, treatises on biochemistry, papers on nuclear physics
and mail-order catalogues is concerned, writing that is poor in imagination is not creative. And imagination is virtually synonymous
with invention.

Great theories in science are always great inventions — products
of the imagination. The universe is an invention, the atom is an invention. There are more conceptions of the universe than there are
models of automobiles. Some have a wide sweep that exceeds any
act of creation described by a poet. The exploits of the heroes who
sweat, fight and outwit one another in *The Iliad* or the Norse sagas
are exciting, but so are the pictures of the birth and death of
worlds that rise like wraiths out of the equations of mathematical
physicists.

A cosmogonist wonders how the universe began. In a daring
flight of imagination he starts with a single bit of matter, causes it

First printed in *The New York Times,* July 19, 1952. Reprinted by permission
of the Estate of Waldemar Kaempffert.

to expand, sees how galaxies, double stars, planets could evolve. Then he looks about him. Far out on the confines of the universe he sees that nebulae are rushing away at a speed of 30,000 miles a second. Manifestly the universe is blowing up like a soap bubble. That is how the currently accepted theory of the expanding universe came into being.

Or take the conception of evolution. For some 2,000 years it remains a philosophic concept. Then comes Darwin with his gift of seeing relationships to which others are blind and weaves into a single logical fabric the protoplasm of the primeval past, the armored fishes that once swam in the ocean, the dinosaurs that were bigger than military tanks and weighed almost as much. There are passages in the Book of Job that go deep into the soul because they express with magnificent finality thoughts that have always harassed the human mind; yet in all literature nothing matches *The Origin of Species* for the scope and splendor of its living pageantry.

When a colossal idea bursts in the mind it overwhelms. Herman Melville testified to that in a letter to Hawthorne about *Moby Dick*. Einstein has stated that his first paper on relativity came to him "like a storm breaking loose." Just how he felt when he arrived at the simple algebraic equation which declares that matter can be converted into energy and energy into matter he has not told us. A man of his deep insight must have been stunned. Out of that equation came atomic bombs. Nothing in Dante's *Inferno* matches it for evil and horror — nothing promises so much material happiness and good.

In an oft-quoted epigram Bertrand Russell remarks that a mathematician does not have to know what he is talking about. Because of this freedom Bolyai, a Hungarian, and Lobachevsky, a Russian, independently formulated geometries in which space is curved and parallel lines meet. The two were considered slightly mad by their colleagues; yet out of this madness came hundreds of pictures of space, one of which proved highly useful in arriving at relativity.

In boldness of imagination the mathematicians stand supreme. It is not only their ideas that startle but the techniques that they invent. There is a character in one of Gogol's novels who is tormented by this question: If an elephant laid eggs what would their color be? That is about the kind of questioning that enabled mathematical physicists to arrive at the prevailing conception of the atom.

If you wonder why no great epic poet has appeared since Milton — unless we consider Goethe's *Faust* an epic poem in dramatic form — consider the mathematical physicists. All the imagination that once found expression in an epic poem — Lucretius' "*De rerum natura*" is an example — is now poured into a theory, like Darwin's natural selection, or into new universes, or into atoms in which events are more important than substance. George Jean Nathan is right. The novelists and dramatists have no monopoly of imagination. With the exception of Balzac, Melville and Dostoevsky few have scaled the heights where the eminent in theoretical science dwell.

From First Step to Last

HANS ZINSSER

IT IS an erroneous impression, fostered by sensational popular biography, that scientific discovery is often made by inspiration — a sort of *coup de foudre* from on high. This is rarely the case. Even Archimedes' sudden inspiration in the bathtub; Newton's experience in the apple orchard; Descartes' geometrical discoveries in his bed; Darwin's flash of lucidity on reading a passage in Malthus; Kekulé's vision of the closed carbon ring which came to him on top of a London bus; and Einstein's brilliant solution of the Michelson puzzle in the patent office in Berne, were not messages out of the blue. They were the final co-ordinations, by minds of genius, of innumerable accumulated facts and impressions which lesser men could grasp only in their uncorrelated isolation, but which — by them — were seen in entirety and integrated into general principles. The scientist takes off from the manifold observations of predecessors, and shows his intelligence, if any, by his ability to discriminate between the important and the negligible, by selecting here and there the significant steppingstones that will lead across the difficulties to new understanding. The one who places the last stone and steps across to the *terra firma* of accomplished discovery gets all the credit. Only the initiated know and honor those whose patient integrity and devotion to exact observation have made the last step possible.

From *As I Remember Him* by Hans Zinsser, by permission of Little, Brown and Company. Copyright 1939, 1940 by Hans Zinsser.

◇◇

⌫ *TWO EUREKAS*

The Golden Crown: Archimedes

ZSOLT DE HARSANYI

KING HIERO sent for his learned kinsman, Archimedes, and put the golden crown into his hand: "Can you find out whether the rascally goldsmith has mixed any base alloy with pure gold? But you must tell me without spoiling my crown with a single scratch." The sage asked for time to think it over and went home. He pondered day and night. Then, when he was having a bath, suddenly the thought came to him: every object submerged in water loses as much of its weight as is equal to the weight of the water supplanted. Overjoyed, he ran stark-naked into the streets calling wildly to the citizens of Syracuse: "Eureka! Eureka!" He had found a method to discover the secret of alloys by calculating their weight, using water scales. He was able to answer the king's question. Then he invented the screw propeller of ships, and later the laws of the balance of levers. He calculated the circle's circumference by its diameter; he constructed catapults; when the Roman soldier broke into his house, trampling out a complicated geometric pattern drawn in the sand, Archimedes shouted at him, "Don't disturb my circles!" And died on a sword.

Swing of a Pendulum: Galileo

ZSOLT DE HARSANYI

ONCE IN THE COURSE of an aimless walk Galileo happened to enter the Campo Santo. He looked vaguely at the three buildings on the square — he knew them so well that he could have drawn them with his eyes closed. On the left the Baptistery, a round building with carved white semicolumns, and above them a row of smaller pillars; the huge white marble Cathedral with all its galleries and arcades; and on the right the surprising Leaning Tower of white carved marble, like the others, but daringly, almost crazily, beautiful, with the fantastic beauty of sugar-ice. It was as though someone had dreamed that a tower was bending in the wind. Suddenly this idle student felt an urge to enter the Cathedral.

Inside the organ was being played; yet a gang of workmen were going about their business undisturbed. Buckets of lime, rafters, and ladders were stacked beside the west door. They were setting up a monument to Archbishop Rinuccini, who had died last year. People were standing about in the center nave staring upward; they were watching the builders, who had just finished fixing the great lamp, clinging to the walls of the dome. Either they had renewed its chain or strengthened its rivets in the ceiling. Anyhow, it was still swinging in a calm, slow arc.

The good-for-nothing student suddenly became alert. His mind, which had for years been trained in such exercises, began to ask questions.

Why did the lamp swing? Because it had been moved from its original position. This, Aristotle had explained in his work *De Motu*. But suppose he had not dealt with the matter; suppose there had never been an Aristotle; suppose that . . . Galileo Galilei, student of Pisa, had never read him? What would he say? For believers, a motionless lamp was one among many; for a young scientist, it was a weight suspended on a chain. This weight longed to fall. It was the personification of stubborn and ceaseless longing to fall, never quiet for a moment, forever tugging at its chain, hoping it would break — but not having the strength to break it. It hung there struggling with the chain, demanding silently day and night to be allowed to fall down. This stubborn urge had probably worn out the

to penetrate into, but his pains, his diligence at these set times made me think he aimed at something beyond the reach of human art and industry. I cannot say I ever saw him drink either wine, ale, or beer, excepting at meals, and then but very sparingly. He very rarely went to dine in the hall, except on some public days, and then if he has not been minded, would go very carelessly, with shoes down at heels, stockings untied, surplice on, and his head scarcely combed.

As for his *Optics* being burned, I knew nothing of it but as I had heard from others, that accident happening before he writ his *Principia.* He was very curious in his garden, which was never out of order, in which he would at some seldom time take a short walk or two, not enduring to see a weed in it. On the left end of the garden was his elaboratory, near the east end of the chapel, where he at these set times employed himself in with a great deal of satisfaction and delight. Nothing extraordinary, as I can remember, happened in making his experiments; which, if there did, he was of so sedate and even temper, that I could not in the least discover it. He very seldom went to the chapel, that being the time he chiefly took his repose; and, as for the afternoon, his earnest and indefatigable studies retained him, so that he scarcely knew the house of prayer. Very frequently, on Sundays, he went to St. Mary's church, especially in the forenoon. I knew nothing of the writings which your honour sent, only that it is his own hand, I am very certain of, believing he might write them at some leisure hours, before he set upon his more serious and weighty matters. Sir Isaac at that time had no pupils nor any chamber-fellow, for that, I would presume to think, would not have been agreeable to his studies. He was only once disordered with pains at the stomach, which confined him for some days to his bed, which he bore with a great deal of patience and magnanimity, seemingly indifferent either to live or die. He seeing me much concerned at his illness, bid me not trouble myself; 'For if,' said he, 'I die, I shall leave you an estate,' which he then mentioned.

Sir, this is what I can at present recollect, hoping it may in some measure satisfy your queries.

My wife at this time is brought to bed of a son, whom I intend to nominate after my dear deceased friend. Would you please to honour me so far as to substitute Dr. Stukeley to stand as witness. I should take it as a very singular favour, and would very much oblige, Sir, your most humble and obedient servant,

HUMPHREY NEWTON.

Grantham, January 17, '27/8.

Sir, — I return your honour a great many thanks for the favour
you have done me in deputing Dr. Stukeley to stand in your stead
as witness to my son. It is out of my sphere to make any grateful
return, therefore doubt not but your goodness will in that point excuse my deficiency. I have bethought myself about Sir Isaac's life as
much as possibly I can. About 6 weeks at spring, and 6 at the fall,
the fire in the elaboratory scarcely went out, which was well
furnished with chemical materials as bodies, receivers, heads, crucibles, etc., which was [sic] made very little use of, the crucibles ex-
cepted, in which he fused his metals; he would sometimes, tho'
very seldom, look into an old mouldy book which lay in his elaboratory, I think it was titled *Agricola de Metallis,* the transmuting of
metals being his chief design, for which purpose antimony was a
great ingredient. Near his elaboratory was his garden, which was
kept in order by a gardener. I scarcely ever saw him do anything as
pruning, etc., at it himself. When he has sometimes taken a turn or
two, has made a sudden stand, turn'd himself about, run up the
stairs like another Archimedes, with an εὕρηκα fall to write on his
desk standing without giving himself the leisure to drew a chair to
sit down on. At some seldom times when he designed to dine in the
hall, would turn to the left hand and go out into the street, when
making a stop when he found his mistake, would hastily turn back,
and then sometimes instead of going into the hall, would return to
his chamber again. When he read in the schools he usually staid
about half an hour; when he had no auditors, he commonly returned in a 4th part of that time or less. Mr. Laughton who was
then the library keeper of Trin. Coll. resorted much to his chamber;
if he commenced Dr. afterwards I know not. His telescope, which
was at that time, as near as I could guess, was near 5 foot long,
which he placed at the head of the stairs going down into the
garden, butting towards the east. What observations he might make
I know not, but several of his observations about comets and the
planets may be found scattered here and there in a book entitled
The Elements of Astronomy, by Dr. David Gregory. He would with
great acuteness answer a question, but would very seldom start one.
Dr. Boerhaave (I think it is), Prof. Lpzg., in some of his writings,
speaking of Sir Is.: "That man," says he, "comprehends as much as
all mankind besides." In his chamber he walked so very much that
you might have thought him to be educated at Athens among the
Aristotelian sect. His brick furnaces, *pro re nata,* he made and altered himself without troubling a brick-layer. He very seldom sat
by the fire in his chamber excepting that long frosty winter, which
made him creep to it against his will. I can't say I ever saw him

wear a night gown, but his wearing clothes that he put off at night, at night do I say, yea, rather towards the morning, he put on again at his rising. He never slept in the daytime that I ever perceived; I believe he grudged the short time he spent in eating and sleeping. Ἀνέχου καὶ ἀπέχου may well and truly be said of him, he always thinking with Bishop Saunderson, temperance to be the best physic. In a morning, he seemed to be as much refreshed with his few hours' sleep as though he had taken a whole night's rest. He kept neither dog nor cat in his chamber, which made well for the old woman his bedmaker, she faring much the better for it, for in a morning she has sometimes found both dinner and supper scarcely tasted of, which the old woman has very pleasantly and mumpingly gone away with. As for his private prayers I can say nothing of them; I am apt to believe his intense studies deprived him of the better part. His behaviour was mild and meek, without anger, peevishness, or passion, so free from that, that you might take him for a stoic. I have seen a small paste-board box in his study set against the open window, no less as one might suppose than a 1000 guin. in it crowded edgeways, whether this was suspicion or carelessness I cannot say; perhaps to try the fidelity of those about him. In winter time he was a lover of apples, and sometimes at a night would eat a small roasted quince. His thoughts were his books; tho' he had a large study seldom consulted with them. When he was about 30 years of age his grey hairs was [sic] very comely, and his smiling countenance made him so much the more graceful. He was very charitable, few went empty handed from him. Mr. Pilkington [his nephew-in-law], who lived at Market Overton, died in a mean condition, (tho' formerly he had a plentiful estate,) whose widow with 5 or 6 children Sir Is. maintained several years together. He commonly gave his poor relations, (for no family so rich but there is some poor among them,) when they apply'd themselves to him, no less than 5 guineas, as they themselves told me. He has given the porters many a shilling not for letting him [in?] at the gates at unreasonable hours, for that he abhorred, never knowing him out of his chamber at such times. No way litigious, not given to law or vexatious suits, taking patience to be the best law, and a good conscience the best divinity. Says Seneca, somebody will demonstrate which way comets wander, why they go so far from the rest of the celestial bodies, how big, and what sort of bodies they are, which had he been contemporary with Sir Is. he might have seen this prophecy of his fulfilled by the wonder of his age. Could your Honour pick somethings out of this indigested mass worthy to be inserted into the life of so great, so good, and so illustrious a person as Sir Isaac Newton, it would be of infinite satisfaction to him, Sir, who is your Honour's most humb. and most obedient servant,

H. NEWTON.

Feb. 14, 1727/8, Grantham.

An Apple Falls

LOUIS TRENCHARD MORE

THE HISTORY of Newton's *Principia* takes us back again to the time when he spent the greater part of the years, 1665 and 1666, quietly at Woolsthorpe to escape the plague. He had just been graduated from college and had been successful enough to be appointed to a scholarship. As a boy, he had spent his days on the farm, meditating on the childish problems which interested him, and now as he comes back, a man, he takes up again his former life; but his mind is now full of profound ideas, and his meditations are to change the course of all future thought. In the long summer afternoons, he sits in the orchard which still stands near the old gray stone house; on one memorable day, an apple falls with a slight thud at his feet. It was a trifling incident which has been idly noticed thousands of times; but now, like the click of some small switch which starts a great machine in operation, it proved to be the jog which awoke his mind to action. As in a vision, he saw that if the mysterious pull of the earth can act through space as far as the top of a tree, of a mountain, and even to a bird soaring high in the air, or to the clouds, so it might even reach so far as the moon. If such were the case, then the moon would be like a stone thrown horizontally, always falling toward the earth, but never reaching the ground, because its swift motion carried it far beyond the horizon. Always falling toward the earth and always passing beyond it, the moon would follow its elliptical path if these two motions were equally balanced. How simple the idea seems to us now as we look backward, but how difficult it was to foresee can be gathered from the fact that even a Galileo, who had solved the problem of the

From *Isaac Newton* by Louis Trenchard More, published by Charles Scribner's Sons.

projectile, did not have sufficient imagination to guess that the moon was only a projectile moving swiftly enough to pass beyond the earth. Nor could Huygens, who formulated the laws of centrifugal force and motion, penetrate the secret. Perhaps even more significant of Newton's genius, was the fact that he not only guessed the law of attraction, but he immediately set himself the task of calculating what would be the law of the force which could hold the moon in her orbit.

All that we know about the initial step of this greatest of discoveries is that Newton did make a calculation to see if a force of attraction, which varied as the inverse square of the distance between the two bodies, would account for the laws of planetary motion; and, having fairly well satisfied himself of its truth, he laid the problem aside to think about other things. Nor did he make any record, at the time, of the sequence of his ideas; and he apparently was unable to tell the story accurately after some years had passed. The earliest account of his discovery was given, in 1694, by Newton to Whiston, who reported it as follows:

"Upon Sir Isaac's first trial, when he took a degree of a great circle on the earth's surface, whence a degree at the distance of the moon was to be determined also, to be 60 measured miles only, according to the gross measures then in use. He was, in some degree, disappointed, and the power that restrained the moon in her orbit, measured by the versed sines of that orbit, appeared not to be quite the same that was to be expected, had it been the power of gravity alone, by which the moon was there influenc'd. Upon this disappointment, which made Sir Isaac suspect that this power was partly that of gravity, and partly that of Cartesius's vortices, he threw aside the paper of his calculation, and went to other studies. However, some time afterward, when Monsieur Picard had much more exactly measured the earth, and found that a degree of a great circle was 69½ such miles, Sir Isaac, in turning over some of his former papers, light [*sic*] upon this old imperfect calculation; and, correcting his former error, discover'd that this power, at the true correct distance of the moon from the earth, not only tended to the earth's centre, as did the common power of gravity with us, but was exactly of the right quantity; and that if a stone was carried up to the moon, or to 60 semidiameters of the earth, and let fall downward by its gravity, and the moon's own menstrual motion was stopt, and she was let fall by that power which before retained her in her orbit, they would exactly fall towards the same point, and with the same velocity; which was therefore no other power than that of gravity. And since that power appear'd to extend as far as the moon, at the distance of 240,000 miles, it was but natural, or rather necessary, to suppose it might reach twice, thrice, four times, etc., the same distance, with the same diminution, according to the squares of such distances perpetually. Which noble discovery proved the happy occasion of the invention of the wonderful Newtonian philosophy."

Pemberton, who edited the third edition of the *Principia,* gives pretty much the same story of the error in the calculation, arising from having taken the wrong diameter of the earth. According to his account Newton, "being absent from books, he took the common estimate in use among geographers and our seamen, before Norwood had measured the earth, that 60 English miles were contained in one degree of latitude on the surface of the earth."

We have one other account of the discovery and later development of the law of gravitation drawn up by Newton, himself, sometime about 1714. While there are some minor mistakes, it is, on the whole, correct. This memorandum has been preserved in the *Portsmouth Collection,* and is as follows:

"In the same year [1666] I began to think of gravity extending to the orb of the moon, and having found out how to estimate the force with which a globe revolving within a sphere presses the surface of the sphere, from Kepler's Rule of the periodical times of the planets being in a sesquialterate proportion of their distances from the centres of their orbs I deduced that the forces which keep the planets in their orbs must [be] reciprocally as the squares of their distances from the centres about which they revolve: and thereby compared the force requisite to keep the moon in her orb with the force of gravity at the surface of the earth, and found them answer pretty nearly. All this was in the two plague years of 1665 and 1666, for in those days I was in the prime of my age for invention, and minded mathematics and philosophy more than at any time since. What Mr. Huygens has published since about centrifugal forces I suppose he had before me. At length in the winter between the years 1676 and 1677 [probably this should be 1679 and 1680] I found the proposition that by a centrifugal force reciprocally as the square of the distance a planet must revolve in an ellipsis about the centre of the force placed in the lower umbilicus of the ellipsis and with a radius drawn to that centre describe areas proportional to the times. And in the winter between the years 1683 and 1684 [this should be the winter between 1684 and 1685] this proposition with the demonstration was entered in the Register book of the R. Society."

On the basis of Newton's conversations with Whiston and Pemberton, the tradition has thus come down to us that, having taken a wrong figure for the earth's diameter, his calculated acceleration of the moon toward the earth did not agree with what it should be, if the attraction varied as the inverse square of the distance from the earth. Such was his modesty and love of accuracy, so we have been taught to believe, that he put away his calculations, supposing that the force of gravity was not sufficient and that an unknown whirling force, perhaps a Cartesian vortex, must be added in order to maintain the moon in her orbit. It was also believed, on a statement of Robison, that, when he afterward learned of Picard's more accurate measurement of the earth's diameter, he went home from London and repeated his old calculations. When he saw his ideas were likely to be confirmed, "he was so much agitated, that he was obliged to desire a friend to finish them."

◇◇

☞ *THROUGH THE MICROSCOPE*

On Certain Animalcules

ANTONY VAN LEEUWENHOEK

On certain Animalcules found in the sediment in gutters on the roofs of houses.

I HAVE BEEN INDUCED to publish my discoveries respecting these creatures, in order to shew how wonderfully Nature has provided for the preservation of their species.

On the 25th of August, I saw in a leaden gutter at the fore part of my house, for the length of about five feet, and the breadth of seven inches, a settlement of rain water, which appeared of a red colour; and, upon considering that perhaps this colour might proceed from some red Animalcules, similar to those which I had seen in muddy ditches, I took a drop of this water, which I placed before the microscope, and in it I discovered a great number of Animalcules, some of them red, and others of them green. The largest of these, viewed through the microscope, did not appear bigger than a large grain of sand to the naked eye; the size of the others was gradually less and less: they were, for the most part, of a round shape; and in the green ones, the middle part of their bodies was of

From the Proceedings of The Royal Society of London.

a yellowish colour. Their bodies seemed composed of particles of an oval shape; they were also provided with certain short and slender organs or limbs, which were protruded a little way out of their bodies, by means of which they caused a kind of circular motion and current in the water: when they were at rest and fixed themselves to the glass, they had the shape of a pear with a short stalk. Upon more carefully examining this stalk, or rather this tail, I found that the extremity of it was divided into two parts, and by the help of these tails the Animalcules fixed themselves to the glass; the lesser of these appeared to me to be the offspring of the larger ones.

Moreover, I saw another kind of Animalcules much smaller, the bodies of them were very transparent; but there seemed to be an hundred of the former species to one of them.

On the 31st of August, the water which I had before observed, was, by three successive days of hot weather, so dried away, that when I pressed my finger on the muddy sediment in the gutter, no more water than about the size of a grain of sand adhered to my finger, in which water I discovered a small number of transparent living Animalcules, but all the green and red ones were dead.

The first of September the sediment in this leaden gutter was so thickened, that it appeared like stiff moist clay; but, with all my endeavours, I could not discover any Animalcules in it of the species I had before seen.

At length I discovered two living Animalcules with oblong bodies, like the largest of those which I had formerly seen in rain water, wherein pepper or ginger had been infused. These Animalcules were almost the thickness of a hair of one's head; but such of them whose bodies were full of young, were twice that size, the ends of their bodies terminating in a point; their tails were provided with six or eight minute organs, by the help of which they could fasten themselves to the glass, and the fore part of their bodies being also provided with certain organs, when they would move from place to place, they brought their hind parts nearer to the fore part, and then, loosing the fore part, they extended it in like manner as we see caterpillars do; and, in swimming, they made use of other organs destined for that purpose. Soon afterwards I observed many of the same species of Animalcules.

The matter in the bowels of these creatures was for the most part red, proceeding (as I imagine) from their feeding on smaller Animalcules of that colour, but some few of them had no red colour in them, especially the smaller ones, which probably had not been long brought forth from the parent.

On the same day the weather was very hot, and, in the afternoon, I took a small part of the sediment from the gutter which was now quite dry, and I saw the surface of it completely red, by reason of the great number of red Animalcules in it, being many more than the green ones; but I could not distinguish them until I had moistened the substance with some rain water.

The following day the sky was again very hot and dry, and, about nine in the morning, I took some of the sediment which had been in the leaden gutter, which was then quite dried, and no thicker than half the back of a knife; it had also lain from the preceding evening in my study; this I put into a glass tube, about the thickness of a swan's quill, and poured on it a small quantity of rain water taken out of my stone cistern, in which water were swimming some of the before mentioned Animalcules of the smaller sort; having poured in this water, I mixed it up with the dry sediment or matter put into the tube, and which seemed very hard and compact, in order to dissolve the same; that thus, if there were still any living Animalcules in it, they might issue forth; though I confess I never thought that there could be any living creature in a substance so dried as this was.

I was, however, mistaken; for scarce an hour had elapsed, when I saw, at least, an hundred of the Animalcules before described; some of them adhering to the glass, some creeping along upon it, and some swimming about. In the evening I computed there were more than three hundred of the same kind of Animalcules, but the most of them were not of full size, as I judged by their bodies being so minute, and so empty of food, as if they were newly born; and in the bodies of some of the larger ones, I could see two, in others three, young ones, folded double: these young ones, when newly born, were as quick in their motions as the full grown ones.

In that part of these Animalcules which may be called the breast, I saw a round particle moving with a reciprocal contraction and dilatation, in the time one might count one: this I did not doubt was the heart.

◇◇

Even a Lady's Teeth

ANTONY VAN LEEUWENHOEK

[*From a letter headed: Of the formation of the Teeth in
several animals: the structure of the human Teeth
explained, and some of the disorders to which the same
are liable accounted for.*]

— *The select Works of Antony van Leeuwenhoek.*
Translated by Samuel Hoole [1800].

IT IS MY CUSTOM, every morning, to rub my teeth with salt,
and afterwards to wash my mouth, and after eating I always clean
my large teeth with a tooth-pick, and sometimes rub them very
hard with a cloth. By these means, my teeth are so clean and white,
that few persons of my age [over fifty] can shew so good a set, nor
do my gums ever bleed, although I rub them hard with salt; and
yet I cannot keep my teeth so clean, but that upon examining them
with a magnifying glass, I have observed a sort of white substance
collected between them, in consistence like a mixture of flour and
water. In reflecting on this substance, I thought it probable, (though
I could not observe any motion in it,) that it might contain some
living creatures. Having therefore mixed it with rain water, which
I knew was perfectly pure, I found, to my great surprise, that it
contained many very small animalcules, the motions of which were
very pleasing to behold. The largest sort of them . . . had the
greatest, and the quickest motion, leaping about in the fluid, like the
fish called a Jack; the number of these was very small. The second
sort . . . often had a kind of whirling motion . . . these were more
in number. Of the third sort, I could not well ascertain the figure,
for sometimes they seemed roundish but oblong, and sometimes
perfectly round. . . . The motion of these little creatures, one
among another, may be imagined like that of a great number of
gnats, or flies sporting in the air. From the appearance of these, to
me, I judged that I saw some thousands of them in a portion of
liquid, no larger than a grain of sand, and this liquid consisted of
eight parts water, and one part only of the before-mentioned substance taken from the teeth.

With the point of a needle, I took some of the same kind of substance from the teeth of two ladies, who I knew were very punctual

in cleaning them every day, and therein I observed as many of these animalcules as I have just mentioned. I also saw the same in the white substance taken from the teeth of a boy about eight years old; and upon examining in like manner, the same substance taken from the teeth of an old gentleman, who was very careless about keeping them clean, I found an incredible number of living animalcules, swimming about more rapidly than any I had before seen, and in such numbers, that the water which contained them, (though but a small portion of the matter taken from the teeth was mixed in it) seemed to be alive.

⊂⊋ LIGHTNING STRIKES

Mr. Franklin: Philadelphia Prometheus

CARL VAN DOREN

. . . A MAN in Philadelphia in America, bred a tradesman, remote from the learned world, hit upon a secret which enabled him, and other men, to catch and tame the lightning, so dread that it was still mythological. To the public, as it gradually heard about him, he seemed a magician. To scientists, from the first, he seemed a master.

Wonders could not run through the world then as they can now, thanks to electricity, but Franklin's fame reached far beyond those who did or could read his books, understand his ingenious experiments, and enjoy his easy, natural expositions. He had made one of the most dramatic guesses in the history of science, and he had verified his guess with a boy's plaything. He had applied his knowledge to making men's houses, barns, ships safe from an incalculable danger. With what seemed the simplest key he had unlocked one of the darkest and most terrifying doors in the unknown universe. Here was another hero of the human race, even as against the terrifying gods. Franklin, Kant said, was a new Prometheus who had stolen fire from heaven.

In the six years between the summer of 1746, when Franklin first saw electrical experiments in Boston, and the summer of 1752,

when he flew the electrical kite in Philadelphia, he made all his
fundamental contributions to electricity. He made them because he
had a fundamental mind, which almost at once mastered the general problem as it then existed and went deeper into it than any
observer had yet gone. He found electricity a curiosity and left it a
science. Indolence, he thought, disposed him too much to the building of hypotheses, and he claimed only to have been lucky in his
guesses. His procedure came from the nature and method of his
mind. But there was more in his science than a few bold conjectures. He steadily insisted on the need of painstaking experiments,
scrupulous accuracy, and a stubborn refusal to surmise what the
tested facts did not warrant. He regretted his weakness in mathematics and the frequent interruptions which broke off the chain
of thought which he believed should be continuous in a scientist.
Nobody ever gave more grateful attention than Franklin to experiments which contradicted this or that theory of his, or more readily
accepted them if he was convinced that he had been in error. His
hypotheses grew as his facts accumulated. It did not matter to him
who got the credit. "These thoughts, my dear friend," he wrote to
Collinson at the end of his letter about lightning rods, "are many
of them crude and hasty; and if I were merely ambitious of acquiring some reputation in philosophy I ought to keep them by me till
corrected and improved by time and farther experience. But since
even short hints and imperfect experiments in any new branch of
science, being communicated, have oftentimes a good effect, in exciting the attention of the ingenious to the subject, and so become
the occasion of more exact disquisition and more complete discoveries; you are at liberty to communicate this paper to whom you
please; it being of more importance that knowledge should increase
than that your friend should be thought an accurate philosopher."

As Franklin was not ambitious, neither did he expect too much
from the world, which he knew as few scientists have known it.
"There are everywhere a number of people who, being totally des-
titute of any inventive faculty themselves, do not readily conceive
that others may possess it," he wrote to John Lining on 18 March
1755. "They think of inventions as miracles: there might be such
formerly, but they are ceased. With these, everyone who offers a
new invention is deemed a pretender: he had it from some other
country or from some book. A man of their own acquaintance, one
who has no more sense than themselves, could not possibly, in their
opinion, have been the inventor of anything. They are confirmed, too,
in these sentiments by frequent instances of pretensions to invention
which vanity is daily producing. That vanity too, though an incite-
ment to invention, is at the same time the pest of inventors. Jealousy

and envy deny the merit or the novelty of your invention; but vanity, when the novelty and merit are established, claims it for its own. . . . Thus through envy, jealousy, and the vanity of competitors for fame, the origin of many of the most extraordinary inventions, though produced within but a few centuries past, is involved in doubt and uncertainty. We scarce know to whom we are indebted for the compass and for spectacles; nor have even paper and printing, that record everything else, been able to preserve with certainty the name and reputation of their inventors. One would not, therefore, of all faculties or qualities of the mind, wish for a friend or a child that he should have that of invention. For his attempts to benefit mankind in that way, however well imagined, if they do not succeed, expose him, though very unjustly, to general ridicule and contempt; and if they do succeed, to envy, robbery, and abuse."

It may have been knowledge of the world as much as modesty that kept Franklin from being too explicit or emphatic about his own inventions. Having no envy, jealousy, or vanity in himself, he would not run the risk of needlessly rousing them in others. When the Abbé Nollet, preceptor to the royal family in France, attacked the theories from America, Franklin did not, after a little reflection, bother to answer him. "I concluded to let my papers shift for themselves, believing it was better to spend what time I could spare from public business in making new experiments than in disputing about those already made." He refused to patent the lightning rod, often called the Franklin rod, or to profit by it. Though he never lost sight of what was being done in electricity during his whole lifetime, he was perfectly willing to have his contributions to it absorbed in the enlarging science. They were absorbed, and it is now difficult to trace the details of his influence. His *Principia* made only a beginning.

But in one discoverable respect he still survives wherever electricity is spoken of. Franklin appears to have been the first to use, at least in print in English, these electrical terms: armature, battery, brush, charged, charging, condense, conductor, discharge, electrical fire, electrical shock, electrician, electrified, electrify, electrized, Leyden bottle, minus (negative or negatively), negatively, non-conducting, non-conductor, non-electric, plus (positive or positively), stroke (electric shock), uncharged. The Philadelphia Prometheus with his kite was also an American Adam in his electrical garden. . . .

Nowhere throughout this first scientific period of his does Franklin appear so nearly full length and to the life as in his accounts of a whirlwind which he observed in 1755. "Being in Maryland, riding with Colonel Tasker and some other gentleman to his country seat where I and my son were entertained by that amiable and worthy man with great hospitality and kindness, we saw, in the vale below us, a small whirlwind beginning in the road and showing itself by the dust it raised and contained. It appeared in the form of a sugar loaf, spinning on its point, moving up the hill towards us, and enlarging as it came forward. When it passed by us, its smaller part near the ground appeared no bigger than a common barrel, but, widening upwards, it seemed at forty or fifty feet high to be twenty or thirty feet in diameter. The rest of the company stood looking after it, but, my curiosity being stronger, I followed it, riding close by its side, and observed its licking up in its progress all the dust that was under its smaller part. As it is a common opinion that a shot fired through a water-spout will break it, I tried to break this little whirlwind by striking my whip frequently through it, but without any effect. Soon after, it quitted the road and took into the woods, growing every moment larger and stronger, raising instead of dust the old dry leaves with which the ground was thick covered, and making a great noise with them and the branches of the trees, bending some tall trees round in a circle swiftly and very surprisingly, though the progressive motion of the whirl was not so swift but that a man on foot might have kept pace with it; but the circular motion was amazingly rapid. By the leaves it was now filled with I could plainly perceive that the current of air they were driven by moved upwards in a spiral line; and when I saw the trunks and bodies of large trees enveloped in the passing whirl, which continued entire after it had left them, I no longer wondered that my whip had no effect on it in its smaller state. I accompanied it about three-quarters of a mile, till some limbs of dead trees, broken off by the whirl, flying about and falling near me, made me more apprehensive of danger; and then I stopped, looking at the top of it as it went on, which was visible by means of the leaves contained in it for a very great height above the trees. Many of the leaves, as they got loose from the upper and widest part, were scattered in the wind; but so great was their height in the air that they appeared no bigger than flies.

"My son, who was by this time come up with me, followed the whirlwind till it left the woods and crossed an old tobacco field, where, finding neither dust nor leaves to take up, it gradually became invisible below as it went away over that field. The course of the general wind then blowing was along with us as we travelled, and the progressive motion of the whirlwind was in a direction nearly opposite, though it did not keep a straight line nor was its progressive motion uniform, it making little sallies on either hand as it went, proceeding sometimes faster and sometimes slower, and seeming sometimes for a few seconds almost stationary, then starting forward pretty fast again. When we rejoined the company, they were admiring the vast height of the leaves now brought by the common wind over our heads. These leaves accompanied us as we travelled, some falling now and then about us, and some not reaching the ground till we had gone near three miles from the place where we first saw the whirlwind begin.

"Upon my asking Colonel Tasker if such whirlwinds were common in Maryland, he answered pleasantly: 'No, not at all common; but we got this on purpose to treat Mr. Franklin.'

"The rest of the company stood looking after it, but, my curiosity being stronger, I followed it, riding close by its side." This is a little symbolical history of Franklin as scientist. Going about his ordinary affairs, he was more curious than ordinary men and followed up what they only looked at. The ants he observed were in his closet, the pigeons in a box on the wall of his house. To warm his house, he devised a new kind of stove. To protect his house, he thought of the lightning rod. Watching the weather, he followed in his mind the course of a northeast storm for a thousand miles. Out of sympathy for his ailing brother he fashioned his catheter. Science came so naturally to him that he blamed himself for not being more patient and systematic. Actually he was, during his first electrical years, as patient and systematic in his studies of electricity as any of the scholars he surpassed. He surpassed them by the speed and reach of the hypotheses of which he spoke slightingly. Franklin, for all his home-made machines to experiment with and his homely inventions and his eagerness to make scientific knowledge immediately useful to mankind, was magnificent in outlook. He saw seashells from the top of a mountain, and saw time stretch out behind him in the great age of the earth. He guessed that light could not come from the sun in particles but on waves in the ether. On the hypothesis that lightning was electricity he built the bolder one that it could be proved. In the one metaphysical sentence in his writings on electricity he referred to "adoring that wisdom which had made all things by weight and measure." Secular as he was, he had often a vision, not unlike religion's, of an enormous universe of order and law which sometime might be understood. Immortal secrets for mortal men. In the meantime, he could be delighted, reasonable, and humorous about the mysteries.

⊂⊟ A CANDLE BURNS

The Discovery of Oxygen

JOSEPH PRIESTLEY

I WISH my reader be not quite tired with the frequent repetition of the word surprize, and others of similar import; but I must go on in that style a little longer.

For the next day I was more surprized than ever I had been before, with finding that, after the above-mentioned mixture of nitrous air and the air from mercurius calcinatus had stood all night (in which time the whole diminution must have taken place; and, consequently, had it been common air, it must have been made perfectly noxious and entirely unfit for respiration or inflammation), a candle burned in it, and even better than in common air.

I cannot, at this distance of time, recollect what it was that I had in view in making this experiment; but I know I had no expectation of the real issue of it. Having acquired a considerable degree of readiness in making experiments of this kind, a very slight and evanescent motive would be sufficient to induce me to do it. If, however, I had not happened, for some other purpose, to have had a lighted candle before me, I should probably never have made the trial; and the whole train of my future experiments relating to this kind of air might have been prevented.

Still, however, having no conception of the real cause of this phenomenon, I considered it as something very extraordinary; . . . I was myself perfectly satisfied of its being common air, as it appeared to be so by the test of nitrous air; though for the satisfaction of others, I wanted a mouse to make the proof quite complete.

On the 8th of this month I procured a mouse, and put it into a glass vessel, containing two ounce-measures of the air from mercurius calcinatus. Had it been common air, a full-grown mouse, as this was, would have lived in it about a quarter of an hour. In this air, however, my mouse lived a full half hour; and though it was taken out seemingly dead, it appeared to have been only exceedingly chilled; for, upon being held to fire, it presently revived and appeared not to have received any harm from the experiment.

From *Experiments and Observations on Different Kinds of Air* by Joseph Priestley. Vol. II. London, 1773.

By this I was confirmed in my conclusion, that the air extracted from mercurius calcinatus, &c., was, *at least, as good* as common air; but I did not certainly conclude that it was any *better;* because, though one mouse would live only a quarter of an hour in a given quantity of air, I knew it was not impossible but that another mouse might have lived in it half an hour; so little accuracy is there in this method of ascertaining the goodness of air: and indeed I have never had recourse to it for my own satisfaction, since the discovery of that most ready, accurate, and elegant test that nitrous air furnishes. But in this case I had a view to publishing the most generally satisfactory account of my experiments that the nature of the thing would admit of.

This experiment with the mouse, when I had reflected upon it some time, gave me so much suspicion that the air into which I had put it was better than common air, that I was induced, the day after, to apply the test of nitrous air to a small part of that very quantity of air which the mouse had breathed so long; so that, had it been common air, I was satisfied it must have been very nearly, if not altogether, as noxious as possible, so as not to be affected by nitrous air; when, to my surprise again, I found that though it had been breathed so long it was still better than common air. For after mixing it with nitrous air, in the usual proportion of two to one, it was diminished in the proportion of 4½ to 3½; that is, the nitrous air had made it two ninths less than before, and this in a very short space of time; whereas I had never found that, in the longest time, any common air was reduced more than one fifth of its bulk by any proportion of nitrous air, nor more than one fourth by any phlogistic process whatever. Thinking of this extraordinary fact upon my pillow, the next morning I put another measure of nitrous air to the same mixture, and to my utter astonishment found that it was farther diminished to almost one half of its original quantity. I then put a third measure to it; but this did not diminish it any farther; but, however, left it one measure less than it was even after the mouse had been taken out of it.

Being now fully satisfied that this air, even after the mouse had breathed it half an hour, was much better than common air; and having a quantity of it still left, sufficient for the experiment, viz., an ounce measure and a half, I put the mouse into it; when I observed that it seemed to feel no shock upon being put into it, evident signs of which would have been visible if the air had not been very wholesome; but that it remained perfectly at its ease another full half hour, when I took it out quite lively and vigorous. Measuring the air the next day, I found it to be reduced from 1½ to ⅔ of an ounce measure. And after this, if I remember well (for in my register of the day I only find it noted, that it was considerably diminished by nitrous air), it was nearly as good as common air. It was evident, indeed, from the mouse having been taken out quite vigorous, that the air could not have been rendered very noxious.

For my further satisfaction, I procured another mouse, and putting it into less than two ounce measures of air extracted from mercurius calcinatus and air from red precipitate (which, having found them to be of the same quality, I had mixed together), it lived three quarters of an hour. But not having had the precaution to set the vessel in a warm place, I suspect that the mouse died of cold. However, as it had lived three times as long as it could probably have lived in the same quantity of common air, and I did not expect much accuracy from this kind of test, I did not think it necessary to make any more experiments with mice.   .

⊂⊑ *IN TRANSIT*

In a Carriage

CHARLES DARWIN

AFTER MY RETURN to England it appeared to me that by following the example of Lyell in Geology, and by collecting all facts which bore in any way on the variation of animals and plants under domestication and nature, some light might perhaps be thrown on the whole subject [origin of species]. . . . My first note-book was opened in July 1837. I worked on true Baconian principles, and without any theory collected facts on a wholesale scale, . . . I soon perceived that selection was the keystone of man's success in making useful races of animals and plants. But how selection could be applied to organisms living in a state of nature remained for some time a mystery to me.

In October 1838, that is, fifteen months after I had begun my systematic inquiry, I happened to read for amusement Malthus on *Population*, and being well prepared to appreciate the struggle for existence which everywhere goes on from long-continued observation of the habits of animals and plants, it at once struck me that

From Charles Darwin's *Autobiography.*

under these circumstances favorable variations would tend to be preserved, and unfavorable ones to be destroyed. The result of this would be the formation of new species. Here then I had at last got a theory by which to work; but I was so anxious to avoid prejudice, that I determined not for some time to write even the briefest sketch of it. In June 1842 I first allowed myself the satisfaction of writing a very brief abstract of my theory in pencil in 35 pages; and this was enlarged during the summer of 1844 into one of 230 pages, which I had fairly copied out and still possess.

But at that time I overlooked one problem of great importance; and it is astonishing to me, except on the principle of Columbus and his egg, how I could have overlooked it and its solution. This problem is the tendency in organic beings descended from the same stock to diverge in character as they become modified. That they have diverged greatly is obvious from the manner in which species of all kinds can be classified under genera, genera under families, families under sub-orders, and so forth; and I can remember the very spot in the road, whilst in my carriage, when to my joy the solution occurred to me; and this was long after I had come to Down. The solution, as I believe, is that the modified offspring of all dominant and increasing forms tend to become adapted to many and highly diverse places in the economy of nature.

On a Bus

FRIEDRICH KEKULÉ

DURING MY STAY in London I resided for a considerable time in Clapham Road in the neighborhood of the Common. I frequently, however, spent my evenings with my friend Hugo Müller at Islington, at the opposite end of the giant town. We talked of many things, but oftenest of our beloved chemistry. One fine summer evening I was returning by the last omnibus, outside, as usual, through the deserted streets of the metropolis, which are at other times so full of life. I fell into a reverie, and lo, the atoms

From a speech given by Friedrich Kekulé before the German Chemical Society in 1890.

were gamboling before my eyes! Whenever, hitherto, these diminutive beings had appeared to me, they had always been in motion; but up to that time I had never been able to discern the nature of their motion. Now, however, I saw how, frequently, two smaller atoms united to form a pair; how a larger one embraced two smaller ones; how still larger ones kept hold of three or even four of the smaller; whilst the whole kept whirling in a giddy dance. I saw how the larger ones formed a chain, dragging the smaller ones after them, but only at the ends of the chain. I saw what our Past Master, Kopp, my highly honored teacher and friend, has depicted with such charm in his *Molekularwelt* but I saw it long before him. The cry of the conductor: "Clapham Road," awakened me from my dreaming but I spent a part of the night in putting on paper at least sketches of these dream forms. This was the origin of the *Structurtheorie*.

◇◇◇◇◇◇◇◇◇◇◇◇◇◇◇◇◇◇◇◇◇◇◇◇◇◇◇◇◇◇◇◇◇◇◇◇

⊂▤ *"CHANCE FAVORS THE PREPARED MIND . . ."*

Chickens, Dogs . . . And a Child's Life Is Saved

RENÉ VALLERY-RADOT

A CHANCE, such as happens to those who have the genius of observation, was now about to mark an immense step in advance and prepare the way for a great discovery. As long as the culture flasks of chicken-cholera microbe had been sown without interruption, at twenty-four hours' interval, the virulence had remained the same; but when some hens were inoculated with an old culture, put away and forgotten a few weeks before, they were seen with surprise to become ill and then to recover. These unexpectedly refractory hens were then inoculated with some new culture, but the phenomenon of resistance recurred. What had happened? What could have attenuated the activity of the microbe? Researches proved that oxygen was the cause; and, by putting between the cul-

From *The Life of Pasteur* by René Vallery-Radot. By permission of Constable and Company, Ltd. © 1901.

tures variable intervals of days, of one, two or three months, variations of mortality were obtained, eight hens dying out of ten, then five, then only one out of ten, and at last, when, as in the first case, the culture had had time to get stale, no hens died at all, though the microbe could still be cultivated.

"Finally," said Pasteur, eagerly explaining this phenomenon, "if you take each of these attenuated cultures as a starting-point for successive and uninterrupted cultures, all this series of cultures will reproduce the attenuated virulence of that which served as the starting-point; in the same way non-virulence will reproduce non-virulence."

And, while hens who had never had chicken-cholera perished when exposed to the deadly virus, those who had undergone attenuated inoculations, and who afterward received more than their share of the deadly virus, were affected with the disease in a benign form, a passing indisposition, sometimes even they remained perfectly well; they had acquired immunity. Was not this fact worthy of being placed by the side of that great fact of vaccine, over which Pasteur had so often pondered and meditated?

He now felt that he might entertain the hope of obtaining, through artificial culture, some vaccinating-virus against the virulent diseases which cause great losses to agriculture in the breeding of domestic animals, and, beyond that, the greater hope of preserving humanity from those contagious diseases which continually decimate it. This invincible hope led him to wish that he might live long enough to accomplish some new discoveries and to see his followers step into the road he had marked out.

Strong in his experimental method which enabled him to produce proofs and thus to demonstrate the truth; able to establish the connection between a virulent and a microbian disease; finally, ready to reproduce by culture, in several degrees of attenuation, a veritable vaccine, could he not now force those of his opponents who were acting in good faith to acknowledge the evidence of facts? Could he not carry all attentive minds with him into the great movement which was about to replace old ideas by new and precise notions, more and more accessible?

Pasteur enjoyed days of incomparable happiness during that period of enthusiasm, joys of the mind in its full power, joys of the heart in all its expansion; for good was being done. He felt that nothing could arrest the course of his doctrine, of which he said — "The breath of Truth is carrying it towards the fruitful fields of the future." He had that intuition which makes a great poet of a great scientist. The innumerable ideas surging through his mind were like so many bees all trying to issue from the hive at the same time.

So many plans and preconceived ideas only stimulated him to further researches; but, when he was once started on a road, he distrusted each step and only progressed in the train of precise, clear and irrefutable experiments. . . .

It was then that it occurred to Pasteur to inoculate the rabic virus directly on the surface of a dog's brain. He thought that, by placing the virus from the beginning in its true medium, hydrophobia would more surely supervene and the incubation might be shorter. The experiment was attempted: a dog under chloroform was fixed to the operating board, and a small, round portion of the cranium removed by means of a trephine (a surgical instrument somewhat similar to a fret-saw); the tough fibrous membrane called the dura-mater, being thus exposed, was then injected with a small quantity of the prepared virus, which lay in readiness in a Pravaz syringe. The wound was washed with carbolic and the skin stitched together, the whole thing lasting but a few minutes. The dog, on returning to consciousness, seemed quite the same as usual. But, after fourteen days, hydrophobia appeared: rabid fury, characteristic howls, the tearing up and devouring of his bed, delirious hallucination, and finally, paralysis and death.

A method was therefore found by which rabies was contracted surely and swiftly. Trephinings were again performed on chloroformed animals — Pasteur had a great horror of useless sufferings, and always insisted on anesthesia. In every case, characteristic hydrophobia occurred after inoculation on the brain. The main lines of this complicated question were beginning to be traceable; but other obstacles were in the way. Pasteur could not apply the method he had hitherto used, *i.e.* to isolate, and then to cultivate in an artificial medium, the microbe of hydrophobia, for he failed in detecting this microbe. Yet its existence admitted of no doubt; perhaps it was beyond the limits of human sight. "Since this unknown being is living," thought Pasteur, "we must cultivate it; failing an artificial medium, let us try the brain of living rabbits; it would indeed be an experimental feat!"

As soon as a trephined and inoculated rabbit died paralyzed, a little of his rabic medulla was inoculated to another; each inoculation succeeded another, and the time of incubation became shorter and shorter, until, after a hundred uninterrupted inoculations, it came to be reduced to seven days. But the virus, having reached this degree, the virulence of which was found to be greater than that of the virus of dogs made rabid by an accidental bite, now became fixed; Pasteur had mastered it. He could now predict the exact time when death should occur in each of the inoculated animals; his predictions were verified with surprising accuracy.

Pasteur was not yet satisfied with the immense progress marked by infallible inoculation and the shortened incubation; he now wished to decrease the degrees of virulence — when the attenuation of the virus was once conquered, it might be hoped that dogs could be made refractory to rabies. Pasteur abstracted a fragment of the medulla from a rabbit which had just died of rabies after an inoculation of the fixed virus; this fragment was suspended by a thread in a sterilized phial, the air in which was kept dry by some pieces of caustic potash lying at the bottom of the vessel and which was closed by a cotton-wool plug to prevent the entrance of atmospheric dusts. The temperature of the room where this desiccation took place was maintained at 23° C. As the medulla gradually became dry, its virulence decreased, until, at the end of fourteen days, it had become absolutely extinguished. This now inactive medulla was crushed and mixed with pure water, and injected under the skin of some dogs. The next day they were inoculated with medulla which had been desiccating for thirteen days, and so on, using increased virulence until the medulla was used of a rabbit dead the same day. These dogs might now be bitten by rabid dogs given them as companions for a few minutes, or submitted to the intracranial inoculations of the deadly virus: they resisted both.

Having at last obtained this refractory condition, Pasteur was anxious that his results should be verified by a Commission. The Minister of Public Instruction acceded to this desire, and a Commission was constituted in May, 1884. . . . The Commission immediately set to work; a rabid dog having succumbed at Alfort on June 1, its carcass was brought to the laboratory of the Ecole Normale, and a fragment of the medulla oblongata was mixed with some sterilized broth. Two dogs, declared by Pasteur to be refractory to rabies, were trephined, and a few drops of the liquid injected into their brains; two other dogs and two rabbits received inoculations at the same time, with the same liquid and in precisely the same manner. . . . On June 3, Bourrel sent word that he had a rabid dog in the kennels of the Rue Fontaine-au-Roi; a refractory dog and a new dog were immediately submitted to numerous bites; the latter was violently bitten on the head in several places. The rabid dog, still living the next day and still able to bite, was given two more dogs, one of which was refractory; this dog, and the refractory dog bitten on the 3rd, were allowed to receive the first bites, the Commission having thought that perhaps the saliva might then be more abundant and more dangerous.

On June 6, the rabid dog having died, the Commission proceeded to inoculate the medulla of the animal into six more dogs, by means of trephining. Three of those dogs were refractory, the three others were fresh from the kennels; there were also two rabbits.

On the 10th, Bourrel telegraphed the arrival of another rabid dog, and the same operations were gone through.

"This rabid, furious dog," wrote Pasteur to his son-in-law, "had spent the night lying on his master's bed; his appearance had been suspicious for a day or two. On the morning of the 10th, his voice became rabietic, and his master, who had heard the bark of a rabid dog twenty years ago, was seized with terror, and brought the dog to M. Bourrel, who found that he was indeed in the biting stage of rabies. Fortunately a lingering fidelity had prevented him from attacking his master. . . .

"This morning the rabic condition is beginning to appear on one of the new dogs trephined on June 1, at the same time as two refractory dogs. Let us hope that the other new dog will also develop it and that the two refractory ones will resist."

At the same time that the Commission examined this dog which developed rabies within the exact time indicated by Pasteur, the two rabbits on whom inoculation had been performed at the same time were found to present the first symptoms of rabic paralysis. "This paralysis," noted Bouley, is revealed by great weakness of the limbs, particularly of the hind quarters; the least shock knocks them over and they experience great difficulty in getting up again." The second new dog on whom inoculation had been performed on June 1 was now also rabid; the refractory dogs were in perfect health. . . .

On Monday, July 6, Pasteur saw a little Alsatian boy, Joseph Meister, enter his laboratory, accompanied by his mother. He was only nine years old, and had been bitten two days before by a mad dog at Meissengott, near Schlestadt.

The child, going alone to school by a little by-road, had been attacked by a furious dog and thrown to the ground. Too small to defend himself, he had only thought of covering his face with his hands. A bricklayer, seeing the scene from a distance, arrived, and succeeded in beating the dog off with an iron bar; he picked up the boy, covered with blood and saliva. The dog went back to his master, Théodore Vone, a grocer at Meissengott, whom he bit on the arm. Vone seized a gun and shot the animal, whose stomach was found to be full of hay, straw, pieces of wood, etc. When little Meister's parents heard all these details they went, full of anxiety, to consult Dr. Weber, at Villé, that same evening. After cauterizing the wounds with carbolic, Dr. Weber advised Mme. Meister to start for Paris, where she could relate the facts to one who was not a physician, but who would be the best judge of what could be done in such a serious case. Théodore Vone, anxious on his own and on the child's account, decided to come also.

Pasteur reassured him; his clothes had wiped off the dog's saliva, and his shirt-sleeve was intact. He might safely go back to Alsace, and he promptly did so.

Pasteur's emotion was great at the sight of the fourteen wounds of the little boy, who suffered so much that he could hardly walk. What should he do for this child? Could he risk the preventive treatment which had been constantly successful on his dogs? Pasteur was divided between his hopes and his scruples, painful in their acuteness. Before deciding on a course of action, he made arrangements for the comfort of this poor woman and her child, alone in Paris, and gave them an appointment for 5 o'clock, after the Institute meeting. He did not wish to attempt anything without having seen Vulpian and talked it over with him. Since the Rabies Commission had been constituted, Pasteur had formed a growing esteem for the great judgment of Vulpian, who, in his lectures on the general and comparative physiology of the nervous system, had already mentioned the profit to human clinics to be drawn from experimenting on animals.

His was a most prudent mind, always seeing all the aspects of a problem. The man was worthy of the scientist: he was absolutely straightforward, and of a discreet and active kindness. He was passionately fond of work, and had recourse to it when smitten by a deep sorrow.

Vulpian expressed the opinion that Pasteur's experiments on dogs were sufficiently conclusive to authorize him to foresee the same success in human pathology. Why not try this treatment? added the professor, usually so reserved. Was there any other efficacious treatment against hydrophobia? If at least the cauterizations had been made with a red-hot iron! but what was the good of carbolic acid twelve hours after the accident. If the almost certain danger which threatened the boy were weighed against the chances of snatching him from death, Pasteur would see that it was more than a right, that it was a duty to apply antirabic inoculation to little Meister.

This was also the opinion of Dr. Grancher, whom Pasteur consulted. M. Grancher worked at the laboratory; he and Dr. Straus might claim to be the two first French physicians who took up the study of bacteriology; these novel studies fascinated him, and he was drawn to Pasteur by the deepest admiration and by a strong affection, which Pasteur thoroughly reciprocated.

Vulpian and M. Grancher examined little Meister in the evening, and, seeing the number of bites, some of which, on one hand especially, were very deep, they decided on performing the first inoculation immediately; the substance chosen was fourteen days old and had quite lost its virulence: it was to be followed by further inoculations gradually increasing in strength.

It was a very slight operation, a mere injection into the side (by means of a Pravaz syringe) of a few drops of a liquid prepared with some fragments of medulla oblongata. The child, who cried very much before the operation, soon dried his tears when he found the slight prick was all that he had to undergo.

Pasteur had had a bedroom comfortably arranged for the mother and child in the old Rollin College, and the little boy was very happy amidst the various animals — chickens, rabbits, white mice, guinea pigs, etc.; he begged and easily obtained of Pasteur the life of several of the youngest of them.

"All is going well," Pasteur wrote to his son-in-law on July 11: "the child sleeps well, has a good appetite, and the inoculated matter is absorbed into the system from one day to another without leaving a trace. It is true that I have not yet come to the test inoculations, which will take place on Tuesday, Wednesday and Thursday. If the lad keeps well during the three following weeks, I think the experiment will be safe to succeed. I shall send the child and his mother back to Meissengott (near Schlestadt) in any case on August 1, giving these good people detailed instruction as to the observations they are to record for me. I shall make no statement before the end of the vacation."

But, as the inoculations were becoming more virulent, Pasteur became a prey to anxiety: "My dear children," wrote Mme. Pasteur, "your father has had another bad night; he is dreading the last inoculations on the child. And yet there can be no drawing back now! The boy continues in perfect health."

Renewed hopes were expressed in the following letter from Pasteur: "My dear René, I think great things are coming to pass. Joseph Meister has just left the laboratory. The three last inoculations have left some pink marks under the skin, gradually widening and not at all tender. There is some action, which is becoming more intense as we approach the final inoculation, which will take place on Thursday, July 16. The lad is very well this morning, and has slept well, though slightly restless; he has a good appetite and no feverishness. He had a slight hysterical attack yesterday."

The letter ended with an affectionate invitation. "Perhaps one of the great medical facts of the century is going to take place; you would regret not having seen it!"

Pasteur was going through a succession of hopes, fears, anguish, and an ardent yearning to snatch little Meister from death; he could no longer work. At nights, feverish visions came to him of this child whom he had seen playing in the garden, suffocating in the mad struggle of hydrophobia, like the dying child he had seen at the Hôpital Trousseau in 1880. Vainly his experimental genius assured him that the virus of that most terrible of diseases was about to be vanquished, that humanity was about to be delivered from this dread horror — his human tenderness was stronger than all, his accustomed ready sympathy for the sufferings and anxieties of others was for the nonce centered in "the dear lad."

The treatment lasted ten days; Meister was inoculated twelve times. The virulence of the medulla used was tested by trephinings on rabbits, and proved to be gradually stronger. Pasteur even inoculated on July 16, at 11 A.M., some medulla only one day old, bound to give hydrophobia to rabbits after only seven days' incubation; it was the surest test of the immunity and preservation due to the treatment.

Cured from his wounds, delighted with all he saw, gaily running about as if he had been on his own Alsatian farm, little Meister, whose blue eyes now showed neither fear nor shyness, merrily received the last inoculation; in the evening, after claiming a kiss from "Dear Monsieur Pasteur," as he called him, he went to bed and slept peacefully. Pasteur spent a terrible night of insomnia; in those slow dark hours of night when all vision is distorted, Pasteur, losing sight of the accumulation of experiments which guaranteed his success, imagined that the little boy would die.

The treatment being now completed, Pasteur left little Meister to the care of Dr. Grancher (the lad was not to return to Alsace until July 27) and consented to take a few days' rest. He spent them with his daughter in a quiet, almost deserted country place in Burgundy, but without however finding much restfulness in the beautiful peaceful scenery; he lived in constant expectation of Dr. Grancher's daily telegram or letter containing news of Joseph Meister.

By the time he went to the Jura, Pasteur's fears had almost disappeared. He wrote from Arbois to his son August 3, 1885: "Very good news last night of the bitten lad. I am looking forward with great hopes to the time when I can draw a conclusion. It will be thirty-one days to-morrow since he was bitten." [It is interesting to know that the little Joseph Meister later became the gatekeeper of the Pasteur Institute. In 1940, fifty-five years after the accident that gave him a lasting place in medical history, he committed suicide to escape being compelled to open for the German invaders the crypt where Pasteur is buried.]

On his return to Paris, Pasteur found himself obliged to hasten the organization of a "service" for the preventive treatment of hydrophobia after a bite. The Mayor of Villers-Farlay, in the Jura, wrote to him that, on October 14, a shepherd had been cruelly bitten by a rabid dog.

Six little shepherd boys were watching over their sheep in a meadow; suddenly they saw a large dog passing along the road, with hanging, foaming jaws.

"A mad dog!" they exclaimed. The dog, seeing the children, left the road and charged them; they ran away shrieking, but the eldest of them, J. B. Jupille, fourteen years of age, bravely turned back in order to protect the flight of his comrades. Armed with his whip, he confronted the infuriated animal, who flew at him and seized his left hand. Jupille, wrestling with the dog, succeeded in kneeling on him, and forcing his jaws open in order to disengage his left hand; in so doing, his right hand was seriously bitten in its turn; finally, having been able to get hold of the animal by the neck, Jupille called to his little brother to pick up his whip, which had fallen during the struggle, and securely fastened the dog's jaws with the lash. He then took his wooden *sabot,* with which he battered the dog's head, after which, in order to be sure it could do no further harm, he dragged the body down to a little stream in the meadow, and held the head under water for several minutes. Death being now certain, and all danger removed from his comrades, Jupille returned to Villers-Farlay.

Whilst the boy's wounds were being bandaged, the dog's carcass was fetched, and a necropsy took place the next day. The two veterinary surgeons who examined the body had not the slightest hesitation in declaring that the dog was rabid.

The Mayor of Villers-Farlay, who had been to see Pasteur during the summer, wrote to tell him that his lad would die a victim of his own courage unless the new treatment intervened. The answer came immediately: Pasteur declared that, after five years' study, he had succeeded in making dogs refractory to rabies, even six or eight days after being bitten; that he had only once yet applied his method to a human being, but that once with success, in the case of little Meister, and that, if Jupille's family consented, the boy might be sent to him. "I shall keep him near me in a room of my laboratory; he will be watched and need not go to bed; he will merely receive a daily prick, not more painful than a pin-prick."

The family, on hearing this letter, came to an immediate decision;

but, between the day when he was bitten and Jupille's arrival in Paris, six whole days had elapsed, whilst in Meister's case there had only been two and a half!

Yet, however great were Pasteur's fears for the life of this tall lad, who seemed quite surprised when congratulated on his courageous conduct, they were not what they had been in the first instance — he felt much greater confidence.

A few days later, on October 26, Pasteur in a statement at the Academy of Sciences described the treatment followed for Meister. Three months and three days had passed, and the child remained perfectly well. Then he spoke of his new attempt. Vulpian rose —

"The Academy will not be surprised," he said, "if, as a member of the Medical and Surgical Section, I ask to be allowed to express the feelings of admiration inspired in me by M. Pasteur's statement. I feel certain that those feelings will be shared by the whole of the medical profession.

"Hydrophobia, that dread disease against which all therapeutic measures had hitherto failed, has at last found a remedy. M. Pasteur, who has been preceded by no one in this path, has been led by a series of investigations unceasingly carried on for several years, to create a method of treatment, by means of which the development of hydrophobia can *infallibly* be prevented in a patient recently bitten by a rabid dog. I say infallibly, because, after what I have seen in M. Pasteur's laboratory, I do not doubt the constant success of this treatment when it is put into full practice a few days only after a rabic bite.

"It is now necessary to see about organizing an installation for the treatment of hydrophobia by M. Pasteur's method. Every person bitten by a rabid dog must be given the opportunity of benefiting by this great discovery, which will seal the fame of our illustrious colleague and bring glory to our whole country."

Pasteur had ended his reading by a touching description of Jupille's action, leaving the Assembly under the impression of that boy of fourteen, sacrificing himself to save his companions. An Academician, Baron Larrey, whose authority was rendered all the greater by his calmness, dignity, and moderation, rose to speak. After acknowledging the importance of Pasteur's discovery, Larrey continued, "The sudden inspiration, agility and courage, with which the ferocious dog was muzzled, and thus made incapable of committing further injury to bystanders, . . . such an act of bravery deserves to be rewarded. I therefore have the honor of begging the Académie des Sciences to recommend to the Académie Française this young shepherd, who, by giving such a generous example of courage and devotion, has well deserved a Montyon prize."

Bouley, then chairman of the Academy, rose to speak in his turn —

"We are entitled to say that the date of the present meeting will remain for ever memorable in the history of medicine, and glorious for French science; for it is that of one of the greatest steps ever accomplished in the medical order of things — a progress realized by the discovery of an efficacious means of preventive treatment for a disease, the incurable nature of which was a legacy handed down by one century to another. From this day, humanity is armed with a means of fighting the fatal disease of hydrophobia and of preventing its onset. It is to M. Pasteur that we owe this, and we could not feel too much admiration or too much gratitude for the efforts on his part which have led to such a magnificent result. . . ."

TEAM WORKERS

<<<<<<<<<<<<<<<<<<<<<<<<<<<<<<

⫷ *THE AIR AGE BEGINS*

The Campers at Kitty Hawk

JOHN DOS PASSOS

ON DECEMBER SEVENTEENTH, nineteen hundred and three, Bishop Wright, of the United Brethren, onetime editor of the *Religious Telescope*, received in his frame house on Hawthorn Street in Dayton, Ohio, a telegram from his boys Wilbur and Orville who'd gotten it into their heads to spend their vacations in a little camp out on the dunes of the North Carolina coast tinkering with a homemade glider they'd knocked together themselves. The telegram read:

SUCCESS   FOUR FLIGHTS THURSDAY MORNING ALL AGAINST
TWENTYONE MILE WIND   STARTED FROM LEVEL WITH
ENGINEPOWER ALONE   AVERAGE SPEED THROUGH AIR
THIRTYONE MILES   LONGEST FIFTYSEVEN SECONDS   INFORM
PRESS   HOME CHRISTMAS

The figures were a little wrong because the telegraph operator misread Orville's hasty penciled scrawl
    but the fact remains
    that a couple of young bicycle mechanics from Dayton, Ohio
    Had designed constructed and flown
    for the first time ever a practical airplane.

After running the motor a few minutes to heat it up I released the wire that held the machine to the track and the machine started forward into the wind. Wilbur ran at the side of the machine holding the wing to balance it on the track. Unlike the start on the 14th made in a calm the machine facing a 27 mile wind started very

*slowly. . . . Wilbur was able to stay with it until it lifted from the
track after a forty-foot run. One of the lifesaving men snapped the
camera for us taking a picture just as it reached the end of the
track and the machine had risen to a height of about two feet. . . .
The course of the flight up and down was extremely erratic, partly
due to the irregularities of the air, partly to lack of experience in
handling this machine. A sudden dart when a little over a hundred
and twenty feet from the point at which it rose in the air ended the
flight. . . . This flight lasted only 12 seconds, but it was nevertheless the first in the history of the world in which a machine carrying a man had raised by its own power into the air in full flight, had
sailed forward without reduction of speed and had finally landed
at a point as high as that from which it started.*

A little later in the day the machine was caught in a gust of wind
and turned over and smashed, almost killing the coastguardsman
who tried to hold it down;
    it was too bad
    but the Wright brothers were too happy to care
    they'd proved that the damn thing flew.

*When these points had been definitely established, we at once
packed our goods and returned home knowing that the age of the
flying machine had come at last.*

They were home for Christmas in Dayton, Ohio, where they'd
been born in the seventies of a family who had been settled west of
the Alleghenies since eighteen fourteen, in Dayton, Ohio, where
they'd been to grammarschool and highschool and joined their
father's church and played baseball and hockey and worked out on
the parallel bars and the flying swing and sold newspapers and
built themselves a printingpress out of odds and ends from the junk-
heap and flown kites and tinkered with mechanical contraptions
and gone around town as boys doing odd jobs to turn an honest
penny.
The folks claimed it was the bishop's bringing home a helicopter,
a fiftycent mechanical toy made of two fans worked by elastic
bands that was supposed to hover in the air, that had got his two
youngest boys hipped on the subject of flight
    so that they stayed home instead of marrying the way the other
boys did, and puttered all day about the house picking up a living
with jobprinting,
    bicyclerepair work,
    sitting up late nights reading books on aerodynamics.

Still they were sincere churchmembers, their bicycle business was prosperous, a man could rely on their word. They were popular in Dayton.

In those days flyingmachines were the big laugh of all the crackerbarrel philosophers. Langley's and Chanute's unsuccessful experiments had been jeered down with an I-told-you-so that rang from coast to coast. The Wrights' big problem was to find a place secluded enough to carry on their experiments without being the horselaugh of the countryside. Then they had no money to spend;

they were practical mechanics; when they needed anything they built it themselves.

They hit on Kitty Hawk,
    on the great dunes and sandy banks that stretch
south towards Hatteras seaward of Albemarle Sound,
    a vast stretch of seabeach
    empty except for a coastguard station, a few fishermen's shacks
and the swarms of mosquitoes and the ticks and chiggers in the
crabgrass behind the dunes
    and overhead the gulls and swooping terns, in the evening fish-
hawks and cranes flapping across the salt-marshes, occasionally
eagles
    that the Wright brothers followed soaring with their eyes
    as Leonardo watched them centuries before
    straining his sharp eyes to apprehend
    the laws of flight.
Four miles across the loose sand from the scattering of shacks,
the Wright brothers built themselves a camp and a shed for their
gliders. It was a long way to pack their groceries, their tools, anything they happened to need; in summer it was hot as blazes, the
mosquitoes were hell;
    but they were alone there
    and they'd figured out that the loose sand was as soft as any-
thing they could find to fall in.
    There with a glider made of two planes and a tail in which they
lay flat on their bellies and controlled the warp of the planes by
shimmying their hips, taking off again and again all day from a big
dune named Kill Devil Hill,
    they learned to fly.
    Once they'd managed to hover for a few seconds
    and soar ever so slightly on a rising aircurrent
    they decided the time had come
    to put a motor in their biplane.

Back in the shop in Dayton, Ohio, they built an airtunnel, which is their first great contribution to the science of flying, and tried out model planes in it.

They couldn't interest any builders of gasoline engines so they had to build their own motor.

It worked; after that Christmas of nineteen three the Wright brothers weren't doing it for fun any more; they gave up their bicycle business, got the use of a big old cowpasture belonging to the local banker for practice flights, spent all the time when they weren't working on their machine in promotion, worrying about patents, infringements, spies, trying to interest government officials, to make sense out of the smooth involved heartbreaking remarks of lawyers.

In two years they had a plane that would cover twenty-four miles at a stretch round and round the cowpasture.

People on the interurban car used to crane their necks out of the windows when they passed along the edge of the field, startled by the clattering pop pop of the old Wright motor and the sight of the white biplane like a pair of ironing boards one on top of the other chugging along a good fifty feet in the air. The cows soon got used to it.

As the flights got longer
the Wright brothers got backers,
engaged in lawsuits,
lay in their beds at night sleepless with the whine of phantom millions, worse than the mosquitoes at Kitty Hawk.

In nineteen-seven they went to Paris,
allowed themselves to be togged out in dress suits and silk hats,
learned to tip waiters
talked with government experts, got used to gold braid and postponements and vandyke beards and the outspread palms of politicos. For amusement
they played diabolo in the Tuileries gardens.

They gave publicized flights at Fort Meyers, where they had their first fatal crackup, St. Petersburg, Paris, Berlin; at Pau they were all the rage,
such an attraction that the hotelkeeper
wouldn't charge them for their room.
Alfonso of Spain shook hands with them and was photographed sitting in the machine,
King Edward watched a flight,

the Crown Prince insisted on being taken up,
the rain of medals began.

They were congratulated by the Czar
and the King of Italy and the amateurs of sport, and the society
climbers and the papal titles,
and decorated by a society for universal peace.

Aeronautics became the sport of the day.
The Wrights don't seem to have been very much impressed by
the upholstery and the braid and the gold medals and the parades
of plush horses,
they remained practical mechanics
and insisted on doing all their own work themselves,
even to filling the gasolinetank.
In nineteen eleven they were back on the dunes
at Kitty Hawk with a new glider.
Orville stayed up in the air for nine and a half minutes, which
remained a long time the record for motorless flight.
The same year Wilbur died of typhoid fever in Dayton.
In the rush of new names: Farman, Blériot, Curtiss, Ferber,
Esnault-Peltrie, Delagrange;
in the snorting impact of bombs and the whine and rattle of
shrapnel and the sudden stutter of machineguns after the motor's
been shut off overhead,
and we flatten into the mud
and make ourselves small cowering in the corners of ruined
walls,
the Wright brothers passed out of the headlines
but not even the headlines or the bitter smear of newsprint or
the choke of smokescreen and gas or chatter of brokers on the stock-
market or barking of phantom millions or oratory of brasshats laying
wreaths on new monuments
can blur the memory
of the chilly December day
two shivering bicycle mechanics from Dayton, Ohio,
first felt their homemade contraption
whittled out of hickory sticks,
gummed together with Arnstein's bicycle cement,
stretched with muslin they'd sewn on their sister's sewing-ma-
chine in their own backyard on Hawthorn Street in Dayton, Ohio,
soar into the air
above the dunes and the wide beach
at Kitty Hawk.

⊂⊇ HUMAN GRANDEUR

Portrait of Madame Curie

ALBERT EINSTEIN

IT WAS MY GOOD FORTUNE to be linked with Mme. Curie through twenty years of sublime and unclouded friendship. I came to admire her human grandeur to an ever growing degree. Her strength, her purity of will, her austerity toward herself, her objectivity, her incorruptible judgment — all these were of a kind seldom found joined in a single individual. She felt herself at every moment to be a servant of society and her profound modesty never left any room for complacency. She was oppressed by an abiding sense for the asperities and inequities of society. This is what gave her that severe outward aspect, so easily misinterpreted by those who were not close to her — a curious severity unrelieved by any artistic strain. Once she had recognized a certain way as the right one, she pursued it without compromise and with extreme tenacity.

The Discovery of Radium

EVE CURIE

WHILE A YOUNG WIFE kept house, washed her baby daughter and put pans on the fire, in a wretched laboratory at the School of Physics a woman physicist was making the most important discovery of modern science.

At the end of 1897 the balance sheet of Marie's activity showed two university degrees, a fellowship and a monograph on the magnetization of tempered steel. No sooner had she recovered from childbirth than she was back again at the laboratory.

The next stage in the logical development of her career was the doctor's degree. Several weeks of indecision came in here. She had to choose a subject of research which would furnish fertile and original material. Like a writer who hesitates and asks himself questions before settling the subject of his next novel, Marie, reviewing the most recent work in physics with Pierre, was in search of a subject for a thesis.

At this critical moment Pierre's advice had an importance which cannot be neglected. With respect to her husband, the young woman regarded herself as an apprentice: he was an older physicist, much more experienced than she. He was even, to put it exactly, her chief, her "boss."

But without a doubt Marie's character, her intimate nature, had a great part in this all-important choice. From childhood the Polish girl had carried the curiosity and daring of an explorer within her. This was the instinct that had driven her to leave Warsaw for Paris and the Sorbonne, and had made her prefer a solitary room in the Latin Quarter to the Dluskis' downy nest. In her walks in the woods she always chose the wild trail or the unfrequented road.

At this moment she was like a traveler musing on a long voyage. Bent over the globe and pointing out, in some far country, a strange name that excites his imagination, the traveler suddenly decides to go there and nowhere else: so Marie, going through the reports of the latest experimental studies, was attracted by the publication of the French scientist Henri Becquerel of the preceding year. She and Pierre already knew this work; she read it over again and studied it with her usual care.

After Roentgen's discovery of X rays, Henri Poincaré conceived the idea of determining whether rays like the X ray were emitted by "fluorescent" bodies under the action of light. Attracted by the same problem, Henri Becquerel examined the salts of a "rare metal," uranium. Instead of finding the phenomenon he had expected, he observed another, altogether different and incomprehensible: he found that uranium salts *spontaneously* emitted, without exposure to light, some rays of unknown nature. A compound of uranium, placed on a photographic plate surrounded by black paper, made an impression on the plate through the paper. And, like the X ray, these astonishing "uranic" salts discharged an electroscope by rendering the surrounding air a conductor.

Henri Becquerel made sure that these surprising properties were not caused by a preliminary exposure to the sun and that they persisted when the uranium compound had been maintained in darkness for several months. For the first time, a physicist had observed the phenomenon to which Marie Curie was later to give the name of *radioactivity*. But the nature of the radiation and its origin remained an enigma.

Becquerel's discovery fascinated the Curies. They asked themselves whence came the energy — tiny, to be sure — which uranium compounds constantly disengaged in the form of radiation. And what was the nature of this radiation? Here was an engrossing subject of research, a doctor's thesis! The subject tempted Marie most because it was a virgin field: Becquerel's work was very recent and so far as she knew nobody in the laboratories of Europe had yet attempted to make a fundamental study of uranium rays. As a point of departure, and as the only bibliography, there existed some communications presented by Henri Becquerel at the Academy of Science during the year 1896. It was a leap into great adventure, into an unknown realm.

There remained the question of where she was to make her experiments — and here the difficulties began. Pierre made several approaches to the director of the School of Physics with practically no results: Marie was given the free use of a little glassed-in studio on the ground floor of the school. It was a kind of storeroom, sweating with damp, where unused machines and lumber were put away. Its technical equipment was rudimentary and its comfort nil.

Deprived of an adequate electrical installation and of everything that forms material for the beginning of scientific research, she kept her patience, sought and found a means of making her apparatus work in this hole.

It was not easy. Instruments of precision have sneaking enemies: humidity, changes of temperature. Incidentally the climate of this little workroom, fatal to the sensitive electrometer, was not much better for Marie's health. But this had no importance. When she was cold, the young woman took her revenge by noting the degrees of temperature in centigrade in her notebook. On February 6, 1898, we find, among the formulas and figures: "Temperature here 6° 25." Six degrees . . . ! * Marie, to show her disapproval, added ten little exclamation points.

The candidate for the doctor's degree set her first task to be the measurement of the "power of ionization" of uranium rays — that is to say, their power to render the air a conductor of electricity and so to discharge an electroscope. The excellent method she used,

---

* About 44° Fahrenheit.

which was to be the key to the success of her experiments, had been invented for the study of other phenomena by two physicists well known to her: Pierre and Jacques Curie. Her technical installation consisted of an "ionization chamber," a Curie electrometer and a piezoelectric quartz.

At the end of several weeks the first result appeared: Marie acquired the certainty that the intensity of this surprising radiation was proportional to the quantity of uranium contained in the samples under examination, and that this radiation, which could be measured with precision, was not affected either by the chemical state of combination of the uranium or by external factors such as lighting or temperature.

These observations were perhaps not very sensational to the uninitiated, but they were of passionate interest to the scientist. It often happens in physics that an inexplicable phenomenon can be subjected, after some investigation, to laws already known, and by this very fact loses its interest for the research worker. Thus, in a badly constructed detective story, if we are told in the third chapter that the woman of sinister appearance who might have committed the crime is in reality only an honest little housewife who leads a life without secrets, we feel discouraged and cease to read.

Nothing of the kind happened here. The more Marie penetrated into intimacy with uranium rays, the more they seemed without precedent, essentially unknown. They were like nothing else. Nothing affected them. In spite of their very feeble power, they had an extraordinary individuality.

Turning this mystery over and over in her head, and pointing toward the truth, Marie felt and could soon affirm that the incomprehensible radiation was an *atomic* property. She questioned: Even though the phenomenon had only been observed with uranium, nothing proved that uranium was the only chemical element capable of emitting such radiation. Why should not other bodies possess the same power? Perhaps it was only by chance that this radiation had been observed in uranium first, and had remained attached to uranium in the minds of physicists. Now it must be sought for elsewhere. . . .

No sooner said than done. Abandoning the study of uranium, Marie undertook to examine *all known chemical bodies*, either in the pure state or in compounds. And the result was not long in appearing: compounds of another element, thorium, also emitted spontaneous rays like those of uranium and of similar intensity. The physicist had been right: the surprising phenomenon was by no means the property of uranium alone, and it became necessary to give it a distinct name. Mme. Curie suggested the name of *radio-activity*. Chemical substances like uranium and thorium, endowed with this particular "radiance," were called *radio elements*.

Radioactivity so fascinated the young scientist that she never tired of examining the most diverse forms of matter, always by the same method. Curiosity, a marvelous feminine curiosity, the first virtue of a scientist, was developed in Marie to the highest degree. Instead of limiting her observation to simple compounds, salts and oxides, she had the desire to assemble samples of minerals from the collection at the School of Physics, and of making them undergo almost at hazard, for her own amusement, a kind of customs inspection which is an electrometer test. Pierre approved, and chose with her the veined fragments, hard or crumbly, oddly shaped, which she wanted to examine.

Marie's idea was simple — simple as the stroke of genius. At the crossroads where Marie now stood, hundreds of research workers might have remained, nonplused, for months or even years. After examining all known chemical substances, and discovering — as Marie had done — the radiation of thorium, they would have continued to ask themselves in vain whence came this mysterious radioactivity. Marie, too, questioned and wondered. But her surprise was translated into fruitful acts. She had used up all evident possibilities. Now she turned toward the unplumbed and the unknown.

She knew in advance what she would learn from an examination of the minerals, or rather she thought she knew. The specimens which contained neither uranium nor thorium would be revealed as totally "inactive." The others, containing uranium or thorium, would be radioactive.

Experiment confirmed this prevision. Rejecting the inactive minerals, Marie applied herself to the others and measured their radioactivity. Then came a dramatic revelation: the radioactivity was a *great deal stronger* than could have been normally foreseen by the quantity of uranium or thorium contained in the products examined!

"It must be an error in experiment," the young woman thought; for doubt is the scientist's first response to an unexpected phenomenon.

She started her measurements over again, unmoved, using the same products. She started over again ten times, twenty times. And she was forced to yield to the evidence: the quantities of uranium and thorium found in these minerals were by no means sufficient to justify the exceptional intensity of the radiation she observed.

Where did this excessive and abnormal radiation come from? Only one explanation was possible: the minerals must contain, in small quantity, a *much more powerfully radioactive substance* than uranium and thorium.

But what substance? In her preceding experiments, Marie had already examined *all known chemical elements.*

The scientist replied to the question with the sure logic and magnificent audaciousness of a great mind: The minerals certainly contained a radioactive substance, which was at the same time a chemical element unknown until this day: *a new element.*

A new element! It was a fascinating and alluring hypothesis — but still a hypothesis. For the moment this powerfully radioactive substance existed only in the imagination of Marie and of Pierre. But it did exist there. It existed strongly enough to make the young woman go to see Bronya one day and tell her in a restrained, ardent voice:

"You know, Bronya, the radiation that I couldn't explain comes from a new chemical element. The element is there and I've got to find it. We are sure! The physicists we have spoken to believe we have made an error in experiment and advise us to be careful. But I am convinced that I am not mistaken."

These were unique moments in her unique life. The layman forms a theatrical — and wholly false — idea of the research worker and of his discoveries. "The moment of discovery" does not always exist: the scientist's work is too tenuous, too divided, for the certainty of success to crackle out suddenly in the midst of his laborious toil like a stroke of lightning, dazzling him by its fire. Marie, standing in front of her apparatus, perhaps never experienced the sudden intoxication of triumph. This intoxication was spread over several days of decisive labor, made feverish by a magnificent hope. But it must have been an exultant moment when, convinced by the rigorous reasoning of her brain that she was on the trail of new matter, she confided the secret to her elder sister, her ally always. . . . Without exchanging one affectionate word, the two sisters must have lived again, in a dizzying breath of memory, their years of waiting, their mutual sacrifices, their bleak lives as students, full of hope and faith.

It was barely four years before that Marie had written:

Life is not easy for any of us. But what of that? we must have perseverance and above all confidence in ourselves. We must believe that we are gifted for something, and that this thing, at whatever cost, must be attained.

That "something" was to throw science upon a path hitherto unsuspected.

In a first communication to the Academy, presented by Prof.
Lippmann and published in the *Proceedings* on April 12, 1898,
"Marie Sklodovska Curie" announced the probable presence in
pitchblende ores of a new element endowed with powerful radioactivity. This was the first stage of the discovery of radium.

By the force of her own intuition the physicist had shown to herself that the wonderful substance must exist. She decreed its existence. But its incognito still had to be broken. Now she would have
to verify hypothesis by experiment, isolate this material and see it.
She must be able to announce with certainty: "It is there."

Pierre Curie had followed the rapid progress of his wife's experiments with passionate interest. Without directly taking part in
Marie's work, he had frequently helped her by his remarks and
advice. In view of the stupefying character of her results, he did not
hesitate to abandon his study of crystals for the time being in order
to join his efforts to hers in the search for the new substance.

Thus, when the immensity of a pressing task suggested and
exacted collaboration, a great physicist was at Marie's side — a
physicist who was the companion of her life. Three years earlier,
love had joined this exceptional man and woman together — love,
and perhaps some mysterious foreknowledge, some sublime instinct
for the work in common.

The available force was now doubled. Two brains, four hands,
now sought the unknown element in the damp little workroom in
the Rue Lhomond. From this moment onward it is impossible to
distinguish each one's part in the work of the Curies. We know that
Marie, having chosen to study the radiation of uranium as the subject of her thesis, discovered that other substances were also radioactive. We know that after the examination of minerals she was
able to announce the existence of a new chemical element, powerfully radioactive, and that it was the capital importance of this
result which decided Pierre Curie to interrupt his very different
research in order to try to isolate this element with his wife. At that
time — May or June 1898 — a collaboration began which was to
last for eight years, until it was destroyed by a fatal accident.

We cannot and must not attempt to find out what should be
credited to Marie and what to Pierre during these eight years. It
would be exactly what the husband and wife did not want. The
personal genius of Pierre Curie is known to us by the original work
he had accomplished before this collaboration. His wife's genius
appears to us in the first intuition of discovery, the brilliant start;
and it was to reappear to us again, solitary, when Marie Curie the
widow unflinchingly carried the weight of a new science and con-

ducted it, through research, step by step, to its harmonious expansion. We therefore have formal proof that in the fusion of their two efforts, in this superior alliance of man and woman, the exchange was equal.

Let this certainty suffice for our curiosity and admiration. Let us not attempt to separate these creatures full of love, whose handwriting alternates and combines in the working notebooks covered with formulae, these creatures who were to sign nearly all their specific publications together. They were to write "We found" and "We observed"; and when they were constrained by fact to distinguish between their parts, they were to employ this moving locution:

> Certain minerals containing uranium and thorium (pitchblende, chalcolite, uranite) are very active from the point of view of the emission of Becquerel rays. In a preceding communication, *one of us* showed that their activity was even greater than that of uranium and thorium, and stated the opinion that this effect was due to some other very active substance contained in small quantity in these minerals.
>
> (Pierre and Marie Curie: *Proceedings of the Academy of Science,* July, 18, 1898.)

Marie and Pierre looked for this "very active" substance in an ore of uranium called pitchblende, which in the crude state had shown itself to be four times more radioactive than the pure oxide of uranium that could be extracted from it. But the composition of this ore had been known for a long time with considerable precision. The new element must therefore be present in very small quantity or it would not have escaped the notice of scientists and their chemical analysis.

According to their calculations — "pessimistic" calculations, like those of true physicists, who always take the less attractive of two probabilities — the collaborators thought the ore should contain the new element to a maximum quantity of one per cent. They decided that this was very little. They would have been in consternation if they had known that the radioactive element they were hunting down did not count for more than a millionth part of pitchblende ore.

They began their prospecting patiently, using a method of chemical research invented by themselves, based on radioactivity: they separated all the elements in pitchblende by ordinary chemical analysis and then measured the radioactivity of each of the bodies thus obtained. By successive eliminations they saw the "abnormal" radioactivity take refuge in certain parts of the ore. As they went on, the field of investigation was narrowed. It was exactly the technique used by the police when they search the houses of a neighborhood, one by one, to isolate and arrest a malefactor.

But there was more than one malefactor here: the radioactivity was concentrated principally in two different chemical fractions of the pitchblende. For M. and Mme. Curie it indicated the existence of two new elements instead of one. By July 1898 they were able to announce the discovery of one of these substances with certainty.

"You will have to name it," Pierre said to his young wife, in the same tone as if it were a question of choosing a name for little Irène.

The one-time Mlle. Sklodovska reflected in silence for a moment. Then, her heart turning toward her own country which had been erased from the map of the world, she wondered vaguely if the scientific event would be published in Russia, Germany and Austria — the oppressor countries — and answered timidly:

"Could we call it 'polonium'?"

In the *Proceedings of the Academy* for July 1898 we read:

> We believe the substance we have extracted from pitchblende contains a metal not yet observed, related to bismuth by its analytical properties. If the existence of this new metal is confirmed we propose to call it *polonium*, from the name of the original country of one of us.

The choice of this name proves that in becoming a Frenchwoman and a physicist Marie had not disowned her former enthusiasms. Another thing proves it to us: even before the note "On a New Radioactive Substance Contained in Pitchblende" had appeared in the *Proceedings of the Academy*, Marie had sent the manuscript to her native country, to that Joseph Boguski who directed the little laboratory at the Museum of Industry and Agriculture where she had made her first experiments. The communication was published in Warsaw in a monthly photographic review called *Swiatlo* almost as soon as in Paris.

Life was unchanged in the little flat in the Rue de la Glacière. Marie and Pierre worked even more than usual; that was all. When the heat of summer came, the young wife found time to buy some baskets of fruit in the markets and as usual, she cooked and put away preserves for the winter, according to the recipes used in the Curie family. Then she locked the shutters on her windows, which gave on burned leaves; she registered their two bicycles at the

Orleans station, and, like thousands of other young women in Paris, went off on holiday with her husband and her child.

This year the couple had rented a peasant's house at Auroux, in Auvergne. Happy to breathe good air after the noxious atmosphere of the Rue Lhomond, the Curies made excursions to Mende, Puy, Clermont, Mont-Dore. They climbed hills, visited grottoes, bathed in rivers. Every day, alone in the country, they spoke of what they called their "new metals," polonium and "the other" — the one that remained to be found. In September they would go back to their damp workroom and the dull minerals; with freshened ardor they would take up their search again. . . .

One grief interfered with Marie's intoxication for work: the Dluskis were on the point of leaving Paris. They had decided to settle in Austrian Poland and to build a sanatorium for tubercular sufferers at Zakopane in the Carpathian Mountains. The day of separation arrived: Marie and Bronya exchanged broken-hearted farewells; Marie was losing her friend and protector, and for the first time she had the feeling of exile.

Marie to Bronya, December 2, 1898:

> You can't imagine what a hole you have made in my life. With you two, I have lost everything I clung to in Paris except my husband and child. It seems to me that Paris no longer exists, aside from our lodging and the school where we work.
>
> Ask Mme. Dluska if the green plant you left behind should be watered, and how many times a day. Does it need a great deal of heat and sun?
>
> We are well, in spite of the bad weather, the rain and the mud. Irène is getting to be a big girl. She is very difficult about her food, and aside from milk tapioca she will eat hardly anything regularly, not even eggs. Write me what would be a suitable menu for persons of her age. . . .

In spite of their prosaic character — or perhaps because of it — some notes written by Mme. Curie in that memorable year 1898 seem to us worth quoting. Some are to be found in the margins of a book called *Family Cooking*, with respect to a recipe for gooseberry jelly:

> I took eight pounds of fruit and the same weight in crystallized sugar. After an ebullition of ten minutes, I passed the mixture through a rather fine sieve. I obtained fourteen pots of very good jelly, not transparent, which "took" perfectly.

In a school notebook covered with gray linen, in which the young
mother had written little Irène's weight day by day, her diet and
the appearance of her first teeth, we read under the date of July
20, 1898, some days after the publication of the discovery of polonium:

> Irène says "thanks" with her hand. She can walk very well
> now on all fours. She says "Gogli, gogli, go." She stays in the
> garden all day at Sceaux on a carpet. She can roll, pick herself
> up, and sit down.

On August 15, at Auroux:

> Irène has cut her seventh tooth, on the lower left. She can
> stand for half a minute alone. For the past three days we have
> bathed her in the river. She cries, but today (fourth bath) she
> stopped crying and played with her hands in the water.
> She plays with the cat and chases him with war cries. She is
> not afraid of strangers any more. She sings a great deal. She gets
> up on the table when she is in her chair.

Three months later, on October 17, Marie noted with pride:

> Irène can walk very well, and no longer goes on all fours.

On January 5, 1899:

> Irène has fifteen teeth!

Between these two notes — that of October 17, 1898, in which
Irène no longer goes on all fours, and that of January 5 in which
Irène has fifteen teeth — and a few months after the note on the
gooseberry preserve, we find another note worthy of remark.

It was drawn up by Marie and Pierre Curie and a collaborator
called G. Bémont. Intended for the Academy of Science, and
published in the *Proceedings* of the session of December 26, 1898,
it announced the existence of a second chemical element in pitchblende.

Some lines of this communication read as follows:

> *The various reasons we have just enumerated lead us to believe
> that the new radioactive substance contains a new element to
> which we propose to give the name of RADIUM.*

The new radioactive substance certainly contains a very strong proportion of barium; in spite of that its radioactivity is considerable. The radioactivity of radium therefore must be enormous.

◇◇◇◇◇◇◇◇◇◇◇◇◇◇◇◇◇◇◇◇◇◇◇◇◇◇◇◇◇◇◇◇◇◇◇◇◇◇

⊂⊋ CONTROLLED NUCLEAR REACTION

Landing in the New World

ARTHUR H. COMPTON

2 DECEMBER 1942. Wednesday, 2 December, was a cold day in Chicago, about 10 degrees, with a raw wind. The "L" and the streetcars were jammed, for it was the second day of gas rationing. Motor traffic was down 40 per cent.

Those fortunate ones who had seats on the bus were reading about the intense air struggle raging over Tunisia. A Los Angeles boy had received the Distinguished Flying Cross from King George of England for services in the Dieppe operation. There was the story of an American submarine that had sunk a Japanese destroyer and four other ships. Admiral Darlan was organizing French forces in Africa. Mussolini's latest address attempted to bolster the sagging morale of the Italians.

2 December 1942 was a day of mourning, prayer, and fasting among the Jews throughout the free countries of the world for the "greatest calamity in Jewish history since the destruction of the Temple." This day, on the eve of the kindling of the Chanukah lights of freedom, was declared a day of mourning by the Chief Rabbinate of Palestine. This followed a statement by the U. S. Department of State that two million Jews had perished and five million more were in danger.

On 2 December 1942 in the city of Chicago, U.S.A., man first liberated and controlled the power within the atom. This event was known only to a few. To those few it was a turning point in history, the birth of a new era.

That morning, on schedule, W. K. Lewis brought his reviewing committee back to Chicago, returning from Lawrence's laboratory in California. They were stopping over between trains. With them they had a draft of their report which was transmitted to General Groves two days later.

It was the separation of the uranium isotopes by gaseous diffusion that the committee believed had the best chance of success. The recommendation was that a plant be erected as rapidly as possible for separating the U-235 in quantity by this method. The committee doubted the usefulness of the magnetic method for full-scale separation but proposed that developmental work on this method should go ahead. It might give experimentally useful amounts of U-235 more promptly. With regard to plutonium, the recommendation was that a pilot plant for further developmental tests be built at once. Though many uncertainties existed, there was a possibility that plutonium production might nevertheless afford the earliest achievement of atomic weapons.

We met the committee in a comfortable conference room of Eckhart Hall. "Where is Fermi?" Lewis inquired. "We would like to talk over these questions with him."

"I'm sorry," I replied, "but Fermi has an important experiment in hand in the laboratory and has asked to be excused. Here are others of us who will be glad to discuss your questions."

The members of the committee surely guessed what Fermi was doing, but in not telling them the code of secrecy was being observed. In any case they went ahead with their discussion, and we did our best to present fairly our view of what needed to be done. We felt that their report as drafted gave a realistic view of the general state of the atomic project. We were relieved at the basic assumption that the program would go ahead with full vigor. We were disappointed that the recommendation did not call for immediate production plans for plutonium. The reviewing committee felt, however, that it was premature to think of plutonium production until pilot plant tests gave us some basis of practical experience about the process.

About the middle of the morning the telephone rang. It was Volney Wilson's voice: "I thought you would want to know that Fermi is ready to start the critical experiment."

This was the call I had been hoping for. The construction crew had been working long hours under the direction of Walter Zinn and Herbert Anderson. Now tests showed that the pile, only about three-fourths of the size that had been thought necessary, was ready to give a chain reaction. This reaction was held down by control rods coated with cadmium that swallowed up all neutrons within reach. To make the reaction work it should now only be necessary to pull these control rods out of the pile. It was this experiment, of removing the control rods by measured steps and noting the effect on the abundance of neutrons in the pile, that was the critical test. If the self-sustaining chain reaction occurred, the neutron abundance should climb slowly but in geometric proportion with the time, continuing to increase without limit until the control rods were pushed back into the pile. It was a fortunate coincidence that the experiment was ready on the day of the reviewing committee's visit.

Wilson explained that space in the laboratory was at a premium but told me that if I wanted to bring with me one other person it should not too greatly disturb the experiment. I passed over the older members of the committee, including W. K. Lewis, its chairman. I picked rather the youngest member of the group, for I reasoned that he would probably remember longer than the others what he would see, and it should be something worth remembering. Thus the lot fell on Crawford H. Greenewalt, then at the age of forty the director of research of one of the important divisions of the du Pont Company. A half a dozen years later he was to become president of du Pont, a destiny that even then seemed not unlikely. Greenewalt was a very competent young man, with unusual knowledge of both research and organizational administration, full of ideas and enthusiasm.

We entered onto a balcony at one end of the squash-court laboratory. At the opposite end of the room was the massive pile of graphite blocks, within which the uranium was embedded. On the balcony with us were twenty others, including Fermi. Most of these were engaged in making various adjustments and reading a variety of meters. On the floor below was George Weil, whose task was to handle the control rods. On a platform over a corner of the pile was a group of three men whom we jokingly called "the suicide squad." It was their responsibility, in case the reaction could not otherwise be stopped, to throw buckets of cadmium solution over the pile. Hilberry was ready with an ax to cut the rope holding a safety rod if the reaction should begin to grow with sudden violence. The door to the balcony was through a concrete wall. A hundred feet farther back, behind a second concrete wall, was another group of men, following the course of the experiments by remote control instruments and an intercommunication system. It was their task, if something should happen to those of us in the laboratory beside the reactor, to throw in the "safety rods" by remote control.

Fermi was conducting a systematic series of experiments, reading the meters as the final control rod was drawn out step by step. The results he plotted against his predictions. The data fitted his calculated line with remarkable precision, showing that as the critical condition for the sustained chain reaction was being approached no detectable new phenomenon was affecting the results. These preliminary tests were time-consuming and we adjourned for lunch.

It was the middle of the afternoon before the preliminary tests were completed. Finally Fermi gave Weil the order to draw out the control rod another foot. This we knew meant that the chain reaction should develop on an expanding scale.

The counters registering the rays from the pile began to click faster and faster until the sound became a rattle. I was watching both a recording meter and a galvanometer. I could see the light from the galvanometer begin to move across the scale. The line traced by the recording stylus was now curved upward. Finally after many minutes the meters showed a reading that meant the radiation reaching the balcony was beginning to be dangerous. "Throw in the safety rods," came Fermi's order. They went in with a clatter. The spot of light from the galvanometer moved back to zero. The rattle of the counters died down to an occasional click. I imagine that I can still hear the sigh of relief from the suicide squad. Eugene Wigner produced a bottle of Italian wine and gave it to Fermi. A little cheer went up.

Atomic power! It had been produced, kept under control, and stopped. The power liberated was less than that needed to light an electric lamp, but that power marked a new era in man's history.

Three faces in that little group stand sharply before me. There was Fermi, swarthy, alert, in as full control of his experimental crew as is the captain of a ship engaged in critical action. At this moment of great achievement his face showed no signs of elation. The experiment had worked precisely as expected. The theoretical calculations were confirmed, and that was that. Now we must get down to the hard work of making the tests needed for the design of the production reactor. This pile, now working, was for him an invaluable experimental tool. The men were weary from days and nights of continual, concentrated effort. To attempt new experiments now would be hazardous. Costly, perhaps dangerous, mistakes might be made.

"We'll call it a day," he announced. "Lock the control rods in the safety position and come back tomorrow morning. Then we'll start the new series of experiments." Cool, collected, Fermi's mind was not dwelling on the significance of what had just been done. He was laying his plans for the next urgent stage of the work.

Volney Wilson's face was troubled. Volney could have stood as a sculptor's model of lithe physical strength, under control and ready for action. But such men are often found to have the most sensitive human sympathies. He was among those who had sincerely hoped that, even at the last moment, something might arise which would make it impossible to effect the chain reaction. The destruction it implied was a nightmare with which he was finding it hard to live. Now the atomic reaction that he had foreseen — first of any of us at Chicago — was an accomplished fact, and the destruction that it portended seemed almost within sight. But Volney was a good soldier. He knew that if atomic weapons could be made we must be sure to have them first, and that his part was essential to our success. Volney Wilson would not fail his duty; but his face mirrored his inner conflict.

But most clearly I see the face of Crawford Greenewalt. His eyes were aglow. He had seen a miracle. Dark, tall, slender, with active imagination, his mind was swarming with ideas of how atomic energy could mean great things in the practical lives of men and women. As an industrial engineer, war at this moment was far from his mind. Here was a source of endless power that could warm people's homes, light their lamps, and turn the wheels of industry. Vast quantities of new radioactive materials would be available for who knew what great new advances in science. As we walked briskly through the cold December air, back across the campus, Greenewalt was telling me of these thoughts. As we rejoined the reviewing committee, Greenewalt did not need to say what he had seen. They could read it on his face.

When the committee had left, I picked up the phone and called Conant. He was reached at the President's office at Harvard University. "Jim," I said, "you'll be interested to know that the Italian navigator has just landed in the new world." Then, half apologetically, because I had led the S-1 Committee to believe that it would be another week or more before the pile could be completed, I added, "The earth was not as large as he had estimated, and he arrived at the new world sooner than he had expected."

"Is that so," was Conant's excited response. "Were the natives friendly?"

"Everyone landed safe and happy."

General Groves could not be reached. He was en route from the Pacific coast where he had been inspecting possible plant sites.

A fortnight later, within the du Pont councils with Colonel Nichols present, Charley Stine told the officers of the company that the production of plutonium was essential to the nation's safety. As Stine's words were reported to me, "du Pont is the only company that can do the task. We must do it, even though it may break the company."

The atmosphere was now one of confidence. The nuclear reaction was an accomplished fact. The Lewis committee had outlined a plan of action for proceeding with the entire atomic project. Du Pont's engineers had given a more reliable estimate of the magnitude of the task than had hitherto been possible. On this basis, in December 1942, Vannevar Bush and the Policy Committee reported to the President on what might be expected from the atomic project. In this report they gave a blueprint of the proposed procedure. With the best of luck we could hope for atomic bombs to be ready for use in the spring of 1945. With an average share of fortune's favors they should be ready by the summer of '45. We should surely be able to count on having the bombs ready, if they could be made at all, by the autumn of '45.

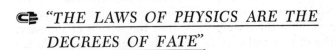

☞ "THE LAWS OF PHYSICS ARE THE DECREES OF FATE"

The Great Theory Tested

PHILIPP FRANK

FOR THE MATHEMATICIAN, Einstein's new conception of gravitation was characterized by beauty and logical simplicity. For the observational astronomer there still remained the disquieting doubt that all this might be mere fantasy. Newton's theory had served them well and it would require more than mathematical elegance to change their views. According to the astronomers, a solar eclipse was needed for the test.

New theories — to use a comparison that Einstein likes to employ — are comparable to beautiful dresses, which when displayed in a dressmaker's salon attract every feminine eye. A celebrated beauty orders this dress, but will it fit her? Will it add to or detract from her beauty? Not until she has worn it in the full glare of lights can she tell. Einstein's theory was a kind of unworn dress that had been in a shop window. The solar eclipse was the first affair at which it was to be worn.

While the war was still in progress, Einstein's papers on the general theory of relativity became known in England. The abstract discussion could be followed only with difficulty, and the new conceptions about motion in the universe could not yet be appreciated in all their logical implications. But their boldness was already admired. For the first time a well-founded proposal had been advanced to change the laws of the universe set up by Isaac Newton, England's pride.

For the English, with their tendency toward experimental verification, one thing was clear. A number of definite experiments had been pointed out to the observer of nature whose results could give decisive evaluation to the merits of the theory. And among these it was pre-eminently Einstein's prediction on the shift in the position of the stellar images during a total solar eclipse that made it possible to test his two theories, the Prague theory of 1911 and the Berlin theory of 1916. As early as March 1917 the Astronomer Royal had pointed out that on March 29, 1919, a total eclipse would take place that would offer unusually favorable conditions for testing Einstein's theories, since the darkened sun would be situated in the midst of a group of particularly bright stars, the Hyades.

Although at that time no one knew whether it would be possible to send expeditions to those regions of the earth where the observation of the total eclipse would be possible, the Royal Society and the Royal Astronomical Society of London appointed a committee to make preparations for an expedition. When the armistice was signed on November 11, 1918, the committee immediately set to work and announced the detailed plans for the expedition on March 27. The committee was headed by Sir Arthur Eddington, one of the few astronomers who were able at that time to delve deeply into the theoretical foundations of Einstein's theories. Eddington, moreover, was a Quaker who had always attached great importance to the maintenance of a friendly feeling between the people of "enemy" nations, and both during and after the war he did not join in the customary feeling of hate for the enemy. He also regarded all new theories about the universe as a means of strengthening religious feeling and of directing the attention of people away from individual and national egoism.

When the sun is eclipsed by the moon, there is only a certain zone on the earth's surface where the entire solar disc is darkened. Since there is the chance that the weather may be poor during the few minutes of darkness and thwart all plans of observation, the Royal Society sent two expeditions to widely separated points within the zone of total eclipse. One set out for Sobral in northern Brazil, while the second sailed for the isle of Principe in the Gulf of

Guinea, West Africa. Eddington was in personal charge of the second group.

When the expedition arrived in Brazil, it aroused not a little astonishment and something of a sensation. The war with Germany was hardly over, and the newspapers were still full of propaganda and counter-propaganda. These had not spared scientific activities, but yet here was a costly expedition coming from England to test the theories of a German scientist. A newspaper in Pará, Brazil, wrote: "Instead of trying to establish a German theory, the members of the expedition, who are well acquainted with the heavens, should rather try to obtain rain for the country, which has suffered from a long drought." The expedition was really in luck, since several days after its arrival it began to rain in Sobral. The savants had justified the public's confidence in science.

I shall not describe the observations made in Brazil, but merely those made by the group on the isle of Principe. The astronomers arrived a month before the date of the eclipse in order to set up their instruments and to make the necessary preparations. And then came the few minutes of total eclipse, with the disquieting uncertainty whether it would be possible to photograph the stars in the neighborhood of the darkened sun, or [if] the clouds would hide the stars and nullify the months of preparation. Sir Arthur Eddington gave the following description of these moments:

> On the day of the eclipse the weather was unfavorable. When totality began, the dark disc of the moon surrounded by the corona was visible through cloud, much as the moon often appears through cloud on a night when no stars can be seen. There was nothing for it but to carry out the arranged program and hope for the best. One observer was occupied changing the plates in rapid succession, whilst the other gave the exposures of the required length with a screen held in front of the object-glass to avoid shaking the telescope in any way.
>
> > For in and out, above, about, below,
> > 'Tis nothing but a Magic *Shadow*-show
> > Played in a Box whose candle is the Sun
> > Round which we Phantom Figures come and go.
>
> Our shadow box takes up all our attention. There is a marvelous spectacle above and as the photographs afterward revealed, a wonderful prominence flame is poised a hundred thousand miles above the surface of the sun. We have not time to snatch a glance at it. We are conscious only of the weird half-light of the

landscape and the hush of nature, broken by the calls of the observers and the beat of the metronome ticking out the 302 seconds of totality.

Sixteen photographs were obtained, with exposures ranging from 2 to 20 seconds. The earlier photographs showed no stars . . . but apparently the cloud lightened toward the end of totality, and a few images appeared on the later plates. In many cases one or the other of the most essential stars was missing through cloud, and no use could be made of them; but one plate was found showing fairly good images of five stars, which were suitable for a determination.

Tense with excitement, Eddington and his collaborators compared the best of the pictures that they had obtained with photographs of the same stars taken in London, where they were far removed from the sun and therefore not exposed to its direct gravitational effect. There actually was a shift of the stellar images away from the sun corresponding to a deflection of the light rays approximately as large as that expected on the basis of Einstein's new theory of 1916.

It was quite a few months, however, before the expeditions had returned to England and the photographic plates were carefully measured in the laboratory, taking into consideration all possible errors. These errors were what actually worried the experts. Around them revolved the discussions in astronomical circles, while the lay public was interested, and could only be interested, in the question whether the observations had demonstrated the "weight of light" or the "curvature of space." The latter was even more exciting since hardly anyone could imagine anything very definite under the phrase "curvature of space."

On November 7, 1919, London was preparing to observe the first anniversary of the armistice. The headlines in the London *Times* were: "THE GLORIOUS DEAD. ARMISTICE OBSERVANCE. ALL TRAINS IN THE COUNTRY STOP." On the same day, however, the *Times* also contained another headline: "REVOLUTION IN SCIENCE. NEWTONIAN IDEAS OVERTHROWN." It referred to the session of the Royal Society on November 6, at which the results of the solar-eclipse expedition were officially announced.

The Royal Society and the Royal Astronomical Society of London had convened a combined session for November 6 to make the formal announcement that the expeditions that had been dispatched by these societies to Brazil and West Africa to observe the total solar eclipse had from their observations reached the conclusion that the rays of light are deflected in the sun's gravitational field and to just the amount predicted by Einstein's new theory of gravitation. This remarkable agreement between a creation of the human mind and the astronomical observations gave the session a wonderful and exciting atmosphere. We have an eyewitness account of this meeting (see below) by one of the most highly regarded philosophers of our time, Alfred North Whitehead. As a mathematician, logician, philosopher, and a man endowed with a fine historical and religious sense, he was better suited to experience the uniqueness of this hour than most scientists. . . .

The psychological situation in Europe at this time increased the interest of the general public in Einstein's theory. English newspapers tried to efface every connection between Germany and the man whom they were honoring. Einstein himself was averse to any tactics of this kind, not because he placed any value on being regarded as a representative of German science, but because he hated every manifestation of narrow-minded nationalism. He also believed that he could advance the cause of international conciliation if he utilized his fame for this purpose. When the *Times* requested him to describe the results of his theory for the London public, he did so on November 28 and used this opportunity to express his opinion in a friendly, humorous way. He wrote:

> The description of me and my circumstances in the *Times* shows an amusing flare of imagination of the part of the writer. By an application of the theory of relativity to the taste of the reader, today in Germany I am called a German man of science and in England I am represented as a Swiss Jew. If I come to be regarded as a "bête noire" the description will be reversed, and I shall become a Swiss Jew for the Germans and a German for the English.

The Order of Nature

ALFRED NORTH WHITEHEAD

. . . THE PILGRIM FATHERS of the scientific imagination as it exists today are the great tragedians of ancient Athens, Aeschylus, Sophocles, Euripides. Their vision of Fate, remorseless and indifferent, urging a tragic incident to its inevitable issue, is the vision possessed by science. Fate in Greek tragedy becomes the order of nature in modern thought. The absorbing interest in the particular heroic incidents, as an example and a verification of the workings of Fate, reappears in our epoch as concentration of interest on the crucial experiments. . . .

It was my good fortune to be present at the meeting of the Royal Society in London when the Astronomer Royal for England announced that the photographic plates of the famous eclipse, as measured by his colleagues in Greenwich Observatory, had verified the prediction of Einstein that rays of light are bent as they pass in the neighborhood of the sun. The whole atmosphere of tense interest was exactly that of the Greek drama: we were the chorus commenting on the decree of Destiny as disclosed in the development of a supreme incident. There was dramatic quality in the very staging: the traditional ceremonial, and in the background the picture of Newton to remind us that the greatest of scientific generalizations was now, after more than two centuries, to receive its first modification. Nor was the personal interest wanting: a great adventure in thought had at length come safe to shore.

Let me here remind you that the essence of dramatic tragedy is not unhappiness. It resides in the solemnity of the remorseless working of things. This inevitableness of Destiny can only be illustrated in terms of human life by incidents which in fact involve unhappiness. For it is only by them that the futility of escape can be made evident in the drama. This remorseless inevitableness is what pervades scientific thought. The laws of physics are the decrees of Fate.

Self-Portrait

ALBERT EINSTEIN

OF WHAT IS SIGNIFICANT in one's own existence one is hardly aware, and it certainly should not bother the other fellow. What does a fish know about the water in which he swims all his life?

The bitter and the sweet come from the outside, the hard from within, from one's own efforts. For the most part I do the thing which my own nature drives me to do. It is embarrassing to earn so much respect and love for it. Arrows of hate have been shot at me, too; but they never hit me, because somehow they belonged to another world, with which I have no connection whatsoever.

I live in that solitude which is painful in youth, but delicious in the years of maturity.

From *Out of My Later Years* by Albert Einstein. Reprinted by permission of the Estate of Albert Einstein.

$E = mc^2$

MORRIS BISHOP

What was our trust, we trust not,
    What was our faith, we doubt;
Whether we must or must not
    We may debate about.
The soul perhaps is a gust of gas
    And wrong is a form of right—
But we know that Energy equals Mass
    By the Square of the Speed of Light.

What we have known, we know not,
    What we have proved, abjure.
Life is a tangled bow-knot,
    But one thing still is sure.
Come, little lad; come, little lass;
    Your docile creed recite:
"We believe that Energy equals Mass
    By the Square of the Speed of Light."

By permission of the Dial Press, publishers of *A Bowl of Bishop* by Morris Bishop.

3

Monuments of Method

Science

Studying the shadow of motion,
The pulses of space, the hours of the star-ocean,
We bring the world to the soul. Let them not say
That deed is sterile. How should our divorced dust
Return to us, but so? Since a man must
Be torment, moisture, pity, and decay,
Seepage, and ruin! Sweep, antennaed notion,
The untunneled dark dimensionless commotion,
Build breathing hills in the eternal clay,
And let earth pulse with you. Long has your rust
Enriched her crimsoned crust.

THE MAN OF SCIENCE

◇◇◇◇◇◇◇◇◇◇◇◇◇◇◇◇◇◇◇◇◇◇◇◇◇◇◇◇◇◇◇◇◇◇◇◇◇

*Sit down before fact as a little child, be prepared to give
up every preconceived notion, follow humbly wherever
and to whatever abysses nature leads, or you shall learn
nothing.*

— T. H. Huxley

The Blood of the Martyrs

STEPHEN VINCENT BENÉT

THE MAN who expected to be shot lay with his eyes open,
staring at the upper left-hand corner of his cell. He was fairly well
over his last beating, and they might come for him any time now.
There was a yellow stain in the cell corner near the ceiling; he had
liked it at first, then disliked it; now he was coming back to liking it.

He could see it more clearly with his glasses on, but he only put
on his glasses for special occasions now — the first thing in the
morning, and when they brought the food in, and for interviews
with the General. The lenses of the glasses had been cracked in a
beating some months before, and it strained his eyes to wear them
too long. Fortunately, in his present life he had very few occasions
demanding clear vision. But, nevertheless, the accident to his
glasses worried him, as it worries all nearsighted people. You put
your glasses on the first thing in the morning and the world leaps
into proportion; if it does not do so, something is wrong with the
world.

The man did not believe greatly in symbols, but his chief nightmare, nowadays, was an endless one in which, suddenly and without warning, a large piece of glass would drop out of one of the
lenses and he would grope around the cell, trying to find out. He
would grope very carefully and gingerly, for hours of darkness, but
the end was always the same — the small, unmistakable crunch of
irreplaceable glass beneath his heel or his knee. Then he would

wake up sweating, with his hands cold. This dream alternated with
the one of being shot, but he found no great benefit in the change.

As he lay there, you could see that he had an intellectual head
— the head of a thinker or a scholar, old and bald, with the big,
domed brow. It was, as a matter of fact, a well-known head; it had
often appeared in the columns of newspapers and journals, sometimes when the surrounding text was in a language Professor Malzius could not read. The body, though stooped and worn, was still a
strong peasant body and capable of surviving a good deal of ill-
treatment, as his captors had found out. He had fewer teeth than
when he came to prison, and both the ribs and the knee had been
badly set, but these were minor matters. It also occurred to him that
his blood count was probably poor. However, if he could ever get
out and to a first-class hospital, he was probably good for at least
ten years more of work. But, of course, he would not get out. They
would shoot him before that, and it would be over.

Sometimes he wished passionately that it would be over — tonight — this moment; at other times he was shaken by the mere
blind fear of death. The latter he tried to treat as he would have
treated an attack of malaria, knowing that it was an attack, but not
always with success. He should have been able to face it better than
most — he was Gregor Malzius, the scientist — but that did not always help. The fear of death persisted, even when one had noted
and classified it as a purely physical reaction. When he was out of
here, he would be able to write a very instructive little paper on the
fear of death. He could even do it here, if he had writing materials,
but there was no use asking for those. Once they had been given
him and he had spent two days quite happily. But they had torn up
the work and spat upon it in front of his face. It was a childish thing
to do, but it discouraged a man from working.

It seemed odd that he had never seen anybody shot, but he
never had. During the war, his reputation and his bad eyesight had
exempted him from active service. He had been bombed a couple
of times when his reserve battalion was guarding the railway
bridge, but that was quite different. You were not tied to a stake,
and the airplanes were not trying to kill you as an individual. He
knew the place where it was done here, of course. But prisoners did
not see the executions, they merely heard, if the wind was from the
right quarter.

He had tried again and again to visualize how it would be, but it
always kept mixing with an old steel engraving he had seen in boy-
hood — the execution of William Walker, the American filibuster,
in Honduras. William Walker was a small man with a white semi-
Napoleonic face. He was standing, very correctly dressed, in front

of an open grave, and before him a ragged line of picturesque natives were raising their muskets. When he was shot he would instantly and tidily fall into the grave, like a man dropping through a trap door; as a boy, the extreme neatness of the arrangement had greatly impressed Gregor Malzius. Behind the wall there were palm trees, and, somewhere off to the right, blue and warm, the Caribbean Sea. It would not be like that at all, for his own execution; and yet, whenever he thought of it, he thought of it as being like that.

Well, it was his own fault. He could have accepted the new regime; some respectable people had done that. He could have fled the country; many honorable people had. A scientist should be concerned with the eternal, not with transient political phenomena; and a scientist should be able to live anywhere. But thirty years at the university were thirty years, and, after all, he was Malzius, one of the first biochemists in the world. To the last, he had not believed that they would touch him. Well, he had been wrong about that.

The truth, of course, was the truth. One taught it or one did not teach it. If one did not teach it, it hardly mattered what one did. But he had no quarrel with any established government; he was willing to run up a flag every Tuesday, as long as they let him alone. Most people were fools, and one government was as good as another for them — it had taken them twenty years to accept his theory of cell mutation. Now, if he'd been like his friend Bonnard — a fellow who signed protests, attended meetings for the cause of world peace, and generally played the fool in public — they'd have had some reason to complain. An excellent man in his field, Bonnard — none better — but, outside of it, how deplorably like an actor, with his short gray beard, his pink cheeks and his impulsive enthusiasm! Any government could put a fellow like Bonnard in prison — though it would be an injury to science and, therefore, wrong. For that matter, he thought grimly, Bonnard would enjoy being a martyr. He'd walk gracefully to the execution post with a begged cigarette in his mouth, and some theatrical last quip. But Bonnard was safe in his own land — doubtless writing heated and generous articles on The Case of Professor Malzius — and he, Malzius, was the man who was going to be shot. He would like a cigarette, too, on his way to execution; he had not smoked in five months. But he certainly didn't intend to ask for one, and they wouldn't think of offering him any. That was the difference between him and Bonnard.

His mind went back with longing to the stuffy laboratory and stuffier lecture hall at the university; his feet yearned for the worn steps he had climbed ten thousand times, and his eyes for the long steady look through the truthful lens into worlds too tiny for the

unaided eye. They had called him "The Bear" and "Old Prickly,"
but they had fought to work under him, the best of the young men.
They said he would explain the Last Judgment in terms of cellular
phenomena, but they had crowded to his lectures. It was Williams,
the Englishman, who had made up the legend that he carried a
chocolate éclair . . . in his battered brief case. Quite untrue, of
course — chocolate always made him ill. . . . And Williams would
never know that he knew the legend, too; for Williams had been
killed long ago in the war. For a moment, Professor Malzius felt
blind hate at the thought of an excellent scientific machine like Williams being smashed in a war. But blind hate was an improper
emotion for a scientist, and he put it aside.

He smiled grimly again; they hadn't been able to break up his
classes — lucky he was The Bear! He'd seen one colleague hooted
from his desk by a band of determined young hoodlums — too bad,
but if a man couldn't keep order in his own classroom, he'd better
get out. They'd wrecked his own laboratory, but not while he was
there.

It was so senseless, so silly. "In God's name," he said reasonably,
to no one, "what sort of conspirator do you think I would make? A
man of my age and habits! I am interested in cellular phenomena!"
And yet they were beating him because he would not tell about the
boys. As if he had even paid attention to half the nonsense! There
were certain passwords and greetings — a bar of music you
whistled, entering a restaurant; the address of a firm that specialized, ostensibly, in vacuum cleaners. But they were not his own
property. They belonged to the young men who had trusted The
Bear. He did not know what half of them meant, and the one time
he had gone to a meeting, he had felt like a fool. For they were fools
and childish — playing the childish games of conspiracy that people
like Bonnard enjoyed. Could they even make a better world than
the present? He doubted it extremely. And yet, he could not betray
them; they had come to him, looking over their shoulders, with
darkness in their eyes.

A horrible, an appalling thing — to be trusted. He had no wish
to be a guide and counselor of young men. He wanted to do his
work. Suppose they were poor and ragged and oppressed; he had
been a peasant himself, he had eaten black bread. It was by his own
efforts that he was Professor Malzius. He did not wish the confi-
dences of boys like Gregopolous and the others — for, after all,
what was Gregopolous? An excellent and untiring laboratory assistant — and a laboratory assistant he would remain to the end of
his days. He had pattered about the laboratory, like a fox terrier,
with a fox terrier's quick bright eyes. Like a devoted dog, he had

made a god of Professor Malzius. "I don't want your problems, man. I don't want to know what you are doing outside the laboratory." But Gregopolous had brought his problems and his terrible trust none the less, humbly and proudly, like a fox terrier with a bone. After that — well, what was a man to do?

He hoped they would get it over with, and quickly. The world should be like a chemical formula, full of reason and logic. Instead, there were all these young men, and their eyes. They conspired, hopelessly and childishly, for what they called freedom against the new regime. They wore no overcoats in winter and were often hunted and killed. Even if they did not conspire, they had miserable little love affairs and ate the wrong food — yes, even before, at the university, they had been the same. Why the devil would they not accept? Then they could do their work. Of course, a great many of them would not be allowed to accept — they had the wrong ideas or the wrong politics — but then they could run away. If Malzius, at twenty, had had to run from his country, he would still have been a scientist. To talk of a free world was a delusion; men were not free in the world. Those who wished got a space of time to get their work done. That was all. And yet, he had not accepted — he did not know why.

Now he heard the sound of steps along the corridor. His body began to quiver and the places where he had been beaten hurt him. He noted it as an interesting reflex. Sometimes they merely flashed the light in the cell and passed by. On the other hand, it might be death. It was a hard question to decide.

The lock creaked, the door opened. "Get up, Malzius!" said the hard, bright voice of the guard. Gregor Malzius got up, a little stiffly, but quickly.

"Put on your glasses, you old fool!" said the guard, with a laugh. "You are going to the General."

Professor Malzius found the stone floors of the corridor uneven, though he knew them well enough. Once or twice the guard struck him, lightly and without malice, as one strikes an old horse with a whip. The blows were familiar and did not register on Professor Malzius' consciousness; he merely felt proud of not stumbling. He was apt to stumble; once he had hurt his knee.

He noticed, it seemed to him, an unusual tenseness and officiousness about his guard. Once, even, in a brightly lighted corridor, the guard moved to strike him, but refrained. However, that, too, happened occasionally, with one guard or another, and Professor Malzius merely noted the fact. It was a small fact, but an important one in the economy in which he lived.

But there could be no doubt that something unusual was going on in the castle. There were more guards than usual, many of them strangers. He tried to think, carefully, as he walked, if it could be one of the new national holidays. It was hard to keep track of them all. The General might be in a good humor. Then they would merely have a cat-and-mouse conversation for half an hour and nothing really bad would happen. Once, even, there had been a cigar. Professor Malzius, the scientist, licked his lips at the thought.

Now he was being turned over to a squad of other guards, with salutings. This was really unusual; Professor Malzius bit his mouth, inconspicuously. He had the poignant distrust of a monk or an old prisoner at any break in routine. Old prisoners are your true conservatives; they only demand that the order around them remain exactly the same.

It alarmed him as well that the new guards did not laugh at him. New guards almost always laughed when they saw him for the first time. He was used to the laughter and missed it — his throat felt dry. He would have liked, just once, to eat at the university restaurant before he died. It was bad food, ill cooked and starchy, food good enough for poor students and professors, but he would have liked to be there, in the big smoky room that smelled of copper boilers and cabbage, with a small cup of bitter coffee before him and a cheap cigarette. He did not ask for his dog or his notebooks, the old photographs in his bedroom, his incomplete experiments or his freedom. Just to lunch once more at the university restaurant and have people point out The Bear. It seemed a small thing to ask, but of course it was quite impossible.

"Halt!" said a voice, and he halted. There were, for the third time, salutings. Then the door of the General's office opened and he was told to go in.

He stood, just inside the door, in the posture of attention, as he had been taught. The crack in the left lens of his glasses made a crack across the room, and his eyes were paining him already, but he paid no attention to that. There was the familiar figure of the General, with his air of a well-fed and extremely healthy tomcat, and there was another man, seated at the General's desk. He could not see the other man very well — the crack made him bulge and waver — but he did not like his being there.

"Well, professor," said the General, in an easy, purring voice.

Malzius' entire body jerked. He had made a fearful, an unpardonable omission. He must remedy it at once. "Long live the state," he shouted in a loud thick voice, and saluted. He knew, bitterly, that his salute was ridiculous and that he looked ridiculous, making it. But perhaps the General would laugh — he had done so before. Then everything would be all right, for it was not quite as easy to beat a man after you had laughed at him.

The General did not laugh. He made a half-turn instead, toward the man at the desk. The gesture said, "You see, he is well trained." It was the gesture of a man of the world, accustomed to deal with unruly peasants and animals — the gesture of a man fitted to be General.

The man at the desk paid no attention to the General's gesture. He lifted his head, and Malzius saw him more clearly and with complete unbelief. It was not a man but a picture come alive. Professor Malzius had seen the picture a hundred times; they had made him salute and take off his hat in front of it, when he had had a hat. Indeed, the picture had presided over his beatings. The man himself was a little smaller, but the picture was a good picture. There were many dictators in the world, and this was one type. The face was white, beaky and semi-Napoleonic; the lean, military body sat squarely in its chair. The eyes dominated the face, and the mouth was rigid. I remember also a hypnotist, and a woman Charcot showed me, at his clinic in Paris, thought Professor Malzius. But there is also, obviously, an endocrine unbalance. Then his thoughts stopped.

"Tell the man to come closer," said the man at the desk. "Can he hear me? Is he deaf?"

"No, Your Excellency," said the General, with enormous, purring respect. "But he is a little old, though perfectly healthy. . . . Are you not, Professor Malzius?"

"Yes, I am perfectly healthy. I am very well treated here," said Professor Malzius, in his loud thick voice. They were not going to catch him with traps like that, not even by dressing up somebody as the Dictator. He fixed his eyes on the big old-fashioned inkwell on the General's desk — that, at least, was perfectly sane.

"Come closer," said the man at the desk to Professor Malzius, and the latter advanced till he could almost touch the inkwell with his fingers. Then he stopped with a jerk, hoping he had done right. The movement removed the man at the desk from the crack in his lenses, and Professor Malzius knew suddenly that it was true. This was, indeed, the Dictator, this man with the rigid mouth. He began to talk.

"I have been very well treated here and the General has acted with the greatest consideration," he said. "But I am Professor Gregor Malzius — professor of biochemistry. For thirty years I have lectured at the university; I am a fellow of the Royal Society, a corresponding member of the Academy of Sciences at Berlin, at Rome, at

Boston, at Paris and Stockholm. I have received the Nottingham Medal, the Lamarck Medal, the Order of St. John of Portugal and the Nobel Prize. I think my blood count is low, but I have received a great many degrees and my experiments on the migratory cells are not finished. I do not wish to complain of my treatment, but I must finish my experiments."

He stopped, like a clock that has run down, surprised to hear the sound of his own voice. He noted, in one part of his mind, that the General had made a move to silence him, but had himself been silenced by the Dictator.

"Yes, Professor Malzius," said the man at the desk, in a harsh, toneless voice. "There has been a regrettable error." The rigid face stared at Professor Malzius. Professor Malzius stared back. He did not say anything.

"In these days," said the Dictator, his voice rising, "the nation demands the submission of every citizen. Encircled by jealous foes, our reborn land yet steps forward toward her magnificent destiny." The words continued for some time, the voice rose and fell. Professor Malzius listened respectfully; he had heard the words many times before and they had ceased to have meaning for him. He was thinking of certain cells of the body that rebel against the intricate processes of Nature and set up their own bellicose state. Doubtless they, too, have a destiny, he thought, but in medicine it is called cancer.

"Jealous and spiteful tongues in other countries have declared that it is our purpose to wipe out learning and science," concluded the Dictator. "That is not our purpose. After the cleansing, the rebirth. We mean to move forward to the greatest science in the world — our own science, based on the enduring principles of our nationhood." He ceased abruptly, his eyes fell into their dream. Very like the girl Charcot showed me in my young days, thought Professor Malzius; there was first the ebullition, then the calm.

"I was part of the cleansing? You did not mean to hurt me?" he asked timidly.

"Yes, Professor Malzius," said the General, smiling, "you were part of the cleansing. Now that is over. His Excellency has spoken."

"I do not understand," said Professor Malzius, gazing at the fixed face of the man behind the desk.

"It is very simple," said the General. He spoke in a slow careful voice, as one speaks to a deaf man or a child. "You are a distinguished man of science — you have received the Nobel Prize. That was a service to the state. You became, however, infected by the wrong political ideas. That was treachery to the state. You had, therefore, as decreed by His Excellency, to pass through a certain period for probation and rehabilitation. But that, we believe, is finished."

"You do not wish to know the names of the young men any more?" said Professor Malzius. "You do not want the addresses?"

"That is no longer of importance," said the General patiently. "There is no longer opposition. The leaders were caught and executed three weeks ago."

"There is no longer opposition," repeated Professor Malzius.

"At the trial, you were not even involved."

"I was not even involved," said Professor Malzius. "Yes."

"Now," said the General, with a look at the Dictator, "we come to the future. I will be frank — the new state is frank with its citizens."

"It is so," said the Dictator, his eyes still sunk in his dream.

"There has been — let us say — a certain agitation in foreign countries regarding Professor Malzius," said the General, his eyes still fixed on the Dictator. "That means nothing, of course. Nevertheless, your acquaintance, Professor Bonnard, and others have meddled in matters that do not concern them."

"They asked after me?" said Professor Malzius, with surprise. "It is true, my experiments were reaching a point that —"

"No foreign influence would turn us from our firm purpose," said the Dictator. "But it is our firm purpose to show our nation first in science and culture as we have already shown her first in manliness and statehood. For that reason, you are here, Professor Malzius." He smiled.

Professor Malzius stared. His cheeks began to tremble.

"I do not understand," said Professor Malzius. "You will give me my laboratory back?"

"Yes," said the Dictator, and the General nodded as one nods to a stupid child.

Professor Malzius passed a hand across his brow.

"My post at the university?" he said. "My experiments?"

"It is the purpose of our regime to offer the fullest encouragement to our loyal sons of science," said the Dictator.

"First of all," said Professor Malzius, "I must go to a hospital. My blood count is poor. But that will not take long." His voice had become impatient and his eyes glowed. "Then — my notebooks were burned, I suppose. That was silly, but we can start in again. I have a very good memory, an excellent memory. The theories are in my head, you know," and he tapped it. "I must have assistants, of course; little Gregopolous was my best one —"

"The man Gregopolous has been executed," said the General, in a stern voice. "You had best forget him."

"Oh," said Professor Malzius. "Well, then, I must have someone else. You see, these are important experiments. There must be some young men — clever ones — they cannot all be dead. I will know them." He laughed a little, nervously. "They used to call me The Bear, you know." He stopped and looked at them for a moment with ghastly eyes. "You are not fooling me?" he said. He burst into tears.

When he recovered he was alone in the room with the General. The General was looking at him as he himself had looked once at strange forms of life under the microscope, with neither disgust nor attraction, but with great interest.

"His Excellency forgives your unworthy suggestion," he said. "He knows you are overwrought."

"Yes," said Professor Malzius. He sobbed once and dried his glasses.

"Come, come," said the General, with a certain bluff heartiness. "We mustn't have our new president of the National Academy crying. It would look badly in the photographs."

"President of the Academy?" said Professor Malzius quickly. "Oh, no; I mustn't be that. They make speeches; they have administrative work. But I am a scientist, a teacher."

"I'm afraid you can't very well avoid it," said the General, still heartily, though he looked at Professor Malzius. "Your induction will be quite a ceremony. His Excellency himself will preside. And you will speak on the new glories of our science. It will be a magnificent answer to the petty and jealous criticisms of our neighbors. Oh, you needn't worry about the speech," he added quickly. "It will be prepared; you will only have to read it. His Excellency thinks of everything."

"Very well," said Professor Malzius; "and then may I go back to my work?"

"Oh, don't worry about that," said the General, smiling. "I'm only a simple soldier; I don't know about those things. But you'll have plenty of work."

"The more the better," said Malzius eagerly. "I still have ten good years."

He opened his mouth to smile, and a shade of dismay crossed the General's face.

"Yes," he said, as if to himself. "The teeth must be attended to. At once. And a rest, undoubtedly, before the photographs are taken. Milk. You are feeling sufficiently well, Professor Malzius?"

"I am very happy," said Professor Malzius. "I have been very well treated and I come of peasant stock."

"Good," said the General. He paused for a moment, and spoke in a more official voice.

"Of course, it is understood, Professor Malzius —" he said.

"Yes?" said Professor Malzius. "I beg your pardon. I was thinking of something else."

"It is understood, Professor Malzius," repeated the General, "that your — er — rehabilitation in the service of the state is a permanent matter. Naturally, you will be under observation, but, even so, there must be no mistake."

"I am a scientist," said Professor Malzius impatiently. "What have I to do with politics? If you wish me to take oaths of loyalty, I will take as many as you wish."

"I am glad you take that attitude," said the General, though he looked at Professor Malzius curiously. "I may say that I regret the unpleasant side of our interviews. I trust you bear no ill will."

"Why should I be angry?" said Professor Malzius. "You were told to do one thing. Now you are told to do another. That is all."

"It is not quite as simple as that," said the General rather stiffly. He looked at Professor Malzius for a third time. "And I'd have sworn you were one of the stiff-necked ones," he said. "Well, well, every man has his breaking point, I suppose. In a few moments you will receive the final commands of His Excellency. Tonight you will go to the capital and speak over the radio. You will have no difficulty there — the speech is written. But it will put a quietus on the activities of our friend Bonnard and the question that has been raised in the British Parliament. Then a few weeks of rest by the sea and dental work, and then, my dear president of the National Academy, you will be ready to undertake your new duties. I congratulate you and hope we shall meet often under pleasant auspices." He bowed from the waist to Malzius, the bow of a man of the world, though there was still something feline in his mustache. Then he stood to attention, and Malzius, too, for the Dictator had come into the room.

"It is settled?" said the Dictator. "Good. Gregor Malzius, I welcome you to the service of the new state. You have cast your errors aside and are part of our destiny."

"Yes," said Professor Malzius, "I will be able to do my work now."

The Dictator frowned a little.

"You will not only be able to continue your invaluable researches," he said, "but you will also be able — and it will be a part of your duty — to further our national ideals. Our reborn nation must rule the world for the world's good. There is a fire within us

that is not in other stocks. Our civilization must be extended everywhere. The future wills it. It will furnish the subject of your first
discourse as president of the Academy."

"But," said Professor Malzius, in a low voice, "I am not a soldier.
I am a biochemist. I have no experience in these matters you speak
of."

The Dictator nodded. "You are a distinguished man of science,"
he said. "You will prove that our women must bear soldiers, our
men abandon this nonsense of republics and democracies for trust
in those born to rule them. You will prove by scientific law that certain races — our race in particular — are destined to rule the world.
You will prove they are destined to rule by the virtues of war, and
that war is part of our heritage."

"But," said Professor Malzius, "it is not like that. I mean," he
said, "one looks and watches in the laboratory. One waits for a long
time. It is a long process, very long. And then, if the theory is not
proved, one discards the theory. That is the way it is done. I probably do not explain it well. But I am a biochemist; I do not know
how to look for the virtues of one race against another, and I can
prove nothing about war, except that it kills. If I said anything else,
the whole world would laugh at me."

"Not one in this nation would laugh at you," said the Dictator.

"But if they do not laugh at me when I am wrong, there is no
science," said Professor Malzius, knotting his brows. He paused. "Do
not misunderstand me," he said earnestly. "I have ten years of good
work left; I want to get back to my laboratory. But, you see, there
are the young men — if I am to teach the young men."

He paused again, seeing their faces before him. There were
many. There was Williams, the Englishman, who had died in the
war, and little Gregopolous with the fox terrier eyes. There were
all who had passed through his classrooms, from the stupidest to the
best. They had shot little Gregopolous for treason, but that did not
alter the case. From all over the world they had come — he remembered the Indian student and the Chinese. They wore cheap overcoats, they were hungry for knowledge, they ate the bad, starchy
food of the poor restaurants, they had miserable little love affairs
and played childish games of politics, instead of doing their work.
Nevertheless, a few were promising — all must be given the truth.
It did not matter if they died, but they must be given the truth.
Otherwise there could be no continuity and no science.

He looked at the Dictator before him — yes, it was a hysteric
face. He would know how to deal with it in his classroom — but
such faces should not rule countries or young men. One was willing
to go through a great many meaningless ceremonies in order to do

one's work — wear a uniform or salute or be president of the Academy. That did not matter; it was part of the due to Caesar. But not to tell lies to young men on one's own subject. After all, they had called him The Bear. . . . They had given him their terrible confidence — not for love or kindness, but because they had found him honest. It was too late to change.

The Dictator looked sharply at the General. "I thought this had been explained to Professor Malzius," he said.

"Why, yes," said Professor Malzius. "I will sign any papers. I assure you I am not interested in politics — a man like myself, imagine! One state is as good as another. And I miss my tobacco — I have not smoked in five months. But, you see, one cannot be a scientist and tell lies."

He looked at the two men.

"What happens if I do not?" he said, in a low voice. But, looking at the Dictator, he had his answer. It was a fanatic face.

"Why, we shall resume our conversations, Professor Malzius," said the General, with a simper.

"Then I shall be beaten again," said Professor Malzius. He stated what he knew to be a fact.

"The process of rehabilitation is obviously not quite complete," said the General, "but perhaps, in time —"

"It will not be necessary," said Professor Malzius. "I cannot be beaten again." He stared wearily around the room. His shoulders straightened — it was so he had looked in the classroom when they had called him The Bear. "Call your other officers in," he said in a clear voice. "There are papers for me to sign. I should like them all to witness."

"Why —" said the General. "Why —" He looked doubtfully at the Dictator.

An expression of gratification appeared on the lean, semi-Napoleonic face. A white hand, curiously limp, touched the hand of Professor Malzius.

"You will feel so much better, Gregor," said the hoarse, tense voice. "I am so very glad you have given in."

"Why, of course, I give in," said Gregor Malzius. "Are you not the Dictator? And besides, if I do not, I shall be beaten again. And I cannot — you understand? — I cannot be beaten again."

He paused, breathing a little. But already the room was full of other faces. He knew them well, the hard faces of the new regime. But youthful some of them too.

The Dictator was saying something with regard to receiving the distinguished scientist, Professor Gregor Malzius, into the service of the state.

"Take the pen," said the General in an undertone. "The inkwell is there, Professor Malzius. Now you may sign."

Professor Malzius stood, his fingers gripping the big, old-fashioned inkwell. It was full of ink — the servants of the Dictator were very efficient. They could shoot small people with the eyes of fox terriers for treason, but their trains arrived on time and their inkwells did not run dry.

"The state," he said, breathing. "Yes. But science does not know about states. And you are a little man — a little, unimportant man."

Then, before the General could stop him, he had picked up the inkwell and thrown it in the Dictator's face. The next moment the General's fist caught him on the side of the head and he fell behind the desk to the floor. But lying there, through his cracked glasses, he could still see the grotesque splashes of ink on the Dictator's face and uniform, and the small cut above his eye where the blood was gathering. They had not fired; he had thought he would be too close to the Dictator for them to fire in time.

"Take that man out and shoot him. At once," said the Dictator in a dry voice. He did not move to wipe the stains from his uniform — and for that Professor Malzius admired him. They rushed then, each anxious to be first. But Professor Malzius made no resistance.

As he was being hustled along the corridors, he fell now and then. On the second fall, his glasses were broken completely, but that did not matter to him. They were in a great hurry, he thought, but all the better — one did not have to think while one could not see.

Now and then he heard his voice make sounds of discomfort, but his voice was detached from himself. There was little Gregopolous — he could see him very plainly — and Williams, with his fresh English coloring — and all the men whom he had taught.

He had given them nothing but work and the truth; they had given him their terrible trust. If he had been beaten again, he might have betrayed them. But he had avoided that.

He felt a last weakness — a wish that someone might know. They would not, of course; he would have died of typhoid in the castle and there would be regretful notices in the newspapers. And then he would be forgotten, except for his work, and that was as it should be. He had never thought much of martyrs — hysterical people in the main. Though he'd like Bonnard to have known about the ink; it was in the coarse vein of humor that Bonnard could not appreciate. But then, he was a peasant; Bonnard had often told him so.

They were coming out into the open courtyard now; he felt the fresh air of outdoors. "Gently," he said. "A little gently. What's the haste?" But already they were tying him to the post. Someone struck him in the face and his eyes watered. "A schoolboy covered with ink," he muttered through his lost teeth. "A hysterical schoolboy, too. But you cannot kill truth."

They were not good last words, and he knew that they were not. He must try to think of better ones — not shame Bonnard. But now they had a gag in his mouth; just as well; it saved him the trouble.

His body ached, bound against the post, but his sight and his mind were clearer. He could make out the evening sky, gray with fog, the sky that belonged to no country, but to all the world.

He could make out the gray high buttress of the castle. They had made it a jail, but it would not always be a jail. Perhaps in time it would not even exist. But if a little bit of truth were gathered, that would always exist, while there were men to remember and rediscover it. It was only the liars and the cruel who always failed.

Sixty years ago, he had been a little boy, eating black bread and thin cabbage soup in a poor house. It has been a bitter life; but he could not complain of it. He had had some good teachers and they had called him The Bear.

The gag hurt his mouth — they were getting ready now. There had been a girl called Anna once; he had almost forgotten her. And his rooms had smelled a certain way and he had had a dog. It did not matter what they did with the medals. He raised his head and looked once more at the gray foggy sky. In a moment there would be no thought, but, while there was thought, one must remember and note. His pulse rate was lower than he would have expected and his breathing oddly even, but these were not the important things. The important thing was beyond, in the gray sky that had no country, in the stones of the earth and the feeble human spirit. The important thing was truth.

"Ready!" called the officer. "Aim! Fire!" But Professor Malzius did not hear the three commands of the officer. He was thinking about the young men.

Portrait of a Scientist

SINCLAIR LEWIS

MAX GOTTLIEB was a German Jew, born in Saxony in 1850.
Though he took his medical degree, at Heidelberg, he was never
interested in practicing medicine. He was a follower of Helmholtz,
and youthful researches in the physics of sound convinced him of
the need of the quantitative method in the medical sciences. Then
Koch's discoveries drew him into biology. Always an elaborately
careful worker, a maker of long rows of figures, always realizing the
presence of uncontrollable variables, always a vicious assailant of
what he considered slackness or lie or pomposity, never too kindly
to well-intentioned stupidity, he worked in the laboratories of Koch,
of Pasteur, he followed the early statements of Pearson in biomet-
rics, he drank beer and wrote vitriolic letters, he voyaged to Italy
and England and Scandinavia, and casually, between two days, he
married (as he might have bought a coat or hired a housekeeper)
the patient and wordless daughter of a Gentile merchant.

Then began a series of experiments, very important, very un-
dramatic-sounding, very long, and exceedingly unappreciated. Back
in 1881 he was confirming Pasteur's results in chicken cholera immunity and, for relief and pastime, trying to separate an enzyme
from yeast. A few years later, living on the tiny inheritance from his
father, a petty banker, and quite carelessly and cheerfully exhaust-
ing it, he was analyzing critically the ptomaine theory of disease,
and investigating the mechanism of the attenuation of virulence of
microorganisms. He got thereby small fame. Perhaps he was over-
cautious, and more than the devil or starvation he hated men who
rushed into publication unprepared.

Though he meddled little in politics, considering them the most
repetitious and least scientific of human activities, he was a sufficiently patriotic German to hate the Junkers. As a youngster he had
a fight or two with ruffling subalterns; once he spent a week in jail;
often he was infuriated by discriminations against Jews; and at
forty he went sadly off to the America which could never become
militaristic or anti-Semitic — to the Hoagland Laboratory in Brooklyn, then to Queen City University as professor of bacteriology.

Here he made his first investigation of toxin-anti-toxin reactions. He announced that antibodies, excepting antitoxin, had no relation to the immune state of an animal, and while he himself was being ragingly denounced in the small but hectic world of scientists, he dealt calmly and most brutally with Yersin's and Marmorek's theories of sera.

His dearest dream, now and for years of racking research, was the artificial production of antitoxin — its production *in vitro*. Once he was prepared to publish, but he found an error and rigidly suppressed his notes. All the while he was lonely. There was apparently no one in Queen City who regarded him as other than a cranky Jew catching microbes by their little tails and leering at them — no work for a tall man at a time when heroes were building bridges, experimenting with Horseless Carriages, writing the first of the poetic Compelling Ads, and selling miles of calico and cigars.

In 1899 he was called to the University of Winnemac, as professor of bacteriology in the medical school, and here he drudged on for a dozen years. Not once did he talk of results of the sort called "practical"; not once did he cease warring on the *post hoc propter hoc* conclusions which still make up most medical lore; not once did he fail to be hated by his colleagues, who were respectful to his face, uncomfortable in feeling his ironic power, but privily joyous to call him Mephisto, Diabolist, Killjoy, Pessimist, Destructive Critic, Flippant Cynic, Scientific Bounder Lacking in Dignity and Seriousness, Intellectual Snob, Pacifist, Anarchist, Atheist, Jew. They said, with reason, that he was so devoted to Pure Science, to art for art's sake, that he would rather have people die by the right therapy than be cured by the wrong. Having built a shrine for humanity, he wanted to kick out of it all mere human beings.

The total number of his papers, in a brisk scientific realm where really clever people published five times a year, was not more than twenty-five in thirty years. They were all exquisitely finished, all easily duplicated and checked by the doubtfulest critics.

At Mohalis he was pleased by large facilities for work, by excellent assistants, endless glassware, plenty of guinea pigs, enough monkeys; but he was bored by the round of teaching, and melancholy again in a lack of understanding friends. Always he sought some one to whom he could talk without suspicion or caution. He was human enough, when he meditated upon the exaltation of doctors bold through ignorance, of inventors who were but tinkers magnified, to be irritated by his lack of fame in America, even in Mohalis, and to complain not too nobly.

He had never dined with a duchess, never received a prize, never been interviewed, never produced anything which the public could understand, nor experienced anything since his schoolboy amours which nice people could regard as romantic. He was, in fact, an authentic scientist.

He was of the great benefactors of humanity. There will never, in any age, be an effort to end the great epidemics or the petty infections which will not have been influenced by Max Gottlieb's researches, for he was not one who tagged and prettily classified bacteria and protozoa. He sought their chemistry, the laws of their existence and destruction, basic laws for the most part unknown after a generation of busy biologists. Yet they were right who called him "pessimist," for this man who, as much as any other, will have been the cause of reducing infectious diseases to almost-zero often doubted the value of reducing infectious diseases at all.

He reflected (it was an international debate in which he was joined by a few and damned by many) that half a dozen generations nearly free from epidemics would produce a race so low in natural immunity that when a great plague, suddenly springing from almost-zero to a world-smothering cloud, appeared again, it might wipe out the world entire, so that the measures to save lives to which he lent his genius might in the end be the destruction of all human life.

He meditated that if science and public hygiene did remove tuberculosis and the other major plagues, the world was grimly certain to become so overcrowded, to become such a universal slave-packed shambles, that all beauty and ease and wisdom would disappear in a famine-driven scamper for existence. Yet these speculations never checked his work. If the future became overcrowded, the future must by birth-control or otherwise look to itself. Perhaps it would, he reflected. But even this drop of wholesome optimism was lacking in his final doubts. For he doubted all progress of the intellect and the emotions, and he doubted, most of all, the superiority of divine mankind to the cheerful dogs, the infallibly graceful cats, the unmoral and unagitated and irreligious horses, the superbly adventuring sea-gulls. . . .

GOTTLIEB'S CREED: ". . . But one thing I keep always pure: the religion of a scientist.

"To be a scientist — it is not just a different job, so that a man should choose between being a scientist and being an explorer or a bond-salesman or a physician or a king or a farmer. It is a tangle of ver-y obscure emotions, like mysticism, or wanting to write poetry; it makes its victim all different from the good normal man. The normal man, he does not care much what he does except that he should eat and sleep and make love. But the scientist is intensely religious — he is so religious that he will not accept quarter-truths, because they are an insult to his faith.

"He wants that everything should be subject to inexorable laws. He is equal opposed to the capitalists who t'ink their silly money-grabbing is a system, and to liberals who t'ink man is not a fighting animal; he takes both the American booster and the European aristocrat, and he ignores all their blithering. Ignores it! All of it! He hates the preachers who talk their fables, but he iss not too kindly to the anthropologists and historians who can only make guesses, yet they have the nerf to call themselves scientists! Oh, yes, he is a man that all nice good-natured people should naturally hate!

"He speaks no meaner of the ridiculous faith-healers and chiro-practors than he does of the doctors what want to snatch our science before it is tested and rush around hoping they heal people, and spoiling all the clues with their footsteps; and worse than the men like hogs, worse than the imbeciles who have not even heard of science, he hates pseudo-scientists, guess-scientists — like these psycho-analysts; and worse than those comic dream-scientists he hates the men that are allowed in a clean kingdom like biology but know only one textbook and how to lecture to nincompoops all so popular. He is the only real revolutionary, the authentic scientist, because he alone knows how liddle he knows.

"He must be heartless. He lives in a cold, clear light. Yet dis is a funny t'ing: really, in private, he is not cold nor heartless — so much less cold than the Professional Optimists. The world has always been ruled by the Philanthropists: by the doctors that want to use therapeutic methods they do not understand, by the soldiers that want something to defend their country against, by the preachers that yearn to make everybody listen to them, by the kind manu-facturers that love their workers, by the eloquent statesmen and soft-hearted authors — and see what a fine mess of hell they haf made of the world! Maybe now it is time for the scientist, who works and searches and never goes around howling how he loves everybody!

"But once again always remember that not all the men who work at science are scientists. So few! The rest — secretaries, press-agents, camp-followers! To be a scientist is like being a Goethe: it is born in you. Sometimes I t'ink you have a liddle of it born in you. If you haf, there is only one t'ing — no, there is two t'ings you must do: work twice as hard as you can, and keep people from using you. I will try to protect you from Success. It is all I can do. So. . . ."

A Letter to Charles Kingsley

THOMAS HENRY HUXLEY

14 WAVERLEY PLACE, SEPT. 23, 1860

My dear Kingsley—

I cannot sufficiently thank you, both on my wife's account and my own, for your long and frank letter, and for all the hearty sympathy which it exhibits — and Mrs. Kingsley will, I hope, believe that we are no less sensible of her kind thought of us. To myself your letter was especially valuable, as it touched upon what I thought even more than upon what I said in my letter to you.

My convictions, positive and negative, on all the matters of which you speak, are of long and slow growth, and are firmly rooted. But the great blow which fell upon me [the death of his son] seemed to stir them to their foundation, and had I lived a couple of centuries earlier I could have fancied a devil scoffing at me and them — and asking me what profit it was to have stripped myself of the hopes and consolations of the mass of mankind? To which my only reply was and is — Oh devil! truth is better than much profit. I have searched over the grounds of my belief, and if wife and child and name and fame were all to be lost to me one after the other as the penalty, still I could not lie.

And now I feel that it is due to you to speak as frankly as you have done to me. An old and worthy friend of mine tried some three or four years ago to bring us together — because, as he said, you were the only man who would do me any good. Your letter leads me to think he was right, though not perhaps in the sense he attached to his own words . . . It [the doctrine of the immortality of man] is not half so wonderful as the conservation of force, or the indestructibility of matter. Whoso clearly appreciates all that is implied in the falling of a stone can have no difficulty about any doctrine simply on account of its marvelousness . . . The universe is one and the same throughout; and if the condition of my success in unraveling some little difficulty of anatomy or physiology is that I shall rigorously refuse to put faith in that which does not rest on sufficient evidence, I cannot believe that the great mysteries of existence will be laid open to me on other terms . . .

Science seems to me to teach in the highest and strongest manner the great truth which is embodied in the Christian conception of entire surrender to the will of God. Sit down before fact as a little child, be prepared to give up every preconceived notion, follow humbly wherever and to whatever abysses nature leads, or you shall learn nothing. I have only begun to learn content and peace of mind since I have resolved at all risks to do this . . .

As I stood behind the coffin of my little son the other day, with my mind bent on anything but disputation, the officiating minister read, as a part of his duty, the words, "If the dead rise not again, let us eat and drink, for tomorrow we die." I cannot tell you how inexpressibly they shocked me. Paul had neither wife nor child, or he must have known that his alternative involved a blasphemy against all that was best and noblest in human nature. I could have laughed with scorn. What! because I am face to face with irreparable loss, because I have given back to the source from whence it came, the cause of a great happiness, still retaining through all my life the blessings which have sprung and will spring from that cause, I am to renounce my manhood, and, howling, grovel in bestiality? Why, the very apes know better, and if you shoot their young, the poor brutes grieve their grief out and do not immediately seek distraction in a gorge.

Kicked into the world a boy without guide or training, or with worse than none, I confess to my shame that few men have drunk deeper of all kinds of sin than I. Happily, my course was arrested in time — before I had earned absolute destruction — and for long years I have been slowly and painfully climbing, with many a fall, toward better things. And when I look back, what do I find to have been the agents of my redemption? The hope of immortality or of future reward? I can honestly say that for these fourteen years such a consideration has not entered my head. No, I can tell you exactly what has been at work. *Sartor Resartus* led me to know that a deep sense of religion was compatible with the entire absence of theology. Secondly, science and her methods gave me a resting place independent of authority and tradition. Thirdly, love opened up to me a view of the sanctity of human nature, and impressed me with a deep sense of responsibility.

If at this moment I am not a worn-out, debauched, useless carcass of a man, if it has been or will be my fate to advance the cause of science, if I feel that I have a shadow of a claim on the love of those about me, if in the supreme moment when I looked down into my boy's grave my sorrow was full of submission and without bitterness, it is because these agencies have worked upon me, and not because I have ever cared whether my poor personality shall remain distinct for ever from the All from whence it came and whither it goes . . .

I have spoken more openly and distinctly to you than I ever have to any human being except my wife.

If you can show me that I err in premises or conclusion, I am ready to give up these as I would any other theories. But at any rate you will do me the justice to believe that I have not reached my conclusions without the care befitting the momentous nature of the problems involved.

And I write this the more readily to you, because it is clear to me that if that great and powerful instrument for good or evil, the Church of England, is to be saved from being shivered into fragments by the advancing tide of science — an event I should be very sorry to witness, but which will infallibly occur if men like Samuel of Oxford are to have the guidance of her destinies — it must be by the efforts of men who, like yourself, see your way to the combination of the practice of the Church with the spirit of science. Understand that all the younger men of science whom I know intimately are *essentially* of my way of thinking. (I know not a scoffer or an irreligious or an immoral man among them, but they all regard orthodoxy as you do Brahmanism.) Understand that this new school of the prophets is the only one that can work miracles, the only one that can constantly appeal to nature for evidence that it is right, and you will comprehend that it is of no use to try to barricade us with shovel hats and aprons, or to talk about our doctrines being "shocking."

. . . If I have spoken too plainly anywhere, or too abruptly, pardon me, and do the like to me.

My wife thanks you very much for your volume of sermons.

Ever yours very faithfully,
T. H. Huxley

◇◇

The Life of Solitude

ALBERT EINSTEIN

I LIVED in solitude in the country and noticed how the monotony of a quiet life stimulates the creative mind. There are certain callings in our modern organization which entail such an isolated life without making a great claim on bodily and intellectual effort. I think of such occupations as the service in lighthouses and lightships. Would it not be possible to fill such places with young people who wish to think out scientific problems, especially of a mathematical or philosophical nature? Very few of such people have the opportunity during the most productive period of their lives to devote themselves undisturbed for any length of time to scientific problems. Even if a young person is lucky enough to obtain a scholarship for a short period he must endeavor to arrive as quickly as possible at definite conclusions. That cannot be of advantage in the pursuit of pure science. The young scientist who carries on an ordinary practical profession which maintains him is in a much better position — assuming of course that this profession leaves him with sufficient spare time and energy. In this way perhaps a greater number of creative individuals could be given an opportunity for mental development than is possible at present.

"In Silent Rooms"

CARL SANDBURG

A father sees a son nearing manhood.
What shall he tell that son? . . .
Tell him to be alone often and get at himself
and above all tell himself no lies about himself
whatever the white lies and protective fronts
he may use amongst other people.
Tell him solitude is creative if he is strong
and the final decisions are made in silent rooms.
Tell him to be different from other people
if it comes natural and easy being different.
Let him have lazy days seeking his deeper motives.
Let him seek deep for where he is a born natural.
   Then he may understand Shakespeare
   and the Wright brothers, Pasteur, Pavlov,
   Michael Faraday and free imaginations
bringing changes into a world resenting change.
   He will be lonely enough
   to have time for the work
   he knows as his own.

THE MANY METHODS OF SCIENCE

◇◇◇

The Wayfarer

The wayfarer,
Perceiving the pathway to truth,
Was struck with astonishment.
It was thickly grown with weeds.
"Ha," he said,
"I see that no one has passed here
In a long time."
Later he saw that each weed
Was a singular knife.
"Well," he mumbled at last,
"Doubtless there are other roads."

— STEPHEN CRANE

We Are All Scientists

THOMAS HENRY HUXLEY

. . . THE METHOD of scientific investigation is nothing but
the expression of the necessary mode of working of the human
mind. It is simply the mode at which all phenomena are reasoned
about, rendered precise and exact. There is no more difference, but
there is just the same kind of difference, between the mental operations of a man of science and those of an ordinary person, as there
is between the operations and methods of a baker or of a butcher
weighing out his goods in common scales, and the operations of a
chemist in performing a difficult and complex analysis by means of
his balance and finely graduated weights. It is not that the action of
the scales in the one case, and the balance in the other, differ in the
principles of their construction or manner of working; but the beam
of one is set on an infinitely finer axis than the other, and of course
turns by the addition of a much smaller weight.

You will understand this better, perhaps, if I give you some
familiar example. You have all heard it repeated, I dare say, that

From *Darwiniana.*

men of science work by means of induction and deduction, and that by the help of these operations, they, in a sort of sense, wring from Nature certain other things, which are called natural laws, and causes, and that out of these, by some cunning skill of their own, they build up hypotheses and theories. And it is imagined by many, that the operations of the common mind can be by no means compared with these processes, and that they have to be acquired by a sort of special apprenticeship to the craft. To hear all these large words, you would think that the mind of a man of science must be constituted differently from that of his fellow men; but if you will not be frightened by terms, you will discover that you are quite wrong, and that all these terrible apparatus are being used by yourselves every day and every hour of your lives.

There is a well known incident in one of Molière's plays, where the author makes the hero express unbounded delight on being told that he had been talking prose during the whole of his life. In the same way, I trust, that you will take comfort, and be delighted with yourselves, on the discovery that you have been acting on the principles of inductive and deductive philosophy during the same period. Probably there is not one who has not in the course of the day had occasion to set in motion a complex train of reasoning, of the very same kind, though differing of course in degree, as that which a scientific man goes through in tracing the causes of natural phenomena.

A very trivial circumstance will serve to exemplify this. Suppose you go into a fruiterer's shop, wanting an apple, — you take up one, and, on biting it, you find it is sour; you look at it, and see that it is hard and green. You take up another one, and that too is hard, green, and sour. The shopman offers you a third; but, before biting it, you examine it, and find that it is hard and green, and you immediately say that you will not have it, as it must be sour, like those that you have already tried.

Nothing can be more simple than that, you think; but if you will take the trouble to analyze and trace out into its logical elements what has been done by the mind, you will be greatly surprised. In the first place, you have performed the operation of induction. You found that, in two experiences, hardness and greenness in apples went together with sourness. It was so in the first case, and it was confirmed by the second. True, it is a very small basis, but still it is enough to make an induction from; you generalize the facts, and you expect to find sourness in apples where you get hardness and greenness. You found upon that a general law, that all hard and green apples are sour; and that, so far as it goes, is a perfect induction. Well, having got your natural law in this way, when you are offered another apple which you find is hard and green, you say, "All hard and green apples are sour; this apple is hard and green, therefore this apple is sour." That train of reasoning is what logicians call a syllogism, and has all its various parts and terms — its major premise, its minor premise, and its conclusion. And, by the help of further reasoning, which, if drawn out, would have to be exhibited in two or three other syllogisms, you arrive at your final determination, "I will not have that apple." So that, you see, you have, in the first place, established a law by induction, and upon that you have founded a deduction, and reasoned out the special conclusion of the particular case. Well now, suppose, having got your law, that at some time afterward, you are discussing the qualities of apples with a friend: you will say to him, "It is a very curious thing, — but I find that all hard and green apples are sour!" Your friend says to you, "But how do you know that?" You at once reply, "Oh, because I have tried them over and over again, and have always found them to be so." Well, if we were talking science instead of common sense, we should call that an experimental verification. And, if still opposed, you go further, and say, "I have heard from the people in Somersetshire and Devonshire, where a large number of apples are grown, that they have observed the same thing. It is also found to be the case in Normandy, and in North America. In short, I find it to be the universal experience of mankind wherever attention has been directed to the subject." Whereupon, your friend, unless he is a very unreasonable man, agrees with you, and is convinced that you are quite right in the conclusion you have drawn. He believes, although perhaps he does not know he believes it, that the more extensive verifications are, — that the more frequently experiments have been made, and results of the same kind arrived at, — that the more varied the conditions under which the same results are attained, the more certain is the ultimate conclusion, and he disputes the question no further. He sees that the experiment has been tried under all sorts of conditions, as to time, place, and people, with the same result; and he says with you, therefore, that the law you have laid down must be a good one, and he must believe it.

In science we do the same thing; — the philosopher exercises precisely the same faculties, though in a much more delicate manner. In scientific inquiry it becomes a matter of duty to expose a supposed law to every possible kind of verification, and to take care, moreover, that this is done intentionally, and not left to a mere accident, as in the case of the apples. And in science, as in common life, our confidence in a law is in exact proportion to the absence of variation in the result of our experimental verifications. For instance, if you let go your grasp of an article you may have in your hand, it will immediately fall to the ground. That is a very common verification of one of the best established laws of nature — that of gravitation. The method by which men of science establish the existence of that law is exactly the same as that by which we have established the trivial proposition about the sourness of hard and green apples. But we believe it in such an extensive, thorough, and unhesitating manner because the universal experience of mankind verifies it, and we can verify it ourselves at any time; and that is the strongest possible foundation on which any natural law can rest.

So much, then, by way of proof that the method of establishing laws in science is exactly the same as that pursued in common life. Let us now turn to another matter (though really it is but another phase of the same question), and that is, the method by which, from the relations of certain phenomena, we prove that some stand in the position of causes toward the others.

I want to put the case clearly before you, and I will therefore show you what I mean by another familiar example. I will suppose that one of you, on coming down in the morning to the parlor of your house, finds that a teapot and some spoons which had been left in the room on the previous evening are gone, — the window is open, and you observe the mark of a dirty hand on the window frame, and perhaps, in addition to that, you notice the impress of a hobnailed shoe on the gravel outside. All these phenomena have struck your attention instantly, and before two seconds have passed you say, "Oh, somebody has broken open the window, entered the room, and run off with the spoons and the teapot!" That speech is out of your mouth in a moment. And you will probably add, "I know there has; I am quite sure of it!" You mean to say exactly what you know; but in reality you are giving expression to what is, in all essential particulars, an hypothesis. You do not *know* it at all; it is nothing but an hypothesis rapidly framed in your own mind. And it is an hypothesis founded on a long train of inductions and deductions.

What are those inductions and deductions, and how have you got at this hypothesis? You have observed, in the first place, that the window is open; but by a train of reasoning involving many inductions and deductions, you have probably arrived long before at the general law — and a very good one it is — that windows do not open of themselves; and you therefore conclude that something has opened the window. A second general law that you have arrived at in the same way is that teapots and spoons do not go out of a window spontaneously, and you are satisfied that, as they are not now where you left them, they have been removed. In the third place, you look at the marks on the window sill, and the shoe marks outside, and you say that in all previous experience the former kind of mark has never been produced by anything else but the hand of a human being; and the same experience shows that no other animal but man at present wears shoes with hobnails in them such as would produce the marks in the gravel. I do not know, even if we could discover any of those "missing links" that are talked about, that they would help us to any other conclusion! At any rate the law which states our present experience is strong enough for my present purpose. You next reach the conclusion, that as these kinds of marks have not been left by any other animals than men, or are liable to be formed in any other way than by a man's hand and shoe, the marks in question have been formed by a man in that way. You have, further, a general law, founded on observation and experience, and that, too, is, I am sorry to say, a very universal and unimpeachable one, — that some men are thieves; and you assume at once from all these premises — and that is what constitutes your hypothesis — that the man who made the marks outside and on the window sill, opened the window, got into the room, and stole your teapot and spoons. You have now arrived at a *vera causa;* — you have assumed a cause which, it is plain, is competent to produce all the phenomena you have observed. You can explain all these phenomena only by the hypothesis of a thief. But that is a hypothetical conclusion, of the justice of which you have no absolute proof at all; it is only rendered highly probable by a series of inductive and deductive reasonings.

I suppose your first action, assuming that you are a man of ordinary common sense, and that you have established this hypothesis to your own satisfaction, will very likely be to go for the police, and set them on the track of the burglar, with the view to the recovery of your property. But just as you are starting with this object, some person comes in, and on learning what you are about, says, "My good friend, you are going on a great deal too fast. How do you know that the man who really made the marks took the spoons? It might have been a monkey that took them, and the man may have merely looked in afterward." You would probably reply, "Well, that is all very well, but you see it is contrary to all experience of the way teapots and spoons are abstracted; so that, at any rate, your hypothesis is less probable than mine." While you are talking the thing over in this way, another friend arrives. And he might say, "Oh, my dear sir, you are certainly going on a great deal too fast. You are most presumptuous. You admit that all these occurrences took place when you were fast asleep, at a time when you could not possibly have known anything about what was taking place. How do you know that the laws of Nature are not suspended during the night? It may be that there has been some kind of supernatural interference in this case." In point of fact, he declares that your hypothesis is one of which you cannot at all demonstrate the truth and that you are by no means sure that the laws of Nature are the same when you are asleep as when you are awake.

Well, now, you cannot at the moment answer that kind of reasoning. You feel that your worthy friend has you somewhat at a disadvantage. You will feel perfectly convinced in your own mind, however, that you are quite right, and you say to him, "My good friend, I can only be guided by the natural probabilities of the case, and if you will be kind enough to stand aside and permit me to pass, I will go and fetch the police." Well, we will suppose that your journey is successful, and that by good luck you meet with a policeman; that eventually the burglar is found with your property on his person, and the marks correspond to his hand and to his boots. Probably any jury would consider those facts a very good experimental verification of your hypothesis, touching the cause of the abnormal phenomena observed in your parlor, and would act accordingly.

Now, in this suppositious case, I have taken phenomena of a very common kind, in order that you might see what are the different steps in an ordinary process of reasoning, if you will only take the trouble to analyze it carefully. All the operations I have described, you will see, are involved in the mind of any man of sense in leading him to a conclusion as to the course he should take in order to make good a robbery and punish the offender. I say that you are led, in that case, to your conclusion by exactly the same train of reasoning as that which a man of science pursues when he is endeavoring to discover the origin and laws of the most occult phenomena. The process is, and always must be, the same; and precisely the same mode of reasoning was employed by Newton and Laplace in their endeavors to discover and define the causes of the movements of the heavenly bodies, as you, with your own common sense, would employ to detect a burglar. The only difference is, that the nature of the inquiry being more abstruse, every step has to be most carefully watched, so that there may not be a single crack or flaw in your hypothesis. A flaw or crack in many of the hypotheses of daily life may be of little or no moment as affecting the general correctness of the conclusions at which we may arrive; but, in a scientific inquiry, a fallacy, great or small, is always of importance, and is sure to be in the long run constantly productive of mischievous, if not fatal results.

Do not allow yourselves to be misled by the common notion that an hypothesis is untrustworthy simply because it is an hypothesis. It is often urged, in respect to some scientific conclusion, that, after all, it is only an hypothesis. But what more have we to guide us in nine-tenths of the most important affairs of daily life than hypotheses, and often very ill-based ones? So that in science, where the evidence of an hypothesis is subjected to the most rigid examination, we may rightly pursue the same course. You may have hypotheses and hypotheses. A man may say, if he likes, that the moon is made of green cheese: that is an hypothesis. But another man, who has devoted a great deal of time and attention to the subject, and availed himself of the most powerful telescopes and the results of the observations of others, declares that in his opinion it is probably composed of materials very similar to those of which our own earth is made up: and that is also only an hypothesis. But I need not tell you that there is an enormous difference in the value of the two hypotheses. That one which is based on sound scientific knowledge is sure to have a corresponding value; and that which is a mere hasty random guess is likely to have but little value. Every great step in our progress in discovering causes has been made in exactly the same way as that which I have detailed to you. A person observing the occurrence of certain facts and phenomena asks, naturally enough, what process, what kind of operation known to occur in Nature applied to the particular case, will unravel and explain the mystery? Hence you have the scientific hypothesis; and its value will be proportionate to the care and completeness with which its basis has been tested and verified. It is in these matters as in the commonest affairs of practical life: the guess of the fool will be folly, while the guess of the wise man will contain wisdom. In all cases, you see that the value of the result depends on the patience and faithfulness with which the investigator applies to his hypothesis every possible kind of verification. . . .

Paradox

CLARENCE R. WYLIE, JR.

Not truth, nor certainty. These I forswore
In my novitiate, as young men called
To holy orders must abjure the world.
"If . . . , then . . . ," this only I assert;
And my successes are but pretty chains
Linking twin doubts, for it is vain to ask
If what I postulate be justified,
Or what I prove possess the stamp of fact.

Yet bridges stand, and men no longer crawl
In two dimensions. And such triumphs stem
In no small measure from the power this game,
Played with the thrice-attenuated shades
Of things, has over their originals.
How frail the wand, but how profound the spell!

By permission of *The Scientific Monthly,* July 1948.

THE UNIQUE ACHIEVEMENT OF GREECE

HERBERT J. MULLER

. . . WITHIN the space of fifty years Athens alone, a little city-state of only a few hundred thousand, produced such men as Pericles, Aeschylus, Sophocles, Euripides, Aristophanes, Socrates, Thucydides, Phidias, the architects of the Parthenon — men whose equals are hardly to be found in our whole history. I do not propose, however, to review this achievement in the detail it deserves. My concern is the Greek spirit — the spirit that led them to embark, without maps, charts, or guides, on the adventure of freedom and the life of reason. It involved the penalties and the paradoxes that are the immediate theme of this book, and are reflected in their own creation of Tragedy. Out of its failures sprang Hagia Sophia: designed by Greek architects, presided over by Greek Patriarchs, but built by a bigoted, despotic emperor who also closed the academies of Athens, to the glory of a faith that was unfree, incurious, and unadventurous. Still, the spirit of Athens proved more vital, inspiring new adventures in the West while Hagia Sophia fell to the Turks; and though it has got us into trouble too, this book is dedicated to its values. For better and worse, it is the primary source of the historical importance of Greece.

The first question, naturally, is how this spirit arose. We cannot explain it by any mystique of race, blood, or Kultur. The Greeks were a mongrel people who never prided themselves on racial purity, were evidently stimulated by their wandering and intermingling with older peoples, and borrowed freely from Crete, Egypt, Phoenicia, Babylonia, Lydia, and other ancient cultures. More helpful is Toynbee's principle of challenge-and-response, or the virtues of adversity. Greece was no comfortable cradle of civilization but a rocky, bony land, which could not support a growing people in its scattered valleys and plains; hence the Greeks had to take to the sea, develop trade and industry, and send out colonizers. Later they rose magnificently to the challenge of invasion by the mighty Persian empire. Yet all this does not really explain the adventure of the Greeks. Countless other wandering, mongrel peoples who faced similar challenges, or had the advantage of adversities, remained barbarians. We do not know just how or why some peoples rise to splendid achievement. All we know for certain is that at least as early as Homer the Greeks were already a free people, standing on their own feet, living their own lives in an ordered world in which monsters, demons, and other irrational horrors had largely been tamed or exterminated.

Now, the Eastern civilizations before them must have had more freedom, variety, initiative, and stir than their rigid structures suggest. They had made remarkable discoveries, carried on extensive trade, created art forms, built imposing cities, organized powerful kingdoms. Nevertheless what we know of these societies indicates that as they became established, they all tended to settle into the same invariable pattern. They were ruled by gods and god-kings who were alike despots. They lived in a profoundly irrational world, haunted by fear, controlled by magic, framed by inviolable custom. Their basic principle was absolute obedience to customs and institutions that were not reasoned about because not regarded as man-made. They had codes of justice and knew some happiness, but they had no idea of personal liberty or a right to happiness. Apparently their subjects never conceived the possibility of a better kind of society, for we do not hear of great rebels or popular uprisings.

Against this historical background the saying of Anaxagoras becomes more luminous: "All things were in chaos when Mind arose and made order." The Greeks were apparently the first to put their trust in Mind and by conscious thought to introduce order into the universe and man's life. When Thales of Miletus stated that "all things are made of water," his apparently naïve fancy was an astonishingly bold advance in thought. In the face of the multifarious, shifting appearances he was assuming that nature was intelligible, in natural rather than supernatural terms; and with this assumption philosophy got under way. "The fact is that invoking the gods to explain diseases and other natural events is all nonsense," declared Hippocrates (or one of the legendary men known as Hippocrates). ". . . In nature all things are alike in this, that they all can be traced to preceding causes." Earlier societies had accumulated considerable medical knowledge and skill, but not until this denial of magical or supernatural causes could medicine become a science. "Hecataeus of Miletus thus speaks: I write what I deem true; for the stories of the Greeks are manifold and seem to me ridiculous" — and with this skeptical utterance the study of history really began. From such beginnings the Greeks went on to make impressive contributions to philosophy, science, and history, but their all-important contribution was the beginnings — the critical, inquiring spirit. And as they discovered Nature, so they discovered Man. The motto inscribed in their national shrine at Delphi was not "Fear God" but "Know Thyself." They created the ideal of culture — the conscious cultivation of human nature.

The Sacred Disease

HIPPOCRATES

I AM about to discuss the disease called "sacred." * It is not in my opinion, any more divine or more sacred than other diseases, but has a natural cause, and its supposed divine origin is due to men's inexperience and to their wonder at its peculiar character. Now while men continue to believe in its divine origin because they are at a loss to understand it, they really disprove its divinity by the facile method of healing which they adopt, consisting as it does of purifications and incantations. But if it is to be considered divine just because it is wonderful, there will be not one sacred disease but many, for I will show that other diseases are no less wonderful and portentous, and yet nobody considers them sacred. For instance quotidian fevers, tertians and quartans, seem to me to be no less sacred and god-sent than this disease, but nobody wonders at them. Then again one can see men who are mad and delirious from no obvious cause, and committing many strange acts, while in their sleep, to my knowledge, men groan and shriek, others choke, others dart up and rush out of doors, being delirious until they wake, when they become as healthy and rational as they were before, though pale and weak; and this happens not once but many times. Many other instances, of various kinds, could be given, but time does not permit us to speak of each separately.

But this disease in my opinion is no more divine than any other; it has the same nature as other diseases, and the cause that gives rise to individual diseases. It is also curable, no less than other illnesses, unless by long lapse of time it be so ingrained as to be more powerful than the remedies that are applied. Its origin, like that of other diseases, lies in heredity. For if a phlegmatic parent has a phlegmatic child, a bilious parent a bilious child, a consumptive parent a consumptive child, and a splenetic parent a splenetic child, there is nothing to prevent some of the children suffering from this disease when one or other of the parents suffered from it; for the seed comes from every part of the body, healthy seed from the healthy parts, diseased seed from the diseased parts. Another strong proof that this disease is no more divine than any other is

From *Hippocrates*, Volumes I and II, translated by W. H. S. Jones. Reprinted by permission of the Harvard University Press and the Loeb Classical Library.

* Epilepsy.

that it affects the naturally phlegmatic, but does not attack the bilious. Yet if it were more divine than others, this disease ought to have attacked all equally, without making any difference between bilious and phlegmatic.

The fact is that the cause of this affection, as of the more serious diseases generally, is the brain.

Case History No. XV

HIPPOCRATES

IN THASOS the wife of Delearces, who lay sick on the plain, was seized after a grief with an acute fever with shivering. From the beginning she would wrap herself up, and throughout, without speaking a word, she would fumble, pluck, scratch, pick hairs, weep and then laugh, but she did not sleep; though stimulated, the bowels passed nothing. She drank a little when the attendants suggested it. Urine thin and scanty; fever slight to the touch; coldness of the extremities.

Ninth day. Much wandering followed by return of reason; silent.

Fourteenth day. Respiration rare and large with long intervals, becoming afterwards short.

Seventeenth day. Bowels under a stimulus passed disordered matters, then her very drink passed unchanged; nothing coagulated. The patient noticed nothing; the skin tense and dry.

Twentieth day. Much rambling followed by recovery of reason; speechless; respiration short.

Twenty-first day. Death.

The respiration of this patient throughout was rare and large; took no notice of anything; she constantly wrapped herself up; either much rambling or silence throughout.

The Training of Aristotle

ALFRED NOYES

. . . I saw among the rocks on my right hand,
Lying, face downward, over a deep rock-pool,
A youth, so still that, till a herring-gull swooped
And sheered away from him with a startled cry
And a wild flutter of its brown mottled wings,
I had not seen him. . . .
               He pored intent
Upon a sea-anemone, like a flower
Opening its disk of blue and crimson rays
Under the lucid water.
               He stretched his hand,
And with a sea-gull's feather, touched its heart.
The bright disk shrank, and closed, as though a flower
Turned instantly to fruit, ripe, soft, and round
As the pursed lips of a sea-god hiding there.
They fastened, sucking, on the quill and held it.
Young Aristotle laughed. He rose to his feet.
"Come and see this!" he called.
               Under the cliff
Nicomachus arose, and drawing his robe
More closely round him, crossed the slippery rocks
To join his son.
             There, side by side, they crouched
Over the limpid pool — the gray physician
And eager boy.
            "See, how it grips the feather!
And grips the rock, too. Yet it has no roots.
Your sea-flowers turn to animals with mouths.
Take out the quill. Now it turns back again
Into a flower; look — look — what lovely colors,
What marvelous artistry.
            This never was formed
By chance. It has an aim beyond this pool.
What does it mean? This unity of design?
This delicate scale of life that seems to ascend
Without a break, through all the forms of earth

From plants to men? The sea-sponge that I found
Grew like a blind rock-rooted clump of moss
Dilating in water, shrinking in the sun;
I know it for a strange sea-animal now,
Shaped like the brain of a man. Can it be true
That, as the poets fable in their songs
Of Aphrodite, life itself was born
Here, in the sea?"
                          Nicomachus looked at him.
"That's a dark riddle, my son. You will not hear
An answer in the groves of Academe,
Not even from Plato. When you go to Athens
Next year, remember among the loftiest flights
Of their philosophy, that the living truth
Is here on earth if we could only see it.
This, this at least, all true Asclepiads know.
Remember, always, in that battle of words,
The truth that father handed down to son
Through the long line of men that served their kind
From Aesculapius, father of us all,
To you his own descendant: — naught avails
In science, till the light you seize from heaven
Shines through the clear sharp fact beneath your feet.
This is the test of both — that, in their wedding,
The light that was a disembodied dream
Burns through the fact, and makes a lanthorn of it,
Transfigures it, confirms it, gives it new
And deeper meanings; and itself, in turn,
Is thereby seen more truly.
                                    Use your eyes;
And you, or those that follow you, will outsoar
Pythagoras."

"Here, Too, Are Gods"

ARISTOTLE

BUT THE FACTS have not yet been sufficiently ascertained; and if at any future time they are ascertained, then credence must be given to the direct evidence of the senses rather than to theories — and to theories too, provided that the results which they show agree with what is observed.

OF THINGS which hold together by nature there are two kinds: those that are unborn, imperishable, and eternal, and those that are subject to generation and decay. The former, although of the highest worth and even divine, are less accessible to our investigation, inasmuch as the findings of sense-experience throw very little light on the questions which we most desire to answer about them. It is much easier to learn about things that perish — i.e., plants and animals — because we live in their midst, and anyone who cares to take the trouble can acquire abundant information about them. . . . [In any case, having discussed elsewhere the apparent nature of divine objects], our present task is to speak about the nature of animals. So far as possible we will omit no species of animal from consideration, however mean its condition. For even animals that are not attractive to sense offer, to the contemplative vision, the immeasurable joy of discovering creative nature at work in them. It would be strangely paradoxical if we enjoyed studying mere likenesses of nature, because of the painter's or carver's art that they embody, while ignoring the even greater delight of studying nature's own works where we are able to discern the formative factors. So we should not childishly refuse to study the meaner animals, for in all works of nature there is something of the marvelous. A story is told of Heraclitus, that when some visitors desired to see him but hesitated when they found him in the kitchen warming himself by the fire, he bade them: "Come in, don't be afraid! for here, too, are gods." In like manner, boldly and without distaste, we ought to pursue the investigation of every sort of animal, for every one of

From Aristotle: *The Parts of Animals*, translated by Philip Wheelwright. Reprinted by permission of the Odyssey Press.

them will reveal to us something both of nature and of beauty. I say beauty, because in nature it is purpose, not haphazard, that predominates; and the purpose which directs and permeates her works is one type of the beautiful. . . .

"See for Yourself"

HIPPOCRATIC COLLECTION

THE EMBRYO is in a membrane and at the center of the embryo is the umbilicus. Now the embryo draws breath to itself and then breathes out. There are membranes connected with the umbilicus. And if you use the evidence I am going to set forth, you will find that the nature of the embryo is in all other respects, from beginning to end, just as I have described it in these discourses. For, if you take twenty or more eggs and put them under two or more hens for hatching, and each day from the second to the last, that is, the day of hatching, take one egg, break it open and examine it, you will find everything as I described it, in so far as the nature of the bird may be compared with that of man. You will find that the membranes stretch from the umbilicus, and that all the other things I spoke of in connection with the human embryo are similarly in a bird's egg, from beginning to end. And if one has not yet seen it, he will be surprised at finding an umbilicus in a bird's egg.

Reprinted by permission of the publishers from M. R. Cohen and I. E. Drabkin: *A Source Book in Greek Science*. Cambridge, Massachusetts: Harvard University Press, 1948.

Eels and Embryo Chicks

ARISTOTLE

IF THERE is any kind of animal which is female and has no male separate from it, it is possible that this may generate a young one from itself without copulation. No instance of this worthy of credit has been observed, up to the present at any rate, but one case in the class of fishes makes us hesitate. No male of the so-called erythrinus[1] has ever yet been seen, but females, and specimens full of roe, have been seen. Of this, however, we have as yet no proof worthy of credit. Again, some members of the class of fishes are neither male nor female, as eels and a kind of mullets found in stagnant waters.[2] But whenever the sexes are separate, the female cannot generate perfectly by herself alone, for then the male would exist in vain, and Nature makes nothing in vain.

Generation from the egg proceeds in an identical manner with all birds, but the full periods from conception to birth differ, as has been said. With the common hen, after three days and three nights there is the first indication of the embryo; with larger birds the interval being longer, with smaller birds shorter. Meanwhile the yolk comes into being, rising toward the sharp end, where the primal element of the egg is situated, and where the egg gets hatched; and the heart appears, like a speck of blood, in the white of the egg. This point beats and moves as though endowed with life, and from it two vein-ducts with blood in them trend in a convoluted course [as the egg-substance goes on growing, toward each of the circumjacent integuments]; and a membrane carrying bloody fibers now envelops the yolk, leading off from the vein-ducts. A little afterward the body is differentiated, at first very small and white. The head is clearly distinguished, and in it the eyes, swollen out to a great extent. This condition of the eyes lasts on for a good while, as it is only by degrees that they diminish in size and collapse. At the outset the

From The Oxford Translation of Aristotle: *The Generation of Animals* and *History of Animals*. By permission of Clarendon Press, Oxford.

[1] Probably the Serranus anthias, a kind of sea-perch. This fish is hermaphrodite, and the male organs are difficult to make out, as may be judged from the fact that the riddle was not solved till near the end of the eighteenth century, and then the solution was much disputed.

[2] The truth about eels has only been quite recently discovered; they do not develop generative organs except in the deep sea (about 500 fathoms), and consequently no sexes are to be observed in any fresh-water eels.

under portion of the body appears insignificant in comparison with the upper portion. Of the two ducts that lead from the heart, the one proceeds toward the circumjacent integument, and the other, like a navel-string, toward the yolk. The life-element of the chick is in the white of the egg, and the nutriment comes through the navel-string out of the yolk.

When the egg is now ten days old the chick and all its parts are distinctly visible. The head is still larger than the rest of its body, and the eyes larger than the head, but still devoid of vision. The eyes, if removed about this time, are found to be larger than beans, and black; if the cuticle be peeled off them there is a white and cold liquid inside, quite glittering in the sunlight, but there is no hard substance whatsoever. Such is the condition of the head and eyes. At this time also the larger internal organs are visible, as also the stomach and the arrangement of the viscera; and the veins that seem to proceed from the heart are now close to the navel. From the navel there stretch a pair of veins; one toward the membrane that envelops the yolk (and, by the way, the yolk is now liquid, or more so than is normal), and the other toward that membrane which envelops collectively the membrane wherein the chick lies, the membrane of the yolk, and the intervening liquid. [For, as the chick grows, little by little one part of the yolk goes upward, and another part downward, and the white liquid is between them; and the white of the egg is underneath the lower part of the yolk, as it was at the outset.] On the tenth day the white is at the extreme outer surface, reduced in amount, glutinous, firm in substance, and sallow in color.

The disposition of the several constituent parts is as follows. First and outermost comes the membrane of the egg, not that of the shell, but underneath it. Inside this membrane is a white liquid; then comes the chick, and a membrane round about it, separating it off so as to keep the chick free from the liquid; next after the chick comes the yolk, into which one of the two veins was described as leading, the other one leading into the enveloping white substance. [A membrane with a liquid resembling serum envelops the entire structure. Then comes another membrane right round the embryo, as has been described, separating it off against the liquid. Underneath this comes the yolk, enveloped in another membrane (into which yolk proceeds the navel-string that leads from the heart and the big vein), so as to keep the embryo free of both liquids.]

About the twentieth day, if you open the egg and touch the chick, it moves inside and chirps; and it is already coming to be covered with down, when, after the twentieth day is past, the chick begins to break the shell. The head is situated over the right leg close to the flank, and the wing is placed over the head; and about this time is plain to be seen the membrane resembling an after-birth that comes next after the outermost membrane of the shell, into which membrane the one of the navel-strings was described as leading (and, by the way, the chick in its entirety is now within it), and so also is the other membrane resembling an after-birth, namely that surrounding the yolk, into which the second navel-string was described as leading; and both of them were described as being connected with the heart and the big vein. At this conjuncture the navel-string that leads to the outer after-birth collapses and becomes detached from the chick, and the membrane that leads into the yolk is fastened on to the thin gut of the creature, and by this time a considerable amount of the yolk is inside the chick and a yellow sediment is in its stomach. About this time it discharges residuum in the direction of the outer after-birth, and has residuum inside its stomach; and the outer residuum is white [and there comes a white substance inside]. By and by the yolk, diminishing gradually in size, at length becomes entirely used up and comprehended within the chick (so that, ten days after hatching, if you cut open the chick, a small remnant of the yolk is still left in connection with the gut), but it is detached from the navel, and there is nothing in the interval between, but it has been used up entirely. During the period above referred to the chick sleeps, wakes up, makes a move and looks up and chirps; and the heart and the navel together palpitate as though the creature were respiring. So much as to generation from the egg in the case of birds.

The Store of Matter

LUCRETIUS

NOR WAS THE STORE of matter ever more closely massed nor held apart by larger spaces between; for nothing is either added to its bulk or lost to it. Wherefore the bodies of the first-beginnings in time gone by moved in the same way in which now they move, and

From Lucretius: *De Rerum Natura*, Book II, translated by H. A. J. Munro.

will ever hereafter be borne along in like manner, and the things which have been wont to be begotten will be begotten after the same law and will be and will grow and will wax in strength so far as is given to each by the decrees of nature. And no force can change the sum of things; for there is nothing outside, either into which any kind of matter can escape out of the universe or out of which a new supply can arise and burst into the universe and change all the nature of things and alter their motions.

And herein you need not wonder at this, that though the first-beginnings of things are all in motion, yet the sum is seen to rest in supreme repose, unless where a thing exhibits motions with its individual body. For all the nature of first things lies far away from our senses beneath their ken; and therefore since they are themselves beyond what you can see, they must withdraw from sight their motion as well; and the more so that the things which we can see, do yet often conceal their motions when a great distance off. Thus often the woolly flocks as they crop the glad pastures on a hill, creep on whither the grass jeweled with fresh dew summons and invites each, and the lambs fed to the full gambol and playfully butt; all which objects appear to us from a distance to be blended together and to rest like a white spot on a green hill. Again when mighty legions fill with their movements all parts of the plains waging the mimicry of war, the glitter then lifts itself up to the sky and the whole earth round gleams with brass and beneath a noise is raised by the mighty trampling of men and the mountains stricken by the shouting re-echo the voices to the stars of heaven, and horse-men fly about and suddenly wheeling scour across the middle of the plains, shaking them with the vehemence of their charge. And yet there is some spot on the high hills, seen from which they appear to stand still and to rest on the plains as a bright spot.

The Study of Anatomy

GALEN

I

. . . I HAVE ATTEMPTED to put together my arguments in the way in which it seems to me the Ancients, had any of them been still alive, would have done, in opposition to those who would over-turn the finest doctrines of our art.

I am not, however, unaware that I shall achieve either nothing at all or else very little. For I find that a great many things which have been conclusively demonstrated by the Ancients are unin-telligible to the bulk of the Moderns owing to their ignorance — nay, that, by reason of their laziness, they will not even make an attempt to comprehend them; and even if any of them have under-stood them, they have not given them impartial examination.

The fact is that he whose purpose is to know anything better than the multitude do must far surpass all others both as regards his nature and his early training. And when he reaches early adoles-cence he must become possessed with an ardent love for truth, like one inspired; neither day nor night may he cease to urge and strain himself in order to learn thoroughly all that has been said by the most illustrious of the Ancients. And when he has learnt this, then for a prolonged period he must test and prove it, observing what part of it is in agreement, and what in disagreement with ob-vious [observed] fact; thus he will choose this and turn away from that. To such an one my hope has been that my treatise would prove of the very greatest assistance. . . . Still, such people may be expected to be quite few in number, while, as for the others, this book will be as superfluous to them as a tale told to an ass.

II

. . . I SHOULD PREFER to finish this present treatise without mentioning the mistakes of others, and so I intended from the be-ginning, but during my discussion of the subject it has occurred to me that when I disagree with the earlier anatomists, my future

I. From *On the Natural Faculties*, translated by Arthur J. Brock, M.D. Re-printed by permission of Harvard University Press and Loeb Classical Li-brary.
II. From *De Usu Partium*, Part II, translated by Mrs. F. A. May and used with her kind permission.

readers may suspect that I am the one who is wrong and not they. For it is reasonable, I suppose, to believe that one man alone is in error rather than everyone else. Moreover, this idea will be even more likely to occur to those who are not familiar with my other anatomical works in which I have shown the mistakes my predecessors made in dissecting and have listed the causes of those mistakes, causes which will even now lead anyone undertaking dissection into errors like theirs, if he is not on his guard. Anyone who sees what I have seen when I dissect will be amazed that these anatomists were ignorant of the tendons and their movements, and that they overlooked whole muscles, and he will call anyone blind who makes such monumental errors. Well then, to omit everything else they missed in the anatomy of the hand, who is there that has eyes and yet fails to see that each finger has lateral movements in addition to its flexion and extension? But nevertheless, when these anatomists mention the tendons moving the fingers, they speak of those that extend and flex them, without taking into consideration that there must also be some sources for the lateral movements. Are you still surprised or incredulous that they are ignorant of some of the more obscure facts of anatomy when they do not even know what is to be seen without dissection? Let me now once for all make this general statement to apply to my whole treatise so as not to be compelled to say the same thing repeatedly: I am now explaining the structures actually to be seen in dissection, and no one before me has done this with any accuracy. Hence, if anyone wishes to investigate the works of Nature, he should put his trust not in books on anatomy, but in his own eyes, and either come to me, or consult one of my associates, or alone by himself industriously practice exercises in dissection; but so long as he only reads, he will be the more likely to believe all the earlier anatomists, because there are many of them.

III

BONY SUBSTANCE is to animals what poles are to tents and walls to houses; for other structures of the body naturally conform to it and change along with it. Thus, if an animal's skull is round, its brain necessarily assumes the same shape, and if the skull is elongate, the brain is elongate too. So also, if the jaws are small and the face somewhat round, the muscles of the jaws and face must be small. Similarly, if the jaws are long, the whole face and its muscles

III.   From Book I of Galen's *Manual of Dissection*, translated by Mrs. F. A. May and used with her kind permission.

will have to be long. This, of course, is the reason why of all animals, the ape most resembles man in viscera, muscles, arteries, veins, and nerves; for its bones are similar in shape to those of man. It is because of the nature of its bones that the ape walks on two feet and uses its fore limbs like hands. So, too, it has the broadest breast of all the quadrupeds, collar bones similar to man's, a round face, and a short neck, and with all these structures similar, it is impossible for the muscles to be different. For the muscles are stretched along the outside of the bones with the result that they copy their shape and size from the bones. The arteries, veins, and nerves follow the muscles, and so they, too, are similar to the similar bones. Since, then, the shape of the body conforms to the bones, and the nature of the other parts is also dependent on them, I think it is of the first importance for you to get an accurate grasp of human osteology. You should not give the bones only a superficial examination, nor should you merely read about them in books, some of which are entitled "Osteology," some "The Skeleton," and some simply "Bones," like that of mine, which, I am convinced, surpasses all previous works on the subject in the accuracy of its facts and the promptitude and clearness of its explanations. Let it be your task and your earnest desire not only to learn perfectly from a book the form of every bone, but also to become a constant observer of human osteology with your own eyes. It is much easier to do this in Alexandria, because physicians there instruct their students in knowledge of the bones by examination of specimens. Hence, for this reason alone, if for no other, I think you should try to spend some time in Alexandria. But if you are unable to do so, it will not be impossible even then for you to inspect human bones; for I have seen them many times when burial places and monuments have been destroyed. Once, a river flooded over a tomb constructed rather carelessly a few months previously and easily washed it out. By the force of the current the cadaver was dragged along, the flesh being already rotted away, but the bones still closely articulated, until it had been carried a stadium [about 600 feet] downstream. It became stranded in a shallow place where the banks sloped gradually, and it looked exactly like a specimen suitably prepared by a physician for the instruction of his young students. Another time I saw, lying only a little distance away by the side of a road in the mountains, the skeleton of a robber whom some traveler, resisting stoutly when attacked, had slain. None of the inhabitants of the region had felt called upon to bury him; but because they had hated him, they were glad to have the body devoured by birds, which ate the flesh in two days' time and left the skeleton picked clean as if for the inspection of a student eager to learn. But if you do not have the chance to observe a specimen of this sort, then dissect an ape, and, carefully removing the flesh, study each bone. Select for your work one of the apes most closely resembling man.

[NOTE: Galen's "ape" was not an anthropoid ape, but a Rhesus monkey or the so-called "Barbary ape." These are still found in diminishing numbers on the Rock of Gibraltar.]

◇◇◇

🖙 *THE WEIGHT OF REASON:*
THE ART OF EXPERIMENT

> *Holy, to be sure, is Lactantius, who denied the spherical form of the earth; holy, too, Augustinus, who admitted the spherical form but denied the Antipodes; holy the officialdom of our day which admits the smallness of the earth but denies its motion; but holier to me is truth . . . In theology the weight of authority, but in philosophy [science] the weight of reason is to be considered.*
>
> — JOHANN KEPLER

> *It is easier to add to things already found out, than to become the first author of new inventions. . . . He that seeks shall find. Wherefore rise from your soft Pillows, and with Smutted Hands touch black Coals, and accurately give heed to the institutions of Art. For with Idleness, Eating, Drinking and playing on Music, you shall never approach to great Mysteries.*
>
> — JOHANN RUDOLPH GLAUBER

Peter Peregrine as Experimentalist

ROGER BACON

I KNOW of only one person who deserves praise for his work in experimental philosophy, for he does not care for the discourses of man and their wordy warfare, but quietly and diligently pursues the works of wisdom. Therefore, what others grope after blindly, as bats in the evening twilight, this man contemplates in all their brilliancy because he is a master of experiment. Hence, he knows all natural science whether pertaining to medicine and alchemy, or to matters celestial and terrestrial. He has worked diligently in the smelting of ores as also in the working of minerals; he is thoroughly acquainted with all sorts of arms and implements used in military service and in hunting, besides which he is skilled in agriculture and in the measurement of lands. It is impossible to write a useful or correct treatise in experimental philosophy without mentioning this man's name. Moreover, he pursues knowledge for its own sake; for if he wished to obtain royal favor, he could easily find sovereigns who would honor and enrich him.

From Introduction to Peter Peregrine's *Letter on the Magnet.*

Experimenting with Magnets

PETER PEREGRINE

. . . BUT THE THINGS that are hidden from the multitude will become clear to astrologers and students of nature, and will constitute their delight, as they will also be of great help to those that are old and more learned. You must know, my dear friend, that whoever wishes to experiment, should be acquainted with the nature of things, and should not be ignorant of the motion of the celestial bodies. He must also be skillful in manipulation in order that, by means of this stone [the lodestone], he may produce these marvelous effects. Through his own industry he can, to some extent, indeed, correct the errors that a mathematician [a theoretical scientist] would inevitably make if he were lacking in dexterity. Besides in such occult experimentation, great skill is required, for very frequently without it the desired result cannot be obtained, because there are many things in the domain of reason which demand this manual dexterity.

From Peter Peregrine: *Letter on the Magnet,* translated by Brother Arnold, La Salle Institute.

A Plea for Experimentation

ROGER BACON

HAVING LAID DOWN fundamental principles of the wisdom of
the Latins so far as they are found in language, mathematics, and
optics, I now wish to unfold the principles of experimental science,
since without experience nothing can be sufficiently known. For
there are two modes of acquiring knowledge, namely, by reasoning and experience. Reasoning draws a conclusion and makes us
grant the conclusion, but does not make the conclusion certain, nor
does it remove doubt so that the mind may rest on the intuition of
truth, unless the mind discovers it by the path of experience; since
many have the arguments relating to what can be known, but because they lack experience they neglect the arguments, and neither
avoid what is harmful nor follow what is good. For if a man who has
never seen fire should prove by adequate reasoning that fire burns
and injures things and destroys them, his mind would not be satisfied thereby, nor would he avoid fire, until he placed his hand or
some combustible substance in the fire, so that he might prove by
experience that which reasoning taught. But when he has had actual experience of combustion his mind is made certain and rests in
the full light of truth. Therefore reasoning does not suffice, but experience does.

This is also evident in mathematics, where proof is most convincing. But the mind of one who has the most convincing proof
in regard to the equilateral triangle will never cleave to the conclusion without experience, nor will he heed it, but will disregard it
until experience is offered him by the intersection of two circles,
from either intersection of which two lines may be drawn to the
extremities of the given line; but then the man accepts the conclusion without any question. Aristotle's statement, then, that proof
is reasoning that causes us to know is to be understood with the
proviso that the proof is accompanied by its appropriate experience,
and is not to be understood of the bare proof. His statement also in
the first book of the Metaphysics that those who understand the
reason and the cause are wiser than those who have empiric knowledge of a fact, is spoken of such as know only the bare truth without
the cause. But I am here speaking of the man who knows the reason

From Roger Bacon: *Opus Majus*, Vol. II, translated by R. B. Burke. Reprinted
by permission of University of Pennsylvania Press.

and the cause through experience. These men are perfect in their wisdom, as Aristotle maintains in the sixth book of the Ethics, whose simple statements must be accepted as if they offered proof, as he states in the same place.

He therefore who wishes to rejoice without doubt in regard to the truths underlying phenomena must know how to devote himself to experiment. For authors write many statements, and people believe them through reasoning which they formulate without experience. Their reasoning is wholly false. For it is generally believed that the diamond cannot be broken except by goat's blood, and philosophers and theologians misuse this idea. But fracture by means of blood of this kind has never been verified, although the effort has been made; and without that blood it can be broken easily. For I have seen this with my own eyes, and this is necessary, because gems cannot be carved except by fragments of this stone. Similarly it is generally believed that the castors employed by physicians are the testicles of the male animal. But this is not true, because the beaver has these under its breast, and both the male and female produce testicles of this kind. Besides these castors the male beaver has its testicles in their natural place; and therefore what is subjoined is a dreadful lie, namely, that when the hunters pursue the beaver, he himself knowing what they are seeking cuts out with his teeth these glands. Moreover, it is generally believed that hot water freezes more quickly than cold water in vessels, and the argument in support of this is advanced that contrary is excited by contrary, just like enemies meeting each other. But it is certain that cold water freezes more quickly for anyone who makes the experiment. People attribute this to Aristotle in the second book of the Meteorologics; but he certainly does not make this statement, but he does make one like it, by which they have been deceived, namely, that if cold water and hot water are poured on a cold place, as upon ice, the hot water freezes more quickly, and this is true. But if hot water and cold are placed in two vessels, the cold will freeze more quickly. Therefore all things must be verified by experience.

Natural Marvels — No Magic

ROGER BACON

I SHALL TELL of certain marvels wrought through the agency of Art and of Nature, and will afterwards assign them to their causes and modes. In these there is no magic whatsoever, because, as has been said, all magical power is inferior to these works and incompetent to accomplish them. First, then, of mechanical devices.

Mechanical Devices. — It is possible that great ships and sea-going vessels shall be made which can be guided by one man and will move with greater swiftness than if they were full of oarsmen.

It is possible that a car shall be made which will move with inestimable speed, and the motion will be without the help of any living creature. Such, it is thought, were the *currus falcati* which the ancients used in combat.

It is possible that a device for flying shall be made such that a man sitting in the middle of it and turning a crank shall cause artificial wings to beat the air after the manner of a bird's flight.

Similarly, it is possible to construct a small-sized instrument for elevating and depressing great weights, a device which is most useful in certain exigencies. For a man may ascend and descend, and may deliver himself and his companions from peril of prison, by means of a device of small weight and of a height of three fingers and a breadth of four.

It is possible also easily to make an instrument by which a single man may violently pull a thousand men toward himself in spite of opposition, or other things which are tractable.

It is possible also that devices can be made whereby, without bodily danger, a man may walk on the bottom of the sea or of a river. Alexander used these to observe the secrets of the sea, as Ethicus the astronomer relates.

These devices have been made in antiquity and in our own time, and they are certain. I am acquainted with them explicitly, except with the instrument for flying which I have not seen. And I know no one who has seen it. But I know a wise man who has thought out the artifice. Infinite other such things can be made, as bridges over rivers without columns or supports, and machines, and unheard-of engines.

From *Letter on the Nullity of Magic,* translated by Professor Davis of the Massachusetts Institute of Technology.

Optical Phenomena and Devices. — Certain physical figurations are especially marvelous, for mirrors and perspective devices can be so arranged that one appears many, one man an army, and the sun and moon as many as we wish. So, mists and vapors sometimes occur in such manner that two suns, or even three, or two moons, appear simultaneously in the heavens, as Pliny narrates in 2 *Nat. Histor.* Since one thing by this means may appear to be many or to be infinite in number, and since it thus actually exceeds its own virtue, then there is no number that is determinate, as Aristotle argues in the chapter *de vacuo.* By this means infinite terror may be cast upon a whole city or upon an army so that it will go entirely to pieces because of the apparent multitude of the stars or of men congregated about it, especially if there be joined to this device another by which perspectives are contrived so that the most distant objects appear near at hand and vice-versa.

We may read the smallest letters at an incredible distance, we may see objects however small they may be, and we may cause the stars to appear wherever we wish. So, it is thought, Julius Cæsar spied into Gaul from the sea shore and by optical devices learned the position and arrangement of the camps and towns of Brittany. Devices may be so contrived that the largest objects appear smallest, that the highest appear low and infamous, and that hidden things appear manifest. Just as Socrates discovered the hiding-place among the hills of a dragon who was corrupting the city and region roundabout with his breath and pestilential influence, so may all that is going on in a city or in a hostile army be learned from the enemy.

Devices may be built to send forth poisonous and infectious emanations and influences wherever a man may wish. Aristotle taught this to Alexander, so that by casting the poison of the basilisk over the walls of a city which held out against his army he conveyed the poison into the city itself.

Mirrors may be so arranged that a man coming into a house shall really see gold, and silver, and precious stones, and whatever a man desires, but whoever approaches the place will find nothing.

But of sublimer powers is that device by which rays of light are led into any place that we wish and are brought together by refractions and reflections in such fashion that anything is burned which is placed there. And these burning glasses function in both directions, as certain authors teach in their books.

The greatest of all devices, however, and the greatest of all things which have been devised is that in which the heavens are described, according to longitude and latitude, with models which actually go through the diurnal movement. This device is worth more than a kingdom to a wise man.

The foregoing are sufficient as examples of constructed devices, though many other wonders might be mentioned in this connection.

Incendiary Compositions. — In addition to these marvels, there are certain others which do not involve particular constructions. We can prepare from saltpeter and other materials an artificial fire which will burn at whatever distance we please. The same may be made from red petroleum and other things, and from amber, and naphtha, and white petroleum, and from similar materials. Pliny reports in his second book that he defended a certain city against the Roman Army, and, by throwing down many incendiaries, burned the soldiers in spite of their armor. Greek Fire and many other combustibles are closely akin to these mixtures.

Further: perpetual lamps may be made, and baths which retain their heat forever, for we know of substances which are not burned by fire but which are purified.

Gunpowder. — Beyond these are still other stupendous things in Nature. For the sound of thunder may be artificially produced in the air with greater resulting horror than if it had been produced by natural causes. A moderate amount of proper material, of the size of the thumb, will make a horrible sound and violent corruscation. Such material may be used in a variety of ways, as, for instance, in a case similar to that in which a whole army and city were destroyed by means of the strategy of Gideon who, with broken jugs and torches, and with fire leaping forth with ineffable thunder, routed the army of the Midianites with three hundred men. These are miracles, if accepted according to their account in size and in substance.

I mention many wonders of another sort, which, though they may have no usefulness, still provide an ineffable spectacle of wisdom and can be applied to inquiring into all those occult matters which the unlearned crowd disbelieve. They are similar to the attraction of iron by the lodestone: for who would believe this attraction unless he should actually see it? There are many wonders of Nature which are not known to the crowd in this attraction of iron, as experience teaches the solicitous inquirer.

But there are still more and still greater than these. For similarly there is an attraction of all metals by the stone of silver and gold. A stone thus runs to vinegar, plants mutually seek one another, and the locally divided parts of animals concur in a natural movement. After I have perceived these things, there is nothing that I find difficult to believe when I reflect that it is either divine or human in its origin.

Self-Activated Working Model of the Heavens.— But there are greater than these. The great power of mathematics can build a spherical instrument, like the artifice of Ptolemy in *Almagest*, in which all heavenly bodies are described veraciously as regards longitude and latitude, but to make them move naturally in their diurnal movement is not within the power of mathematics. A faithful and magnificent experimenter might aspire to construct an instrument of such materials and of such an arrangement that it would move naturally in the diurnal motion of the heavens, a thing which seems possible because many things are determined by the movement of the heavens, such as comets, and the tides of the sea, and other things wholly and in part. In the presence of this instrument all other apparatus of the Astrologers, whether the product of wisdom or mere vulgar equipment, would cease to count any more. The treasure of a king would scarcely merit comparison with it.

"We Are Beholden to Experiments . . ."

THOMAS SPRAT

THE POETS of old, to make all things look more venerable than they were, devised a thousand false Chimaeras; on every Field, River, Grove and Cave, they bestowed a fantasm of their own making: with this they amazed the world. . . . And in the modern age these fantastical forms were revived and possessed Christendom, in the very height of the Schoolmens time: an infinite number of fairies haunted every house; all Churches were filled with apparitions; men began to be frighted from their cradles. . . . All which abuses if those acute philosophers did not promote, yet they were never able to overcome; nay, even not so much as King Oberon and his invisible army.

But from the time in which the real philosophy [science] has appeared there is scarce any whisper remaining of such horrors;

From *History of the Royal Society of London*, 1667.

every man is unshaken at those tales at which his ancestors trembled: the course of things goes quietly along, in its true channel of natural causes and effects. For this we are beholden to experiments; which though they have not yet completed the discovery of the true world, yet they have already vanquished those wild inhabitants of the false world, that used to astonish the minds of men.

⊂ξ *WHAT LANGUAGE FOR SCIENCE?*

English for the English

GEOFFREY CHAUCER

LITEL LOWIS my sone, I have perceived wel by certeyne evidences thyn abilite to lerne sciencez touchinge noumbres and proporciouns; and as wel considere I thy bisy preyere in special to lerne the Tretis of the Astrolabie. Than, for as mechel as a philosofre seith, 'he wrappeth him in his frend, that condescendeth to the rightful preyers of his frend,' ther-for have I geven thee a suffisaunt Astrolabie as for oure orizonte, compowned after the latitude of Oxenford; up-on which, by mediacion of this litel tretis, I purpose to teche thee a certein nombre of conclusions apertening to the same instrument. I seye a certein of conclusiouns, for three causes. The furste cause is this: truste wel that alle the conclusiouns that han ben founde, or elles possibly mighten be founde in so noble an instrument as an Astrolabie, ben un-knowe perfitly to any mortal man in this regioun, as I suppose. A-nother cause is this; that sothly, in any tretis of the Astrolabie that I have seyn, there ben some conclusions that wole nat in alle thinges performen hir bihestes; and some of hem ben to harde to thy tendre age of ten yeer to conseyve. This tretis, divided in fyve parties, wole I shewe thee under ful lighte rewles and naked wordes in English; for Latin ne canstow yit but smal, my lyte sone. But natheles, suffyse to thee thise trewe conclusiouns in English, as wel as suffyseth to thise noble clerkes Grekes thise same conclusiouns in Greek, and to Arabiens in Arabik, and to Jewes in Ebrew, and to the Latin folk in Latin; whiche Latin folk han hem furst out of othre diverse langages, and written in

From *A Treatise on the Astrolabe* by Geoffrey Chaucer.

hir owne tonge, that is to sein, in Latin. And god wot, that in alle thise langages, and in many mo, han thise conclusiouns ben suffisantly lerned and taught, and yit by diverse rewles, right as diverse pathes leden diverse folk the righte wey to Rome. Now wol I prey meekly every discreet persone that redeth or hereth this litel tretis, to have my rewde endyting for excused, and my super-fluite of wordes, for two causes. The firste cause is, for that curious endyting and hard sentence is ful hevy atones for swich a child to lerne. And the seconde cause is this, that sothly me semeth betre to wryten un-to a child twyes a good sentence, than he forgete it ones. And Lowis, yif so be that I shewe thee in my lighte English as trewe conclusiouns touching this matere, and naught only as trewe but as many and as subtil conclusiouns as ben shewed in Latin in any commune tretis of the Astrolabie, con me the more thank; and preye god save the king, that is lord of this langage, and alle that him feyth bereth and obeyeth, everech in his degree, the more and the lasse. But considere wel, that I ne usurpe nat to have founde this werk of my labour or of myn engyn. I nam but a lewd compilatour of the labour of olde Astrologiens, and have hit trans-lated in myn English only for thy doctrine; and with this swerd shal I sleen envye.

Words and Matter

FRANCIS BACON

HERE THEREFORE is the first distemper of learning, when men study words and not matter; whereof, though I have represented an example of late times, yet it hath been and will be *secundum majus et minus* in all time. And how is it possible but this should have an operation to discredit learning, even with vulgar capacities, when they see learned men's works like the first letter of a patent, or limned book; which though it hath large flourishes, yet it is but a letter? It seems to me that Pygmalion's frenzy is a good emblem or portraiture of this vanity: for words are but the images of matter;

From Francis Bacon: *The Advancement of Learning*, Clarendon Press, Oxford.

and except they have life of reason and invention, to fall in love with them is all one as to fall in love with a picture.

But yet notwithstanding it is a thing not hastily to be condemned, to clothe and adorn the obscurity even of philosophy itself with sensible and plausible elocution. . . .

The second [distemper] which followeth is in nature worse than the former: for as substance of matter is better than beauty of words, so contrariwise vain matter is worse than vain words: wherein it seemeth the reprehension of Saint Paul was not only proper for those times, but prophetical for the times following; and not only respective to divinity, but extensive to all knowledge: *Devita profanas vocum novitates, et oppositiones falsi nominis scientiae.* For he assigneth two marks and badges of suspected and falsified science: the one, the novelty and strangeness of terms; the other, the strictness of positions, which of necessity doth induce oppositions, and so questions and altercations. Surely, like as many substances in nature which are solid do putrify and corrupt into worms; so it is the property of good and sound knowledge to putrify and dissolve into a number of subtle, idle, unwholesome, and (as I may term them) vermiculate questions, which have indeed a kind of quickness and life of spirit but no soundness of matter or goodness of quality. This kind of degenerate learning did chiefly reign amongst the schoolmen: who having sharp and strong wits, and abundance of leisure, and small variety of reading, but their wits being shut up in the cells of a few authors (chiefly Aristotle their dictator) as their persons were shut up in the cells of monasteries and colleges, and knowing little history, either of nature or time, did out of no great quantity of matter and infinite agitation of wit spin out unto us those laborious webs of learning which are extant in their books. For the wit and mind of man, if it work upon matter, which is the contemplation of the creatures of God, worketh according to the stuff and is limited thereby; but if it work upon itself, as the spider worketh his web, then it is endless, and brings forth indeed cobwebs of learning, admirable for the fineness of thread and work, but of no substance or profit.

◇◇

Marriage of the Faculties

FRANCIS BACON

TIME IS LIKE A RIVER, which has brought down to us things light and puffed up, while those which are weighty and solid have sunk. Nay, those very authors who have usurped a kind of dictatorship in the sciences and taken upon them to lay down the law with such confidence, yet when from time to time they come to themselves again, they fall to complaints of the subtlety of nature, the hiding-places of truth, the obscurity of things, the entanglement of causes, the weakness of the human mind; wherein nevertheless they show themselves never the more modest, seeing that they will rather lay the blame upon the common condition of men and nature than upon themselves. And then whatever any art fails to attain, they ever set it down upon the authority of that art itself as impossible of attainment; and how can art be found guilty when it is judge in its own cause? So it is but a device for exempting ignorance from ignominy. Now for those things which are delivered and received, this is their condition: barren of works, full of questions; in point of enlargement slow and languid; carrying a show of perfection in the whole, but in the parts ill filled up; in selection popular, and unsatisfactory even to those who propound them; and therefore fenced round and set forth with sundry artifices. And if there be any who have determined to make trial for themselves, and put their own strength to the work of advancing the boundaries of the sciences, yet have they not ventured to cast themselves completely loose from received opinions or to seek their knowledge at the fountain, but they think they have done some great thing if they do but add and introduce into the existing sum of science something of their own; prudently considering with themselves that by making the addition they can assert their liberty, while they retain the credit of modesty by assenting to the rest. But these mediocrities and middle ways so much praised, in deferring to opinions and customs, turn to the great detriment of the sciences. . . . And if there have been any who, not binding themselves either to other men's opinions or to their own, but loving liberty, have desired to engage others along with themselves in search, these, though honest in intention, have been weak in endeavor. For they have been content to follow probable reasons, and are carried round in a

From *The Great Instauration* (Preface) by Francis Bacon.

whirl of arguments, and in the promiscuous liberty of search have relaxed the severity of inquiry. There is none who has dwelt upon experience and the facts of nature as long as is necessary. Some there are indeed who have committed themselves to the waves of experience, and almost turned mechanics; yet these again have in their very experiments pursued a kind of wandering inquiry, without any regular system of operations. And besides they have mostly proposed to themselves certain petty tasks, taking it for a great matter to work out some single discovery; — a course of proceeding at once poor in aim and unskillful in design. For no man can rightly and successfully investigate the nature of anything in the thing itself; let him vary his experiments as laboriously as he will, he never comes to a resting place, but still finds something to seek beyond. And there is another thing to be remembered: namely, that all industry in experimenting has begun with proposing to itself certain definite works to be accomplished, and has pursued them with premature and unseasonable eagerness; it has sought, I say, experiments of Fruit, not experiments of Light: not imitating the divine procedure, which in its first day's work created light only and assigned to it one entire day; on which day it produced no material work, but proceeded to that on the days following.

Upon the whole, therefore, it seems that men have not been happy hitherto either in the trust which they have placed in others or in their own industry with regard to the sciences; especially as neither the demonstrations nor the experiments as yet known are much to be relied upon. But the universe to the eye of the human understanding is framed like a labyrinth; presenting as it does on every side so many ambiguities of way, such deceitful resemblances of objects and signs, natures so irregular in their lines, and so knotted and entangled. And then the way is still to be made by the uncertain light of the sense, sometimes shining out, sometimes clouded over, through the woods of experience and particulars; while those who offer themselves for guides are (as was said) themselves also puzzled, and increase the number of errors and wanderings. In circumstances so difficult, neither the natural force of man's judgment nor even any accidental felicity offers any chance of success. No excellence of wit, no repetition of chance experiments, can overcome such difficulties as these. Our steps must be guided by a clue, and the whole way from the very first perception of the senses must be laid out upon a sure plan. Not that I would be understood to mean that nothing whatever has been done in so many ages by so great labors. We have no reason to be ashamed of the discoveries which have been made, and no doubt the ancients prove themselves in everything that turns on wit and abstract meditation, wonderful men. But as in former ages when men sailed only by observation of the stars, they could indeed coast along the shores of the old continent or cross a few small and mediterranean seas; but before the ocean could be traversed and the new world discovered, the use of the mariner's needle, as a more faithful and certain guide, had to be found out: in like manner the discoveries which have been hitherto made in the arts and sciences are such as might be made by practice, meditation, observation, argumentation — for they lay near to the senses, and immediately beneath common notions; but before we can reach the remoter and more hidden parts of nature, it is necessary that a more perfect use and application of the human mind and intellect be introduced.

For my own part at least, in obedience to the everlasting love of truth, I have committed myself to the uncertainties and difficulties and solitudes of the ways, and relying on the divine assistance have upheld my mind both against the shocks and embattled ranks of opinion, and against my own private and inward hesitations and scruples, and against the fogs and clouds of nature, and the phantoms flitting about on every side; in the hope of providing at last for the present and future generations guidance more faithful and secure. Wherein if I have made any progress, the way has been opened to me by no other means than the true and legitimate humiliation of the human spirit. For all those who before me have applied themselves to the invention of arts have but cast a glance or two upon facts and examples and experience, and straightway proceeded, as if invention were nothing more than an exercise of thought, to invoke their own spirits to give them oracles. I, on the contrary, dwelling purely and constantly among the facts of nature, withdraw my intellect from them no further than may suffice to let the images and rays of natural objects meet in a point, as they do in the sense of vision; whence it follows that the strength and excellency of the wit has but little to do in the matter. And the same humility which I use in inventing I employ likewise in teaching. For I do not endeavor either by triumphs of confutation, or pleadings of antiquity, or assumption of authority, or even by the veil of obscurity, to invest these inventions of mine with any majesty; which might easily be done by one who sought to give luster to his own name rather than light to other men's minds. I have not sought (I say) nor do I seek either to force or ensnare men's judgments; but I lead them to things themselves and the concordance of things, that they may see for themselves what they have, what they can dispute, what they can add and contribute to the common stock. And for myself, if in anything I have been either too credulous or

too little awake and attentive, or if I have fallen off by the way and
left the inquiry incomplete, nevertheless I so present these things
naked and open, that my errors can be marked and set aside before
the mass of knowledge be further infected by them; and it will be
easy also for others to continue and carry on my labors. And by
these means I suppose that I have established for ever a true and
lawful marriage between the empirical and the rational faculty, the
unkind and ill-starred divorce and separation of which has thrown
into confusion all the affairs of the human family.

◇◇

◖ MATHEMATICS AND THE LAWS
OF NATURE

HERMANN WEYL

KNOWLEDGE in all physical sciences — astronomy, physics,
chemistry — is based on observation. But observation can only ascertain what is. How can we predict what will be? To that end
observation must be combined with mathematics.

One of the ancient Greek philosophers, Anaxagoras, first explained solar and lunar eclipses by means of the shadows of moon
and earth intercepting the rays of the sun. You may say that he
applied the idea of perspective to the heavenly bodies. Just a few
years before, perspective had begun to be used for the stage decorations in the Athenian theater. Anaxagoras had the imagination to
see something in common between stage decorations and eclipses.
What made his approach possible? First this: that the Greeks had
developed geometry as a mathematical science proceeding by pure
reasoning from a few basic laws or axioms. "Through two distinct
points there goes one and only one straight line" is one of these
axioms that everybody takes for granted. Geometry had made the
behavior of straight lines predictable. The second prerequisite for
Anaxagoras' achievement is the conception of light rays as the

First given as a talk during the intermission of a New York Philharmonic-
Symphony broadcast sponsored by the U.S. Rubber Company. Reprinted by
permission of F. Joachim Weyl.

agents that carry messages from the object to our eyes and thus give rise to our visual image of the object. This conception is purely hypothetical — a flash of genius as it were.

Third: a mathematical theory of light rays, namely that they are straight lines. That theory is suggested by experience. By combining these three ingredients — geometry, the conception of light rays, and the theory that they are straight — one can account for all the familiar facts of shadows and perspective.

It is on the same theoretical foundation that a surveyor determines the distance of a remote object: he measures his base and certain angles and then draws his conclusions by means of the geometry of light rays. In very much the same way Anaxagoras made his indirect measurement of the moon's distance from us. That distance is certainly not directly measurable by tapeline. With this example in mind you will understand the following general statements: All indirect measurements, like that of the distance of the moon, are ultimately anchored in direct measurements. The link between the indirect and the direct measurements must be furnished by theory — in this case by the theory of perspective. A theory makes good when all indirect measurements based on it check. This is a methodic principle of paramount importance.

Anaxagoras could have carried out his construction with pencil on paper, or rather with a reed on papyrus. But diagrams thus drawn are far too inaccurate for the purposes of astronomy.

Numbers, on the other hand, are capable of truly unlimited accuracy; and the use of numbers instead of geometric diagrams becomes indispensable anyhow as soon as time and such entities as mass, electrical charge, force, temperature have to be dealt with. The latter are all measurable quantities, though accessible to indirect measurement only. It was Galileo who said: "Measure what is measurable, and make measurable what is not so."

Mathematicians got along with geometry all right, but with the numbers they really come into their own. For the sequence of the natural numbers, 1, 2, 3, . . . is our minds' own free creation. It starts with 1, and any number is followed by the next one. That is all. According to this simple procedure the numbers march on toward infinity. 2 is the number that follows 1, 3 the number that follows 2, etc. Nothing else. You know very little about Henry VIII when you know that he followed Henry VII on the English throne. But you know all about 8 when you know that it follows 7. Man has his substantial existence; the words of our language have meanings with shifting subtle nuances; the tones of our musical compositions have their sensuous qualities. But numbers have neither substance, nor meaning, nor qualities. They are nothing but marks, and all that is in them we have put into them by the simple rule of straight succession.

It is therefore no wonder that we can predict what they do: for instance, that 7 plus 5 makes 12, or that an even number is always followed by an odd one. But do not imagine that all arithmetical laws are that trivial. As a matter of fact the mathematicians have been busy for many generations to discover more and more profound and universal laws, and they find that every progress raises new problems. I think the difficulty of their task is mainly due to the fact that the sequence of numbers is infinite.

After this digression about mathematics I resume my story. Passing on from Anaxagoras, and skipping 2000 years, I come to Kepler. He established his famous three laws about the motion of the planets. The only one that concerns us here is his first law: The planetary orbits are ellipses with the sun as their common focus. The Greek mathematicians had come upon the ellipses as the simplest curves after the straight lines and circles. Kepler had first tried circles; they did not fit the observations. He then turned to the only slightly more complicated ellipses and they fitted; they did so to an extraordinary degree of accuracy, and have not ceased to do so up to this date. Three remarks are here in order.

First: Kepler could not derive his laws from observation; for observation indicates merely the varying direction of the line joining our planet the earth, with the planet under observation.

Second: his idea of the elliptic orbit depended on the preliminary discovery of the ellipses by the Greek mathematicians.

Third: whatever the observations are, they could always have been fitted by a suitable curve; the point is that a vast number of detailed observations fit with such a simple curve as the ellipse. Kepler shared with Pythagoras and his followers a deep belief in the harmony of the universe. But for the Pythagoreans this was a sort of mystic creed. With Kepler it became a fact, in my opinion the most important fact we know about the universe. I formulate it this way: There is inherent in nature a hidden harmony that reflects itself in our minds under the image of simple mathematical laws. That then is the reason why events in nature are predictable by a combination of observation and mathematical analysis. Again and again in the history of physics this conviction, or should I say this dream, of harmony in nature has found fulfillments beyond expectation.

Now I can be brief. The conceptual basis of Kepler's theory was still the same as with Anaxagoras. Galileo, the father of modern science, brought in a new conception: he visualized motion as a struggle between inertia and force. A moving body has mass and momentum, and is acted upon by forces. This conception has remained the firm foundation of our physical understanding to this day, unshaken even by atomic and quantum physics.

And so has his basic law: Force changes momentum at a rate equal to the force. Rate of change is a mathematical notion that is defined in calculus. Newton added the idea of a universal force of gravitation acting between any two mass particles. His dynamical law of gravitation, the simplest that algebra can devise, is essentially simpler than the medley of Kepler's three kinematical laws, but covers and predicts a far wider range of phenomena with the minutest accuracy. Again we find the three characteristic features: the necessary mathematics, here calculus and algebra, developed beforehand by the mathematicians; a basic conception about the nature of things; and a theory expressed in terms of both. Many more illustrations could be adduced from modern physics. Digging for the roots of the phenomena we drive the spade deeper and deeper. Galileo and Newton reached a deeper layer than their predecessor Kepler, and we continue their labors. But thereby the gap between theory and observation becomes ever wider. Mathematics has to work harder and harder to bridge this gap. Newton himself was held up by a mathematical difficulty of this sort for twenty years.

A peculiar situation prevails in quantum physics: The mathematical apparatus, in terms of which Schrödinger expressed the basic law of quantum physics, had indeed been developed by the mathematicians beforehand — as in the other cases we discussed.

But the stimulus to this mathematical development had originally come from a ground where music and physics meet, the acoustics of vibrating bodies. Studies undertaken to understand musical harmony have thus finally enabled us to understand the richest harmony in the visible world — that of the spectral lines emitted by radiating atoms.

"Bring Arguments and Proofs"

GALILEO GALILEI

Second Day

SIMPLICIO: I must confess that I have reflected all night upon what happened yesterday [examination of the principles of Ptolemy and Copernicus], and truth to tell, I have discovered many shrewd, new and plausible notions; yet nevertheless I find that I am swayed by the opinion of so many great writers, and in particular . . . I see you shake your head, Sagredo, and smile to yourself as if I had uttered some great absurdity.

SAGREDO: I not only smile, but to tell you the truth I am bursting with restraining myself from laughing outright; for you have reminded me of a very pretty story that I have witnessed not so many years ago, in the company of some of my other worthy friends, whom I could name to you.

SALVIATI: It would be well if you told us about it, so that Simplicio might not think it was he who caused your laughter.

SAGREDO: Very well. One day, in his home at Venice, I found a famous physician, to whom some flocked for their studies and others out of curiosity to see some dissections by the hands of this learned, careful and experienced anatomist. On that day, it so happened that, while I was there, he was in search of the origin and rise of the nerves about which there is a famous controversy between the Galenists and the Peripatetics [followers of Aristotle]. While the anatomist demonstrated how the great many nerves starting from the brain, their root, and then passing by the nape of the neck, distend thereafter along the backbone and branch out through all the body and that a very small filament, as fine as a thread, went to the heart; he turned to a gentleman whom he knew to be a peripatetic philosopher, and for whose sake he had, with extraordinary exactness, demonstrated and proved everything, and asked him if he was at length satisfied and persuaded that the origin of the nerves proceeded from the brain, and not from the heart. To which the philosopher, after he had stood musing awhile, answered: "You have made me see this business so plainly and sensibly, that did not the text of Aristotle assert the contrary, which positively affirmed

From *Dialogue About the Two Chief World Systems* by Galileo, based on the Salusbury translation, in Werner Heisenberg: *The Physicist's Conception of Nature*. Reprinted by permission of Messrs. Hutchinson and Co., Ltd. and Harcourt, Brace and Company, Inc.

the nerves to proceed from the heart, I should be constrained to confess your opinion to be true."

SIMPLICIO: I would have you know, masters, that this controversy about the origin of the nerves is by no means as proved and decided as some may perhaps persuade themselves.

SAGREDO: Nor doubtless will it ever be, if it find such contradictions; but what you say by no means lessens the extravagance of the answer of that Peripatetic, who against such sensible experience produced not other experiments nor yet the arguments of Aristotle, but his mere authority and pure *ipse dixit*.

SIMPLICIO: Aristotle has gained his authority by the force of his demonstrations and by the profoundness of his arguments; but it is essential that we understand him, and not only understand but have so great familiarity with his books that we form a perfect idea of them in our minds, so that every saying of his might always, as it were, be present in our memory; for he did not write for the crowd, nor did he feel obliged to spin out his syllogisms with the trivial method of disputes; indeed he has sometimes made free to place the proof of one proposition amongst facts which seem to treat of quite another point; and therefore it is essential to be master of all that vast idea, and to learn how to connect this passage with that and how to combine this text with another far remote from it; for it is beyond doubt that who has thus studied him knows how to gather from his books the demonstrations of every knowable deduction, for they contain everything.

SAGREDO: But, good Simplicio, just as the things scattered here and there in Aristotle give you no trouble in their collection, and in persuading yourself that by comparing and connecting several small sentences you can extract the juice of some desired conclusion, so what you and other brave philosophers do with the text of Aristotle, I could do by the verses of Virgil or Ovid, composing thereof Centones wherewith I could explain the entire affairs of man, and the secrets of nature. But why do I speak of Virgil or any other poet? I have a little book, much shorter than Aristotle or Ovid, in which are contained all the sciences, and with very little study one may gather out of it a most perfect idea, and this is the Alphabet; and there is no doubt but that he who knows how to combine and dispose aright this or that vowel, with such and such consonants may gather thence the infallible answer to all doubts, and deduce from them the principles of all Sciences and all Arts; just in the same manner as the painter from diverse simple colors, laid severally upon his palette, proceeds by mixing a little of this and that with a little of a third, to represent to the life men, plants, buildings, birds, fishes, and in a word reproducing whatever object is visible; though there be never upon the palette either eyes, feathers, fins, leaves or stones. Indeed, it is essential that none of the things to be imitated, or any part of them, be actually among the colors if you want the latter for representing all things; for should there be, for instance, feathers amongst them, these would serve to represent nothing but birds and plumed creatures.

SALVIATI: And there are certain gentlemen yet living and in health who were present when a doctor who happened to be Professor in a famous Academy, hearing the description of the telescope, by him not seen before, said that the invention was taken from Aristotle, and causing his works to be fetched, he turned to a place where the philosopher gives the reason why, from the bottom of a deep well, one may see the stars in Heaven at noon; and addressing himself to the company, "See here," he says, "the well which represents the tube; see here the gross vapors from which is taken the invention of lenses, and see here lastly the intensification of the powers of sight by the passage of light-rays through a denser, dark and transparent medium."

SAGREDO: This manner of understanding all that is knowable, is like that whereby a piece of marble contains in it one, indeed a thousand, very beautiful statues, but the difficulty lies in discovering them, or we may say that it is like the prophecies of the Abbot Joachim, or the answers of the Heathen Oracles, which cannot be understood till all the things foretold have come to pass.

SALVIATI: And why do you not add the predictions of the Astrologers which with equal cleverness can be seen after the event, in horoscopes or, if you will, the configuration of the Heavens. . . .

SIMPLICIO: But if we should recede from Aristotle, whom are we to take for our guide in philosophy? Name me another.

SALVIATI: We need a guide when we are in unknown and uncouth lands, but in the open plains the blind alone stand in need of a leader, and for such it is better that they stay at home. But he that has eyes in his head, and in his mind, him should we choose as our guide. Yet mistake me not, thinking that because I say this I would not listen to Aristotle; on the contrary I commend the reading and diligent study of his works, and only deplore a slavish surrender to him, a blind acceptance of any of his *dicta* without any search for further reasons to take these for inviolable laws. This is an abuse that carries with it another inconvenience, to wit, that others will no longer take pains to understand the validity of his proofs. And what is more shameful in the middle of public disputes, while one person is treating of provable conclusions, than to hear the other parry with a passage from Aristotle, often written with quite a different aim, and thus to stop the mouth of his opponent? But if you will continue to study in this manner, I would have you lay aside the name of philosopher [i.e. scientist] and call yourselves either historians or Doctors of Memory, for it is not fit that those who never philosophize should usurp the honorable title of philosophers. But it is best for us to return to shore, and not launch further into a boundless gulf, out of which we shall not be able to get before night. Therefore, Simplicio, come either with arguments and proof of your own, or those of Aristotle, and bring us no more texts and naked authorities, for our disputes are about the sensible world and not about paper.

A New Theory about Light and Colors

ISAAC NEWTON

Numb. 80.

PHILOSOPHICAL
TRANSACTIONS.

February 19. 1671/72.

The CONTENTS.

A Letter of Mr. Isaac Newton, *Mathematick Professor in the University of Cambridge; containing his New Theory about* Light *and* Colors: *Where* Light *is declared to be not Similar or Homogeneal, but consisting of difform rays, some of which are more refrangible than others: And* Colors *are affirm'd to be not Qualifications of* Light, *deriv'd from Refractions of natural Bodies, (as 'tis generally believed;) but Original and Connate properties, which in divers rays are divers: Where several Observations and Experiments are alledged to prove the said Theory. An Accompt of some Books:* I. *A Description of the* EAST-INDIAN COASTS, MALABAR, COROMANDEL, CEYLON, &c. in Dutch, by Phil. Baldæus.

From the *Philosophical Transactions of the Royal Society of London.*

II. Antonii le Grand *INSTITUTIO PHILOSOPHIÆ*, secun-
dùm principia Renati Des-Cartes; *novâ methodo adornata & ex-
plicata*. III. *An Essay to the Advancement of MUSICK; by*
Thomas Salmon *M. A. Advertisement about* Thæon Smyrnæus.
An Index *for the Tracts of the Year* 1671.

A *letter of Mr.* Isaac Newton, *Professor of the Mathematicks in the
University of Cambridge; containing his New Theory about* Light
and Colors: *sent by the Author to the Publisher from Cambridge,
Febr.* 6. 1671/72; *in order to be communicated to the* R. Society.

SIR,

To perform my late promise to you, I shall without further ceremony
acquaint you, that in the beginning of the Year 1666 (at which time
I applyed my self to the grinding of Optick glasses of other figures
than *Spherical,*) I procured me a Triangular glass-Prisme, to try
therewith the celebrated *Phænomena* of *Colours*. And in order
thereto having darkened my chamber, and made a small hole in my
window-shuts, to let in a convenient quantity of the Suns light, I
placed my Prisme at his entrance, that it might be thereby refracted
to the opposite wall. It was at first a very pleasing divertisement, to
view the vivid and intense colours produced thereby; but after a
while applying my self to consider them more circumspectly, I became surprised to see them in an *oblong* form; which, according to
the received laws of Refraction, I expected should have been *circular*.

They were terminated at the sides with streight lines, but at the
ends, the decay of light was so gradual, that it was difficult to determine justly, what was their figure; yet they seemed *semicircular*.

Comparing the length of this coloured *Spectrum* with its breadth,
I found it about five times greater; a disproportion so extravagant,
that it excited me to a more then ordinary curiosity of examining,
from whence it might proceed. I could scarce think, that the various
Thickness of the glass, or the termination with shadow or darkness,
could have any Influence on light to produce such an effect; yet I
thought it not amiss, first to examine those circumstances, and so
tryed, what would happen by transmitting light through parts of
the glass of divers thicknesses, or through holes in the window of
divers bignesses, or by setting the Prisme without so, that the light
might pass through it, and be refracted before it was terminated by
the hole: But I found none of those circumstances material. The
fashion of the colours was in all these cases the same.

Then I suspected, whether by any *unevenness* in the glass, or other
contingent irregularity, these colours might be thus dilated. And to

try this, I took another Prisme like the former, and so placed it, that the light, passing through them both, might be refracted contrary ways, and so by the latter returned into that course, from which the former had diverted it. For, by this means I thought, the *regular* effects of the first Prisme would be destroyed by the second Prisme, but the *irregular* ones more augmented, by the multiplicity of refractions. The event was, that the light, which by the first Prisme was diffused into an *oblong* form, was by the second reduced into an *orbicular* one with as much regularity, as when it did not at all pass through them. So that, what ever was the cause of that length, 'twas not any contingent irregularity.

I then proceeded to examin more critically, what might be effected by the difference of the incidence of Rays coming from divers parts of the Sun; and to that end, measured the several lines and angles, belonging to the Image. Its distance from the hole or Prisme was 22 foot; its utmost length 13¼ inches; its breadth 2⅜; the diameter of the hole ¼ of an inch; the angle, with the Rays, tending towards the middle of the image, made with those lines, in which they would have proceeded without refraction, was 44.deg.56'. And the vertical Angle of the Prisme, 63 deg. 12'. Also the Refractions on both sides of the Prisme, that is, of the Incident, and Emergent Rays, were as near, as I could make them, equal, and consequently about 54 deg. 4'. And the Rays fell perpendicularly upon the wall. Now subducting the diameter of the hole from the length and breadth of the Image, there remains 13 Inches the length, and 2⅙ the breadth, comprehended by those Rays, which passed through the center of the said hole, and consequently the angle of the hole, which that breadth subtended, was about 31', answerable to the Suns Diameter; but the angle, which its length subtended, was more than five such diameters, namely 2 deg. 49'.

Having made these observations, I first computed from them the refractive power of that glass, and found it measured by the *ratio* of the sines, 20 to 31. And then, by that *ratio*, I computed the Refractions of two Rays flowing from opposite parts of the Sun's *discus*, so as to differ 31' in their obliquity of Incidence, and found, that the emergent Rays should have comprehended an angle of about 31', as they did, before they were incident.

But because this computation was founded on the Hypothesis of the proportionality of the *sines* of Incidence, and Refraction, which though by my own Experience I could not imagine to be so erroneous, as to make that Angle but 31', which in reality was 2 deg. 49'; yet my curiosity caused me again to take my Prisme. And having placed it at my window, as before, I observed, that by turning it a little about its *axis* to and fro, so as to vary its obliquity to the light, more then an angle of 4 or 5 degrees, the Colours were not thereby sensibly translated from their place on the wall, and consequently by that variation of Incidence, the quantity of Refraction was not sensibly varied. By this Experiment therefore, as well as by the former computation, it was evident, that the difference of the Incidence of Rays, flowing from divers parts of the Sun, could not make them after decussation diverge at a sensibly greater angle, than that at which they before converged; which being, at most, but about 31 or 32 minutes, there still remained some other cause to be found out, from whence it could be 2 degr. 49'.

Then I began to suspect, whether the Rays, after their trajection through the Prisme, did not move in curve lines, and according to their more or less curvity tend to divers parts of the wall. And it increased my suspition, when I remembred that I had often seen a Tennis ball, struck with an oblique Racket, describe such a curve line. For, a circular as well as a progressive motion being communicated to it by that stroak, its parts on that side, where the motions conspire, must press and beat the contiguous Air more violently than on the other, and there excite a reluctancy and reaction of the Air proportionably greater. And for the same reason, if the Rays of light should possibly be globular bodies, and by their oblique passage out of one medium into another acquire a circulating motion, they ought to feel the greater resistance from the ambient Æther, on that side, where the motions conspire, and thence be continually bowed to the other. But notwithstanding this plausible ground of suspition, when I came to examine it, I could observe no such curvity in them. And besides (which was enough for my purpose) I observed, that the difference 'twixt the length of the Image, and diameter of the hole, through which the light was transmitted, was proportionable to their distance.

The gradual removal of these suspitions, at length led me to the *Experimentum Crucis,* which was this: I took two boards, and placed one of them close behind the Prisme at the window, so that the light might pass through a small hole, made in it for the purpose, and fall on the other board, which I placed at about 12 feet distance, having first made a small hole in it also, for some of that Incident light to pass through. Then I placed another Prisme behind this second board, so that the light, trajected through both the boards, might pass through that also, and be again refracted before it arrived at the wall. This done, I took the first Prisme in my hand, and turned it to and fro slowly about its *Axis,* so much as to make the several parts of the Image, cast on the second board, successively pass through the hole in it, that I might observe to what places on the wall the second Prisme would refract them. And I saw by the variation of those places, that the light, tending to that end of the Image, towards which the refraction of the first Prisme was made, did in the second Prisme suffer a Refraction considerably greater then the light tending to the other end. And so the true cause of the length of that Image was detected to be no other, then that *Light* consists of *Rays differently refrangible,* which, without any respect to a difference in their incidence, were, according to their degrees of refrangibility, transmitted towards divers parts of the wall.

When I understood this, I left off my aforesaid Glass works; for I saw, that the perfection of Telescopes was hitherto limited, not so much for want of glasses truly figured according to the prescriptions of Optick Authors, (which all men have hitherto imagined,) as because that Light it self is a *Heterogeneous mixture of differently refrangible Rays.* So that, were a glass so exactly figured, as to collect any one sort of rays into one point, it could not collect those also into the same point, which having the same Incidence upon the same Medium are apt to suffer a different refraction. Nay, I wondered, that seeing the difference of refrangibility was so great, as I found it, Telescopes should arrive to that perfection they are now at. For, measuring the refractions in one of my Prismes, I found, that supposing the common *sine* of Incidence upon one of its planes was 44 parts, the *sine* of refraction of the utmost Rays on the red end of the Colours, made out of the glass into the Air, would be 68 parts, and the *sine* of refraction of the utmost rays on the other end, 69 parts: So that the difference is about a 24*th* or 25*th* part of the whole refraction. And consequently, the object-glass of any Telescope cannot collect all the rays, which come from one point of an object so as to make them convene at its *focus* in less room then in a circular space, whose diameter is the 50*th* part of the Diameter of its Aperture; which is an irregularity, some hundreds of times greater, then a circularly figured *Lens,* of so small a section as the Object glasses of long Telescopes are, would cause by the unfitness of its figure, were Light *uniform.*

This made me take *Reflections* into consideration, and finding them regular, so that the Angle of Reflection of all sorts of Rays was equal to their Angle of Incidence; I understood, that by their mediation Optick instruments might be brought to any degree of perfection imaginable, provided a *Reflecting* substance could be found, which would polish as finely as Glass, and *reflect* as much light, as glass *transmits,* and the art of communicating to it a *Parabolick* figure be also attained. But there seemed very great difficulties, and I have almost thought them insuperable, when I further considered, that every irregularity in a reflecting superficies makes the rays stray 5 or 6 times more out of their due course, than the like irregularities in a refracting one: So that a much greater curiosity would be here requisite, than in figuring glasses for Refraction.

Amidst these thoughts I was forced from *Cambridge* by the Intervening Plague, and it was more then two years, before I proceeded further. But then having thought on a tender way of polishing, proper for metall, whereby, as I imagined, the figure also would be corrected to the last; I began to try, what might be effected in this kind, and by degrees so far perfected an Instrument (in the essential parts of it like that I sent to *London*,) by which I could discern Jupiters 4 Concomitants, and shewed them divers times to two others of my acquaintance. I could also discern the Moon-like phase of *Venus*, but not very distinctly, nor without some niceness in disposing the Instrument.

From that time I was interrupted till this last Autumn, when I made the other. And as that was sensibly better then the first (especially for Day-Objects,) so I doubt not, but they would be still brought to a much greater perfection by their endeavours, who, as you inform me, are taking care about it at *London*.

I have sometimes thought to make a *Microscope*, which in like manner should have, instead of an Object-glass, a Reflecting piece of metall. And this I hope they will also take into consideration. For those Instruments seem as capable of improvement as *Telescopes*, and perhaps more, because but one reflective piece of metall is requisite in them, as you may perceive by the annexed diagram, where A B representeth the object metall, C D the eye glass, F their common Focus, and O the other focus of the metall, in which the object is placed.

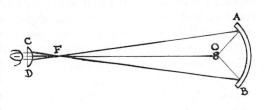

But to return from this digression, I told you, that Light is not similar, or homogeneal, but consists of *difform* Rays, some of which are more refrangible than others: So that of those, which are alike incident on the same medium, some shall be more refracted than others, and that not by any virtue of the glass, or other external cause, but from a predisposition, which every particular Ray hath to suffer a particular degree of Refraction.

I shall now proceed to acquaint you with another more notable difformity in its Rays, wherein the *Origin of Colours* is unfolded: Concerning which I shall lay down the *Doctrine* first, and then, for its examination, give you an instance or two of the *Experiments,* as a specimen of the rest.

The Doctrine you will find comprehended and illustrated in the following propositions.

1. As the Rays of light differ in degrees of Refrangibility, so they also differ in their disposition to exhibit this or that particular colour. Colours are not *Qualifications of Light,* derived from Refractions, or Reflections of natural Bodies (as 'tis generally believed,) but *Original* and *connate properties,* which in divers Rays are divers. Some Rays are disposed to exhibit a red colour and no other; some a yellow and no other, some a green and no other, and so of the rest. Nor are there only Rays proper and particular to the more eminent colours, but even to all their intermediate gradations.

2. To the same degree of Refrangibility ever belongs the same colour, and to the same colour ever belongs the same degree of Refrangibility. The *least Refrangible* Rays are all disposed to exhibit a *Red* colour, and contrarily those Rays, which are disposed to exhibit a *Red* colour, are all the least refrangible: So the *most refrangible* rays are all disposed to exhibit a deep *Violet-Colour,* and contrarily those which are apt to exhibit such a violet colour, are all the most Refrangible. And so to all the intermediate colours in a continued series belong intermediate degrees of refrangibility. And this Analogy 'twixt colours, and refrangibility, is very precise and strict; the Rays always either exactly agreeing in both, or proportionally disagreeing in both.

3. The species of colour, and degree of Refrangibility proper to any particular sort of Rays, is not mutable by Refraction, nor by Reflection from natural bodies, nor by any other cause, that I could yet observe. When any one sort of Rays hath been well parted from those of other kinds, it hath afterwards obstinately retained its colour, notwithstanding my utmost endeavours to change it. I have refracted it with Prismes, and reflected it with Bodies, which in Day-light were of other colours; I have intercepted it with the coloured film of Air interceding two compressed plates of glass; transmitted it through coloured Mediums, and through Mediums irradiated with other sorts of Rays, and diversly terminated it; and yet could never produce any new colour out of it. It would by contracting or dilating become more brisk, or faint, and by the loss of many Rays, in some cases very obscure and dark; but I could never see it changed *in specie.*

[4.] Yet seeming transmutations of Colours may be made, where there is any mixture of divers sorts of Rays. For in such mixtures, the component colours appear not, but, by their mutual allaying each other, constitute a midling colour. And therefore, if by refraction, or any other of the aforesaid causes, the difform Rays, latent in such a mixture, be separated, there shall emerge colours different from the colour of the composition. Which colours are not New generated, but only made Apparent by being parted; for if they be again intirely mix't and blended together, they will again compose that colour, which they did before separation. And for the same reason, Transmutations made by the convening of divers colours are not real; for when the difform Rays are again severed, they will exhibit the very same colours, which they did before they entered the composition; as you see, *Blew* and *Yellow* powders, when finely mixed, appear to the naked eye *Green,* and yet the Colours of the Component corpuscles are not thereby really transmuted, but only blended. For, when viewed with a good Microscope, they still appear *Blew* and *Yellow* interspersedly.

5. There are therefore two sorts of Colours. The one original and simple, the other compounded of these. The Original or primary colours are, *Red, Yellow, Green, Blew,* and a *Violet-purple,* together with Orange, Indico, and an indefinite variety of Intermediate gradations.

6. The same colours in *Specie* with these Primary ones may be also produced by composition: For, a mixture of *Yellow* and *Blew* makes *Green;* of *Red* and *Yellow* makes *Orange;* of *Orange* and *Yellowish green* makes *yellow.* And in general, if any two Colours be mixed, which in the series of those, generated by the Prisme, are not too far distant one from another, they by their mutual alloy compound that colour, which in the said series appeareth in the mid-way between them. But those, which are situated at too great a distance, do not so. *Orange* and *Indico* produce not the intermediate Green, nor Scarlet and Green the intermediate yellow.

7. But the most surprising and wonderful composition was that of *Whiteness.* There is no one sort of Rays which alone can exhibit this. 'Tis ever compounded, and to its composition are requisite all the aforesaid primary Colours, mixed in a due proportion. I have often with Admiration beheld, that all the Colours of the Prisme being made to converge, and thereby to be again mixed as they were in the light before it was Incident upon the Prisme, reproduced light, intirely and perfectly white, and not at all sensibly differing from a *direct* Light of the Sun, unless when the glasses, I used, were not sufficiently clear; for then they would a little incline it to *their* colour.

8. Hence therefore it comes to pass, that *Whiteness* is the usual colour of *Light;* for, Light is a confused aggregate of Rays indued with all sorts of Colors, as they are promiscuously darted from the

various parts of luminous bodies. And of such a confused aggregate, as I said, is generated Whiteness, if there be a due proportion of the Ingredients; but if any one predominate, [the] Light must incline to that colour; as it happens in the Blew flame of Brimstone; the yellow flame of a Candle; and the various colours of the Fixed stars.

9. These things considered, the *manner*, how colours are produced by the Prisme, is evident. For, of the Rays, constituting the incident light, since those which differ in Colour proportionally differ in Refrangibility, *they* by their unequall refractions must be severed and dispersed into an oblong form in an orderly succession from the least refracted Scarlet to the most refracted Violet. And for the same reason it is, that objects, when looked upon through a Prisme, appear coloured. For, the difform Rays, by their unequal Refractions, are made to diverge towards several parts of the *Retina*, and there express the Images of things coloured, as in the former case they did the Suns Image upon a wall. And by this inequality of refractions they become not only coloured, but also very confused and indistinct.

10. Why the colours of the *Rainbow* appear in falling drops of Rain, is also from hence evident. For, those drops, which refract the Rays, disposed to appear purple, in greatest quantity to the Spectators eye, refract the Rays of other sorts so much less, as to make them pass beside it; and such are the drops on the inside of the *Primary* Bow, and on the outside of the *Secondary* or Exteriour one. So those drops, which refract in greatest plenty the Rays, apt to appear red, toward the Spectators eye, refract those of other sorts so much more, as to make them pass beside it; and such are the drops on the exteriour part of the *Primary*, and interiour part of the *Secondary* Bow.

Rules of Reasoning in Philosophy

ISAAC NEWTON

Rule I. We are to admit no more causes of natural things, than such as are both true and sufficient to explain their appearances.

To this purpose the philosophers say, that Nature do's nothing in vain, and more is in vain, when less will serve; For Nature is pleas'd with simplicity, and affects not the pomp of superfluous causes.

Rule II. Therefore to the same natural effects we must, as far as possible, assign the same causes.

As to respiration in a man, and in a beast; the descent of stones in *Europe* and in *America;* the light of our culinary fire and of the Sun; the reflection of light in the Earth, and in the Planets.

Rule III. The qualities of bodies, which admit neither intension nor remission of degrees, and which are found to belong to all bodies within the reach of our experiments, are to be esteemed the universal qualities of all bodies whatsoever.

For since the qualities of bodies are only known to us by experiments, we are to hold for universal, all such as universally agree with experiments; and such as are not liable to diminution, can never be quite taken away. *We are certainly not to relinquish the evidence of experiments for the sake of dreams and vain fictions of our own devising; nor are we to recede from the analogy of Nature, which uses to be simple, and always consonant to itself.* We no otherways know the extension of bodies, than by our senses, nor do these reach it in all bodies; but because we perceive extension in all that are sensible, therefore we ascribe it universally to all others also. That abundance of bodies are hard we learn by experience. And because the hardness of the whole arises from the hardness of the parts, we therefore justly infer the hardness of the undivided particles not only of the bodies we feel but of all others. That all bodies are impenetrable, we gather not from reason, but from sensation. The bodies which we handle we find impenetrable, and thence conclude impenetrability to be an universal property of all bodies whatsoever. That all bodies are moveable, and endow'd with certain powers (which we call the *vires inertiæ*) of persevering in their motion or in their rest, we only infer from the like properties observ'd in the bodies which we have seen. The extension, hardness, impenetrability, mobility and *vis inertiæ* of the whole,

From Isaac Newton: *Philosophiae Naturalis Principia Mathematica*, Book III.

result from the extension, hardness, impenetrability, mobility and *vires inertiæ* of the parts: and thence we conclude the least particles of all bodies to be also all extended, and hard, and impenetrable, and moveable, and endow'd with their proper *vires inertiæ*. And this is the foundation of all philosophy. Moreover, that the divided but contiguous particles of bodies may be separated from one another, is matter of observation; and, in the particles that remain undivided, our minds are able to distinguish yet lesser parts, as is mathematically demonstrated. But whether the parts so distinguish'd, and not yet divided, may, by the powers of nature, be actually divided and separated from one another, we cannot certainly determine. Yet had we the proof of but one experiment, that any undivided particle, in breaking a hard and solid body, suffer'd a division, we might by virtue of this rule, conclude, that the undivided as well as the divided particles may be divided and actually separated to infinity.

Lastly, If it universally appears, by experiments and astronomical observations, that all bodies about the Earth, gravitate towards the Earth; and that in proportion to the quantity of matter which they severally contain; that the Moon likewise, according to the quantity of its matter, gravitates towards the Earth; that on the other hand our Sea gravitates towards the Moon; and all the Planets mutually one towards another; and the Comets in like manner towards the Sun; we must, in consequence of this rule, universally allow, that all bodies whatsoever are endow'd with a principle of mutual gravitation. For the argument from the appearances concludes with more force for the universal gravitation of all bodies, than for their impenetrability; of which among those in the celestial regions, we have no experiments, nor any manner of observation. Not that I affirm gravity to be essential to bodies. By their *vis insita* [inherent forces] I mean nothing but their *vis inertia* [inertial forces]. This is immutable. Their gravity is diminished as they recede from the Earth.

Rule IV. In experimental philosophy we are to look upon propositions collected by general induction from phaenomena as accurately or very nearly true, notwithstanding any contrary hypotheses that may be imagined, till such time as other phaenomena occur, by which they may either be made more accurate, or liable to exceptions.

This rule we must follow that the argument of induction may not be evaded by hypotheses.

"I Frame No Hypotheses"

ISAAC NEWTON

HITHERTO we have explain'd the phænomena of the heavens
and of our sea, by the power of Gravity, but have not yet assign'd
the cause of this power. This is certain, that it must proceed from a
cause that penetrates to the very centers of the Sun and Planets,
without suffering the least diminution of its force; that operates, not
according to the quantity of the surfaces of the particles upon
which it acts, (as mechanical causes use to do,) but according to
the quantity of the solid matter which they contain, and propagates
its virtue on all sides, to immense distances, decreasing always in
the duplicate proportion of the distances. Gravitation towards the
Sun is made up out of the gravitations towards the several particles
of which the body of the Sun is compos'd; and in receding from the
Sun, decreases accurately in the duplicate proportion of the distances, as far as the orb of Saturn, as evidently appears from the
quiescence of the aphelions of the Planets; nay, and even to the remotest aphelions of the Comets, if those aphelions are also quies-
cent. But hitherto I have not been able to discover the cause of
those properties of gravity from phænomena, and I frame no hypotheses. For whatever is not deduc'd from the phænomena, is to be
called an hypothesis; and hypotheses, whether metaphysical or
physical, whether of occult qualities or mechanical, have no place
in experimental philosophy. In this philosophy particular propositions are inferr'd from the phænomena, and afterwards render'd
general by induction. Thus it was that the impenetrability, the mobility, and the impulsive force of bodies, and the laws of motion
and of gravitation, were discovered. And to us it is enough, that
gravity does really exist, and acts according to the laws which we
have explained, and abundantly serves to account for all the motions of the celestial bodies, and of our sea.

And now we might add something concerning a certain most
subtle Spirit, which pervades and lies hid in all gross bodies; by the
force and action of which Spirit, the particles of bodies mutually
attract one another at near distances, and cohere, if contiguous;
and electric bodies operate to greater distances, as well repelling as
attracting the neighbouring corpuscles; and light is emitted, reflected, refracted, inflected, and heats bodies; and all sensation is

From the *Principia*, 1729 edition, translated by Benjamin Motte.

excited, and the members of animal bodies move at the command of the will, namely, by the vibrations of this Spirit, mutually propagated along the solid filaments of the nerves, from the outward organs of sense to the brain, and from the brain into the muscles. But these are things that cannot be explain'd in few words, nor are we furnish'd with that sufficiency of experiments which is required to an accurate determination and demonstration of the laws by which this electric and elastic spirit operates.

<><><><><><><><><><><><><><><><><><><><><><><><><><><><>

📎 *NO HOLDS BARRED*

The scientific method, as far as it is a method, is nothing more than doing one's damnedest with one's mind, no holds barred. What primarily distinguishes science from other intellectual enterprises in which the right answer has to be obtained is not the method but the subject matter. . . . Science has made a step-by-step progress, starting with a patient analysis of the complex situations of experience into as simple components as possible, acquiring mastery of these simple components, and then applying the results of the accumulated experience to more complex situations until we have the irresistible and accelerated progress of the present.

— From Percy W. Bridgman: *Reflections of a Physicist,* Philosophical Library.

Benjamin Franklin: Electrician

CARL VAN DOREN

NOW THAT ELECTRICITY has become a daily commonplace it is hard to realize what fresh, strange news it was when Franklin first thought — perhaps first heard — of it in Boston in the summer of 1746. Before that year he might have known that various bodies may be electrified by rubbing, so that they will attract lighter ob-

jects, and that the attracting force may be transferred to other
bodies. He might have read of frictional machines, mounted rotat-
ing spheres of sulphur or glass, which could be used to charge insulated conductors with what was called the electric fluid. European
scientists already distinguished two kinds of electricity: vitreous,
produced on glass rubbed with silk, and resinous, produced on
resin rubbed with wool or fur. But not until January 1746 had Pieter
van Musschenbroek at Leyden discovered the electric bottle later
known as the Leyden jar, the simplest and for years the only known
condenser, which was the basis of early electrical research. William
Watson in London quickly followed Musschenbroek in his experiments and concluded that all bodies contained electricity: uncharged bodies the normal or equilibrium amount, charged bodies
more or less than that as they contained vitreous or resinous electricity, or vice versa. Franklin in the fall or winter of the year went
forward from the year's chief discovery in science.

"My house," he says, "was continually full, for some time, with
people who came to see these new wonders. To divide a little this
encumbrance among my friends, I caused a number of similar
tubes" — similar to the one Collinson had sent the Library Company — "to be blown at our glass-house, with which they furnished
themselves, so that we had at length several performers." Philip
Syng, a member of the Junto and a skilled silversmith contrived a
machine to save them labor. "The European papers on electricity,"
Franklin wrote in the earliest of the reports which he regularly
made to Collinson, "frequently speak of rubbing the tube as a
fatiguing exercise. Our spheres are fixed on iron axes which pass
through them. At one end of the axis there is a small handle with
which you turn the sphere like a common grindstone." Thomas
Hopkinson, president of the American Philosophical Society, first
noticed that points "throw off the electrical fire." Ebenezer Kinnersley, a Baptist minister with no pastorate, discovered that the Leyden jar could be electrified as strongly through the tinfoil coating as
through the wire leading into it, and independently rediscovered
the "contrary electricities" of glass and sulphur. His lectures —
planned and encouraged by Franklin — in Philadelphia, Boston,
Newport, and New York during 1751–52 made Kinnersley's experiments nearly as famous in America as Franklin's.

But Franklin, carefully crediting his friends with whatever they
found out, was the real master of the new knowledge. In his busy
house in Market Street, working with such pieces of apparatus as a
saltcellar, a vinegar cruet, a pump handle, or the gold on the binding of a book, and "little machines I had roughly made for myself,"
he had the most spacious views and the most painstaking methods.

Within a few months he could write to Collinson, on 28 March 1747, that "we have observed some particular phenomena that we look upon to be new." By 11 July, when he wrote at length, he had already hit upon two of his fundamental contributions: his conception of electricity as a single fluid, and his substitution of the terms positive and negative, or plus and minus, for vitreous and resinous electricity; and he was full of "the wonderful effect of pointed bodies, both in drawing off and throwing off the electrical fire," which was to suggest the lightning rod.

Within another month he had written Collinson two more long letters, and then on 14 August sent a hurried note after them. "On some further experiments since, I have observed a phenomenon or two that I cannot at present account for on the principle laid down in those letters, and am therefore become a little diffident of my hypothesis and ashamed that I expressed myself in so positive a manner. In going on with these experiments how many pretty systems do we build which we soon find ourselves obliged to destroy! If there is no other use discovered of electricity, this however is something considerable, that it may help to make a vain man humble. I must now request that you would not expose those letters; or if you communicate them to any friends you would at least conceal my name." In a letter dated 1 September, he began: "The necessary trouble of copying long letters which perhaps, when they come to your hands, may contain nothing new or worth your reading (so quick is the progress made with you in electricity) half discourages me from writing any more on that subject."

. . . In the report to Collinson of 29 April 1749 Franklin, continuing his observation on the Leyden jar, first pointed out the great part played by the dielectric — the glass — and told of making, for the first time in history, "what we called an electrical battery, consisting of eleven panes of large sash-glass, armed with thin leaden plates pasted on each side, placed vertically and supported at two inches' distance on silk cords, with thick hooks of leaden wire, one from each side, standing upright, distant from each other, and convenient communications of wire and chain from the giving side of one pane to the receiving side of the other; that so the whole might be charged together and with the same labour as one single pane." How important these matters were he could not know. He gave nearly as much space to telling of devices he and his friends had worked out to astound the curious. "Chagrined a little that we have been hitherto able to produce nothing in this way of use to mankind, and the hot weather coming on when electrical experiments are not so agreeable, it is proposed to put an end to them for this season, somewhat humorously, in a party of pleasure on the banks of

Schuylkill. Spirits, at the same time, are to be fired by a spark sent from side to side through the river, without any other conductor than the water: an experiment which we some time since performed, to the amazement of many. A turkey is to be killed for our dinner by the electrical shock, and roasted by the electrical jack, before a fire kindled by the electrified bottle; when the healths of all the famous electricians in England, Holland, France, and Germany are to be drank in electrified bumpers, under the discharge of guns from the electrical battery."

Later that year Franklin made an entry in "the minutes I used to keep of the experiments I made, with memorandums of such as I purposed to make. . . . *November 7, 1749.* Electrical fluid agrees with lightning in these particulars. 1. Giving light. 2. Colour of the light. 3. Crooked direction. 4. Swift motion. 5. Being conducted by metals. 6. Crack or noise in exploding. 7. Subsisting in water or ice. 8. Rending bodies it passes through. 9. Destroying animals. 10. Melting metals. 11. Firing inflammable substances. 12. Sulphureous smell. The electric fluid is attracted by points. We do not know whether this property is in lightning. But since they agree in all particulars wherein we can already compare them, is it not probable they agree likewise in this? Let the experiment be made." Other scientists before Franklin had suspected that lightning was electricity. He set out to find a method of proving it.

A use for the discovery was promptly in his mind. It cannot have been more than a few weeks before he wrote a letter which Collinson sent to the *Gentleman's Magazine* for May 1750, where it has eluded Franklin's editors. "There is something, however, in the experiments of points, sending off or drawing on the electrical fire, which has not been fully explained, and which I intend to supply in my next. For the doctrine of points is very curious, and the effects of them truly wonderful; and, from what I have observed on experiments, I am of opinion that houses, ships, and even towers and churches may be effectually secured from the strokes of lightning by their means; for if, instead of the round balls of wood or metal which are commonly placed on the tops of weathercocks, vanes, or spindles of churches, spires, or masts, there should be a rod of iron eight or ten feet in length, sharpened gradually to a point like a needle, and gilt to prevent rusting, or divided into a number of points, which would be better, the electrical fire would, I think, be drawn out of a cloud silently, before it could come near enough to strike; and a light would be seen at the point, like the sailors' corpuzante [corposant: St. Elmo's fire]. This may seem whimsical, but let it pass for the present until I send the experiments at large." Here is Franklin's earliest suggestion of the lightning rod, made when he seems not yet to have thought of the need of a ground wire.

Now he turned his attention to thunderstorms — which he called thunder-gusts — and wrote out a new hypothesis for Collinson which, though undated, must belong to the first half of 1750. Franklin then supposed that clouds formed over the ocean had more electricity in them than clouds formed over the land, and that when they came close enough together their different charges were equalized by the passage of lightning between them. "If two gun barrels electrified will strike at two inches' distance, and make a loud snap, to what a great distance may 10,000 acres of electrified cloud strike and give its fire, and how loud must be that crack?" When clouds came close to the earth their electricity was discharged through "high hills and high trees, lofty towers, spires, masts of ships, chimneys, etc., as so many prominencies and points."

By 29 July 1750 Franklin was ready to draw up for Collinson, who had sent the first electrical tube, and Thomas Penn, who had sent the Library Company "a complete electrical apparatus," a summary of the *Opinions and Conjectures, concerning the Properties and Effects of the Electrical Matter, Arising from Experiments and Observations, Made at Philadelphia, 1749*. Now, nine months after he had privately determined to make his great experiment, he publicly proposed it, through Collinson to the Royal Society. Let the experiment be made. Make the truth useful to mankind. "Nor is it of much importance to us to know the manner in which nature executes her laws: 'tis enough if we know the laws themselves. 'Tis of real use to know that china left in the air unsupported will fall and break; but how it comes to fall, and why it breaks, are matters of speculation. 'Tis a pleasure indeed to know them, but we can preserve our china without it."

Now repeating his suggestion of lightning rods, Franklin provided also for "a wire down the outside of the building into the ground, or down round one of the shrouds of a ship and down her side till it reaches the water. . . . To determine the question whether the clouds that contain lightning are electrified or not, I would propose an experiment to be tried where it may be done conveniently. On the top of some high tower or steeple place a kind of sentry box . . . big enough to contain a man and an electrical stand [an insulator]. From the middle of the stand let an iron rod rise and pass bending out of the door, and then upright twenty or thirty feet, pointed very sharp at the end. If the electrical stand be kept clean and dry, a man standing on it when such clouds are passing low might be electrified and afford sparks, the rod drawing fire to him from a cloud. If any danger to the man should be apprehended (though I think there would be none), let him stand on the floor of his box and now and then bring near to the rod the loop of a wire that has one end fastened to the leads, he holding it by a wax handle; so the sparks, if the rod is electrified, will strike from the rod to the wire and not affect him."

Franklin did not know enough about lightning to know how dangerous such an experiment might be, and the experience he had two days before Christmas the same year did not disturb his plans. "Being about to kill a turkey by the shock from two large glass jars, containing as much electrical fire as forty common phials, I inadvertently took the whole through my own arms and body, by receiving the fire from the united top wires with one hand while the other held a chain connected with the outsides of both jars. The company present (whose talking to me, and to one another, I suppose occasioned my inattention to what I was about) say that the flash was very great and the crack as loud as a pistol; yet, my senses being instantly gone, I neither saw the one nor heard the other; nor did I feel the stroke on my hand. . . . I then felt what I know not well how to describe: a universal blow throughout my whole body from head to foot, which seemed within as well as without; after which the first thing I took notice of was a violent quick shaking of my body, which gradually remitting, my sense as gradually returned. . . . That part of my hand and fingers which held the chain was left white, as though the blood had been driven out, and remained so eight or ten minutes after, feeling like dead flesh; and I had a numbness in my arms and the back of my neck which continued till the next morning but wore off. . . . I am ashamed to have been guilty of so notorious a blunder; a match for that of the Irishman . . . who, being about to steal powder, made a hole in the cask with a hot iron." "The greatest known effects of common lightning," Franklin thought the next year, might be exceeded by linking up enough electric bottles, "which a few years since could not have been believed and even now may seem to many a little extravagant to suppose. So we are got beyond the skill of Rabelais's devils of two years old, who, he humorously says, had only learnt to thunder and lighten a little round the head of a cabbage."

Incidental Discovery: What Is Heat?

BENJAMIN THOMPSON

IT FREQUENTLY HAPPENS that in the ordinary affairs and occupations of life opportunities present themselves of contemplating some of the most curious operations of nature; and very interesting philosophical experiments might often be made, almost without trouble or expense, by means of machinery contrived for the mere mechanical purposes of the arts and manufactures.

. . . Being engaged, lately, in superintending the boring of cannon in the workshops of the military arsenal at Munich, I was struck with the very considerable degree of heat which a brass gun acquires, in a short time, in being bored; and with the still more intense heat (much greater than that of boiling water, as I found by experiment) of the metallic chips separated from it by the borer. . . .

From whence comes the heat actually produced in the mechanical operation above mentioned?

Is it furnished by the metallic chips which are separated by the borer from the solid mass of metal?

If this were the case, then, according to the modern doctrines of latent heat, and of caloric, the capacity for heat of the parts of the metal, so reduced to chips, ought not only to be changed, but the change undergone by them should be sufficiently great to account for all the heat produced.

But no such change had taken place; for I found, upon taking equal quantities, by weight, of these chips, and of thin slips of the same block of metal separated by means of a fine saw, and putting them, at the same temperature (that of boiling water) into equal quantities of cold water (that is to say, at the temperature of $59\frac{1}{2}°$ F.), the portion of water into which the chips were put was not, to all appearance, heated either less or more than the other portion, in which the slips of metal were put.

This experiment being repeated several times, the results were always so nearly the same that I could not determine whether any, or what change, had been produced in the metal, in regard to its capacity for heat, by being reduced to chips by the borer.

From hence it is evident that the heat produced could not possibly have been furnished at the expense of the latent heat of the metallic chips. But, not being willing to rest satisfied with these trials, however conclusive they appeared to me to be, I had recourse to [a] still more decisive experiment:

[Thompson designed an apparatus in which a blunt borer was forced against the bottom of a metal cylinder that was rotated by machinery operated by horses. The cylinder was enclosed in a box containing about two gallons of water.]

At the end of one hour I found, by plunging a thermometer into the water in the box . . . that its temperature had been raised no less than 47 degrees; being now 107° of Fahrenheit's scale. . . . At 2 hours 20 minutes it was at 200°; and at 2 hours 30 minutes it *actually boiled!*

It would be difficult to describe the surprise expressed in the countenances of the bystanders on seeing so large a quantity of water heated and actually made to boil without any fire.

Though there was, in fact, nothing that could justly be considered as surprising in this event, yet I acknowledge fairly that it afforded me a degree of childish pleasure, which, were I ambitious of the reputation of a *grave philosopher,* I ought most certainly rather to hide than to discover. . . .

And in reasoning on this subject we must not forget that the most remarkable circumstance, that the source of the heat generated by friction in these experiments, appears evidently to be *inexhaustible.*

It is hardly necessary to add, that any thing which any *insulated* body, or system of bodies, can continue to furnish, *without limitation,* cannot possibly be a *material substance:* and it appeared to me to be extremely difficult, if not quite impossible, to form any distinct idea of any thing, capable of being excited, and communicated, in the manner the heat was excited and communicated in the experiments, except it be *motion.*

Accidental Discovery: Galvani and Volta

JAMES B. CONANT

THE LAYMAN is often confused in regard to the role of the accidental discovery on the one hand and the planned experiment on the other. This is particularly true in connection with the development of new techniques and the evolution of new concepts from experiment. The case history which I recommend for a study of these topics is the work of Galvani and Volta on the electric current. This case history illustrates the fact that an accidental discovery may lead by a series of experiments (which must be well planned) to a new technique or a new concept or both; it also shows that in the exploration of a new phenomenon the experiments may be well planned without any "working hypothesis" as to the nature of the phenomenon, but that shortly an explanation is sure to arise. A new conceptual scheme will be evolved. This may be on a grand scale and have wide applicability, or may be strictly limited to the phenomenon in question. A test of the new concept or group of concepts in either instance will probably lead to new discoveries and the eventual establishment, modification, or overthrow of the conceptual scheme in question.

The case history begins with certain observations made by Luigi Galvani, an Italian physician, a professor at Bologna, some time before 1786. This investigator noted the twitching of a frog's leg when the crural nerves were touched by a metallic scalpel in the neighborhood of an electrostatic machine from which sparks were drawn. *He followed up his observation.* At this point in a course on the Tactics and Strategy of Science the instructor would wax eloquent. He would remind the class that time and time again throughout the history of science the consequences of following up or not following up accidental discoveries have been very great. The analogy of a general's taking advantage of an enemy's error or a lucky break, like the capture of the Remagen bridge, could hardly fail to enter the discussion. Pasteur once wrote that "chance favors only the prepared mind." This is excellently illustrated by the case history at hand. The Dutch naturalist, Swammerdam, had previously discovered that if you lay bare the muscle of a frog in much the same way

From *On Understanding Science* by James B. Conant. Reprinted by permission of Yale University Press, publishers.

as Galvani did, grasp a tendon in one hand and touch the frog's nerve with a scalpel held in the other hand, a twitching will result. But Swammerdam never followed up his work. Galvani did. In his own words, "I had dissected and prepared a frog . . . and while I was attending to something else, I laid it on a table on which stood an electrical machine at some distance. . . . Now when one of the persons who were present touched accidentally and lightly the inner crural nerves of the frog with the point of a scalpel all the muscles of the legs seemed to contract again and again. . . . Another one who was there, who was helping us in electrical researches, thought that he had noticed that the action was excited when a spark was discharged from the conductor of the machine. Being astonished by this new phenomenon he called my attention to it, who at that time had something else in mind and was deep in thought. Whereupon I was inflamed with an incredible zeal and eagerness to test the same and to bring to light what was concealed in it."

Galvani did not succeed in bringing to light all that was concealed in the new phenomenon. But he proceeded far enough to make the subsequent discoveries inevitable. In a series of well-planned experiments he explored the obvious variables, but without a clear-cut, over-all hypothesis. This is the usual situation when a new phenomenon is encountered by a gifted experimenter. A series of working hypotheses spring to mind, are tested and either discarded or incorporated into a conceptual scheme which gradually develops. For example, Galvani first determined whether or not sparks had to be drawn from the electrical machine in order to occasion twitching. He found "Without fail there occurred lively contractions . . . at the same instant as that in which the spark jumped. . . ."

The nerves and muscles of the frog's leg constituted a sensitive detector of an electric charge. Galvani found that not only must a spark be passing from the electrostatic machine but the metallic blade of the scalpel must be in contact with the hand of the experimenter. In this way a small charge originating from the electrical disturbance, namely the spark, passed down the conducting human body through the scalpel to the nerve. So far the physician was on sound and fruitful ground. There now occurred one of those coincidences which more than once have initially baffled an investigator but eventually led to great advances. The frog's leg could under certain circumstances act not only as a sensitive electrical detector but as a source of electricity as well. When this happened, the electricity self-generated so to speak actuated the detector. One can readily see that the superposition of these two effects could be most bewildering and misleading. This was particularly so since the conditions under which the frog's leg became a source of electricity were totally unconnected with any electrical phenomena then known. The variable was the nature of the metal or I should say metals used. For Galvani discovered and duly recorded that the electrostatic machine could be dispensed with if the leg and the nerve were connected together by two *different* metals. Under these conditions the twitching occurred. (The experiment was usually performed as follows: a curved rod was made to touch simultaneously both a hook passing through the spinal cord of the frog and the "muscles of the leg or the feet.") "Thus, for example," wrote Galvani, "if the whole rod was iron or the hook was iron . . . the contractions either did not occur or were very small. But if one of them was iron and the other brass, or better if it was silver (silver seems to us the best of all the metals for conducting animal electricity) there occur repeated and much greater and more prolonged contractions."

Galvani had discovered the principle of the electric battery without knowing it. His two metals separated by the moist animal tissue were a battery, the frog's leg the detector. Every reader can perform the equivalent of Galvani's experiment himself. A copper coin and a silver one placed above and below the tongue when touched together produce in the tongue a peculiar "taste." A very small electric current flows and our tongue records the fact through a series of interactions of electricity and nerves much in the same way as did Galvani's "prepared" frogs. Not having a suspicion of all this, however, Galvani developed a conceptual scheme (an hypothesis on the grand scale, we might say) to account for all the phenomena in terms of what was then known about electricity, which was derived entirely from experiment with electrostatic machines. Having found outside electrical disturbances unnecessary (when he unwittingly used the *right* metallic combination!) the experiments, he says, "cause us to think that possibly the electricity was present in the animal itself." Galvani's following up of an accidental discovery by a series of controlled experiments had led to a recording of the significant facts, but it was to be another Italian who developed the fruitful concept. It was Volta who in the late 1790s, continuing the study of the production of electricity by the contact of two different metals, invented the electric battery as a source of what we now often call Galvanic electricity.

Alessandro Volta (1745–1827) of Padua had earlier invented a new form of instrument for detecting small charges of electricity. He began by agreeing with Galvani about animal electricity and went about studying it. With his new instrument, a sensitive condensing electrometer, Volta explored various combinations of variables related to Galvani's early experiments and found that the frog could be eliminated in favor of almost any moist material. This discovery might be considered an example of the accidental discovery, but if so it is of a different order from that of Galvani. Explorations with new techniques and tools, if undertaken in a more or less orderly fashion, almost always turn up unexpected facts. In this sense a great majority of new facts of science are accidental discoveries. But the difference between this sort of experience and the example afforded by Galvani's work is obvious. Volta's new discovery amounted, of course, to the invention of the electric battery; for he showed that electricity was produced when two different metals were separated by water containing salt or lye. This was most conveniently done by using moistened paper. In a letter to the President of the Royal Society of London in 1800 Volta wrote "30, 40, 60 or more pieces of copper, or rather of silver, each in contact with a piece of tin, or of zinc, which is much better, and as many layers of water or of some other liquid which is a better conductor than pure water, such as salt-water or lye and so forth, or pieces of pasteboard or of leather, etc. well soaked with these liquids; . . . such an alternative series of these three sorts of conductors always in the same order, constitutes my new instrument; which imitates . . . the effects of Leyden jars . . ." [See diagram on page 331.] This new battery was a source of electricity different from the electrostatic generator already known in 1800; it was the first source of continuous current. The battery produced electricity of low potential but of considerable quality (low voltage, relatively high amperage); the sparks from a frictional machine are brief spasms of current of high potential but very low amperage.

There was a hot controversy between Galvani's disciples (Galvani died in 1798) and Volta about whether or not there was such a thing as animal electricity, and what caused the twitching of the frog's leg in the first experiments. Volta soon lost interest in the quarrel and devoted his attention to the study of his new battery. Today we have a rather complete and highly satisfactory conceptual scheme in which all the facts about electric batteries find their place. This is not the case, however, with observations about muscles, nerves, and electric currents in animal tissue. In this field one working hypothesis still replaces another and new experiments are still throwing new light on an ancient phenomenon. In a sense, we have not yet finished with Galvani's very first observation, but have finished with Volta's discovery. The original controversy centered on the question, is there animal electricity? This has now become largely a meaningless question, but in attempting to find an answer Volta discovered the electric battery. Such is often the course of scientific history. We end by solving a problem other than the one first at issue.

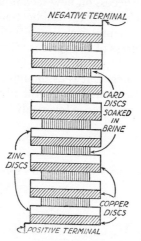

One form of Volta's battery or pile.

Another case history which illustrates the role of the accidental discovery, the well-planned experiments by which it may be followed up, the role of the working hypothesis, the development of an hypothesis on the grand scale, and the rapid emergence of both a new technique and a new concept is furnished by a study of the discovery of X rays. The story is familiar to all scientists though perhaps it is not generally known that before Roentgen announced his discovery, several other investigators had noticed the fogging of photographic plates near an electric discharge tube. Roentgen followed up his accidental observation. For pedagogic purposes in a course on the Tactics and Strategy of Science this case history could be used to supplement the one just given or in place of it. Roentgen's work is both simpler and more complex than Galvani's and Volta's; the experimentation and reasoning are more straightforward, but to understand the discovery of the X rays the student should have a considerable background of physics. Therefore, the eighteenth-century example is better in that it almost explains itself as far as technical terms are involved. On the other hand, it is more remote and perhaps less interesting to the average layman.

Both the case of the discovery of the electric battery and that of X rays show in a dramatic fashion a point I referred to in the last chapter, namely, that a new technique may have an almost revolutionary effect. With the new electric battery in the beginning of the nineteenth century, Humphry Davy and many others discovered all sorts of new electrochemical and physical phenomena; from them in turn came in rapid succession new techniques and new concepts. Likewise in our own day after the publication of an account of the X-ray tube, new experimental facts came forth in torrents. Tremendous spurts in the progress of the various sciences are almost always connected with the development of a new technique or the sudden emergence of a new concept. It is as though a group of prospectors were hunting in barren ground and suddenly struck a rich vein of ore. All at once everyone works feverishly and the gold begins to flow.

The Blunderbuss Method

PAUL DE KRUIF

"I WILL FIND a chemical to cure diphtheria!" [Behring] cried, and inoculated herds of guinea pigs with cultivations of virulent diphtheria bacilli. They got sick, and as they got sicker he shot various chemical compounds into them. He tried costly salts of gold, he tried naphthylamine, he tested more than thirty different strange or common substances. He believed innocently because these things could kill microbes in a glass tube without damaging the tube, they would also hit the diphtheria bacilli under a guinea pig's hide without ruining the guinea pig. But alas, from the slaughterhouse of dead and dying guinea pigs his laboratory was, you would suppose he would have seen there was little to choose between the deadly microbes and his equally murderous cures. . . . Nevertheless, being a poet, Behring did not have too great a reverence for facts; the hecatombs of corpses went on piling up, but they failed to shake his faith in some marvelous unknown remedy for diphtheria hidden somewhere among the endless rows of chemicals in existence. Then,

From *Microbe Hunters*, copyright 1926, 1953 by Paul de Kruif. Reprinted by permission of Harcourt, Brace and Company, Inc.

in his enthusiastic — but random — search he came upon the tri-chloride of iodine.

Under the skins of several guinea pigs he shot a dose of diphtheria bacilli sure to kill them. In a few hours these microbes began their work; the spot of the injection became swollen, got ominously hot, the beasts began to droop — then, six hours after the fatal dose of the bacilli, Behring shot in his iodine tri-chloride. . . . "It is no good, once more," he muttered. The day passed with no improvement and the next morning the beasts began to go into collapse. Solemnly he put the guinea pigs on their backs, then poked them with his finger to see if they could still scramble back on their feet. . . . "If the guinea pig can still get up when you poke him, there may be yet a chance for him," explained Behring to his amazed assistants. What a test that was — think of a doctor having a test like this to see whether or no his patient would live! And what an abominably crude test! Less and less the iodine-treated guinea pigs moved when he poked them — there was now no longer any hope. . . .

Then one morning Behring came into his laboratory to see those guinea pigs on their feet! Staggering about, and dreadfully scraggly looking beasts they were, but they were getting better from diphtheria, these creatures whose untreated companions had died days before. . . .

"I have cured diphtheria!" whispered Behring.

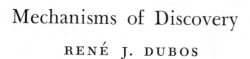

Mechanisms of Discovery

RENÉ J. DUBOS

. . . THE USE of intuition as a guide to discovery is perhaps a more common procedure than some exponents of the scientific method are inclined to believe. An extreme interpretation of Francis Bacon's writings has led to the view that the accumulation of well-established facts is sufficient to the elaboration of scientific truth, that facts speak for themselves and become automatically translated into general laws. It is indeed certain that the experimen-

From *Louis Pasteur, Free Lance of Science* by René Dubos, by permission of Little, Brown and Company.

tal method has a self-propelling force, and that many discoveries have been made by the routine and faithful application of its rules without an obvious use of hypotheses or intuition, but it is also true that scientific creation often involves the selection, from the wealth of amorphous data, of those facts which are relevant to a problem formulated in advance from abstract concepts.

In this respect the progress of science depends to a large extent upon anticipatory ideas. These give rise to the working hypothesis that constitutes the imaginative component and one of the mainsprings of scientific discovery. Before addressing himself to nature for a definite answer from results of experiments, every investigator formulates tentative answers to his problem. The experiment serves two purposes, often independent one from the other: it allows the observation of new facts, hitherto either unsuspected, or not yet well defined; and it determines whether a working hypothesis fits the world of observable facts. The precision and the frequency with which the hypotheses hit the target of reality constitute a measure of the intuitive endowment of their author. Needless to say, successful guesses are not sufficient for the instrumentation of discovery. The scientist must also be able to demonstrate the validity and to exploit the consequences of his intuitions if they are not to be stillborn.

Only few of the great experimenters have described the mental processes by which they discovered new facts or formulated new generalizations. Some, it must be admitted, assure us that their method consists merely in the use of their eyes, their ears, and other physical senses to perceive and describe reality as it presented itself to them. This view is illustrated in the picturesque words of the physiologist François Magendie: "I am a mere street scavenger of science. With hook in hand and basket on my back, I go about the streets of science collecting whatever I find." Others have told a very different story. They report how a period of intense preoccupation with a given problem was followed by a flash of inspiration often occurring under odd circumstances, away from the bench or the desk, in the course of which the solution presented itself, readymade, as emerging from some subconscious labor. Examples of inspired creations are common from the world of arts and letters, and many scientists, several of them Pasteur's contemporaries, have acknowledged a similar origin to their discoveries.

In the course of an address on his seventieth birthday, Helmholtz thus described how his most important thoughts had come to him. "After previous investigation of the problem in all directions . . . happy ideas come unexpectedly without effort, like an inspiration. . . . They have never come to me when . . . I was at my working table. . . . They come . . . readily during the slow ascent of hills on a sunny day."

According to William Thompson (Lord Kelvin), the idea of the mirror galvanometer occurred to him at a moment when he happened to notice a reflection of light from his monocle. The theories of the structure of the atom and of the benzene ring were formulated by Kekulé under the following circumstances. He had been visiting a friend in London and was riding home on the last bus. Falling into a revery, he saw atoms flitting before his eyes, two coupled together, with larger atoms seizing the smaller ones, then still larger atoms seizing three and even four smaller atoms, all whirling around in a bewildering dance, the larger atoms forming a row and dragging still smaller atoms at the end of the chain. Arriving home, he spent the night sketching pictures of the "structural theory."

At the time of the discovery of the benzene ring theory, Kekulé was working on a textbook. Turning from his desk toward the fireplace, he fell into a hypnotic state of mind, seeing the same atoms flitting again before his eyes, long rows of them assuming serpentine forms. All at once, one of the serpents seized his own tail "and whirled mockingly before his eyes." Flashing awake at once, Kekulé began writing the benzene ring theory.

To the uninitiated, it appears even more remarkable that many mathematicians like Gauss, Poincaré and Einstein have traced some of their greatest discoveries to a sudden illumination. Einstein said, in *Physics and Reality*:

> There is no inductive method which could lead to the fundamental concepts of physics. Failure to understand this fact constituted the basic philosophical error of so many investigators of the nineteenth century. . . . We now realize with special clarity, how much in error are those theorists who believe that theory comes inductively from experience. . . .

Even Clerk Maxwell, probably the most rigorous and logical scientific mind of the nineteenth century, has emphasized that purely imaginative mechanical models and analogies are often the precursors of mathematical abstractions. As is well known, Faraday evolved many of his discoveries from the mechanical concept of lines of forces; for twenty-five years, he used and elaborated this model until the lines of forces became to him as real as matter, and he mentally constructed a model of the universe in such terms. Maxwell at first borrowed from Faraday a similar model of the electromagnetic field. True enough, he discarded its use after he had reached an adequate mathematical formulation of electromagnetism with its help, but he acknowledged his indebtedness to Faraday's mechanical concept and added: "For the sake of persons of different types of mind, scientific truth should be presented in different forms and should be regarded as equally scientific whether it appears in the robust form and vivid coloring of a physical illustration or in the tenuity and paleness of a symbolical expression."

Elsewhere, Maxwell attempted to analyze Faraday's method of discovery [and suggested]: "there may be a mathematical method in which we move from the whole to the parts instead of from the parts to the whole." Is not this apprehension of the whole responsible in part for some of the mysterious processes of intuition that have so often been claimed by men of science? Was it not such a process which made Gauss reply, when asked how soon he expected to reach certain mathematical conclusions, "that he had them long ago, all he was worrying about was how to reach them"?

In certain respects, Darwin used this unanalytical intuitive approach in formulating the theory of evolution based on natural selection. He became convinced of the fact of organic evolution — the variability of species — during his short stay in the Galapagos Islands, and the hypothesis of natural selection came to him in a flash while reading Malthus' essay on population. Twenty years elapsed before he would publish his theory, a period devoted to the accumulation of the detailed body of facts required to bolster his preconceived views.

◇◇◇

Planning Unplanned Research

IRVING LANGMUIR

YOU CAN'T PLAN to make discoveries. But you can plan work that will probably lead to discoveries.

Dr. Willis Whitney discovered a word which is in the dictionary — serendipity — and I don't like the definition that is given. Let me suggest this one: "The art of profiting from unexpected occurrences." Now, it seems to me a large part of the Laboratory work is

Reproduced by permission of the General Electric Research Laboratory.

amidst a litter of slides, slide boxes, and notebooks. Stools and some shelves filled with culture flasks, bottles of stain, and other specimens of laboratory glassware complete the equipment. WALTER REED, *Major, Medical Corps — slim, distinguished, Virginian, fifty — sits at the workbench. In the meanwhile.*]

1ST ORDERLY: Go easy, there!

2ND ORDERLY: Let me get hold!

1ST ORDERLY: Hands slipping?

2ND ORDERLY: It's hot! I'm sweating. (*The stretcher is set down while he mops his brow.*) Hope they get the door of that autopsy room unlocked and don't keep us waiting where everybody can see. (*The stretcher resumes its course.*)

1ST ORDERLY: Straight ahead. (*They are going.* REED *looks up from the papers* MISS BLAKE *has handed him.*)

REED: Name: John Davis. Age: twenty-two. He wasn't married. That's always some consolation. I must write to his mother.

MISS BLAKE: Yes, doctor.

BRINKERHOF: I knew that boy. He came from Indiana near where I come from. I was pitching horseshoes with him last Friday. (*He turns sorrowfully apart.*) Now he's dead.

REED (*calling*):   Brinkerhof! (BRINKERHOF *goes up into the laboratory and salutes.*)

MC CLELLAND: This Cuba's a fine place to spend the summer.

REED (*to* BRINKERHOF):   Get word to Agramonte that there's a subject for him in the autopsy room. Say I'll join him there. (BRINKERHOF *salutes and goes.* REED *buries his head in his hands.*) That's all, Miss Blake. (MISS BLAKE *hesitates an instant, then turns out of the laboratory.* BRINKERHOF *returns.*)

REED: Yes, Mr. Brinkerhof?

[BRINKERHOF *proffers the document.*]

BRINKERHOF: From General Wood's headquarters. For you, sir.

REED: What is it?

BRINKERHOF: The army death list brought up to date, sir.

REED (*wincing as he takes the document*):   Thank you, Mr. Brinkerhof. (*He turns and goes somberly up into the laboratory, studying the document as he goes. The sky is reddening with sunset. He is surprised to find* AGRAMONTE *working at the microscope.* BRINKERHOF *goes.*) I didn't know you'd come in, Agramonte.

AGRAMONTE (*not looking up*):   Just now, doctor. To examine this.

REED: Is it . . . Is it from the dead boy you've just had down there?

AGRAMONTE (*as before*): You didn't join me.

REED (*turning distressfully away*):   I was waiting for Carroll
to get back from Pinar. I didn't feel up to another autopsy today.

AGRAMONTE (*as before*):   I can understand that.

REED: Still nothing?

AGRAMONTE: Did you expect anything? After two months of
this? And how many boys cut up? Did you still expect anything?
We've made a record for thoroughness at any rate, doctor.

REED (*shaken*):   I can't stand much more of this, Agramonte.
Have you looked over the army death list lately? They're our boys!

AGRAMONTE: Yes, doctor.

REED: And I look out there over the sea and watch our trans-
ports steaming home and I daren't think what they may be carrying!
And we've taken Cuba on! Taken it on with this awful thing smoldering in it! Smoldering and waiting for fresh fuel. For fresh American fuel now, Agramonte! Waiting its chance to jump over home
to us! As its been doing for over a hundred years! To Philadelphia
and New Orleans and . . . And to know we've had it under our
microscopes a thousand times and never seen it! And men will die
and go on dying for all . . .

AGRAMONTE: It is not an agreeable condition from my point
of view either, doctor. I am Cuban-born.

REED: I didn't mean to offend you, Agramonte. It isn't easy
to admit one's failed. It shakes one's nerve. (*He sits smiling.*) I've
said to myself all this afternoon: "If Carroll brings me back anything from Pinar, anything that even looks like a new lead . . ."
(CARROLL *has entered through the gathering dusk outside.*) Carroll!

CARROLL: Well, I did get here.

REED: What news from the camp at Pinar?

CARROLL: There's no doubt about your diagnosis. Pernicious
malaria my eye! It's yellow jack and going great guns, too! They're
dropping like flies! (REED *turns away.*)

AGRAMONTE: Is that all you have to tell us?

CARROLL: I can't tell you a damned thing that we don't know
already! There's nothing to do but wait and see how bad it gets.

AGRAMONTE: And I'm told General Wood's lost a third of his
staff in the past month!

REED: At his mess they've been drinking toasts to the last to
go. Now they've begun drinking to the next.

CARROLL (*nodding*):   And Wood knows it was yellow jack,
not Rough Riders, that licked the Spaniards here. And it will lick us
if we don't lick it first.

AGRAMONTE: There's no doubt about that.

REED: And our commission — you, Agramonte and you, Carroll, and Lazear and I — we were sent down here to stop this horror! To isolate a microbe and find a cure! And we've failed! It isn't easy to admit that.

CARROLL: It's better than pretending you're getting somewhere.

REED: If I could only think of some fresh angle. . . .

CARROLL: We've tried every angle! Give it up, Chief! It's no use!

REED: I'm calling the Commission to disband it tonight. It won't be a long session. Then we'll go home.

CARROLL: Thank God! I hate wasting time! I've got to have something I can *see* and *get* at! Like that typhoid job before we came down here! Those flies traveled straight as an arrow from backhouse to mess hall! That was a job you could get some enjoyment out of! Let's go home and get on to something else! Only you'd keep me with you, wouldn't you, Chief? You know I'm a one-man dog. I know how you feel, though! (*An affectionate gesture from* REED *to* CARROLL.)

AGRAMONTE: The most we could do would be to keep on working. We have at least discredited everyone else.

REED (*desperate*): And we're quitting. We're breaking the chain! Have we the right?

CARROLL: I can see I've stayed away from you too long.

REED: We know so little, Carroll. We know so little!

CARROLL: I ran into one puzzler out there at Pinar.

REED: I've heard enough puzzlers I can't solve.

CARROLL: This is a funny one. Case of a soldier. Sick July 12th. Died on the 18th.

REED: You reported him.

CARROLL: Didn't know he hadn't been near the disease for over a month before he took sick.

REED (*looking up*): How was that?

CARROLL: They had him locked up in the guardhouse!

AGRAMONTE: Sure of that, Carroll?

CARROLL: And there he lay in that guardhouse for three days after, with eight other prisoners and they didn't catch it. Not even the one who slept in his blankets after he'd died. (*"Mess Call" sounds.*)

REED (*sharply*): How about contaminated food or water?

CARROLL: The whole outfit ate and drank the same.

REED: The other eight may have been immunes.

CARROLL: Records don't show it. One came from Iowa, one from Maine, two from Wisconsin . . .

REED: The man may have been extra susceptible.

CARROLL: That might explain. If we could explain why *we* don't catch it. (*But* REED, *caught in sudden thought, holds up his hand for silence.*) What?

REED: Nothing. I'll see you tonight. (AGRAMONTE *and* CARROLL *exchange a glance, but decide against asking questions.*)

CARROLL: After supper. All right.

AGRAMONTE: We'll go clean up.

REED: Eight-thirty, gentlemen. (AGRAMONTE *and* CARROLL *go out into the dusk, leaving* REED *alone. "Mess Call" sounds again, nearer and louder. The light concentrates upon the tensely thoughtful* REED, *until only his figure remains of the entire scene. A pause, then solo.*) What was it crawled or jumped or flew through that guardhouse window, bit that one prisoner and went back where it came from?

> [*The scene goes into complete darkness. "Tattoo" sounds. Then the sky freezes to the green of tropic night and shows* CARROLL, AGRAMONTE, GORGAS, *and* TORY *talking easily on one of the flights of steps.* REED *stands apart on the edge of the shadow and* LAZEAR *lounges in the shadow above.* GORGAS, *aged forty-six, is friendly, keen, and humorous.* LAZEAR, *aged thirty-four, is imaginative and wildly alive. Again the summer uniforms of officers of the Medical Corps.* TORY, *Colonel of the Marine Hospital Corps, is sixty, pompous, and objectionable.*]

TORY (*as the last notes of "Tattoo" die away*):   If you really have reached the end of your tether, Major Reed, my advice to you and to the members of your Commission is to call it a day. Go home. Give out a salty personal interview. Say your accomplishment here has been too technical for popular consumption. You will thus preserve the atmosphere of success which we all require for our reputations and to safeguard our service of our glorious mistress, Science! You will then feel free to move on to pastures new, as the farmers say, and, as my friend, Major Gorgas, can assure you, you will be leaving this epidemic in worthy hands. The Marine Hospital Corps with which I have the honor to be connected. . . .

> [LAZEAR *stirs irritably.* CARROLL *sits nodding approval.* REED *steps forward. But* GORGAS *interrupts.*]

GORGAS: Aren't you rather missing the point of this conference, Colonel Tory? It isn't General Wood's idea for anyone to go home. Wood wants us all working together on this. Wood's getting anxious for action. He watches me scrubbing and you fumigating and they tell him Reed's busy with microscopes. But he doesn't see any results. And it isn't only Cuba he's got on his mind. It's this whole Caribbean and Central American part of the world that we're getting involved in. It's Panama! How can we talk about a Panama Canal with yellow jack rampaging all over the place? This is the toughest problem Wood's governor-generalship has to grapple with and he's not going to let anyone quit. And neither am I, if I can help it! I'm the one Wood gets after and I'm tired of taking all the blame alone!

REED: I called the Commission to disband it tonight. Three hours ago I was certain we should disband. I hesitate now to propose continuing. The only course which remains open to us leads so far afield, seems so blocked with difficulty and beset with danger that I stand appalled before it.

GORGAS: You're being damn mysterious!

TORY: What is the course?

REED: To set our microscopes aside.

CARROLL: Say!

REED: And concentrate on new methods for prevention.

AGRAMONTE: How?

REED: By turning our minds to how yellow fever spreads, Agramonte. From man to man and village to village and even across the sea.

GORGAS: I should like to know something about that!

CARROLL: Not me. It's not my line. I'm a microscope man. I don't give a hoot how it spreads. I'll work on cause or nothing.

TORY: I admire determination in men of science and if the Marine Hospital Corps hadn't covered the ground . . .

AGRAMONTE: Yes, doctor. What more can this Commission add?

REED (*to* AGRAMONTE). I've come to suspect a middleman here. An infection carrier. In all likelihood an insect. Which we might hope to identify and which you, Gorgas, might subsequently wipe out.

AGRAMONTE: What kind of insect?

REED: Present evidence seems to point to a mosquito.

LAZEAR (*coming forward*): Did you say mosquito?

GORGAS (*a weary smile*): You're not going off on that tangent are you, Reed?

TORY: You can't be serious!

REED: I couldn't be more so.

LAZEAR: And why not, Colonel Tory? If we find that a mosquito is the carrier of yellow fever and stop that, won't we have done our job? And what a job finding it is going to be! The kind that comes once in a lifetime! God bless you, Reed! Mosquitoes are meat and drink to me. (*General laughter except from* TORY.)

TORY: These fads are the curse of modern medicine!

LAZEAR: I hadn't thought of that.

TORY: Think of it now and tell me how you could hope to test Dr. Finlay's mosquitoes by any conceivable experiment.

REED (*quietly*):   We haven't yet tried experimenting on men.

[*A general gasp.* TORY *rises astounded.*]

CARROLL: For God's sake, Reed!

LAZEAR: By heaven! Get the mosquitoes! Feed 'em on sick men! Let 'em bite healthy men! See what happens!

TORY (*stammering*):   You don't propose using human guinea pigs!

REED: I hadn't thought of calling them by that name.

TORY: I can't believe my ears! Doctors you call yourselves! Do you realize this is human vivisection! And might be manslaughter! Or even murder!

[*More or less together.*]
{
GORGAS: He's got you there, Reed!
CARROLL: You *are* going it pretty strong!
AGRAMONTE: Yes, I admit I hadn't thought of . . .
}

TORY: If Finlay were right and one of your victims died!

REED: If we fail at this, our victims, as you call them, will be none the worse for a few harmless mosquito bites. If we succeed, we shall have risked a few dozen lives to save countless thousands.

TORY: No! No! You've got to be stopped!

LAZEAR: We haven't started yet!

TORY: You're not going to start! Wait until General Wood hears of this!

REED: I'll take my chances, Colonel, with Leonard Wood, and if the members of this Commission . . .

AGRAMONTE: You can count on me, doctor!

CARROLL: We stand by, of course, Reed!

LAZEAR: This is an independent Commission, Colonel!

TORY: It isn't independent of Washington!

LAZEAR: Even Washington will think twice before it . . .

TORY (*shouting him down*):   American public opinion won't think twice! The American press and pulpit won't think twice! You know how they stand on animal vivisection! I'll go to them before I let you disgrace science and the army with this monstrous . . .

LAZEAR: Do you mean you'd run to yellow journals! Obstructing the very thing you pretend to . . .

TORY: If you're ready, Major Gorgas, I'll bid these gentlemen a very good evening.

REED (*steadily*):   Good evening, Colonel.

[*But the colonel is already on his way.*]

GORGAS (*to* REED, *somewhat apologetic*):   Well, it turned out livelier than most medical meetings. Sorry I couldn't give you more support. It wouldn't have panned out, though. I'm right about Finlay.

REED: You may be. Good night, Gorgas.

[*Ad lib good nights as "Call to Quarters" sounds.* GORGAS *goes.* REED *turns up in the laboratory,* LAZEAR *following, letting out the full hurt of his disappointment. The others in their turn follow into the laboratory.*]

LAZEAR: Reed, if you had this in the back of your head, why didn't you just tell us? Why did you have to let them in on it? We could have tackled it alone!

CARROLL: If you ask me, it's just as well!

LAZEAR (*hotly*):   I don't agree! We might have made history!

CARROLL: Yes. Or made damn fools of ourselves!

LAZEAR: Don't be so sure of that!

REED (*quietly*):   Did you think I'd be stopped by anything they said?

LAZEAR: Reed!

CARROLL: Now listen, Reed! You know what Tory can do to you!

REED (*strong because imperturbable*):   There's no doubt of what Colonel Tory can do; I see no reason, though, why he or anyone should know what we're up to from now on. (*Pause, then.*)

AGRAMONTE (*low*):   But, doctor, would it be possible to experiment on men in secret?

LAZEAR (*quick and low*).   It's got to be!

CARROLL: Men, though!

[*Off stage the* QUARTET *begins singing very softly.*]

THE QUARTET:

"Oh, the moonlight's fair tonight along the Wabash,
  From the fields there comes the breath of new-mown hay;
  Through the sycamores the candle lights are gleaming,
    On the banks of the Wabash, far away."

CARROLL: Men, God Almighty!

LAZEAR (*quickly*):   That's got to be, too!

REED (*low but stern*):   I'm afraid so. I'm afraid so.

CARROLL (*a whisper*):   Men . . . (*The light dies on the laboratory as the screen closes.*)

Men. But first mosquitoes — and the Commission visits the Cuban DR. FINLAY, *"cracked old Finlay" whose theories of the carrier of yellow fever have been laughed at by scientists for nineteen years.* MAJOR REED *and his men do not laugh, as they plead with the old man for his mosquitoes. . . .*

FINLAY (*scornful*):   You live in your own little world of professionals. You forget that other world outside, where the humane and kindhearted and Christian live and love their fellow men! They may send their sons off to be butchered in battle, but let one of you lift one finger in this war and they will engulf you! You will be destroyed! There will arise such power of public fury . . .

LAZEAR (*in a whisper of suppressed excitement*):   All right, Dr. Finlay! Let the soldiers wait! They'll keep! They'll be there any time we need 'em! We'll start this off ourselves!

FINLAY: You, gentlemen!

REED (*kindling*):   The four of us!

LAZEAR: No. Only three. Agramonte's had yellow fever.

AGRAMONTE (*regretful*):   Yes.

CARROLL: Am I in on this?

LAZEAR: Don't you want to be?

CARROLL: I like to be consulted before I . . .

LAZEAR: I'll try it first. You can follow me.

CARROLL: I can follow you, can I?

LAZEAR (*nodding*):   You've got five kids.

CARROLL: You've got a kid yourself.

LAZEAR: That's four less than you. We'll hold Reed back to see that we don't bungle and . . .

REED: Why didn't we think of this before?

LAZEAR: What a job it's turning out to be!

FINLAY (*his vocal powers only just restored*):   But I can't have it, gentlemen! You must put this idea out of your minds at once!

LAZEAR (*laughing*):   Thought you wanted us to be ruthless!

FINLAY: But this is carrying things too far!

CARROLL: After all, there may not be any risk.

FINLAY: There is, doctor! Believe me, there is!

REED: Then the three of us should make easy marks!

CARROLL: If you're right!

LAZEAR: And your mosquitoes aren't too fastidious!

FINLAY: No! You are men of science! Your lives are valuable!

REED: Is any man's life worth more than the cause he risks it on? (*Pause, then.*)

FINLAY (*deeply stirred*):   You must let me thank you. Major Reed. My friends, all of you. You come to me after nineteen years. Strangers. You fill my life with hope as sudden music fills our Cuban nights. I concede your skepticism and revere your courage. I am honored. Tell me how I may serve you.

AGRAMONTE (*suavely covering the embarrassment of the others*): Let them have the eggs, doctor. I think you had better let them have the eggs.

FINLAY: When I give them into your hands I give you nineteen years of my life. Well, I do it gladly.

[*He goes out. The four members of the Commission eye each other in the most intense excitement, but each one in his own mood,* AGRAMONTE *worried,* CARROLL *amused,* REED *solemn,* LAZEAR *white hot.* FINLAY *returns carrying a porcelain dish covered with a gauze. He sets it down on the table to uncover it, the four members of the Commission leaning eagerly forward. The light begins imperceptibly to fade until only the five faces are visible, the old Scotchman's lit with a religious fervor as he describes his great discovery.*]

FINLAY: You have only to raise the water in that dish and those eggs will hatch the criminal. Beware of her. She isn't one of your wild marsh mosquitoes. She's your domestic pet. Shares your home with you, takes her siesta underneath your eaves, raises her family in your patio fountain and rewards your hospitality with death. How do I know? I know! I have a mystic's faith in this mosquito! You hold the key to yellow fever in your hands. I pray for your sake and all humanity's that you may turn the lock I failed to turn.

REED: Curious. Very curious.

CARROLL: They look like little black cigars.

LAZEAR (*a dry whisper*): Come on! Let's get going! (*Darkness. Then the* QUARTET *is singing again.*)

THE QUARTET:
"After the din of the battle's roar,
    Just at the close of day,
Wounded and bleeding upon the field,
    Two dying soldiers lay.
One held a ringlet of thin gray hair.
    One held a lock of brown,
Bidding each other a last farewell,
    Just as the sun went down."

[AMES *is standing, below, between two cots in which* SOLDIERS *lie sick of yellow fever and* MISS BLAKE *looks on as he speaks over the singing.*]

AMES: I don't know any more about it than you do, boys. I'm only a doctor. These lab experiments are 'way over my head. I get my orders to let 'em bring their mosquitoes in here to the ward to suck a few yellow fever germs out of your blood. You've got plenty to spare, so there's nothing for you to get excited about. One little mosquito bite won't make you feel any worse than you do already.

[AGRAMONTE *enters above and comes quickly down the stairs. He carries a wire basket filled with test tubes, the mouths of which are covered with tightly stretched gauze.*]

You back so soon?

AGRAMONTE: Don't tell me I'm wearing out my welcome.

AMES: Oh, no! I was just preparing these new arrivals, that's all.

AGRAMONTE (*hesitant*):   I don't like to trouble them, but if you've explained . . .

AMES: Go ahead. They're too sick to mind. Skeeters hungry?

AGRAMONTE: They've been crying like babies. (*Then, to* MISS BLAKE.) If you'll turn back the blankets so I can get at him, Miss Blake . . .

MISS BLAKE (*as she turns the blankets back from the first cot*): Don't be afraid. Doctor isn't going to hurt you. (AGRAMONTE *selects a test tube from the basket and deftly inverts it, applying its mouth to the patient's abdomen. He taps the end lightly to jar the mosquito down toward the flesh.*)

AGRAMONTE: Tap. Tap. There!

AMES: Once you get your skeeters filled up with yellow-jack blood, though . . .

AGRAMONTE (*wary*):   Yes, Ames?

AMES: What do you do with 'em back there in that lab of yours? (*Pause, then.*)

AGRAMONTE (*evasive*):   Oh, various things. (*Then.*) Why?

AMES: I was wondering. There are some pretty brutal rumors going around.

AGRAMONTE: You mustn't believe everything you hear, Ames. (*Then, to* MISS BLAKE.) Next. (*Business as before.*)

MISS BLAKE: Don't be afraid. Doctor isn't going to hurt you.

AGRAMONTE: Tap. Tap.

THE QUARTET:

> "One thought of mother at home, alone,
>   Feeble and old and gray,
> One of the sweetheart he left in town,
>   Happy and young and gay.
> One kissed a ringlet of thin gray hair,
>   One kissed a lock of brown,
> Bidding farewell to the Stars and Stripes,
>   Just as the sun went down."

[*Darkness, under cover of which the cots vanish.*] . . .

Tap. Tap. DR. LAZEAR *is bitten by the infected mosquito — and becomes the first of the human guinea pigs. But* MAJOR REED *is ordered home, and the others must carry on without him.*

They do — with unhappy results. LAZEAR *does not become ill.* CARROLL, *who is next, does; but he has spoiled the experiment by having performed an autopsy on a victim of yellow jack. . . .*

[*Light on the laboratory and* LAZEAR *sits in his shirt sleeves at the microscope, while* AGRAMONTE, *now in uniform, paces to and fro evidently under a severe strain.* FINLAY *enters to them in a tremolo of mingled delight and awe.*]

FINLAY: I have seen Dr. Carroll! Whatever doubts you may have had yesterday, there can be no question now! First I was sorry for him! Then I remembered to thank God!

LAZEAR (*looking up in excitement from the microscope*): There's not a trace of malaria in the blood! Malaria would have shown itself by this! (*He is on his feet.*) Let's celebrate, Dr. Finlay! Let's get drunk!

AGRAMONTE (*full force at both of them*):   What you and Dr. Finlay may or may not believe is not evidence, and you cannot deceive yourselves that it is!

[*The pair fairly scream back at him.*]

FINLAY: A man has been bitten by my mosquito!

LAZEAR: And has got yellow jack as a result!

AGRAMONTE: Not necessarily as a result!

FINLAY: What he did, where he went yesterday, is of no importance!

AGRAMONTE: It is of the most disastrous importance!

LAZEAR: He came through three months of exposure before he was bitten!

AGRAMONTE: That is not proof!

FINLAY: It was my mosquito that infected him!

AGRAMONTE: We don't *know* that!

LAZEAR: You're splitting hairs!

AGRAMONTE: I'm talking science! You know that we have bungled Carroll's sickness! You know his life will be wasted if he dies!

LAZEAR: There's no good looking on the dark side, is there?

AGRAMONTE: You know that is what you must report to Reed!

LAZEAR: Reed will know that we've got this! Here! Under our fingers!

AGRAMONTE: Where?

have cleared away, leaving one — PRIVATE DEAN, *a nondescript, hick American — looking up at the laboratory.*)

LAZEAR: Do you know that cavalryman out there, Agramonte?

AGRAMONTE: No, I don't think so. (*Then he understands.*) No, Lazear! Not that! (LAZEAR *is on his way out of the laboratory.*)

LAZEAR: Why not?

AGRAMONTE (*stopping him*): Will your conscience let you?

LAZEAR: What's conscience got to do with it?

[*He has broken away and runs down the steps to* DEAN.]

AGRAMONTE (*to* FINLAY): Stop him, Dr. Finlay!

FINLAY: And let Dr. Carroll die without confirmation?

[*He follows* LAZEAR *down. Off stage the* QUARTET *strikes into "Good-by, Dolly Gray."*] . . .

DEAN, *all innocence, is given the "Tap Tap." Now the scene changes. On a hospital cot* CARROLL *lies dying, while* DR. AMES *applies a stethoscope to the patient's heart.*

CARROLL (*feeble, but in the best of good humor*): If you can keep that heart of mine going, Ames, you're a better man than I think.

[LAZEAR *turns wretchedly.*]

AMES: I can't even hear your heart till you quit talking!

CARROLL: Helps me to talk. Keeps me from going out.

AMES: Go out if you want to. Won't hurt you any.

CARROLL: Going out's not so bad. Coming back's getting harder.

LAZEAR: Damn us both for a pair of incompetent bunglers! When I think of the waste of this! (*But* CARROLL *is laughing.*)

CARROLL: You know I was the first. That's some satisfaction. You can't curse me out of that.

LAZEAR: I didn't mean to curse you.

CARROLL: Some day, when you get a second to back me up and break out in print, find room for me in a footnote, will you?

[AGRAMONTE *enters.*]

AGRAMONTE: Lazear . . .

[LAZEAR *turns and fairly runs to him.*]

LAZEAR: News?

AGRAMONTE (*holding out a paper*): His name's on the sick list.

LAZEAR (*examining*): Oh, God bless you, Private Dean! (*He turns back in great exultation.*) Carroll, you're set! We've got your confirmation! (*But* CARROLL *has gone out again.*) Oh . . .

AGRAMONTE: What?

LAZEAR: No. He comes and goes like that. (*Then.*) He was
just asking me to . . . (*He stops to control himself. Then.*) I guess
I'm tired. (*He sits again.*) Time like this you forget what it's all
about. What was it all about? The chase of the carrier of yellow
fever. That was it, wasn't it? The chase. (*He smiles.*) I might remember to ask how Dean is.

AGRAMONTE: I don't know. (AMES *returns carrying, in his
hand, the hypodermic needle for* CARROLL'S *injection. He goes to the
bed.* LAZEAR *follows. Then.*) Didn't you find any new yellow-jack
cases?

AMES: No.

LAZEAR: Nor hear of any?

AMES (*surprised*): No!

LAZEAR: Go on, Agramonte! (AGRAMONTE *goes, troubled.*)
Can I help you?

AMES: Alcohol. (LAZEAR *applies the alcohol to* CARROLL'S
arm.) Hold it. (LAZEAR *holds the arm while* AMES *makes the injection.*) Here.

[LAZEAR *takes the needle and sets it aside.* AMES *listens with
his stethoscope again.* LAZEAR *comes back to the bedside.*
AMES *looks up. Pause, then.*]

LAZEAR: How long do you give him?

AMES: I don't know. If we could make him fight . . .

[MISS BLAKE *has entered.*]

MISS BLAKE: Dr. Ames.

AMES: Yes?

MISS BLAKE: Can you get away to look at a new case? (LA-
ZEAR'S *head comes up.*) It's a soldier they . . .

LAZEAR (*almost fainting*): What's the soldier's name?

MISS BLAKE (*consulting a scrap of paper*): Dean. William H.
Troop A. Seventh Cavalry. (LAZEAR'S *eyes close as she continues to
*AMES.) And everybody's upset because he insists he hasn't been out
of camp for weeks and they're afraid of its breaking out here again
and . . .

AMES (*to* LAZEAR): Good God!

LAZEAR (*low*): Hadn't you better take a look at him?

[AMES *hands* LAZEAR *his stethoscope.*]

AMES: You watch that heart.

[*He goes,* MISS BLAKE *following.*]

MISS BLAKE: I'm afraid there's no doubt but it *is* yellow . . .

[*They are gone.* LAZEAR *turns toward* CARROLL.]

LAZEAR (*behind his voice that grim pressure which doctors
employ to reach through unconsciousness*): I'll make you fight

now, you bloody bonehead! (*He kneels beside the bed. His tone is low but shaken with all the force in him.*) You did it after all . . . in spite of yourself . . .

CARROLL (*as he comes to somewhat*): I was the first. Remember that. . . . I was the first . . .

LAZEAR (*the pressure increasing as the tone drops in pitch*): Damn right you were! And nobody's ever going to forget it! . . . We've got your second now! . . . We know now, Carroll! We know! Do you get that! We know!

[*Darkness, but not before we have seen the smile on the sick man's face. Then.*]

MISS BLAKE (*calling frantically through the darkness*): Dr. Ames! Dr. Ames!

[*Light strikes her from behind* AMES *as he enters.*]

AMES: What are you doing up at this time of night?

MISS BLAKE: It's Dr. Lazear . . .

AMES: What's wrong with him?

MISS BLAKE: I don't know! I'm afraid! I went in just now. I was ready to make my report on what fine progress Dr. Carroll's making. And he . . . (*Her voice chokes with tears.*) He's very sick, Dr. Ames . . .

AMES: Lazear, too! (*They cross through the darkness, the light increasing to show* LAZEAR *seated at the laboratory workbench, haggard and ill, notebooks and sheets of paper scattered before him. The sky remains unlighted.*)

LAZEAR (*pushing the words out as he writes*): I don't deny I bungled Carroll's case, though Dean seems to have confirmed him. Now they're both out of the woods, I have to confess to you about myself. I can't account for it, but I'm beginning to be afraid . . . (MISS BLAKE *and* AMES *have entered to him.*) Go away. I'm busy.

AMES: She tells me you're under the weather.

LAZEAR: I'd have told you myself if I'd wanted you to know!

AMES: You don't have to tell me. I can see.

LAZEAR: I've got a touch of malaria.

AMES: Sure it isn't the same malaria Carroll had?

LAZEAR (*low and stubborn*): Carroll got yellow jack from our mosquitoes. I haven't taken a bite myself for weeks. Whatever this is, it can't be yellow jack!

AMES (*eying him sharply*): The fact remains . . .

MISS BLAKE: Oh, if doctors would only take care of themselves!

[AGRAMONTE *has entered.*]

AGRAMONTE: What's this about Lazear?

AMES: Looks to me very much like . . .

It is yellow fever — without the mosquito's bite! He lies dying, as GORGAS *and* FINLAY *and* CARROLL *sit waiting. . . .*

GORGAS: Men can't go against death and not risk death themselves. Pasteur sent Thuillier to Alexandria for the cholera there. Thuillier didn't come back. Lazear won't be the last.

FINLAY: Humanity won't have done asking this sacrifice of his kind for a long time yet. Science won't have done.

CARROLL: His wife's just had another baby. He won't ever see it.

[*Light grows on the screened bed on which* LAZEAR *lies dying.* MISS BLAKE *attends him.* AMES *is just leaving him to approach the other doctors.*]

AMES: Make Carroll go back to bed, Major Gorgas.

CARROLL: How much sleep did he get the nights you thought I was a goner?

GORGAS: He hadn't just been sick. You have.

CARROLL: Lazear's dying! For a lot of God-forsaken half-wits of men and women! Will they ever appreciate what he's done for them? Will they even hear of him?

FINLAY: Neither death nor what he's dying for belong in words.

CARROLL: I haven't got your philosophy, Dr. Finlay. Lazear's the best fellow I've ever known.

GORGAS: And his death is so much waste.

LAZEAR (*faintly from behind the screen*):   Waste! Waste!

CARROLL (*on his feet*):   He heard you! He understood! Lazear!

AMES: Keep your shirt on, Carroll! He's beyond understanding now.

[*The bugle sounds the thin, solemn strains of "Taps." On the last note* REED's *voice is heard barking sharply through the darkness.*]

REED: Didn't I warn both you and Lazear the night I left you! Unimpeachable workmanship, I demanded! And what have you given me? (*Bright daylight shows that the flag has disappeared and that* REED *is striding to and fro in the laboratory, while* CARROLL, AGRAMONTE, *and* GORGAS *sit morosely apart.*) You at death's door for no purpose and he dead for less!

CARROLL: Be fair, Reed!

REED: I'm not being unfair! God honor both of you for gallant men!

GORGAS: Reed! You've done enough! The summer's over and the epidemic with it!

REED: There'll be other summers and worse epidemics! There's knowledge and this fact's not yet established!

GORGAS: It's got away from you!

AGRAMONTE: I'm afraid it has.

REED: Gorgas, I can't let go!

AGRAMONTE: What have you to hang on to?

CARROLL: Let Agramonte go back on this if he wants to, Reed! I'm convinced!

AGRAMONTE: I cannot be romantic about this, Carroll! Scientifically, we have no evidence that Finlay's mosquito played any part either in Lazear's death or in your sickness! And I must agree with Major Gorgas that . . .

[*But* BRINKERHOF *has entered.*]

BRINKERHOF: Colonel Tory is here asking for you, Major.

[TORY *enters. The entire company rises.* BRINKERHOF *goes.*]

TORY: I welcome your return to Cuba, Major. All my sympathy for your young colleague's death. I call on you to serve a notice on you. The American Public Health Association will hold its annual conference next month. My staff in the Marine Hospital Corps has been invited to report on yellow fever. Since we shall criticize your experiment and you, it seems only fair that you should read what we have to say. (*He proffers a manuscript with a smile of triumph.*) So you may prepare your defense. If you have one.

REED: The usual course would have been to wait for us to make some public assertion. (*He indicates the paper.*) This may prevent the continuance of our work.

TORY: I venture to hope it will.

REED: Death has given tragic testimony in our behalf.

TORY: More tragic than conclusive.

REED: I can say no more.

TORY: Major.

REED: Colonel. (*Salutes.* TORY *goes.* REED *turns desperately to* GORGAS.) I need your support desperately now, Gorgas!

GORGAS: Wouldn't you have it if I could give it, Reed? But Lazear did catch yellow fever without your mosquito and you can't keep on in the face of that!

CARROLL: I got yellow jack from a mosquito! You can't account for my case any other way!

REED: There's another case I can't account for either, except . . .

AGRAMONTE (*alarmed*): Careful, doctor!

REED: We've got to play the ace now, Agramonte. Have you got your Private X. Y. Dean handy? Call him in. Let's see him. I want Major Gorgas to hear me talk to him! . . .

PRIVATE DEAN *is convincing enough — but not for the cautious scientist. . . .*

GORGAS (*embarrassment*): I know what it is to hope, Reed, but I can't accept a soldier's word in lieu of demonstration.

REED (*frantic*): Surely that story of his indicates something!

GORGAS: If you could substantiate every word he said you'd still have to admit he was in this lab that day with three doctors any one of whom might have carried the infection from Carroll's bedside! If he's all the defense you have against Tory, I'm sorry for you!

AGRAMONTE: He's perfectly right. We haven't any defense.

CARROLL: Do we sit tight, then, and let Tory do his worst?

REED: No! I believe our mosquitoes have the real deadly stuff in 'em! I believe Lazear really did find the catch before he died! In spite of his death and Gorgas' doubts I believe it!

GORGAS: You've all gone off your heads over this!

REED: I can see I'm in no shape to convince you, Gorgas! But, by God, we *have* got enough to take to Leonard Wood!

[*Both* CARROLL *and* AGRAMONTE *are on their feet in great excitement.*]

CARROLL: Wood!

REED: He's our last chance, Carroll!

AGRAMONTE: What can Wood do for us?

REED: I can't tell you that! I can only tell you what I shall ask him for!

GORGAS: And what will that be?

REED (*full blast*): Facilities for a fool-proof demonstration of this mosquito! The full power of his governor-generalship behind us! Ten thousand dollars for operating expenses! An isolation camp where we can experiment under ideal conditions! And his leave to call for volunteers to experiment on! I think the time has come for that at last!

[*Sensation.*]

CARROLL: So we fall back on the army after all!

REED: As soldiers should, Carroll! As soldiers should! (*The light dims, concentrating on the four officers.*)

GORGAS: Do you think Wood will even consider that?

REED: I don't know, Gorgas. All I know is: Lazear and Carroll showed the way! And I know this will give the army a new kind of hero! Do you think Leonard Wood won't see that?

[*Darkness, the* QUARTET *swelling. At the same time light strikes* AMES, *where he is talking to a sergeant.*]

thought still another thought in the nick of time. "If I do give my life," I said to myself, "it may be noble, but will it be a start?"

BUSCH: It's a thing any radical could go into and not be ashamed of, only I got to have more time on it.

MISS BLAKE: Won't the Major get a single volunteer?

BRINKERHOF: I wouldn't know.

MISS BLAKE: I want him to get one.

O'HARA: Don't be using your sex to shame us into this!

MISS BLAKE: I'm talking to Mr. Brinkerhof now. To Mr. Brinkerhof, who wants to stay in the army. Drill. Ten, maybe twenty years of drill. Then another war. And more lives thrown away. Then drill again. Then a pension and the old soldiers' home. If that's all being a soldier comes to!

BRINKERHOF: It ain't much.

MISS BLAKE: Now, maybe for the first time since armies began, soldiers are given a chance to do good, not harm. To make the world better, not worse, as a place to live in. (*They listen hypnotized,* O'HARA *rising slowly to his feet.*) You'd get well! We'd take care of you! Don't be afraid!

BRINKERHOF: But I *am* afraid.

MISS BLAKE: That makes it all the braver!

BRINKERHOF: I wouldn't do it for money!

MISS BLAKE: For your sergeancy then!

BRINKERHOF: That'd be just as bad.

MISS BLAKE: For science and humanity!

BRINKERHOF: Oh, I'd never be up to anything like that!

MISS BLAKE: Choose your own reason!

BRINKERHOF: There'd be a lot of satisfaction in it.

MISS BLAKE: Indeed there would!

BRINKERHOF: No! Just to me, I mean!

MISS BLAKE: But that's enough!

BRINKERHOF: I ain't committed myself! I only said, for the sake of argument . . .

MISS BLAKE: "If one, only one, of our boys will step forward," the Major said, "he'll make this reach and touch the heart of the world and the world will weep and have faith in this!"

O'HARA: By God, I'll do it for the heck of it!

[*A glad cry from* MISS BLAKE. *"Call to Quarters" sounds.*]

BRINKERHOF: Oh, I'm coming, John! I'm coming!

BUSCH: Stop him!

MC CLELLAND (*to* MISS BLAKE): You talked him into this!

MISS BLAKE: Thank God if I did!

MC CLELLAND: You're responsible if they . . .

MISS BLAKE: I can't help that! I can't help wanting them to . . .

They have volunteered. An isolation camp has been set up for them; Camp Lazear, they call it. O'HARA *and* BRINKERHOF *are placed in a clean tent;* BUSCH *and* MC CLELLAND, *the controls, in the "dirty house," to sleep in the unwashed and undisinfected bedding on which yellow fever victims have died. The first two have had* FINLAY'S *mosquitoes bite them; and now* BRINKERHOF *sits on his cot taking his temperature while* O'HARA *lounges before the tent gazing toward his friends' clean wooden shack. . . .*

O'HARA: Being a hero should be quickly over and on to the glory that comes after.

MC CLELLAND: Will you listen to all that quiet!

BUSCH: I heard it before and I didn't like it. They'd ought to have give us a bugler out here.

MC CLELLAND: I never expected this to be this way. This was some Thanksgiving Day!

BUSCH: I ain't complaining. I'm putting on weight living in that stink.

O'HARA (*to* BRINKERHOF): Will you take that thermometer out of your mouth, John!

BRINKERHOF: I'm hot.

O'HARA: It's a cold night with a wintry dampness in it the way you could see your breath if you troubled to blow it!

MC CLELLAND: O'Hara!

O'HARA: What is it?

MC CLELLAND: How are you feeling?

O'HARA: I'm feeling fine.

BUSCH: How's Brinkerhof feeling?

O'HARA: He feels better than me.

BRINKERHOF: I don't feel well, John! I got vertigo.

O'HARA: If you don't feel right, it's your willful imagination! If you felt bad, I'd feel worse than you! Do you think it's friendly to try stealing a march on me? We started on this together and we'll finish together or not finish at all!

BRINKERHOF: This is the night of the fourth day. The Major said things ought to begin to happen the fourth day.

O'HARA: For the last time I tell you, if you've got a fever you're no friend of mine!

MC CLELLAND: Quit scrapping, O'Hara!

[GORGAS *and* FINLAY *see* REED'S *point and go to* MISS BLAKE.]

GORGAS: Yes, I expect we were being a bit inhuman.

FINLAY: That's one of the drawbacks of experiment, Major Gorgas.

[*They have crossed to* MISS BLAKE, *who hands them each a file of the record. They sit to study them in silence while she looks on and* CARROLL *and* AGRAMONTE *watch from above.* REED *has gone to* BRINKERHOF'S *bedside and stands looking down on him.*]

REED: That was part of the game, Brinkerhof. An essential part from my point of view. I hope you didn't mind it too much.

BRINKERHOF: I wouldn't feel up to minding anything, doctor.

REED: It's a bad sickness, I know that. We got your case at the beginning, though, so you're going to be all right. Don't worry.

BRINKERHOF: I wouldn't feel up to worrying, either. (REED'S *hand is on the boy's forehead.*)

REED: They tell me you didn't drink the champagne I sent you.

BRINKERHOF: Do I have to drink it, sir?

REED: It might make you feel less sick at your stomach.

BRINKERHOF: I ain't used to it and I didn't care for it. (REED *smiles, then.*)

REED: My wife's just sent me a fine fruit cake. I'm saving it for you. For your Christmas dinner. We'll try to have you on your feet by then. So you can get sick all over again. Not for science, though. Just for the fun of it. Nothing else we can do for you now? (*A pause.* BRINKERHOF *manages to lift his head a little. Then.*)

BRINKERHOF: Why was it, sir, yellow jack took me and give O'Hara the go-by?

REED (*surprised*):   I don't know, Brinkerhof. Some men seem to be born immune to some diseases.

BRINKERHOF: Could a man be immune one time and catch it another?

REED: It's possible. We don't know much about immunity.

BRINKERHOF: John O'Hara, he's quite a friend of mine, sir. You just asked me what more you could do for me. John set his heart on getting this disease for the start it'd give him practicing medicine. It's likely the only start he'll ever get. Would you give John another chance at it, sir?

REED: It's hard for me to say no to you, Brinkerhof. I'm afraid O'Hara's a waste of time for my purposes. I can't afford to break our record of success. I'll do what I can to help him with his

medical studies. But I wish you'd ask me for something else now.
(BRINKERHOF *sinks back.*)

BRINKERHOF: Give John my best. Ask him not to be angry with me if he can help it.

REED: I'll do that much.

[*But* GORGAS, *going through the file, has come to the fever chart.*]

GORGAS (*low and quick*): A hundred and three and six tenths last night. Dropped again, though, at six this morning and again at eight.

FINLAY: You've noticed the granular casts in the urine, I hope? (REED *goes toward them.*)

GORGAS: Oh, yes.

FINLAY: The eyes were beautifully jaundiced today, too.

GORGAS (*to* MISS BLAKE): How about the gums?

MISS BLAKE: A little bleeding.

FINLAY: Headache and nausea still troublesome, though?

MISS BLAKE: He's very uncomfortable.

FINLAY: Splendid! I should defer to the Major's diagnosis, but I can't think of a symptom the boy's omitted! It's beautiful! Beautiful! The fourth day of his sickness, too! (*Then, to* REED.) And how long did you say between the bite and the first symptom?

REED: Three days, nine and a half hours.

FINLAY: Nineteen years for me. Three days, nine and a half hours for Major Reed! (*He is pumping* REED's *hand.*) I conceived a truth! You delivered it into life! Together we have added to the world's arsenal of knowledge!

GORGAS: You promised you'd make me eat my doubts, Reed. Didn't know eating doubts could be such a pleasure! Damned if this isn't an impressive moment! I'm going out after this mosquito now. And after that, Panama! You've made the Panama Canal possible now! May I? (*He holds out his hand.*)

REED (*sternly*): If that boy's convinced you, Gorgas, that he did get the infection from the mosquito and if those other two, healthy as ever in the filth of that dirty house, have shown you the disease cannot in nature be contracted except from the mosquito, then you may! But if you have any shadow of reservation on either point . . .

[AMES *has entered hastily to the second cot.*]

AMES: You certainly are knocking 'em over out at that camp, Major! Will you fix up this cot, Miss Blake?

[MISS BLAKE *goes to prepare the cot.*]

CARROLL: What do you mean?

The Story of the Electron Microscope

JAMES HILLIER

OUR STORY concerns one of the latest developments of modern science, but its beginnings go back some two hundred and fifty years. At that time there was a certain merchant in the city of Delft, Holland, who had a curious hobby. This man, Antony Leeuwenhoek, was possessed with the idea of making a perfect optical lens, and after his store closed for the day he used to spend his nights patiently grinding small bits of glass and shaping them into carefully curved surfaces. This inspired amateur became an expert. He made for himself a microscope and was fascinated by the world of little things which it brought into his view.

For centuries, scientists had speculated on the nature and structure of the invisible world that lies beyond the range of the unaided eye. It was for Leeuwenhoek to open the door and take a look. What he saw was enough to show the possibilities of microscopy. Gradually the microscope was accepted as a regular tool of science. In the nineteenth century Pasteur, Koch, and others made spectacular advances in biology and medicine through the use of the relatively crude microscopes of their time.

In the early days it was assumed that there was no theoretical limit to the magnifying power of microscopes. It was supposed that as lenses became improved, one could see continuously smaller and smaller objects. A rude awakening came, however, about seventy years ago. At that time the German physicist, Ernest Abbe, pointed out that it would never be possible to observe directly an object which was considerably smaller than the wave length of the light used to illuminate it.

In effect, what Abbe said was this: That no microscope using ordinary light could usefully magnify an object by more than about 1000 diameters, no matter how perfect its lenses. He showed by optical theory why this must be so.

But, as so often happens in science, the theory which sets a limit to what can be accomplished with existing methods at the same time points out the way in which those methods can be improved and the limit thus removed. If ordinary light is too coarse, reasoned the scientists, why not use ultraviolet light since its wave lengths

First given as part of a symposium broadcast sponsored by the U.S. Rubber Company. Reprinted by permission of Dr. James Hillier.

are only about one-half that of ordinary blue light? This stratagem was tried and it worked. By making their lenses of special materials which are transparent to ultraviolet light, the optical experts were able to construct an ultraviolet microscope with a magnification of 2500 diameters. This was more than double the power of the ordinary microscope.

Of course it was natural to think of further extending the method and using still shorter wave lengths, for there are many rays beyond the ultraviolet. But this time the physical properties of the rays put a stop to progress. For either the waves were absorbed by the lenses, as was the case with the extremely short ultraviolet rays; or else the waves were so penetrating that they passed through the lenses without being affected and focusing became impossible, as was the case with X rays, for example.

Thus we have the situation in the 1920s. Research scientists were becoming more and more aware of the existence of many small structures that could best be studied through a microscope, if only a microscope powerful enough could be devised. Probably no one was more surprised than the microscopists themselves when the solution came not from students of optics, but from the atomic physicists studying electrons.

Electrons are the particles of negative electricity whose flow through wires and vacuum tubes constitutes an electric current. In 1924 the French physicist, Louis DeBroglie, presented a thesis in which he suggested that a beam of electrons had what we may call a dual personality. He pointed out that such a beam was not just a stream of particles but that it also had associated with it something in the nature of a wave.

Later, when the truth of DeBroglie's theory was demonstrated, the wave length associated with an electron beam was found to be almost inconceivably small. Actually, the electron wave length is one hundred thousand times as short as that of visible light. The conclusion was obvious. If a microscope could be devised to use a beam of electrons in place of the usual beam of light, it should bring to visibility objects far, far smaller than anything previously seen. It was an exciting idea, but there was one forbidding detail. Nobody knew a way of focusing electrons, and until the electron beam could be focused there was no prospect of constructing an electron microscope.

Meanwhile, and quite apart from these desires and speculations, a certain Dr. Busch in a physical laboratory in Germany was having difficulties with an experiment in electronics. Busch decided to calculate the magnitude of his errors. History doesn't tell whether he was successful in tracking down the degree of those errors, for in where we like, is made up precisely of seven of one and three of the other. And of course it is quite impossible to write them down so that any choice of ten letters picked here and there will contain just seven As.

Then what do I mean by saying that we expect A to turn up seven times to every three times which B turns up? I mean that among all the sets of ten trials which we can choose from an extended series, picking as we like, the greatest number will contain seven As and three Bs. This is the same thing as saying that if we have enough trials, the proportion of As to Bs will tend to the ratio of seven to three. But of course, no run of trials, however extended, is necessarily long enough. In no run of trials can we be sure of reaching precisely the balance of seven to three.

Then how do I know that the law is in fact seven As and three Bs? What do I mean by saying that the ratio tends to this in a long trial, when I never know if the trial is long enough? And more, when I know that at the very moment when we have reached precisely this ratio, the next single trial must upset it — because it must add either a whole A or a whole B, and cannot add seven tenths of one and three tenths of the other. I mean this. After ten trials, we may have eight As and only two Bs; it is not at all improbable. It is not very improbable that we may have nine As, and it is not even excessively improbable that we may have ten. But it is very improbable that, after a hundred trials, we shall have as many as eighty As. It is excessively improbable that after a thousand trials we shall have as many as eight hundred As; indeed it is highly improbable that at this stage the ratio of As and Bs departs from seven to three by as much as five per cent. And if after a hundred thousand trials we should get a ratio which differs from our law by as much as one per cent, then we should have to face the fact that the law itself is almost certainly in error. . . .

· This is the method to which modern science is moving. It uses no principle but that of forecasting with as much assurance as possible, but with no more than is possible. That is, it idealizes the future from the outset, not as completely determined, but as determined within a defined area of uncertainty. Let me illustrate the kind of uncertainty. We know that the children of two blue-eyed parents will certainly have blue eyes; at least, no exception has ever been found. By contrast, we cannot be certain that all the children of two brown-eyed parents will have brown eyes. And we cannot be certain of it even if they have already had ten children with brown eyes. The reason is that we can never discount a run of luck of the kind which Dr. Johnson once observed when a friend of his was breeding horses. "He has had," said Dr. Johnson, "sixteen fillies without one colt, which is an accident beyond all computation of chances." But what we can do is to compute the *odds* against such a run; this is not as hard as Johnson supposed. And from this we can compute the likelihood that the next child will have brown eyes. That is, we can make a forecast which states our degree of uncertainty in a precise form. Oddly enough, it is just here that Mendel's own account of his work is at fault. He assumed in effect that once a couple has had ten brown-eyed children, the chance that they may yet have blue-eyed children is negligible. But it was not.

This area of uncertainty shrinks very quickly in its proportion if we make our forecasts not about one family but about many. I do not know whether this or that couple will have a child next year; I do not even know whether I shall. But it is easy to estimate the number of children who will be born to the whole population, and to give limits of uncertainty to our estimate. The motives which lead to marriage, the trifles which cause a car to crash, the chanciness of today's sunshine or tomorrow's egg, are local, private and incalculable. Yet, as Kant saw long ago, their totals over the country in a year are remarkably steady; and even their ranges of uncertainty can be predicted.

This is the revolutionary thought in modern science. It replaces the concept of the *inevitable effect* by that of the *probable trend*. Its technique is to separate so far as possible the steady trend from local fluctuations. The less the trend has been overlaid by fluctuations in the past, the greater is the confidence with which we look along the trend into the future. We are not isolating a cause. We are tracing a pattern of nature in its whole setting. We are aware of the uncertainties which that large, flexible setting induces in our pattern. But the world cannot be isolated from itself: the uncertainty *is* the world. The future does not already exist; it can only be predicted. We must be content to map the places into which it may move, and to assign a greater or less likelihood to this or that of its areas of uncertainty.

These are the ideas of chance in science today. They are new ideas: they give chance a kind of order; they re-create it as the life within reality. These ideas have come to science from many sources. Some were invented by Renaissance brokers; some by seventeenth-century gamblers; some by mathematicians who were interested in aiming-errors and in the flow of gases and more recently in radioactivity. The most fruitful have come from biology within little more than the last fifty years. I need not stress again how successful they have been in the last few years, for example in physics: Nagasaki is a monument to that. . . .

of ichthyological knowledge. In short, what my net can't catch isn't
fish." Or — to translate the analogy — "If you are not simply guessing, you are claiming a knowledge of the physical universe discovered in some other way than by the methods of physical science
and admittedly unverifiable by such methods. You are a metaphysician. Bah!"

The dispute arises, as many disputes do, because the protagonists are talking about different things. The onlooker has in mind
an objective kingdom of fishes. The ichthyologist is not concerned
as to whether the fishes he is talking about form a subjective or objective class; the property that matters is that they are catchable.

. . . When the ichthyologist rejected the onlooker's suggestion
of an objective kingdom of fishes as too metaphysical, and explained that his purpose was to discover laws (i.e. generalizations)
which were true for catchable fish, I expect the onlooker went away
muttering: "I bet he does not get very far with his ichthyology of
catchable fish. I wonder what his theory of the reproduction of
catchable fish will be like. It is all very well to dismiss baby fishes
as metaphysical speculation; but they seem to me to come into the
problem."

◇◇

Epilogue: New Pathways in Science

SIR ARTHUR EDDINGTON

OUR HOME, the Earth, is the fifth or sixth largest planet belonging to a middle grade star in the Milky Way. Within our galaxy
alone there are perhaps a thousand million stars as large and as luminous as the sun; and this galaxy is one of many millions which
formed part of the same creation but are now scattering apart.
Amid this profusion of worlds there are perhaps other globes that
are or have been inhabited by beings as highly developed as Man;
but we do not think they are at all common. The present indications
seem to be that it is very long odds against a particular star undergoing the kind of accident which gave birth to the solar system. It

From *New Pathways in Science* by Sir Arthur Eddington. Reprinted by permission of Cambridge University Press, publishers.

was breeding horses. "He has had," said Dr. Johnson, "sixteen fillies without one colt, which is an accident beyond all computation of chances." But what we can do is to compute the *odds* against such a run; this is not as hard as Johnson supposed. And from this we can compute the likelihood that the next child will have brown eyes. That is, we can make a forecast which states our degree of uncertainty in a precise form. Oddly enough, it is just here that Mendel's own account of his work is at fault. He assumed in effect that once a couple has had ten brown-eyed children, the chance that they may yet have blue-eyed children is negligible. But it was not.

This area of uncertainty shrinks very quickly in its proportion if we make our forecasts not about one family but about many. I do not know whether this or that couple will have a child next year; I do not even know whether I shall. But it is easy to estimate the number of children who will be born to the whole population, and to give limits of uncertainty to our estimate. The motives which lead to marriage, the trifles which cause a car to crash, the chanciness of today's sunshine or tomorrow's egg, are local, private and incalculable. Yet, as Kant saw long ago, their totals over the country in a year are remarkably steady; and even their ranges of uncertainty can be predicted.

This is the revolutionary thought in modern science. It replaces the concept of the *inevitable effect* by that of the *probable trend*. Its technique is to separate so far as possible the steady trend from local fluctuations. The less the trend has been overlaid by fluctuations in the past, the greater is the confidence with which we look along the trend into the future. We are not isolating a cause. We are tracing a pattern of nature in its whole setting. We are aware of the uncertainties which that large, flexible setting induces in our pattern. But the world cannot be isolated from itself: the uncertainty *is* the world. The future does not already exist; it can only be predicted. We must be content to map the places into which it may move, and to assign a greater or less likelihood to this or that of its areas of uncertainty.

These are the ideas of chance in science today. They are new ideas: they give chance a kind of order; they re-create it as the life within reality. These ideas have come to science from many sources. Some were invented by Renaissance brokers; some by seventeenth-century gamblers; some by mathematicians who were interested in aiming-errors and in the flow of gases and more recently in radio-activity. The most fruitful have come from biology within little more than the last fifty years. I need not stress again how successful they have been in the last few years, for example in physics: Nagasaki is a monument to that. . . .

The idea of chance as I have explained it here is not difficult. But it is new and unfamiliar. We are not used to handling it. So it does not seem to have the incisiveness of the simple laws of cause and effect. We seem to be in a land of sometimes and perhaps, and we had hoped to go on living with always and with certainly.

Yet I believe that the difficulty is only one of habit. We shall become accustomed to the new ideas just as soon as we are willing and as we have to. And we are having to. On all sides science is crowding into fields of knowledge which cannot be isolated in the laboratory, and asking us to come to conclusions in matters where we cannot hope to trace a causal mechanism. It may seem to be overtaxing our notion of science to hope that we shall find some common method of tackling the problems of physics and economics, of evolution and soil chemistry, of medicine and meteorology, of psychology and aerial bombardment. We have grown accustomed to thinking of science itself as divided into smaller and smaller pieces of specialization, an atomic universe of knowledge of its own, which no one and nothing can again hope to master. But this may well be an illusion. The different branches of science may seem so far apart only because we lack the common method on which they grow and which holds them together organically. Look back to the state of knowledge in the year 1600: the branches of science and of speculation seemed as diverse and as specialized, and no one could have foreseen that they would all fall into place as soon as Descartes and Hobbes introduced the unifying concept of cause and effect. The statistical concept of chance may come as dramatically to unify the scattered pieces of science in the future. What Hobbes and Newton did was to change the whole concept of natural law: instead of basing it on the analogy of the human will, they built it on cause and on force. But this analogy with human effort is now breaking down. We are on the threshold of another scientific revolution. The concept of natural law is changing. The laws of chance seem at first glance to be lawless. But I have shown in this chapter that they can be formulated with as much rigor as the laws of cause. Certainly they can be seen already to cover an infinitely wider field of human experience in nature and in society. And it may be that they will give to that field the unity which the last fifty years have lacked. If they do, they will give us all also a new confidence. We have been swept by a great wave of pessimism, which rises from our own feeling of helplessness in the recognition that none of us understands the great workings of the world. As science and knowledge have been broken into pieces, there has come upon us all a loss of nerve. That happened to the old classical culture of the Mediterranean in the seventeenth century. The future lay with the driving and purposeful optimists of the North, who seized the notion of cause and purpose, and with it conquered nature and the world together. We are looking for another such universal concept to unify and to enlighten our world. Chance has a helpless ring in our ears. But the laws of chance are lively, vigorous and human; and they may give us again that forward look which in the last half century has so tragically lowered its eyes.

Parable of the Fishing Net

SIR ARTHUR EDDINGTON

LET US SUPPOSE that an ichthyologist is exploring the life of the ocean. He casts a net into the water and brings up a fishy assortment. Surveying his catch he proceeds in the usual manner of a scientist to systematize what it reveals. He arrives at two generalizations.

(1) No sea-creature is less than two inches long.

(2) All sea-creatures have gills.

These are both true of his catch, and he assumes tentatively that they will remain true however often he repeats it.

In applying this analogy, the catch stands for the body of knowledge which constitutes physical science, and the net for the sensory and intellectual equipment which we use in obtaining it. The casting of the net corresponds to observation: for knowledge which has not been or could not be obtained by observation is not admitted into physical science.

An onlooker may object that the first generalization is wrong. "There are plenty of sea-creatures under two inches long, only your net is not adapted to catch them." The ichthyologist dismisses the objection contemptuously. "Anything uncatchable by my net is *ipso facto* outside the scope of ichthyological knowledge, and is not part of the kingdom of fishes which has been defined as the theme

From *The Philosophy of Physical Science* by Sir Arthur Eddington. Reprinted by permission of Cambridge University Press, publishers.

of ichthyological knowledge. In short, what my net can't catch isn't fish." Or — to translate the analogy — "If you are not simply guessing, you are claiming a knowledge of the physical universe discovered in some other way than by the methods of physical science and admittedly unverifiable by such methods. You are a metaphysician. Bah!"

The dispute arises, as many disputes do, because the protagonists are talking about different things. The onlooker has in mind an objective kingdom of fishes. The ichthyologist is not concerned as to whether the fishes he is talking about form a subjective or objective class; the property that matters is that they are catchable.

. . . When the ichthyologist rejected the onlooker's suggestion of an objective kingdom of fishes as too metaphysical, and explained that his purpose was to discover laws (i.e. generalizations) which were true for catchable fish, I expect the onlooker went away muttering: "I bet he does not get very far with his ichthyology of catchable fish. I wonder what his theory of the reproduction of catchable fish will be like. It is all very well to dismiss baby fishes as metaphysical speculation; but they seem to me to come into the problem."

◇◇◇

Epilogue: New Pathways in Science

SIR ARTHUR EDDINGTON

OUR HOME, the Earth, is the fifth or sixth largest planet belonging to a middle grade star in the Milky Way. Within our galaxy alone there are perhaps a thousand million stars as large and as luminous as the sun; and this galaxy is one of many millions which formed part of the same creation but are now scattering apart. Amid this profusion of worlds there are perhaps other globes that are or have been inhabited by beings as highly developed as Man; but we do not think they are at all common. The present indications seem to be that it is very long odds against a particular star undergoing the kind of accident which gave birth to the solar system. It

From *New Pathways in Science* by Sir Arthur Eddington. Reprinted by permission of Cambridge University Press, publishers.

seems that normally matter collects in big masses with excessively high temperature, and the formation of small cool globes fit for habitation is a rare occurrence. Nature seems to have been intent on a vast evolution of fiery worlds, an epic of milliards of years. As for Man — it seems unfair to be always raking up against Nature her one little inadvertence. By a trifling hitch of machinery — not of any serious consequence in the development of the universe — some lumps of matter of the wrong size have occasionally been formed. These lack the purifying protection of intense heat or the equally efficacious absolute cold of space. Man is one of the gruesome results of this occasional failure of antiseptic precautions.

To realize the insignificance of our race before the majesty of the universe may be healthful; but it brings to us an alarming thought. For Man is the typical custodian of certain qualities or illusions, which make a vital difference to the significance of things. He displays purpose in an inorganic world of chance. He can represent truth, righteousness, sacrifice. In him there flickers for a few brief years a spark from the divine spirit. Are these of as little account in the universe as he is?

It may be going too far to say that our bodies are pieces of stellar matter which, by a contingency not sufficiently guarded against in Nature, have evaded the normal destiny, and have taken advantage of low temperature conditions to assume unusual complication and perform the series of antics we call "life." I neither assert nor deny this view; but I regard it as so much of an open question that I am unwilling to base my philosophy or my religion on the assumption that it must necessarily break down. But there is another approach to the problem. Science is an attempt to read the cryptogram of experience; it sets in order the facts of sensory experience of human beings. Everyone will agree that this attempt has met with considerable success; but it does not start quite at the beginning of the Problem of Experience. The first question asked about scientific facts and theories, such as we have been discussing in this book, is "Are they true?" I would emphasize that even more significant than the scientific conclusions themselves is the fact that this question so urgently arises about them. The question "Is it true?" changes the complexion of the world of experience — not because it is asked *about* the world, but because it is asked *in* the world. When we go right back to the beginning, the first thing we must recognize in the world of experience is something intent on truth — something to which it matters intensely that beliefs should be true. This is no elusive cryptogram; it is not written in the symbolic language in which we describe the unknowable activities of unknown agents in the physical universe. Before we invite science to take the problem in hand and put in order the facts of sensory experience, we have settled the first ingredient of the world of experience. If science in its survey rediscovers that ingredient, well and good. If not, then science may claim to account for the universe, but what is there to account for science?

What is the ultimate truth about ourselves? Various answers suggest themselves. We are a bit of stellar matter gone wrong. We are physical machinery — puppets that strut and talk and laugh and die as the hand of time pulls the strings beneath. But there is one elementary inescapable answer. *We are that which asks the question.* Whatever else there may be in our nature, responsibility toward truth is one of its attributes. This side of our nature is aloof from the scrutiny of the physicist. I do not think it is sufficiently covered by admitting a mental aspect of our being. It has to do with conscience rather than with consciousness. Concern with truth is one of those things which make up the spiritual nature of Man. There are other constituents of our spiritual nature which are perhaps as self-evident; but it is not so easy to force an admission of their existence. We cannot recognize a problem of experience without at the same time recognizing ourselves as truth-seekers involved in the problem. The strange association of soul and body — of responsibility toward truth with a particular group of carbon compounds — is a problem in which we naturally feel intense interest; but it is not an anxious interest, as though the existence of a spiritual significance of experience were hanging in the balance. That significance is to be regarded rather as a datum of the problem; and the solution must fit the data; we must not alter the data to fit an alleged solution.

I do not regard the phenomenon of life (in so far as it can be separated from the phenomenon of consciousness) as necessarily outside the scope of physics and chemistry. Arguments that because a living creature is an organism it *ipso facto* possesses something which can never be understood in terms of physical science do not impress me. I think it is insufficiently recognized that modern theoretical physics is very much concerned with the study of organization; and from organization to organism does not seem an impossible stride. But equally it would be foolish to deny the magnitude of the gulf between our understanding of the most complex form of inorganic matter and the simplest form of life. Let us suppose, however, that some day this gulf is bridged, and science is able to show how from the entities of physics creatures might be formed which are counterparts of ourselves even to the point of being endowed with life. The scientist will perhaps point out the nervous mechanism of the creature, its powers of motion, of growth, of reproduction, and end by saying, "That's you." But it has yet to satisfy the inescapable test. Is it concerned with truth as I am? Then I will acknowledge that it is indeed myself. The scientist might point to motions in the brain and say that these really mean sensations, emotions, thoughts; and perhaps supply a code to translate the motions into the corresponding thoughts. Even if we could accept this inadequate substitute for consciousness as we intimately know it, we must still protest: "You have shown us a creature which thinks and believes; you have not shown us a creature to whom it *matters* that what it thinks and believes should be true." The inmost ego, possessing what I have called the inescapable attribute, can never be part of the physical world unless we alter the meaning of the word "physical" so as to be synonymous with "spiritual" — a change scarcely to the advantage of clear thinking. But having disowned our supposed double, we can say to the scientist: "If you will hand over this Robot who pretends to be me, and let it be filled with the attribute at present lacking and perhaps other spiritual attributes which I claim as equally self-evident, we may arrive at something that is indeed myself."

A few years ago the suggestion of taking the physically constructed man and adapting him to a spiritual nature by casually adding something, would have been a mere figure of speech — a verbal gliding over of insuperable difficulties. In much the same way we talk loosely of constructing a Robot and then breathing life into it. A Robot is presumably not constructed to bear such last-minute changes of design; it is a delicate piece of mechanism made to work mechanically, and to adapt it to anything else would involve entire reconstruction. To put it crudely, if you want to fill a vessel with anything you must make it hollow, and the old-fashioned material body was not hollow enough to be a receptacle of mental or of spiritual attributes. The result was to place consciousness in the position of an intruder in the physical world. We had to choose between explaining it away as an illusion or perverse misrepresentation of what was really going on in the brain, and admitting an extraneous agent which had power to suspend the regular laws of Nature and asserted itself by brute interference with the atoms and molecules in contact with it.

Our present conception of the physical world is *hollow* enough to hold almost anything. I think the reader will agree. There may indeed be a hint of ribaldry in his hearty assent. What we are dragging to light as the basis of all phenomena is a scheme of symbols connected by mathematical equations. That is what physical reality boils down to when probed by the methods which a physicist can apply. A skeleton scheme of symbols proclaims its own hollowness.

It can be — nay it cries out to be — filled with something that shall transform it from skeleton into substance, from plan into execution, from symbols into an interpretation of the symbols. And if ever the physicist solves the problem of the living body, he should no longer be tempted to point to his result and say, "That's you." He should say rather, "That is the aggregation of symbols which stands for you in my description and explanation of those of your properties which I can observe and measure. If you claim a deeper insight into your own nature by which you can interpret these symbols — a more intimate knowledge of the reality which I can only deal with by symbolism — you can rest assured that I have no rival interpretation to propose." The skeleton is the contribution of physics to the solution of the Problem of Experience; from the clothing of the skeleton it stands aloof. . . .

The stress here laid on the limitations of physical science will, I hope, not be misunderstood by the reader. There is no suggestion that science has become a declining force; rather we obtain a clearer appreciation of the contribution which it is able to make, both now and in the future, to human development and culture. Within its own limitations physical science has become greatly strengthened by the changes. It has become more sure of its aims — and perhaps less sure of its achievements. Since the last most bewildering revolution of physical theory (wave mechanics) there has been an interval of some years during which it has been possible to settle down to steady progress. Recently the most striking developments have been on the experimental side. In quick succession the artificial transmutation of the elements, the discovery of the neutron and the discovery of the positive electron have startled the scientific world and opened up new realms for exploration. But I count this as normal prosperity rather than revolution.

In contemplating the gradually developing scheme of scientific knowledge which never seems to reach finality in any direction, there are times when we are tempted to doubt the substantiality of our gains. Questions, which seem to have been settled, become unsettled:

> Nature and Nature's laws lay hid in night:
> God said, "Let Newton be!" and all was light.
> But not for long. The devil howling, "Ho!
> Let Einstein be!" restored the *status quo*.

In my own subject of astronomy it is particularly difficult to know how far we may feel certain of our ground. So many conclusions have to be guarded by an "if." And it is sometimes those results which have been most widely accepted that prove to have been most insecure. Finding ourselves unable to decide some of those simple fundamental questions, which to a large extent control the course of astronomical theory, we begin to doubt whether there has been any real progress. And then we realize with a start that ten years ago we did not know enough even to formulate the doubts that now beset us. I sometimes think that the progress of knowledge is to be measured not by the questions that it has answered but by the questions that it provokes us to ask.

In writing of the new pathways in science it is natural that the changes should be emphasized rather than the continuity with the past. It may seem that this is an age when we have scant respect for tradition, and are pulling to pieces all that our forerunners so laboriously erected. We have to show unsparingly the way in which the scientists of an earlier generation were misled by false assumptions, and the direction in which their conceptions of the universe have proved inadequate; but we utilize the positive contributions that they made, bringing us step by step nearer to the ideal. Progress has a ruthless side, but it is not an indiscriminate ruthlessness. We are not the less tenderly cherishing the seed planted by our predecessors because from time to time we transplant it into new soil where it may grow more freely. That is what a revolution in science means. When Einstein overthrew Newton's theory, he took Newton's plant, which had outgrown its pot, and transplanted it to a more open field.

All this new growth of science has its roots in the past. If we see farther than our predecessors it is because we stand on their shoulders — and it is not surprising if they receive a few kicks as we scramble up. A new generation is climbing on to the shoulders of the generation to which I belong; and so it will go on. Each phase of the scientific advance has contributed something that is preserved in the succeeding phase. That, indeed, is our ground for hope that the coming generation will find something worth preserving — something that is not wholly illusory — in the scientific thought of the Universe as it stands today.

When we see these new developments in perspective they appear as the natural unfolding of a flower:

> For out of olde feldes, as men seith,
> Cometh al this newe corn fro yere to yere;
> And out of olde bokes, in good feith,
> Cometh al this newe science that men lere.

4

Literary Naturalists

better engines than those of a *Mauretania*, life's power of multiplying itself, so that in a few hours an invisible microbe may become a fatal million.

Another, also old-fashioned, basis for wonder is to be found in the immensities. It takes light eight minutes to reach us from the sun, though it travels at the maximum velocity — of about 186,300 miles per second. So we see the nearest star by the light that left it four years ago, and Vega as it was twenty-seven years ago, and most of the stars that we see without a telescope as they were when Galileo Galilei studied them in the early years of the seventeenth century. In any case it is plain that we are citizens of no mean city.

A third basis for rational wonder is to be found in the intricacy and manifoldness of things. We get a suggestion of endless resources in the creation of individualities. Over two thousand years ago Aristotle knew about five hundred different kinds of animals; and now the list of the named and known includes twenty-five thousand different kinds of backboned animals, and a quarter of a million — some insist on a minimum of half a million — backboneless animals, each itself and no other. For "all flesh is not the same flesh, but there is one kind of flesh of men, another flesh of beasts, another of fishes, and another of birds." The blood of a horse is different from that of an ass, and one can often identify a bird from a single feather or a fish from a few scales. One is not perhaps greatly thrilled by the fact that the average man has twenty-five billions of oxygen-capturing red blood corpuscles, which if spread out would occupy a surface of 3,300 square yards; but there is significance in the calculation that he has in the cerebral cortex of his brain, the home of the higher intellectual activities, some nine thousand millions of nerve cells, that is to say, more than five times the present population of the globe — surely more than the said brain as yet makes use of.

So it must be granted that we are fearfully and wonderfully made! Our body is built up of millions of cells, yet there is a simplicity amid the multitudinousness, for each cell has the same fundamental structure. Within the colloid cell-substance there floats a kernel or nucleus, which contains forty-seven (or in woman forty-eight) chromosomes, each with a beadlike arrangement of smaller microsomes, and so on, and so on. Similarly, while eighty-nine different elements have been discovered out of the theoretically possible ninety-two [many more by now, of course], we know that they differ from one another only in the number and distribution of the electrons and protons that make up their microcosmic planetary system. What artistry to weave the gorgeously varied tapestry of the world out of two kinds of physical thread — besides, of course, Mind, which eventually searches into the secret of the loom.

A fourth basis for rational wonder is in the orderliness of Nature, and that is almost the same thing as saying its intelligibility. What implications there are in the fact that man has been able to make a science of Nature! Given three good observations of a comet, the astronomer can predict its return to a night. It is not a phantasmagoria that we live in, it is a rationalizable cosmos. The more science advances the more the fortuitous shrivels, and the more the power of prophecy grows. Two astronomers foretold the discovery of Neptune; the chemists have anticipated the discovery of new elements; the biologist can not only count but portray his chickens before they are hatched. The Order of Nature is the largest of all certainties; and leading authorities in modern physics tell us that we cannot think of it as emerging from the fortuitous. It is time that the phrase "a fortuitous concourse of atoms" was buried. Even the aboriginal nebula was not *that!* No doubt there have been diseases and tragedies among men, cataclysms and volcanic eruptions upon the earth, and so on — no one denies the shadows; but even these disturbances are not disorderly; the larger fact is the absence of all caprice. To refer to the poet's famous line, no one any longer supposes that gravitation can possibly cease when he goes by the avalanche. Nor will a microbe's insurgence be influenced by the social importance of the patient.

Corresponding to the intelligibility of Nature is the pervasiveness of beauty — a fifth basis of rational wonder, appealing to the emotional side of our personality. Surely Lotze was right, that it is of high value to look upon beauty not as a stranger in the world, nor as a casual aspect of certain phenomena, but as "the fortunate revelation of that principle which permeates all reality with its living activity."

A sixth basis of rational wonder is to be found in the essential characteristics of living creatures. We need only add the caution that the marvel of life is not to be taken at its face value; as Coleridge wisely said, the first wonder is the child of *ignorance;* we must attend diligently to all that biochemistry and biophysics can discount; we must try to understand all that can be formulated in terms of colloids, and so on. Yet when all that is said, there seem to be large residual phenomena whose emergence in living creatures reveals a new depth in Nature. Life is an enduring, insurgent activity, growing, multiplying, developing, enregistering, varying, and above all else evolving.

For this is the seventh wonder — Evolution. It is not merely that all things flow; it is that life flows uphill. Amid the ceaseless flux there is not only conservation, there is advancement. The changes are not those of a kaleidoscope, but of "an onward advancing melody." As the unthinkably long ages passed the earth became the cradle and home of life; nobler and finer kinds of living creatures appeared; there was a growing victory of life over things and of "mind" over "body"; until at last appeared Man, who is Life's crowning wonder, since he has given to everything else a higher and deeper significance. And while we must consider man in the light of evolution, as most intellectual combatants admit, there is the even more difficult task of envisaging evolution in the light of Man. *Finis coronat opus* — a wise philosophical axiom; and yet the scientist must qualify it by asking who can say Finis to Evolution.

Brute Neighbors

HENRY DAVID THOREAU

WHY DO PRECISELY these objects which we behold make a world? Why has man just these species of animals for his neighbors; as if nothing but a mouse could have filled this crevice? I suspect that Pilpay & Co. have put animals to their best use, for they are all beasts of burden, in a sense, made to carry some portion of our thoughts.

The mice which haunted my house were not the common ones, which are said to have been introduced into the country, but a wild native kind not found in the village. I sent one to a distinguished naturalist, and it interested him much. When I was building, one of these had its nest underneath the house, and before I had laid the second floor, and swept out the shavings, would come out regularly at lunch time and pick up the crumbs at my feet. It probably had never seen a man before; and it soon became quite familiar, and would run over my shoes and up my clothes. It could readily ascend the sides of the room by short impulses, like a squirrel, which it re-

From *Walden* by Henry David Thoreau.

sembled in its motions. At length, as I leaned with my elbow on the bench one day, it ran up my clothes, and along my sleeve, and round and round the paper which held my dinner, while I kept the latter close, and dodged and played at bopeep with it; and when at last I held still a piece of cheese between my thumb and finger, it came and nibbled it, sitting in my hand, and afterward cleaned its face and paws, like a fly, and walked away.

A phoebe soon built in my shed, and a robin for protection in a pine which grew against the house. In June the partridge (*Tetrao umbellus*), which is so shy a bird, led her brood past my windows, from the woods in the rear to the front of my house, clucking and calling to them like a hen, and in all her behavior proving herself the hen of the woods. The young suddenly disperse on your approach, at a signal from the mother, as if a whirlwind had swept them away, and they so exactly resemble the dried leaves and twigs that many a traveler has placed his foot in the midst of a brood, and heard the whir of the old bird as she flew off, and her anxious calls and mewing, or seen her trail her wings to attract his attention, without suspecting their neighborhood. The parent will sometimes roll and spin round before you in such a dishabille, that you cannot, for a few moments, detect what kind of creature it is. The young squat still and flat, often running their heads under a leaf, and mind only their mother's directions given from a distance, nor will your approach make them run again and betray themselves. You may even tread on them, or have your eyes on them for a minute, without discovering them. I have held them in my open hand at such a time, and still their only care, obedient to their mother and their instinct, was to squat there without fear or trembling. So perfect is this instinct, that once, when I had laid them on the leaves again, and one accidentally fell on its side, it was found with the rest in exactly the same position ten minutes afterward. They are not callow like the young of most birds, but more perfectly developed and precocious even than chickens. The remarkably adult yet innocent expressions of their open and serene eyes is very memorable. All intelligence seems reflected in them. They suggest not merely the purity of infancy, but a wisdom clarified by experience. Such an eye was not born when the bird was, but is coeval with the sky it reflects. The woods do not yield another such a gem. The traveller does not often look into such a limpid well. The ignorant or reckless sportsman often shoots the parent at such a time, and leaves these innocents to fall a prey to some prowling beast or bird, or gradually mingle with the decaying leaves which they so much resemble. It is said that when hatched by a hen they will directly disperse on some alarm, and so are lost, for they never hear the mother's call which gathers them again. These were my hens and chickens.

It is remarkable how many creatures live wild and free though secret in the woods, and still sustain themselves in the neighborhood of towns, suspected by hunters only. How retired the otter manages to live here! He grows to be four feet long, as big as a small boy, perhaps without any human being getting a glimpse of him. I formerly saw the raccoon in the woods behind where my house is built, and probably still heard their whinnering at night. Commonly I rested an hour or two in the shade at noon, after planting, and ate my lunch, and read a little by a spring which was the source of a swamp and of a brook, oozing from under Brister's Hill, half a mile from my field. The approach to this was through a succession of descending grassy hollows, full of young pitch pines, into a larger wood about the swamp. There, in a very secluded and shaded spot, under a spreading white pine, there was yet a clean, firm sward to sit on. I had dug out the spring and made a well of clear gray water, where I could dip up a pailful without roiling it, and thither I went for this purpose almost every day in midsummer, when the pond was warmest. Thither, too, the woodcock led her brood, to probe the mud for worms, flying but a foot above them down the bank, while they ran in a troop beneath; but at last, spying me, she would leave her young and circle round and round me, nearer and nearer till within four or five feet, pretending broken wings and legs, to attract my attention, and get off her young, who would already have taken up their march, with faint, wiry peep, single file through the swamp, as she directed. Or I heard the peep of the young when I could not see the parent bird. There too the turtle doves sat over the spring, or fluttered from bough to bough of the soft white pines over my head; or the red squirrel, coursing down the nearest bough, was particularly familiar and inquisitive. You only need sit still long enough in some attractive spot in the woods that all its inhabitants may exhibit themselves to you by turns.

I was witness to events of a less peaceful character. One day when I went out to my woodpile, or rather my pile of stumps, I observed two large ants, the one red, the other much larger, nearly half an inch long, and black, fiercely contending with one another. Having once got hold they never let go, but struggled and wrestled and rolled on the chips incessantly. Looking farther, I was surprised to find that the chips were covered with such combatants, that it was not a *duellum,* but a *bellum,* a war between two races of ants, the red always pitted against the black, and frequently two red ones to one black. The legions of these Myrmidons covered all the hills and vales in my wood yard, and the ground was already strewn with the dead and dying, both red and black. It was the only battle which I have ever witnessed, the only battlefield I ever trod while the battle was raging; internecine war; the red republicans on the one hand, and the black imperialists on the other. On every side they were engaged in deadly combat, yet without any noise that I could hear, and human soldiers never fought so resolutely. I watched a couple that were fast locked in each other's embraces, in a little sunny valley amid the chips, now at noonday prepared to fight till the sun went down, or life went out. The smaller red champion had fastened himself like a vise to his adversary's front, and through all the tumblings on that field never for an instant ceased to gnaw at one of his feelers near the root, having already caused the other to go by the board; while the stronger black one dashed him from side to side, and, as I saw on looking nearer, had already divested him of several of his members. They fought with more pertinacity than bulldogs. Neither manifested the least disposition to retreat. It was evident that their battle cry was "Conquer or die." In the meanwhile there came along a single red ant on the hillside of this valley, evidently full of excitement, who either had despatched his foe, or had not yet taken part in the battle; probably the latter, for he had lost none of his limbs; whose mother had charged him to return with his shield or upon it. Or perchance he was some Achilles, who had nourished his wrath apart, and had now come to avenge or rescue his Patroclus. He saw this unequal combat from afar — for the blacks were nearly twice the size of the red; he drew near with rapid pace till he stood on his guard within half an inch of the combatants; then, watching his opportunity, he sprang upon the black warrior, and commenced his operations near the root of his right fore leg, leaving the foe to select among his own members; so there were three united for life, as if a new kind of attraction had been invented which put all other locks and cements to shame. I should not have wondered by this time to find that they had their respective musical bands stationed on some eminent chip, and playing their national airs the while, to excite the slow and cheer the dying combatants. I was myself excited somewhat even as if they had been men. The more you think of it, the less the difference. And certainly there is not the fight recorded in Concord history, at least, if in the history of America, that will bear a moment's comparison with this, whether for the numbers engaged in it, or for the patriotism and heroism displayed. For numbers and for carnage it was an Austerlitz or Dresden. Concord fight! Two killed on the patriots' side, and Luther Blanchard wounded! Why here every ant was a Buttrick, — "Fire! for God's sake fire!" — and thousands shared the fate of Davis and Hosmer. There was not one hireling there. I have no doubt that it was a principle they fought for, as much as our ancestors, and not to avoid a three-penny tax on their tea; and the results of this battle will be as important and memorable to those whom it concerns as those of the battle of Bunker Hill, at least.

I took up the chip on which the three I have particularly described were struggling, carried it into my house, and placed it under a tumbler on my window-sill, in order to see the issue. Holding a microscope to the first-mentioned red ant, I saw that, though he was assiduously gnawing at the near fore leg of his enemy, having severed his remaining feeler, his own breast was all torn away, exposing what vitals he had there to the jaws of the black warrior, whose breastplate was apparently too thick for his to pierce; and the dark carbuncles of the sufferer's eyes shone with ferocity such as war only could excite. They struggled half an hour longer under the tumbler, and when I looked again the black soldier had severed the heads of his foes from their bodies, and the still living heads were hanging on either side of him like ghastly trophies at his saddle-bow, still apparently as firmly fastened as ever, and he was endeavoring with feeble struggles, being without feelers and with only the remnant of a leg, and I know not how many other wounds, to divest himself of them; which at length, after half an hour or more, he accomplished. I raised the glass, and he went off over the window-sill in that crippled state. Whether he finally survived that combat, and spent the remainder of his days in some Hôtel des Invalides, I do not know; but I thought that his industry would not be worth much thereafter. I never learned which party was victorious, nor the cause of the war; but I felt for the rest of that day as if I had had my feelings excited and harrowed by witnessing the struggle, the ferocity and carnage, of a human battle before my door.

Kirby and Spence tell us that the battles of ants have long been celebrated and the date of them recorded, though they say that Huber is the only modern author who appears to have witnessed them. "Aeneas Sylvius," say they, "after giving a very circumstantial account of one contested with great obstinacy by a great and small species on the trunk of a pear tree," adds that " 'this action was fought in the pontificate of Eugenius the Fourth, in the presence of Nicholas Pistoriensis, an eminent lawyer, who related the whole history of the battle with the greatest fidelity.' A similar engagement between great and small ants is recorded by Olaus Magnus, in which the small ones, being victorious, are said to have buried the bodies of their own soldiers, but left those of their giant enemies a prey to the birds. This event happened previous to the expulsion of the tyrant Christian the Second from Sweden." The battle which I witnessed took place in the Presidency of Polk, five years before the passage of Webster's Fugitive-Slave Bill.

Many a village Bose, fit only to course a mud-turtle in a victualing cellar, sported his heavy quarters in the woods, without the knowledge of his master, and ineffectually smelled at old fox burrows and woodchucks' holes; led perchance by some slight cur which nimbly threaded the wood, and might still inspire a natural terror in its denizens; — now far behind his guide, barking like a canine bull toward some small squirrel which had treed itself for scrutiny, then, cantering off, bending the bushes with his weight, imagining that he is on the track of some stray member of the jerbilla family. Once I was surprised to see a cat walking along the stony shore of the pond, for they rarely wander so far from home. The surprise was mutual. Nevertheless the most domestic cat, which has lain on a rug all her days, appears quite at home in the woods, and, by her sly and stealthy behavior, proves herself more native there than the regular inhabitants. Once, when berrying, I met with a cat with young kittens in the woods, quite wild, and they all, like their mother, had their backs up and were fiercely spitting at me. A few years before I lived in the woods there was what was called a "winged cat" in one of the farmhouses in Lincoln nearest the pond, Mr. Gilian Baker's. When I called to see her in June 1842 she was gone a-hunting in the woods, as was her wont (I am not sure whether it was a male or female, and so use the more common pronoun), but her mistress told me that she came into the neighborhood a little more than a year before, in April, and was finally taken into their house; that she was of a dark brownish-gray color, with a white spot on her throat, and white feet, and had a large bushy tail like a fox; that in the winter the fur grew thick and flatted out along her sides, forming strips ten or twelve inches long by two and a half wide, and under her chin like a muff, the upper side loose, the under matted like felt, and in the spring these appendages dropped off. They gave me a pair of her "wings," which I keep still. There is no appearance of a membrane about them. Some thought it was part flying squirrel or some other wild animal, which is not impossible, for, according to naturalists, prolific hybrids have been produced by the union of the marten and domestic cat. This would have been the right kind of cat for me to keep, if I had kept any; for why should not a poet's cat be winged as well as his horse?

In the fall the loon (*Colymbus glacialis*) came, as usual, to moult and bathe in the pond, making the woods ring with his wild laughter before I had risen. At rumor of his arrival all the Mill-dam sportsmen are on the alert, in gigs and on foot, two by two and three by three, with patent rifles and conical balls and spy-glasses. They come rustling through the woods like autumn leaves, at least ten men to one loon. Some station themselves on this side of the pond, some on that, for the poor bird cannot be omnipresent; if he dive here he must come up there. But now the kind October wind rises, rustling the leaves and rippling the surface of the water, so that no loon can be heard or seen, though his foes sweep the pond with spy-glasses, and make the woods resound with their discharges. The waves generously rise and dash angrily, taking sides with all water-fowl, and our sportsmen must beat a retreat to town and shop and unfinished jobs. But they were too often successful. When I went to get a pail of water early in the morning I frequently saw this stately bird sailing out of my cove within a few rods. If I endeavored to overtake him in a boat, in order to see how he would manœuvre, he would dive and be completely lost, so that I did not discover him again, sometimes, till the latter part of the day. But I was more than a match for him on the surface. He commonly went off in a rain.

As I was paddling along the north shore one very calm October afternoon, for such days especially they settle on to the lakes, like the milkweed down, having looked in vain over the pond for a loon, suddenly one, sailing out from the shore toward the middle a few rods in front of me, set up his wild laugh and betrayed himself. I pursued with a paddle and he dived, but when he came up I was nearer than before. He dived again, but I miscalculated the direc-tion he would take, and we were fifty rods apart when he came to the surface this time, for I had helped to widen the interval; and again he laughed long and loud, and with more reason than before. He manœuvred so cunningly that I could not get within half a dozen rods of him. Each time, when he came to the surface, turning his head this way and that, he coolly surveyed the water and the land, and apparently chose his course so that he might come up where there was the widest expanse of water and at the greatest distance from the boat. It was surprising how quickly he made up his mind and put his resolve into execution. He led me at once to the widest part of the pond, and could not be driven from it. While he was thinking one thing in his brain, I was endeavoring to divine his thought in mine. It was a pretty game, played on the smooth surface of the pond, a man against a loon. Suddenly your adversary's checker disappears beneath the board, and the problem is to place yours nearest to where his will appear again. Sometimes he would come up unexpectedly on the opposite side of me, having appar-ently passed directly under the boat. So long-winded was he and so unweariable, that when he had swum farthest he would immediately plunge again, nevertheless; and then no wit could divine where in the deep pond, beneath the smooth surface, he might be speeding his way like a fish, for he had time and ability to visit the bottom of the pond in its deepest part. It is said that loons have been caught in the New York lakes eighty feet beneath the surface, with hooks set for trout, — though Walden is deeper than that. How surprised must the fishes be to see this ungainly visitor from another sphere speeding his way amid their schools! Yet he appeared to know his course as surely under water as on the surface, and swam much faster there. Once or twice I saw a ripple where he approached the surface, just put his head out to reconnoitre, and instantly dived again. I found that it was as well for me to rest on my oars and wait his reappearing as to endeavor to calculate where he would rise; for again and again, when I was straining my eyes over the surface one way, I would suddenly be startled by his unearthly laugh behind me. But why, after displaying so much cunning, did he invariably betray himself the moment he came up by that loud laugh? Did not his white breast enough betray him? He was indeed a silly loon, I thought. I could commonly hear the splash of the water when he came up, and so also detected him. But after an hour he seemed as fresh as ever, dived as willingly, and swam yet farther than at first. It was surprising to see how serenely he sailed off with unruffled breast when he came to the surface, doing all the work with his webbed feet beneath. His usual note was this demoniac laughter, yet somewhat like that of a water-fowl; but occasionally, when he had balked me most successfully and come up a long way off, he uttered a long-drawn unearthly howl, probably more like that of a wolf than any bird; as when a beast puts his muzzle to the ground and deliberately howls. This was his looning — perhaps the wildest sound that is ever heard here, making the woods ring far and wide. I concluded that he laughed in derision of my efforts, confident of his own resources. Though the sky was by this time overcast, the pond was so smooth that I could see where he broke the surface when I did not hear him. His white breast, the stillness of the air, and the smoothness of the water were all against him. At length, having come up fifty rods off, he uttered one of those prolonged howls, as if calling on the god of loons to aid him, and immediately there came a wind from the east and rippled the surface, and filled the whole air with misty rain, and I was impressed as if it were the prayer of the loon answered, and his god was angry with me; and so I left him disappearing far away on the tumultuous surface.

For hours, in fall days, I watched the ducks cunningly tack and veer and hold the middle of the pond, far from the sportsman;

tricks which they will have less need to practice in Louisiana ba-
yous. When compelled to rise they would sometimes circle round
and round and over the pond at a considerable height, from which
they could easily see to other ponds and the river, like black motes
in the sky; and, when I thought they had gone off thither long since,
they would settle down by a slanting flight of a quarter of a mile on
to a distant part which was left free; but what beside safety they got
by sailing in the middle of Walden I do not know, unless they love
its water for the same reason that I do.

A Descent into Perpetual Night

WILLIAM BEEBE

MORE THAN THREE AND A HALF YEARS AGO I dived to a depth of
fourteen hundred and twenty-six feet, and here I was on the self-
same ancient barge with the identical bathysphere, and within a
mile and a half of the very spot where I made the former descent.
An equal distance to the east marked the spot of a more recent dive
to twenty-two hundred feet.

At 9:41 in the morning we splashed beneath the surface, and
often as I have experienced it, the sudden shift from a golden yellow
world to a green one was unexpected. After the foam and bubbles
passed from the glass, we were bathed in green; our faces, the tanks,
the trays, even the blackened walls were tinged. Yet seen from the
deck, we apparently descended into sheer, deep ultramarine. The
only hint of this change of color vouchsafed those above was the increasing turquoise of the bathysphere as it approached the vanish-
ing point, about 100 feet.

We were dropped several fathoms and dangled there awhile,
until all the apparatus on deck was readapted to the vertical cable
close to the ship's side. I made the most of my last glimpse of the
upper world. By peering up I could see the watery ceiling crinkling,
and slowly lifting and settling, while here and there, pinned to this

ceiling, were tufts of sargassum weed. I could see small dots moving just below the weed, and for the first time I tried, and successfully, to focus low power binoculars through the water. I had no trouble in recognizing a small ocean turbot and a flyingfish, trailing its half-spread wings as it swam. The bathysphere then revolved slightly and the hull of the *Ready* came into view. It was even more like a coral reef than it had appeared four years ago, great streamers of plant and animal life floating out from it. There is something wholly unreal and at the same time rather amusing about an upward view of the slow-rolling bottom of an unanchored boat, whose deck, a few minutes before, had seemed so solid and stanch.

The sun was blazing over the ocean, the surface was unusually quiet; conditions were perfect for whatever the eyes could carry to the brain. A question came over the phone, an answer went, and down we slipped through the water. As I have said, the first plunge erases, to the eye, all the comforting, warm rays of the spectrum. The red and the orange are as if they had never been, and soon the yellow is swallowed up in the green. We cherish all these on the surface of the earth and when they are winnowed out at 100 feet or more, although they are only one-sixth of the visible spectrum, yet, in our mind, all the rest belongs to chill and night and death. Even modern war bears this out; no more are red blood and scarlet flames its symbols, but the terrible grayness of gas, the ghastly blue of Very lights.

The green faded imperceptibly as we went down, and at 200 feet it was impossible to say whether the water was greenish-blue or bluish-green. At this depth I made my eyes focus in mid-water and saw small creatures clearly, copepods and others of the innumerable swarms which haunt the upper layers.

At 320 feet a lovely colony of siphonophores drifted past. At this level they appeared like spun glass. Others which I saw at far greater and blacker depths were illumined, but whether by their own or by reflected light I cannot say. These are colonial creatures like submerged Portuguese men-o'-war, and similar to those beautiful beings are composed of a colony of individuals, which perform separate functions, such as flotation, swimming, stinging, feeding, and breeding, all joined by the common bond of a food canal. Here in their own haunts they swept slowly along like an inverted spray of lilies-of-the-valley, alive and in constant motion. In our nets we find only the half-broken swimming bells, like cracked, crystal chalices, with all the wonderful loops and tendrils and animal flowers completely lost or contracted into a mass of tangled threads. Twenty feet lower a pilotfish looked in upon me — the companion of sharks and turtles, which we usually think of as a surface fish, but with only our pitiful, two-dimensional, human observation for proof.

When scores of bathyspheres are in use we shall know much more about the vertical distribution of fish than we do now. For example, my next visitors were good-sized yellow-tails and two blue-banded jacks which examined me closely at 400 and 490 feet respectively. Here were so-called surface fish happy at 80 fathoms. Several silvery squid balanced for a moment, then shot past, and at 500 feet a pair of lanternfish with no lights showing looked at the bathysphere unafraid.

At 600 feet the color appeared to be a dark, luminous blue, and this contradiction of terms shows the difficulty of description. As in former dives, it seemed bright, but was so lacking in actual power that it was useless for reading and writing.

There are certain nodes of emotion in a descent such as this, the first of which is the initial flash. This came at 670 feet, and it seemed to close a door upon the upper world. Green, the world-wide color of plants, had long since disappeared from our new cosmos, just as the last plants of the sea themselves had been left behind far overhead.

At 700 feet the light beam from our bulb was still rather dim; the sun had not given up and was doing his best to assert his power. At 800 feet we passed through a swarm of small beings, copepods, sagitta or arrow worms and every now and then a worm which was not a worm but a fish, one of the innumerable round-mouths or *Cyclothones*. Eighty feet farther and a school of about 30 lanternfish passed, wheeled and returned; I could guess *Myctophum laternatum*, but I cannot be certain. The beam of light drove them away.

At 1000 feet we took stock of our surroundings. The stuffing box and the door were dry, the noise of the blower did not interfere with the telephone conversation, the humidity was so well taken care of that I did not need a handkerchief over nose and mouth when talking close to the glass. The steel was becoming very cold. I tried to name the water; blackish-blue, dark gray-blue. It is strange that as the blue goes, it is not replaced by violet — the end of the visible spectrum. That has apparently already been absorbed. The last hint of blue tapers into a nameless gray, and this finally into black, but from the present level down, the eye falters, and the mind refuses any articulate color distinction. The sun is defeated and color has gone forever, until a human at last penetrates and flashes a yellow electric ray into what has been jet black for two billion years.

I kept the light on for a while and at 1050 feet through a school of little flying snails there suddenly passed a "large dark body, over four feet long" (so I telephoned it). I shut off the light, but looked into empty gray space without a trace of lumination — the fish had dissolved. Later, with the light on again, ten feet lower, a pilotfish appeared, showing how easily his kind can adapt itself to a shift of more than 30 atmospheres and from 15 pounds an inch at the surface to 480 at this level.

Lights now brightened and increased, and at 1100 feet I saw more fish and other organisms than my prebathysphere experience had led me to hope to see on the entire dive. With the light on, several chunky little hatchet-fish approached and passed through; then a silver-eyed larval fish two inches long; a jelly; suddenly a vision to which I can give no name, although I saw others subsequently. It was a network of luminosity, delicate, with large meshes, all aglow and in motion, waving slowly as it drifted. Next a dim, very deeply built fish appeared and vanished; then a four-inch larval eel swimming obliquely upward; and so on. This ceaseless telephoning left me breathless and I was glad of a hundred feet of only blue-blackness and active sparks.

At 1200 feet an explosion occurred, not at the window but a few feet away, so baffling that I decided to watch intently for repetitions. The large fish came again, and a loose, open school of pteropods and small shrimps bobbed about. The snails were shield-shaped as I well knew from having handled thousands in the deep-sea nets. Their empty shells form most of the sea bottom hereabouts.

Suddenly in the distance a strong glow shot forth, covering a space of perhaps eight inches. Not even the wildest guess would help with such an occurrence. Then the law of compensation sent, close to the window, a clear-cut, three-inch, black anglerfish with a pale, lemon-colored light on a slender tentacle. All else my eye missed, so I can never give it a name.

One great source of trouble in this bathysphere work is the lag of mind behind instantaneous observation. For example, at 1300 feet a medium-sized, wide-mouthed angler came in sight, then vanished, and I was automatically describing an eight-inch larval eel looking like a transparent willow leaf, when my mind shot back to the angler and demanded how I had seen it. I had recorded no individual lights on body or tentacle, and now I realized that the teeth had glowed dully, the two rows of fangs were luminous. It is most baffling to gaze into outer darkness, suddenly see a vision, record the bare facies — the generality of the thing itself — and then, in the face of complete distraction by another spark or organism, to have to hark back and recall what special characters escaped the mind but were momentarily etched upon the retina. On this point I had thoroughly coached Miss Hollister at the other end of the telephone, so I constantly received a fire of questions, which served to focus my attention and flick my memory. Again and again when such a question came, I willfully shut my eyes or turned them into the bathysphere to avoid whatever bewilderment might come while I was searching my memory for details of what had barely faded from my eye. At a few stops on the descent, as I have said, I permitted myself a minute or two of emotional debauch, of reciting to myself the where and the what of locality, surroundings, time of day, pressure, temperature, and so on. But all the rest of the time I allowed myself no rest from direct observation and reporting. The unproductive Oh's! and Ah's! of my first few dives were all too vivid in my mind.

Just above 1400 feet two black eels, about eighteen inches in length, went through the beam — distinctly *Serrivomer*. At 1400 feet my recent studies came to mind, and told me that I saw a male golden-tailed sea-dragon with a big cheek light (*Idiacanthus*), but before it vanished I saw it was black, and considerably larger even than the giant female of the species. So it was wholly unknown.

At 1500 I swung for two and a half minutes, and here occurred the second memorable moment in these dives — opportunity for the deliberate, accurate record of a fish wholly new to science, seen by one or both of us, the proof of whose existence, other than our word, must await the luck of capture in nets far more effective than those we now use in our oceanographic work. First, a quartet of slender, elongate fish passed through the electric light literally like arrows, about twenty inches long, whether eels or not I shall never know; then a jelly, so close that it almost brushed the glass. Finally, without my seeing how it got there, a large fish swung suspended, half in, half out of the beam. It was poised with only a slow waving of fins. I saw it was something wholly unknown, and I did two things at once; I reached behind for Mr. Barton, to drag him away from his camera preparations to the windows, to see and corroborate, and I disregarded Miss Hollister's insistent questions in my ears. I had to grunt or say something in reply to her, for I had already exceeded the five seconds which was our danger duration of silence throughout all the dives. But all this time I sat absorbing the fish from head to tail through the wordless, short-circuiting of sight, later to be materialized into spoken and written words, and finally into a painting dictated by what I had seen through the clear quartz.

The strange fish was at least two feet in length, wholly without lights or luminosity, with a small eye and good-sized mouth. Later, when it shifted a little backward I saw a long, rather wide, but evidently filamentous pectoral fin. The two most unusual things were first, the color, which, in the light, was an unpleasant pale, olive drab, the hue of water-soaked flesh, an unhealthy buff. It was a color worthy of these black depths, like the sickly sprouts of plants in a cellar. Another strange thing was its almost tailless condition, the caudal fin being reduced to a tiny knob or button, while the vertical fins, taking its place, rose high above and stretched far beneath the body, these fins also being colorless. I missed its pelvic fins and its teeth, if it had any, while such things as nostrils and ray counts were, of course, out of the question.

There is a small family of deep-sea fish known as *Cetomimidæ*, and somewhere in or close to this the strange apparition belongs. Only three species are known, and only twenty-four individuals have so far been captured, sixteen of which have been in our own deep nets drawn through these very waters. I have called the fish we saw the Pallid Sailfin, and am naming it *Bathyembryx istiophasma*, which is a Grecian way of saying that it comes from deep in the abyss and swims with ghostly sails.

Although I had already seen many deep-sea forms on this dive, yet here was one larger than any we had ever taken in nets. The Sailfin was alive, quiet, watching our strange machine, apparently oblivious that the hinder half of its body was bathed in a strange luminosity. Preëminently, however, it typified the justification of the money, time, trouble, and worry devoted to bringing the bathysphere to its present efficiency. Amid nameless sparks, unexplained luminous explosions, abortive glimpses of strange organisms, there came, now and then, adequate opportunity to add a definite new fish or other creature to our knowledge of the life of the deep sea. At the possible risk of cumbering taxonomy with a *nomen nudum*, I have chosen to give definite names to a very few of these clearly seen fish, the physical type of which must, for a time, be represented by a drawing, made under my direction, with only the characters of which I am certain. With no visible increase of fin vibration, my Pallid Sailfin moved into outer darkness, and when I had finished telephoning the last details I ordered a further descent. This entire volume would not contain the detailed recital of even a fraction of all the impressive sights and forms I saw, and nothing at these depths can be spoken of without superlatives.

At 1630 feet a light grew to twice its diameter before our eyes, until it was fully the diameter of a penny, appearing to emanate from some creature which bore irregular patches of dull luminosity on its body. The outline was too indistinct to tell whether it was with or without a backbone.

At 1900 feet, to my surprise, there was still the faintest hint of dead gray light, 200 feet deeper than usual, attesting the almost complete calm of the surface and the extreme brilliancy of the day far overhead. At 2000 feet the world was forever black. And this I count as the third great moment of descent, when the sun, source of all light and heat on the earth, has been left behind. It is only a psychological milepost, but it is a very real one. We had no realization of the outside pressure but the blackness itself seemed to close in on us.

At 2000 feet I made careful count and found that there were never less than ten or more lights — pale yellow and pale bluish — in sight at any one time. Fifty feet below I saw another pyrotechnic network, this time, at a conservative estimate, covering an extent of two by three feet. I could trace mesh after mesh in the darkness, but could not even hazard a guess at the cause. It must be some invertebrate form of life, but so delicate and evanescent that its abyssal form is quite lost if ever we take it in our nets. Another hundred feet and Mr. Barton saw two lights blinking on and off, obviously under control of the fish.

At this level and again on the way up, I saw at the very end of our beam some large form swimming. On earlier dives I had observed this and hesitated even to mention it, for it savored too much of imagination backed by imperfect observation. But here it was again. The surface did not seem black, and what outline came momentarily to view was wholly problematic. But that it was some very large creature or creatures of which we had glimpses five separate times on dives separated by years, we are certain. Whether fish or squid or other organism we cannot say.

At 2300 some exclamation of mine was interrupted by a request from above to listen to the tug's whistles saluting our new record, and my response was, "Thanks ever so much, but take this: two very large leptocephali have just passed through the light, close together, vibrating swiftly along; note — why should larval eels go in pairs?" And with this the inhabitants of our dimly remembered upper world gave up their kindly efforts to honor us. On down we went through a rich, light-filled 2400, and to rest at 2500 feet, for a long half hour.

A pair of large, coppery-sided scimitar-mouths (*Gonostoma elongatum*) swam past; *Sternoptyx*, the skeletonfish, appeared in a group of four; a fish as flat as a moonfish entered the beam, and banking steeply, fled in haste. One flying snail, from among the countless billions of his fellows, flapped back and forth across my glass. Three times, at different levels, creatures had struck against the glass and, utterly meaningless as it sounds, exploded there, so abruptly that we instinctively jerked back our heads.

We tried out the full power of the 1500-watt light, heating the bathysphere and window considerably, but not too dangerously. At 11:17 o'clock I turned the light on suddenly, and saw a strange quartet of fish to which I have not been able to fit genus or family. Shape, size, color, and one fin I saw clearly, but Abyssal Rainbow Gars is as far as I dare go, and they may be anything but gars. About four inches over all, they were slender and stiff with long, sharply pointed jaws. They were balanced in the center of the electric ray when it was first turned on, and the unheard-of glare affected them not at all. There they stood, for they were almost upright, and I could see only a slight fanning with a dorsal fin. Keeping equal distances apart, and maintaining their upright pose, they swam slowly into the uttermost dark. The amazing thing about them was their unexpected pattern and color. The jaws and head were brilliant scarlet, which, back of the gills, changed abruptly into a light but strong blue and this merged insensibly into clear yellow on the posterior body and tail. Unless in the light of some other fish, or in my electric path, their colors could never have been visible, and were assuredly useless by-products.

I alternated with Mr. Barton's camera at the window and there were hardly any seconds without lights or definite organisms coming into view. In one period of this duration, chosen at random, I counted 46 lights, ten of which were of unusual size, most of them pale yellow, but a few bluish. The sight I enjoyed most was a momentary glimpse of what I am certain was the same, or another, Pallid Sailfin. In all this vast extent in three dimensions, of black water, the chance of confirming at a wholly different depth a new observation made my satisfaction complete.

The change in the electric beam itself from 1000 feet downward was interesting. At the upper layers it was weak but decidedly yellow, with a turquoise cap at the farther end of the oblique luminous shaft. As we descended, the yellow changed to a luminous gray, and the turquoise crept down, until, at this extreme depth, it reached to the very window. Along each side of the sharply marked beam extended a broad border of rich, velvety, dark blue, and abruptly outside of this came the black pit itself. At two well-separated depths, I focused very carefully on the rain of small creatures passing and repassing through the farthest extreme end of the light. In both cases the focus was the same and I brought the glass to the surface without changing it. On deck, walking back from the bow until it was in perfect focus with the glass, I found that the visible end of the beam of electric light was 45 feet distant from the bathysphere window, five feet farther than I had been estimating.

The several nodes of high lights of which I have written occur on every descent, but there is in addition a compounding of sensations. At first we are quick to see every light, facile in sending up notes, but when we have used up most of our adjectives it is difficult to ring changes on sparks, lights, and darkness. More and more complete severance with the upper world follows, and a plunging into new strangenesses, unpredictable sights continually opening up, until our vocabularies are pauperized, and our minds drugged.

Over two hours had passed since we left the deck and I knew that the nerves both of my staff and myself were getting ragged with constant tenseness and strain. My eyes were weary with the flashing of eternal lights, each of which had to be watched so carefully, and my mind was surfeited with visions of the continual succession of fish and other organisms, and alternately encouraged and depressed by the successful or abortive attempts at identification. So I asked for our ascent.

One minute later, at 2470 feet, all my temporarily relaxed attention was aroused and focused on another splendid piece of luck. A tie rope had to be cut and in this brief interval of suspension, extended by my hurried order, a new anglerfish came out of all the ocean and hesitated long enough close to my window for me to make out its dominant characters. I am calling it the Three-starred Anglerfish, *Bathyceratias trilynchnus*. It was close in many respects to the well-known genera *Ceratias* and *Cryptosparas*, but the flattened angle of the mouth and the short, even teeth were quite different. It was six inches long, typically oval in outline, black, and with small eye. The fin rays were usual except that it had three tall tentacles or illicia, each tipped with a strong, pale yellow light organ. The light was clearly reflected on the upper side of the fish. In front of the dorsal fin were two pear-shaped organs exactly like those of the common *Cryptosparas*. The paired fins escaped me. No pioneer, peering at a Martian landscape, could ever have a greater thrill than did I at such an opportunity.

Once more I rearranged my aching limbs, stretched and twisted to make my muscles cease complaining, and watched the small fry slip downward through the beam, as the winch drew us steadily upward. Everything of interest was still relayed through the phone, but I was slumped down, relaxed. Suddenly I leaned forward, banging my head against the steel but not losing a second of observation. A small school of luminous fish had just passed, when, fortunately at a moment of suspension, came a new and gorgeous creature. I yelled for continuance of the stop, which was at 1900 feet, and began to absorb what I saw; a fish almost round, with long, moderately high, continuous, vertical fins; a big eye, medium mouth, and small pectoral fins. The skin was decidedly brownish. We swung around a few degrees to port, bringing the fish into the dark blue penumbra of the beam, and then I saw its real beauty. Along the sides of the body were five unbelievably beautiful lines of light, one equatorial, with two curved ones above and two below. Each line was composed of a series of large, pale yellow lights, and every one of these was surrounded by a semicircle of very small, but intensely purple photophores.

The fish turned slowly and, head on, showed a narrow profile. If it were at the surface and without lights I should, without question, have called it a butterflyfish (*Chætodon*) or a surgeonfish (*Acanthurus*). But this glowing creature was assuredly neither, unless a distant relation, adapted for life at three hundred fathoms. My name for it is *Bathysidus pentagrammus*, the Five-lined Constellationfish. In my memory it will live throughout the rest of my life as one of the loveliest things I have ever seen.

Soon after I returned to the surface I reviewed my telephoned notes, especially of the several new fish of which I had been given such excellent sights. I added all the details that came to mind. Then, with my artist Mrs. Bostelmann, I went into an artistic huddle, made scrawling attempts myself, and then carefully corrected her trained drawing. Little by little my brain fish materialized, its proportions, size, color, lights, fins interdigitated with those of my memory, and we have a splendid finished painting which represents the vision in front of my window at 11:52 in the morning of August eleventh, 1900 feet below the surface of the Atlantic Ocean.

In the never-ceasing excitement of abounding life I had completely forgotten the idea of a half-mile record, and when on deck, in exactly another hour, we were reminded that an additional 130 feet would have done the trick, I had no regrets. A man-made unit of measure is of far less importance than my Three-starred Angler which otherwise we should surely have missed. . . .

I have spoken of the three outstanding moments in the mind of a bathysphere diver, the first flash of animal light, the level of eternal darkness, and the discovery and description of a new species of fish. There is a fourth, lacking definite level or anticipation, a roving moment which might very possibly occur near the surface or at the greatest depth, or even as one lies awake, days after the dive, thinking over and reliving it. It is, to my mind, the most important of all, far more so than the discovery of new species. It is the explanation of some mysterious occurrence, of the display of some inexplicable habit which has taken place before our eyes, but which, like a sublimated trick of some master fakir, evades understanding.

This came to me on this last deep dive at 1680 feet, and it explained much that had been a complete puzzle. I saw some creature, several inches long, dart toward the window, turn sideways and — explode. This time my eyes were focused and my mind ready, and at the flash, which was so strong that it illumined my face and the inner sill of the window, I saw the great red shrimp and the outpouring fluid of flame. This was a real Fourth Moment, for many "dim gray fish" as I had reported them, now resolved into distant clouds of light, and all the previous "explosions" against the glass became intelligible. At the next occurrence the shrimp showed plainly before and during the phenomenon, illustrating the value in observation of knowing what to look for. The fact that a number of the deep-sea shrimps had this power of defense is well known, and I have had an aquarium aglow with the emanation. It is the abyssal complement of the sepia smoke screen of a squid at the surface.

Before this dive was completed, I had made a still greater refinement in discernment, perceiving that there were two very distinct types of defense clouds emitted, one which instantly diffused into a glowing mist or cloud, and the other which exploded in a burst of individual sparks, for all the world like a diminutive roman candle. Both occurred at the window or near it a number of times, but it was the latter which was the more startling. . . .

At 11:12 A.M. we came to rest gently at 3000 feet, and I knew that this was my ultimate floor; the cable on the winch was very near its end. A few days ago the water had appeared blacker at 2500 feet than could be imagined, yet now to this same imagination it seemed to show as blacker than black. It seemed as if all future nights in the upper world must be considered only relative degrees of twilight. I could never again use the word BLACK with any conviction.

I looked out and watched an occasional passing light and for the first time I realized how completely lacking was the so-called phosphorescence with which we are familiar at the surface. There, whenever an ordinary fish passes, it becomes luminous by reflection from the lights of the myriads of the minute animals and plants floating in the water. Here each light is an individual thing, often under direct control of the owner. A gigantic fish could tear past the window, and if unillumined might never be seen.

My eyes became so dark adapted at these depths that there was no possibility of error; the jet blackness of the water was broken only by sparks and flashes and steadily glowing lamps of appreciable diameter, varied in color and of infinite variety as regards size and juxtaposition. But they were never dimmed or seen beyond or through any lesser mist or milky-way of organisms. The occasional, evanescent, defense clouds of shrimps hence stand out all the more strongly as unusual phenomena, and are quite apart from the present theme. If the surface light is emitted chiefly by *Noctiluca* and single-celled plants, the explanation of its abyssal absence is easy, for all surface forms of these groups have died out hundreds of feet overhead.

A second thing which occurred to me as I sat coiled in the bathysphere, *more* than half a mile down, was the failure of our powerful beam of light to attract organisms of any kind. Some fled at its appearance, others seemed wholly unconcerned, but not a single copepod or worm or fish gathered along its length or collected against the starboard window from which it poured. We sometimes kept the lesser beam on for three minutes at a time, so there was abundance of time for the plankton, which abounded in all parts of the path of light, to feel and react to its influence. The reason for this demands far more study than I have been able to give it. One factor is doubtless not only lack of the rhythm of day and night, but the eternal absence of all except animal light.

Even in this extremity of blackness I sensed the purity of the water, its freedom from sediment and roiling; six miles from shore and a full mile from the bottom insured this. So there was no diffusion of light, no trails, no refraction. When sparks or larger lights moved they were as distinct as when they were motionless. But reflection was noticeable, as upon the eye or skin from a sub-ocular or a lateral photophore, or upon my face when a shrimp exploded close in front.

Now and then I felt a slight vibration and an apparent slacking off of the cable. Word came that a cross swell had arisen, and when the full weight of bathysphere and cable came upon the winch, Captain Sylvester let out a few inches to ease the strain. There were only about a dozen turns of cable left upon the reel, and a full half of the drum showed its naked, wooden core. We were swinging at 3028 feet, and, Would we come up? We would.

Whatever I thought about the relative value of intensive observation as compared with record-breaking, I had to admit that this ultimate depth which we had attained showed a decided increase in the number of large fish — more than a dozen from three to twenty feet having been seen — and a corresponding greater number of lights, though not in actual size of their diameters.

Now and then, when lights were thickest, and the watery space before me seemed teeming with life, my eyes peered into the distance beyond them, and I thought of the lightless creatures forever invisible to me, those with eyes which depended for guidance through life upon the glow from the lamps of other organisms, and, strangest of all the inhabitants of the deeper parts of the ocean, those blind from birth to death, whose sole assistants, to food, to mates and from enemies, were cunning sense organs in the skin, or long, tendril-like rays of their fins.

Before we began to ascend, I had to stop making notes of my own, so numb were my fingers from the cold steel of the window sill, and to change from my cushion to the metal floor, was like shifting to a cake of ice. Of the blackness of the outside water I have already written too much. As to pressure, there seemed no reason why we should not be outside in a diving helmet as well as in. I thought of a gondola 60,000 feet up in the stratosphere with a pressure of one pound to the square inch. And then through the telephone we learned that at this moment we were under a pressure of 1360 pounds to each square inch, or well over half a ton. Each window held back over nineteen tons of water, while a total of 7016 tons were piled up in all directions upon the bathysphere itself. Yes, we had heard clearly, we were ready to be pulled up at once!

At 2929 feet I heard a metallic twang through the phone, asked what it was, and got some noncommittal answer. I found out later that one of the guy ropes used in spooling the incoming cable on the drum had suddenly given way with a terrific report — a ghastly shock to everyone on deck until they realized it was a rope and not the cable. Truly we in the bathysphere had the best of it at all times.

Whenever I sink below the last rays of light, similes pour in upon me. Throughout all this account I have consciously rejected the scores of "as ifs" which sprang to mind. The stranger the situation the more does it seem imperative to use comparisons. The eternal one, the one most worthy and which will not pass from mind, the only other place comparable to these marvelous nether regions, must surely be naked space itself, out far beyond atmosphere, between the stars, where sunlight has no grip upon the dust and rubbish of planetary air, where the blackness of space, the shining planets, comets, suns, and stars must really be closely akin to the world of life as it appears to the eyes of an awed human being, in the open ocean, one half mile down.

Fishes in Armor

MYRON GORDON

FISHES had elaborate styles of personal armor long before ancient man learned to use a simple shield in self-defense.

In the days before the age of dinosaurs, the most popular of all styles in apparel for fishes was a stiff suit of bony scales, movable only along the scale's beveled edges. Then with the arrival of the huge newly evolved plesiosaurs and other fish-swallowing, bone-crushing monsters in the age of reptiles, the former advantages of protective armor were practically nil. The fishes in the Mesozoic seas faced a changing tempo. The "speed-up" movement arrived.

Predatory sharks and larger fishes swam faster after their prey. Speed, not armament, was necessary for survival. Small fishes with fast, flexible bodies, streamlined for speed and powered for a quick getaway, met the challenge of the new mode of life. They fled from the triple threat of reptiles, sharks and larger fishes. Their kind flourished and multiplied.

Nearly all modern fishes have long since discarded the last vestiges of the ancient suits of bony armor. But the modern trunkfishes have re-adopted, with modifications, the old-fashioned, prehistoric style of armor suiting. Like up-to-date dress designers, the trunkfishes have copied merely the spirit of the old style; they have evolved entirely new methods of covering their bodies.

The scales in the trunkfish's body constitute a solid series of hard hexagonal plates, firmly joined together to form a single, inflexible bony case. A tortoise in its shell can move its head in and out and twist it, if it wishes, from side to side; but the only independent movement of the head that a trunkfish can execute, is to ogle its eyes and to pucker its lips. The head is joined immovably to the trunk.

Confined permanently within these strait-jackets of their own making, it is a mystery how trunkfishes get along. Certainly few would have predicted success for fishes outfitted with this ungainly body style of a past age in this modern world with its ferocious marauders, like barracudas and morays, and the ancient predatory sharks that continue to snatch their living from all creatures weaker than themselves.

The return of armored styles to modern fishes has its human par-

From *Natural History* Magazine. By kind permission of the author.

allel. Old-fashioned costumes of past centuries reappear with modern flares to clothe the fashionable ladies of today. And personal armor of King Arthur's day has returned in part in the bullet-proof vest and the steel helmet of the modern infantryman. One man was fascinated by this piscine-human parallelism. Bashford Dean was an expert in ichthyology. He was first of all an authority on fishes of the past and present. He knew how they lived and the factors that determined why some of them failed in the past and became extinct while others succeeded in their struggle for existence until the present day. His studies of fish armor led him to a study of evolution of human armor. Dean took time off from his duties as curator of fishes at the American Museum of Natural History to establish and study the collection of human armor at the Metropolitan Museum of Art. He had long been an expert on the kinds of metallic suits of armor well-dressed knights wore in medieval times. He was appointed curator of human armor at the Metropolitan Museum of Art.

The story of evolution of armor among men is more complete than the story of evolution of armor in fishes. The human record is infinitely shorter, the number of styles invented by man are fewer, and the materials used are simpler in composition. But the development of both piscine and human armor have had their period of crude beginnings, their period of rapid development, their period of florescence, and finally their period of decline almost to the point of extinction. Trunkfish and men in bullet-proof vests are modern representatives of different ancestral stocks, but their costumes have a common purpose.

The porcupine fish's scales are modified and form a globular series of sharply pointed spines. These jagged needles form an effective coat of mail and oppose the enemy from all points of the compass. The South American armored catfish, on the other hand, is literally sandwiched in between two solid plates of bone. The unfish-like sea horses, that swim so slowly and gracefully through the water by imperceptible movement of their semi-transparent fins, are encased within a series of bony rings. Their heads are constantly erect like the heads of trotting horses on parade. Sea horses need no over-check straps to keep their heads up: their necks are encircled with collars of bone. They are stiff-necked from the cradle to the grave. When dead, their bodies, or rather their bony shells, shrink hardly at all; and dried sea horses are sometimes marketed as curios. The helpless fish are caught, their bodies dried in the sun and preserved by a coat of shellac. Thus the armor which normally serves to protect the fish becomes its tomb. Some curio vendors sacrilegiously lacquer and paint sea horses with gaudy colors.

The trigger fishes of the tropics have many small, hard, stud-like tubercles in their skin. They are tough-skinned, indeed; but their pugnacious relatives, the file-fishes, are even tougher. As a matter of fact, the skins of larger file-fishes, when peeled from their carcasses and dried, are actually used as abrasives. But all these fishes with tough hides are amateurs in the art of passive self-defense when compared with the trunkfishes, for these have the most completely enclosed of all the styles of protective armor.

The trunkfish and their allies live in the coral community of tropical American waters. The seas about the coral archipelago of the Florida Keys is a Paris style-center in the fishes' world. Man lacks the imagination to design the diversity of outlandish styles displayed by the fishes in this marine style-center. A menagerie of fish types pass constantly in review. There are sea horses, of course; then there are pork fish, goat fish and mutton fish; then there are squirrel fish, rabbit fish and lion fish; there are scorpion fish, louse fish and butterfly fish; parrot fish and snipe fish; frog fish, snake fish and lizard fish; and there are monk fish and angle fish! And, to return to the category of trunkfish, there are cowfish.

No contest was ever proposed, no prizes were ever offered for the best choice of a name to suit the personality of the cowfish, a trunkfish which scientists call *Lactophrys tricornis*. If there had been a contest, perhaps someone might have thought of a more dignified name. And yet these curious twelve-inch fishes of the coral reefs do resemble, in a most superficial manner to be sure, a staid milch cow. They have the same wide-eyed, vacuous expression, although on rare occasions they seem to express a mood of deep sadness. When disturbed they appear to be bewildered and amazed.

William Swainson, the English naturalist, writing in 1839, must have had an amusing time in choosing the cowfish's technical name of *Lactophrys*. The horn-like protuberances must have reminded him of a cow. That would account for the "lacto" portion of *Lactophrys*, for "lactoria" means milch cow in Latin. Then there was something appealing about the sad eyes of the cowfish, something about their overhanging, brooding, eyebrow-like eye-sockets that attracted Swainson's sensitive attention, so that he added "ophrys," which means eyebrow in Greek. Could Swainson have meant, then, that this mournful fish looked like a cow with prominent eyebrows? *Tricornis*, the cowfish's specific name, refers to three horns. Actually the cowfish, like its bovine namesake, has but two horns on its head; but in addition, in the rear, pointing backward, there are three horns on each side of the shell.

You might think that the ichthyologist is bothered by such names as *Lactophrys tricornis* for the cowfish and *Lactophrys trigonus* for the common trunkfish, but as a matter of fact the fish scientist is happy about it. Years ago, in 1738, toward the end of the dark ages of biology, the educated fish man had to remember this name for the cowfish: *Ostracion triangulatus duobus aculeis in fronte et totidem in imo ventre subcaudalesque binis.* The author of this prayer-like appellation was Pedrus Artedi, a native of Sweden.

Artedi had traveled widely in his lifetime. When in England he made the rounds of the taverns in and about London. He specifically mentions "The Nagg's Head," "The White Bear" and the "Green Dragon in Stepney." These visits were strictly on business, for it was in these and other inns that various natural history curiosities from the new world of America were exhibited. The trunk-fishes as a group became well known to European naturalists because of the heavy demand for, and the extensive traffic in, the dried shells of these fishes. So thorough were the catches of trunk-fish hunters in American seas that every species now recognized as distinct had been described some two hundred years ago from curio specimens.

It was at the height of this trunkfish curio fad period that Artedi described several of them. In London Artedi visited Sir Hans Sloane and saw his collection of natural history specimens from the West Indies, a collection which was destined to be the beginning of the British Museum of Natural History. There Artedi spotted a rare cowfish. He was convinced that this particular cowfish had never before been recognized or described to the scientific world. Forthwith he supplied the necessary baptismal papers. The words he used were in Latin, the language in vogue at the time for scientific treatises. From that baptismal record, the name *Ostracion triangulatus duobus,* etc. of the cowfish was derived.

But the records show that Pedrus Artedi was fifty years too late in his naming of the cowfish. He was beaten by Dr. Martin Lister, who is not to be confused with Lord Lister of antiseptic fame. Dr. Martin Lister, the original cowfish man, had his own ideas about names for the cowfish. His 1686 name is: *Piscis triangularis capite cornutus cui e media cauda cutacea aculeus longue erigitus.* Lister's and Artedi's names for the cowfish stood on the fish catalogues until 1758, when von Linné gave naturalists the world over a new deal by systematically cutting down the long names of all living things to two words. All naturalists cheered. This practice is still in vogue today. When the modern naturalist thinks back to the days of Lister and Artedi and recalls the long quotations these gentlemen used as names for their specimens, he feels that remembering and saying *Lactophrys tricornis* is almost as easy as saying Jack Robinson.

Yet the honor of having discovered the very first American

trunkfish must go, not to Dr. Martin Lister or Pedrus Artedi, but to an unknown member of Columbus' crew. On their first voyage to America in 1492, while at anchor on the coast of Cuba, this unknown sailor-fisherman caught a fish which "was like a swine, all covered with a very hard skin, no part whereof was soft but the tail."

Other fishes may have shapes that please the human eye better than the angular conformations of the trunkfish, but no fish can claim more dazzling colors, a more intriguing color pattern, and a greater repertoire of color changes than they.

England's fish expert, J. R. Norman, keeper of fishes at the British Museum, votes the trunkfish of the Great Barrier Reef of Australia the most colorful of all fishes. They have all the colors of the rainbow and can change at will from one color scheme to another. The Florida trunkfishes are brilliant, too, and their remarkable ability to change color is manifest when at one moment they are vivid green, at the next a nut-brown, and a moment later as white as the bleached coral sand. And in the intervals between these definite color phases, intermediate transitional stages are flashed in a continuous series of complex combinations.

There certainly is no correlation at all between their beautiful colors and beauty of body lines for they are grotesque and unbelievable. Detached from their normal surroundings they appear clownishly out of place. But swimming slowly among the living coral heads they are dignified and even stately. Their bodies can never relax from their stiff-necked posture, for they are of one piece. When forced to rapid movement they are ludicrous. They have penguin-on-land actions in getting about.

When removed from the water their behavior is pathetic, for they are absolutely helpless, being unable to move their solid bodies. When placed upon a stone, out of water, trunkfishes foam at the mouth in their distress. Some say that they make small grunting noises; others say that they growl like dogs. Large trunkfishes will live two to three hours out of water, all the time, Goode comments, "solemnly fanning their fins." When restored to their native element they cannot immediately sink to the bottom for they have absorbed much air in their sojourn above the water line; but after a short time they seem none the worse for their emersion.

Viewed head-on the chinless face of a trunkfish presents a grotesque appearance, with its lips perpetually pursed as if forever ready to kiss the world. From their funnel-shaped head small jaws protrude which are capable of limited movement only. They have a strong set of teeth, designed to break down hard coral structures which are inhabited by worms, shrimps and other small animals on which they feed. With these powerful teeth they can defend themselves from smaller fishes at close quarters, but in the confinement of an aquarium the trunkfish is at a distinct disadvantage. Its fins are constantly being ripped to pieces by fishes that are in the habit of biting at anything that moves and then darting away. Trunkfish have lived for long periods in an aquarium, but their cell-mates have been chosen with great care.

Trunkfishes have regained a degree of protection within their rigid bony shell but only at the expense of speed. They do not have the smooth contours and perfect tear-drop streamline form displayed by fast-swimming fishes like mackerel and swordfish. Rather their body styles follow motifs of sharp angles, pointed projections and grotesque elevations, all molded into a single bony frame. Cleave a swordfish in two behind the head and the outline of the cut is an oval. Split a trunkfish similarly and the outline is a triangle. The back of the swordfish is nicely curved; the back of the trunkfish is a pyramid. The belly of the swordfish is well rounded like the bottom of a trim, speedy canoe; the belly region of a trunkfish is as level as the underside of a flat-bottomed rowboat. This flat nether surface enables the trunkfish to execute a safe, upright landing on the bottom of the sea; and here it spends much time resting quietly.

Living their lives encased permanently in bony armor, these small, individual, aquatic tanks, being unable to execute body undulations, move slowly through the water, relying upon their fins alone to project them forward. From the rigid case, and joined to it by thin folds of skin, project small, flabby fins; one on each side of the body, one on top, and one on the bottom. From the rear a thin, naked tailpiece with its ridiculously small flap of tail fin sticks out like a stiff whisk-broom tail on a hobby horse. This fin, so important in other fishes' swimming strokes, merely serves the trunkfish as a rudder. Only when the trunkfish is pressed for utmost haste does its tail revert to the time-honored task of active locomotion. When forced, it will lash its tail from side to side in the best fish manner. In doing this the motion of its tail fin may be likened to the sculling action of the gondolier's single oar at the stern of his boat.

The burden of locomotion falls upon the small upper and lower fins. These have a half rotary sculling action resembling, but, of course, never effecting, the movement of a screw propeller. Oftentimes the movement of these transparent fins is hardly perceptible and the chunky trunkfish seems to glide through the water without effort and with great dignity.

The fins on the port and starboard side of a trunkfish have a special duty. They not only keep the fish upright, but they prevent it from being projected forward like a rocket by the powerful force of the water ejected backward from the small gill openings. When the fish is at rest, the pectoral fins wave vigorously at the rate of one hundred and eighty times a minute.

Trunkfish have put their trust in the principle that a strong defense is the best offense. They have been practicing this policy successfully for the past fifty million years. This may seem a long time for humans, but the modern age for fishes started millions of years before the form of man was conceived.

There is no question, as far as trunkfishes are concerned, that the exchange of speed for security was profitable. They are not likely to be attacked by fishes of their own size, with which they have to compete most of the time. The trunkfish live among the living coral heads in tropic seas, among which the watery paths are often narrow and tortuous. A coral reef community is a city of narrow streets and crooked alleys. The denizens of the coral city rarely stray into the boulevards and highways of open water. If they do, they are soon taken out of their native course: the Gulf Stream will carry them to northern waters that are colder and uncongenial. They cannot live a normal life outside their coral community. Sharks, barracudas, and other predators of the sea patrol the outskirts and await their chance to pounce, unhindered by the many pillars and posts within the coral city, upon those that stray outside.

Shark stomachs tell stories that cannot be denied. Sharks have swallowed trunkfish. Unless trunkfish are swallowed whole they are not likely to be attacked at all. What, after all, has the trunkfish to tempt its smaller pursuers? Its fins are thin and small. Its tailpiece is a little insignificant morsel of flesh hardly worth the effort of a fight. And the trunkfish has a strong set of teeth with which it can defend itself at close quarters. But it cannot defend itself as it passes down the gullet of a shark. Gudger, American Museum fish expert, found an empty and perfectly polished shell of a trunkfish inside the stomach of a shark at Dry Tortugas, Florida. The six-sided, fused plates of the unfortunate trunkfish's bony jacket were worn down so smooth that they revealed their beautiful mosaic construction. The fine striations and scrolls upon each piece appeared as clear as the grain in a slab of well-rubbed curly maple. Sharks have an efficient digestive mill to handle these tough but tempting morsels. When a shark is through with a trunkfish, it discards a shell that is as completely freed of soft parts as a skeleton that has been picked clean by the combined efforts of buzzards, ants and dermestids, experts in this funereal job.

Sharks discovered that trunkfishes were good eating long before man did — long before man existed. Even now sharks are beating man in trunkfish hunting — they are nearer the source of supply. Trunkfish are a treat for the epicure, according to America's expert in fisheries, G. Brown Goode. Serious cases of poisoning have resulted from eating the spoiled meat of the trunkfish, but these cases occurred in tropical countries where, if care is not taken, the flesh decomposes rapidly. There is little danger of poisoning if the fish are fresh. Seafood connoisseur Goode says that the flesh of these fishes is delicate in texture and exceptionally pleasant in taste. Goode likes his fishes prepared by first boiling them whole, like lobsters, in salt water, then scooping out the meat; the meat is then mixed with cracker crumbs, eggs, butter and red pepper, and this promising combination is stuffed back into the original trunkfish shell and roasted until nicely browned. Those who have eaten this fish agree with Goode that it is a rare delicacy. Trunkfish eating has not reached commercial proportions as yet. Some enterprising composer of sea food menus could scoop the shore dinner trade by glorifying them as the treasure-chests of the sea.

So enthusiastic was the French fish scientist and fish gourmet, Lacépède, of the delicacy of the flesh of the trunkfish that he wrote at great length, in 1798, of a method by which the trunkfish of the American tropical seas might be induced to live in the temperate fresh waters of France. "The exquisite flavor and exceedingly wholesome nature of the flesh of the 'triangulaire' should encourage us to make persevering and well considered experiments in this direction." His plan was to acclimatize the fish by gradual, insensible changes in temperature and salinity of the sea water until the cool, fresh water level was reached. There was one serious difficulty to this plan: the trunkfish refused stubbornly to co-operate.

European waters do not provide the coral homesteads necessary for the trunkfishes, and none are found along European coasts of the Atlantic. But the tropical shores of the American Atlantic provide suitable places for them, and here they flourish. They are abundant in the vicinity of the laboratories of the Marine Biological Station of the Carnegie Institute at Loggerhead Key of the Dry Tortugas, the last of the Keys of Florida.

One day in the shallow seas surrounding Bush Key, just opposite Garden Key or Fort Jefferson, the "Shark Island" of Dr. Samuel Mudd fame, we hauled a fine-meshed seine at low tide along the outskirts of a fine stand of living coral heads. We walked shoulder-high in the warm, crystal-clear waters, scarcely seeing the well-camouflaged sea creatures that we knew were there. We worked blindly in our attempt to surround a section of the coral community and capture its inhabitants. Three of us dragged the seine for some thirty yards toward still shallower waters at the beach. Then those on opposite ends of the seine approached one another in a circling maneuver, and gradually the net completely surrounded a crowded, milling mob of fish, crabs, shrimps, sea urchins, sea cucumbers, snails, sponges, algae of all shapes and colors. Everything was entwined in strands of fantastic seaweeds, bits of broken coral, and masses of sponges.

We were obliged to remove these entwining objects before we could safely select the living fishes we wanted for closer study. As we hauled out pieces of seaweeds of many colors and curious designs, I noticed a number of green globules of jelly-like algae, suspended in the water enclosed by the net. They moved almost imperceptibly, as if carried by the tide. As I reached down to remove these bits of plant masses, they moved a trifle faster than my open hand. I tried again, with the same empty result; then it dawned upon me that those globs of algae were not algae at all but were some form of animal life. I made a deliberate lunge at one of them and found that I had a baby trunkfish in my hand.

My first impression of having to deal with green masses of plant life was so strong that the realization that they were representatives of the animal world came as a definite mental shock. I had the sensation for an instant of acting as a magician and at the same time of being one whom the magician held spellbound. It was almost as if I had pulled a rabbit out of the net.

I looked at the baby trunkfish again. Its body was already hardened with bone and its small mosaic green shell was beautifully sculptured in an intricate design that followed a hexagonal pattern. Its tiny, transparent fins were hardly visible in my hand; they were entirely invisible in the water. It was these translucent fins that had enabled the little trunkfish to move away in an unfishlike manner from my hand. When I replaced it in the water, the little green fishy ball made off with the smoothness of a toy balloon in a quiet breeze.

The Changing Year

RACHEL CARSON

FOR THE SEA as a whole, the alternation of day and night, the passage of the seasons, the procession of the years, are lost in its vastness, obliterated in its own changeless eternity. But the surface waters are different. The face of the sea is always changing. Crossed by colors, lights, and moving shadows, sparkling in the sun, mysterious in the twilight, its aspects and its moods vary hour by hour. The surface waters move with the tides, stir to the breath of the winds, and rise and fall to the endless, hurrying forms of the waves. Most of all, they change with the advance of the seasons. Spring moves over the temperate lands of our Northern Hemisphere in a tide of new life, of pushing green shoots and unfolding buds, all its mysteries and meanings symbolized in the northward migration of the birds, the awakening of sluggish amphibian life as the chorus of frogs rises again from the wet lands, the different sound of the wind which stirs the young leaves where a month ago it rattled the bare branches. These things we associate with the land, and it is easy to suppose that at sea there could be no such feeling of advancing spring. But the signs are there, and seen with understanding eye, they bring the same magical sense of awakening.

In the sea, as on land, spring is a time for the renewal of life. During the long months of winter in the temperate zones the surface waters have been absorbing the cold. Now the heavy water begins to sink, slipping down and displacing the warmer layers below. Rich stores of minerals have been accumulating on the floor of the continental shelf — some freighted down the rivers from the lands; some derived from sea creatures that have died and whose remains have drifted down to the bottom; some from the shells that once encased a diatom, the streaming protoplasm of a radiolarian, or the transparent tissues of a pteropod. Nothing is wasted in the sea; every particle of material is used over and over again, first by one creature, then by another. And when in spring the waters are deeply stirred, the warm bottom water brings to the surface a rich supply of minerals, ready for use by new forms of life.

Just as land plants depend on minerals in the soil for their growth, every marine plant, even the smallest, is dependent upon the nutrient salts or minerals in the sea water. Diatoms must have silica, the element of which their fragile shells are fashioned. For these and all other microplants, phosphorus is an indispensable mineral. Some of these elements are in short supply and in winter may be reduced below the minimum necessary for growth. The diatom population must tide itself over this season as best it can. It faces a stark problem of survival, with no opportunity to increase, a problem of keeping alive the spark of life by forming tough protective spores against the stringency of winter, a matter of existing in a dormant state in which no demands shall be made on an environment that already withholds all but the most meager necessities of life. So the diatoms hold their place in the winter sea, like seeds of wheat in a field under snow and ice, the seeds from which the spring growth will come.

These, then, are the elements of the vernal blooming of the sea: the "seeds" of the dormant plants, the fertilizing chemicals, the warmth of the spring sun.

In a sudden awakening, incredible in its swiftness, the simplest plants of the sea begin to multiply. Their increase is of astronomical proportions. The spring sea belongs at first to the diatoms and to all the other microscopic plant life of the plankton. In the fierce intensity of their growth they cover vast areas of ocean with a living blanket of their cells. Mile after mile of water may appear red or brown or green, the whole surface taking on the color of the infinitesimal grains of pigment contained in each of the plant cells.

The plants have undisputed sway in the sea for only a short time. Almost at once their own burst of multiplication is matched by a similar increase in the small animals of the plankton. It is the spawning time of the copepod and the glassworm, the pelagic shrimp and the winged snail. Hungry swarms of these little beasts of the plankton roam through the waters, feeding on the abundant plants and themselves falling prey to larger creatures. Now in the spring the surface waters become a vast nursery. From the hills and valleys of the continent's edge lying far below, and from the scattered shoals and banks, the eggs or young of many of the bottom animals rise to the surface of the sea. Even those which, in their maturity, will sink down to a sedentary life on the bottom, spend the first weeks of life as freely swimming hunters of the plankton. So as spring progresses new batches of larvae rise into the surface each day, the young of fishes and crabs and mussels and tube worms, mingling for a time with the regular members of the plankton.

Under the steady and voracious grazing, the grasslands of the surface are soon depleted. The diatoms become more and more scarce, and with them the other simple plants. Still there are brief explosions of one or another form, when in a sudden orgy of cell division it comes to claim whole areas of the sea for its own. So, for a time each spring, the waters may become blotched with brown, jellylike masses, and the fishermen's nets come up dripping a brown slime and containing no fish, for the herring have turned away from these waters as though in loathing of the viscid, foul-smelling algae. But in less time than passes between the full moon and the new, the spring flowering of Phaeocystis is past and the waters have cleared again.

In the spring the sea is filled with migrating fishes, some of them bound for the mouths of great rivers, which they will ascend to deposit their spawn. Such are the spring-run chinooks coming in from the deep Pacific feeding grounds to breast the rolling flood of the Columbia, the shad moving in to the Chesapeake and the Hudson and the Connecticut, the alewives seeking a hundred coastal streams of New England, the salmon feeling their way to the Penobscot and the Kennebec. For months or years these fish have known only the vast spaces of the ocean. Now the spring sea and the maturing of their own bodies lead them back to the rivers of their birth.

Other mysterious comings and goings are linked with the advance of the year. Capelin gather in the deep, cold water of the Barents Sea, their shoals followed and preyed upon by flocks of auks, fulmars, and kittiwakes. Cod approach the banks of Lofoten, and gather off the shores of Iceland. Birds whose winter feeding territory may have encompassed the whole Atlantic or the whole Pacific converge upon some small island, the entire breeding population arriving within the space of a few days. Whale suddenly appear off the slopes of the coastal banks where the swarms of shrimplike krill are spawning, the whales having come from no one knows where, by no one knows what route.

With the subsiding of the diatoms and the completed spawning of many of the plankton animals and most of the fish, life in the surface waters slackens to the slower pace of midsummer. Along the meeting places of the currents the pale moon jelly Aurelia gathers in thousands, forming sinuous lines or windrows across miles of sea, and the birds see their pale forms shimmering deep down in the green water. By midsummer the large red jellyfish Cyanea may have grown from the size of a thimble to that of an umbrella. The great jellyfish moves through the sea with rhythmic pulsations, trailing long tentacles and as likely as not shepherding a little group of young cod or haddock, which find shelter under its bell and travel with it.

A hard, brilliant, coruscating phosphorescence often illuminates the summer sea. In waters where the protozoan Noctiluca is abundant it is the chief source of this summer luminescence, causing fishes, squids, or dolphins to fill the water with racing flames and to clothe themselves in a ghostly radiance. Or again the summer sea may glitter with a thousand thousand moving pinpricks of light, like an immense swarm of fireflies moving through a dark wood. Such an effect is produced by a shoal of the brilliantly phosphorescent shrimp Meganyctiphanes, a creature of cold and darkness and of the places where icy water rolls upward from the depths and bubbles with white ripplings at the surface.

Out over the plankton meadows of the North Atlantic the dry twitter of the phalaropes, small brown birds, wheeling and turning, dipping and rising, is heard for the first time since early spring. The phalaropes have nested on the arctic tundras, reared their young, and now the first of them are returning to the sea. Most of them will continue south over the open water far from land, crossing the equator into the South Atlantic. Here they will follow where the great whales lead, for where the whales are, there also are the swarms of plankton on which these strange little birds grow fat.

As the fall advances, there are other movements, some in the surface, some hidden in the green depths, that betoken the end of summer. In the fog-covered waters of Bering Sea, down through the treacherous passes between the islands of the Aleutian chain and southward into the open Pacific, the herds of fur seals are moving. Left behind are two small islands, treeless bits of volcanic soil thrust up into the waters of Bering Sea. The islands are silent now, but for the several months of summer they resounded with the roar of millions of seals come ashore to bear and rear their young — all the fur seals of the eastern Pacific crowded into a few square miles of bare rock and crumbling soil. Now once more the seals turn south, to roam down along the sheer underwater cliffs of the continent's edge, where the rocky foundations fall away steeply into the deep sea. Here, in a blackness more absolute than that of arctic winter, the seals will find rich feeding as they swim down to prey on the fishes of this region of darkness.

Autumn comes to the sea with a fresh blaze of phosphorescence, when every wave crest is aflame. Here and there the whole surface may glow with sheets of cold fire, while below schools of fish pour through the water like molten metal. Often the autumnal phosphorescence is caused by a fall flowering of the dinoflagellates, multiplying furiously in a short-lived repetition of their vernal blooming.

Sometimes the meaning of the glowing water is ominous. Off the Pacific coast of North America, it may mean that the sea is filled with the dinoflagellate Gonyaulax, a minute plant that contains a poison of strange and terrible virulence. About four days after Gonyaulax comes to dominate the coastal plankton, some of the fishes and shellfish in the vicinity become toxic. This is because, in their normal feeding, they have strained the poisonous plankton out of the water. Mussels accumulate the Gonyaulax toxins in their livers, and the toxins react on the human nervous system with an effect similar to that of strychnine. Because of these facts, it is generally understood along the Pacific coast that it is unwise to eat shellfish taken from coasts exposed to the open sea where Gonyaulax may be abundant, in summer or early fall. For generations before the white men came, the Indians knew this. As soon as the red streaks appeared in the sea and the waves began to flicker at night with the mysterious blue-green fires, the tribal leaders forbade the taking of mussels until these warning signals should have passed. They even set guards at intervals along the beaches to warn inlanders who might come down for shellfish and be unable to read the language of the sea.

But usually the blaze and glitter of the sea, whatever its meaning for those who produce it, implies no menace to man. Seen from the deck of a vessel in open ocean, a tiny, man-made observation point in the vast world of sea and sky, it has an eerie and unearthly quality. Man, in his vanity, subconsciously attributes a human origin to any light not of moon or stars or sun. Lights on the shore, lights moving over the water, mean lights kindled and controlled by other men, serving purposes understandable to the human mind. Yet here are lights that flash and fade away, lights that come and go for reasons meaningless to man, lights that have been doing this very thing over the eons of time in which there were no men to stir in vague disquiet.

On such a night of phosphorescent display Charles Darwin stood on the deck of the *Beagle* as she plowed southward through the Atlantic off the coast of Brazil.

"The sea from its extreme luminousness presented a wonderful and most beautiful appearance [he wrote in his diary]. Every part of the water which by day is seen as foam, glowed with a pale light. The vessel drove before her bows two billows of liquid phosphorus, and in her wake was a milky train. As far as the eye reached the crest of every wave was bright; and from the reflected light, the sky just above the horizon was not so utterly dark as the rest of the Heavens. It was impossible to behold this plain of matter, as it were melted and consuming by heat, without being reminded of Milton's description of the regions of Chaos and Anarchy."

Like the blazing colors of the autumn leaves before they wither and fall, the autumnal phosphorescence betokens the approach of winter. After their brief renewal of life the flagellates and the other minute algae dwindle away to a scattered few; so do the shrimps and the copepods, the glassworms and the comb jellies. The larvae of the bottom fauna have long since completed their development and drifted away to take up whatever existence is their lot. Even the roving fish schools have deserted the surface waters and have migrated into warmer latitudes or have found equivalent warmth in the deep, quiet waters along the edge of the continental shelf. There the torpor of semihibernation descends upon them and will possess them during the months of winter.

The surface waters now become the plaything of the winter gales. As the winds build up the giant storm waves and roar along their crests, lashing the water into foam and flying spray, it seems that life must forever have deserted this place.

For the mood of the winter sea, read Joseph Conrad's description:

"The greyness of the whole immense surface, the wind furrows upon the faces of the waves, the great masses of foam, tossed about and waving, like matted white locks, give to the sea in a gale an appearance of hoary age, lustreless, dull, without gleams, as though it had been created before light itself."

But the symbols of hope are not lacking even in the grayness and bleakness of the winter sea. On land we know that the apparent lifelessness of winter is an illusion. Look closely at the bare branches of a tree, on which not the palest gleam of green can be discerned. Yet, spaced along each branch are the leaf buds, all the spring's magic of swelling green concealed and safely preserved under the insulating, overlapping layers. Pick off a piece of the rough bark of the trunk; there you will find hibernating insects. Dig down through the snow into the earth. There are the eggs of next summer's grasshoppers; there are the dormant seeds from which will come the grass, the herb, the oak tree.

So, too, the lifelessness, the hopelessness, the despair of the winter sea are an illusion. Everywhere are the assurances that the cycle has come to the full, containing the means of its own renewal. There is the promise of a new spring in the very iciness of the winter sea, in the chilling of the water, which must, before many weeks, become so heavy that it will plunge downward, precipitating the overturn that is the first act in the drama of spring. There is the promise of new life in the small plantlike things that cling to the rocks of the underlying bottom, the almost formless polyps from which, in spring, a new generation of jellyfish will bud off and rise into the surface waters. There is unconscious purpose in the sluggish forms of the copepods hibernating on the bottom, safe from the surface storms, life sustained in their tiny bodies by the extra store of fat with which they went into this winter sleep.

Already, from the gray shapes of cod that have moved, unseen by man, through the cold sea to their spawning places, the glassy globules of eggs are rising into the surface waters. Even in the harsh world of the winter sea, these eggs will begin the swift divisions by which a granule of protoplasm becomes a living fishlet.

Most of all, perhaps, there is assurance in the fine dust of life that remains in the surface waters, the invisible spores of the diatoms, needing only the touch of warming sun and fertilizing chemicals to repeat the magic of spring.

The Sperm Whale's Head

HERMAN MELVILLE

HERE, NOW, are two great whales, laying their heads together; let us join them, and lay together our own.

Of the grand order of folio Leviathans, the Sperm Whale and the Right Whale are by far the most noteworthy. They are the only whales regularly hunted by man. To the Nantucketer, they present the two extremes of all the known varieties of the whale. As the external difference between them is mainly observable in their heads; and as a head of each is this moment hanging from the *Pequod's* side; and as we may freely go from one to the other, by merely stepping across the deck; — where, I should like to know, will you obtain a better chance to study practical cetology than here?

In the first place, you are struck by the general contrast between these heads. Both are massive enough in all conscience; but there is a certain mathematical symmetry in the Sperm Whale's which the Right Whale's sadly lacks. There is more character in the Sperm Whale's head. As you behold it, you involuntarily yield the immense superiority to him, in point of pervading dignity. In the present

From *Moby Dick* by Herman Melville.

instance, too, this dignity is heightened by the pepper and salt color of his head at the summit, giving token of advanced age and large experience. In short, he is what the fishermen technically call a "gray-headed whale."

Let us now note what is least dissimilar in these heads — namely, the two most important organs, the eye and the ear. Far back on the side of the head, and low down, near the angle of either whale's jaw, if you narrowly search, you will at last see a lashless eye, which you would fancy to be a young colt's eye; so out of all proportion is it to the magnitude of the head.

Now, from this peculiar sideway position of the whale's eyes, it is plain that he can never see an object which is exactly ahead, no more than he can one exactly astern. In a word, the position of the whale's eyes corresponds to that of a man's ears; and you may fancy, for yourself, how it would fare with you, did you sideways survey objects through your ears. You would find that you could only command some thirty degrees of vision in advance of the straight side-line of sight; and about thirty more behind it. If your bitterest foe were walking straight toward you, with dagger uplifted in broad day, you would not be able to see him, any more than if he were stealing upon you from behind. In a word, you would have two backs, so to speak; but, at the same time, also, two fronts (side fronts): for what is it that makes the front of a man — what, indeed, but his eyes?

Moreover, while in most other animals that I can now think of, the eyes are so planted as imperceptibly to blend their visual power, so as to produce one picture and not two to the brain; the peculiar position of the whale's eyes, effectually divided as they are by many cubic feet of solid head, which towers between them like a great mountain separating two lakes in valleys; this, of course, must wholly separate the impressions which each independent organ imparts. The whale, therefore, must see one distinct picture on this side, and another distinct picture on that side; while all between must be profound darkness and nothingness to him. Man may, in effect, be said to look out on the world from a sentry-box with two joined sashes for his window. But with the whale, these two sashes are separately inserted, making two distinct windows, but sadly impairing the view. This peculiarity of the whale's eyes is a thing always to be borne in mind in the fishery; and to be remembered by the reader in some subsequent scenes.

A curious and most puzzling question might be started concerning this visual matter as touching the Leviathan. But I must be content with a hint. So long as a man's eyes are open in the light, the act of seeing is involuntary; that is, he cannot then help mechanically seeing whatever objects are before him. Nevertheless, anyone's experience will teach him, that though he can take in an indiscriminating sweep of things at one glance, it is quite impossible for him, attentively, and completely, to examine any two things — however large or however small — at one and the same instant of time; never mind if they lie side by side and touch each other. But if you now come to separate these two objects, and surround each by a circle of profound darkness; then, in order to see one of them, in such a manner as to bring your mind to bear on it, the other will be utterly excluded from your contemporary consciousness. How is it, then, with the whale? True, both his eyes, in themselves, must simultaneously act; but is his brain so much more comprehensive, combining, and subtle than man's, that he can at the same moment of time attentively examine two distinct prospects, one on one side of him, and the other in an exactly opposite direction? If he can, then is it as marvelous a thing in him, as if a man were able simultaneously to go through the demonstrations of two distinct problems in Euclid. Nor, strictly investigated, is there any incongruity in this comparison.

It may be but an idle whim, but it has always seemed to me, that the extraordinary vacillations of movement displayed by some whales when beset by three or four boats; the timidity and liability to queer frights, so common to such whales; I think that all this indirectly proceeds from the helpless perplexity of volition, in which their divided and diametrically opposite powers of vision must involve them.

But the ear of the whale is full as curious as the eye. If you are an entire stranger to their race, you might hunt over these two heads for hours, and never discover that organ. The ear has no external leaf whatever; and into the hole itself you can hardly insert a quill, so wondrously minute is it. It is lodged a little behind the eye. With respect to their ears, this important difference is to be observed between the Sperm Whale and the Right. While the ear of the former has an external opening, that of the latter is entirely and evenly covered over with a membrane, so as to be quite imperceptible from without.

Is it not curious, that so vast a being as the whale should see the world through so small an eye, and hear the thunder through an ear which is smaller than a hare's? But if his eyes were as broad as the lens of Herschel's great telescope; and his ears capacious as the porches of cathedrals; would that make him any longer of sight, or sharper of hearing? Not at all. — Why then do you try to "enlarge" your mind? Subtilize it.

Let us now with whatever levers and steam-engines we have at hand, cant over the Sperm Whale's head, so that it may lie bottom up; then, ascending by a ladder to the summit, have a peep down the mouth; and were it not that the body is now completely separated from it, with a lantern we might descend into the great Kentucky Mammoth Cave of his stomach. But let us hold on here by this tooth, and look about us where we are. What a really beautiful and chaste-looking mouth! from floor to ceiling, lined, or rather papered with a glistening white membrane, glossy as bridal satins.

But come out now, and look at this portentous lower jaw, which seems like the long narrow lid of an immense snuff-box, with the hinge at one end, instead of one side. If you pry it up, so as to get it overhead, and expose its rows of teeth, it seems a terrific portcullis; and such, alas! it proves to many a poor wight in the fishery, upon whom these spikes fall with impaling force. But far more terrible is it to behold, when fathoms down in the sea, you see some sulky whale, floating there suspended, with his prodigious jaw, some fifteen feet long, hanging straight down at right-angles with his body, for all the world like a ship's jib-boom. This whale is not dead; he is only dispirited; out of sorts, perhaps; hypochondriac; and so supine, that the hinges of his jaw have relaxed, leaving him there in that ungainly sort of plight, a reproach to all his tribe, who must, no doubt, imprecate lockjaws upon him.

In most cases this lower jaw — being easily unhinged by a practiced artist — is disengaged and hoisted on deck for the purpose of extracting the ivory teeth, and furnishing a supply of that hard white whalebone with which the fishermen fashion all sorts of curious articles, including canes, umbrella-stocks, and handles to riding-whips.

With a long, weary hoist the jaw is dragged on board, as if it were an anchor; and when the proper time comes — some few days after the other work — Queequeg, Daggoo, and Tashtego, being all accomplished dentists, are set to drawing teeth. With a keen cutting spade, Queequeg lances the gums; then the jaw is lashed down to ringbolts, and a tackle being rigged from aloft, they drag out these teeth, as Michigan oxen drag stumps of old oaks out of wild woodlands. There are generally forty-two teeth in all; in old whales, much worn down, but undecayed; nor filled after our artificial fashion. The jaw is afterward sawn into slabs, and piled away like joists for building houses.

The Intelligence of Birds

JULIAN HUXLEY

A CENTURY AND A HALF AGO, it was generally accepted, even by professional naturalists, that nature represented a single scale, culminating in man. There existed, they supposed, a ladder of life, each rung of which was represented by a different type of animal, with humanity as the highest of all. And from this point of view, each kind of living creature represented merely a step on the way to man, its nature an incomplete realization of human nature.

But with further study, especially after it was illuminated by the theory of evolution, a wholly different and more interesting picture emerged. The various types of animals — insects, fish, crustaceans, birds and the rest — could not be thought of as the rungs of one ladder, the steps of a single staircase; they now appeared as the branches of a tree, the ever-growing tree of evolving life. And with this, they took on a new interest. It might still be that man was at the summit of the whole; but he was at the top of the tree only by being at the top of one particular branch. There existed many other branches, quite different in their nature, in which life was working out its ends in a different way from that she had adopted in the human branch. By looking at these branches we are able to see not merely our own natures in an incomplete state, but quite other expressions of life, quite other kinds of nature from our own. Life appears not as a single finished article, but as a whole series of diverse and fascinating experiments to deal with the problems of the world. We happen to be the most successful experiment, but we are not therefore the most beautiful or the most ingenious.

Of these various experiments, the two which are the most interesting are on the one hand the insects, with their bodies confined within the armor of their skeletons, their minds cramped within the strange rigidity of instinct, and on the other hand the birds.

It is with these latter that I am concerned here; and I shall try to picture some of the differences between their minds and our own. But first we need a little evolutionary background so as to grasp some of the main characters of this particular branch of life. Birds, then, branched off from reptiles somewhere about a hundred million years ago, a good long time after our own mammalian ancestry had

From *Man Stands Alone* by Julian Huxley, copyright 1926, 1954 by Julian S. Huxley. By permission of Harper and Brothers, publishers.

taken its origin from another branch of the great reptilian stock. The birds' whole nature was of course remodeled in connection with flight, so that their fore-limb was irrevocably converted into a wing, and no chance was left of remolding it into a hand. They clung obstinately to one important character of their reptilian ancestry — the shelled egg, whereas their mammalian rivals came to specialize in the internal nourishment of the young inside the mother's body; and by this the birds debarred themselves from ever being born into the world at such an advanced state of development as is possible to man and other higher mammals. But in one thing at least they went further than any mammal; they not only developed a constant temperature, but kept it constant at a greater height. Birds and mammals are unique among living things in having evolved the self-regulating central heating system that we call "warm blood," a system which is of the utmost importance, since it enables their activities of body and mind to continue on a more or less constant level instead of being slowed down by cold, speeded up by heat, as is the case with all other kinds of animals, and makes it possible for them to laugh at extremes of temperature which send insects or reptiles into the sleep of hibernation or aestivation. But birds have pushed the invention to its limits: they live at temperatures which would be the extremes of fever for us.

It is this extremely high temperature, 105 degrees or over, combined with the agility that comes of flight, which gives birds their fascinating quality of seeming always so intensely alive. But being intensely alive does not necessarily, as we know from human examples, mean being intensely intelligent. And in fact, in respect to their minds just as much as their bodies, birds have developed along other lines than mammals. Mammals have gradually perfected intelligence and the capacity for learning by experience, until this line has culminated in that conscious reason and in that deliberate reliance upon the accumulated experience of previous generations, which are unique properties of the human species. And with the gradual rise of intelligence, the power and fixity of the instincts has diminished. Birds, on the other hand, have kept instinct as the mainstay of their behavior; they possess, like all other backboned animals, some intelligence and some power of profiting by experience, but these are subordinate, used merely to polish up the outfit of instincts which is provided by heredity without having to be paid for in terms of experience. Indeed, the anatomist could tell you as much by looking at the brains of bird and mammal, even if he had never studied the way the creatures behave. For whereas in mammals we can trace a steady increase in the size and elaboration of the cerebral hemispheres, the front part of the brain which we know to be the seat of intelligence and learning, this region is never highly developed in any bird, but remains relatively small, without convolutions on its surface; while other parts which are known to be the regulating machinery for complicated but more automatic and more emotional actions, are in birds relatively larger than in four-footed creatures.

But enough of this generalizing. What I wanted to show at the outset was the fact that in the lives of birds we are not merely studying the actions of creatures which, though small and feathered, had minds of the same type as ourselves, albeit on a lower level, but of a branch of the tree of life which, in mind as in body, has specialized along a line of its own, showing us mind of a different quality from ours. They have raised emotion to the highest pitch found in animals; the line of mammals has done the same thing for intelligence.

Perhaps the most obvious way in which birds differ from men in their behavior is that they can do all that they have to do, including some quite complicated things, without ever being taught. Flying, to start with, is an activity which, for all its astonishing complexity of balance and aeronautical adjustment, comes untaught to birds. Young birds very frequently make their first flight when their parents are out of sight. Practice of course makes perfect and puts a polish on the somewhat awkward first performance; but there is no elaborate learning needed as with our learning of golf or tennis or figure-skating. Furthermore, the stories of old birds "teaching" their young to fly seem all to be erroneous. Some kinds of birds, once their young are full-fledged, do try to lure them away from the nest. But this merely encourages them to take the plunge; there is no instruction by the old bird in the movements of flight, no conscious imitation by the young.

But flight, after all, is something very organic. What is much more extraordinary than that a bird should be able to fly untaught (though this demands a formidable complexity of self-regulating machinery provided ready-made by Nature in the form of muscles and skeleton, nerves and nerve centers, eyes and balance organs) is that it should be able to build its nest untaught. And of this there can be no manner of doubt. Young birds, mating for the first time, can make perfectly good nests, and nests of the usual type found among their particular species. Some people have suggested that this may be due to their having absorbed the necessary knowledge from contemplating the structure of the nest in which they were brought up. But even if we were to admit that this was possible — which is very unlikely, considering that the young of small birds are very stupid, only live a few days in the nest after their eyes are open, and are never given any lessons in nest-building by their parents — it is negatived by the facts. For instance, the celebrated mound-builders or brush-turkeys of the Australian region build large mounds of rubbish and decaying leaves and deposit their eggs at the end of tunnels in the mounds, leaving them to be hatched out by the heat of the fermenting vegetation. The young brush-turkey on hatching scrambles out of the tunnel; it can get no instruction from its parents, since they have long since gone about their own business; and not only does it not stay around the mound long enough to observe how it is constructed, but does not bestow on it so much as a look. Nonetheless, when the time comes for it to mate, it will build a mound just as its ancestors have done.

Secondly, even young birds which have been brought up by hand in artificial nests — boxes lined by cotton wool or what not — will build the proper kind of nest for their species when the time comes for mating, and will not attempt to reproduce their own early homes. We are reminded of Dr. Johnson's comment on the suggestion that the attraction which woman's bosom has for the male sex is due to its pleasurable association with foods during infancy. He did not notice, he said, that those who had been hand-fed when babies evinced any passionate fondness for bottles. In fact, the impulse of sex attraction in the one case, the impulse to construct a nest of a certain type in the other, cannot be explained by any rationalistic arguments of this sort; the one and the other are based not upon reason, not upon association, but upon instinct. The finch, for instance, has the impulse, when its mating urge is upon it, to weave coarse material into a rough cup, and then to line this with some finer material; the tailor-bird has the impulse to take leaves and sew them together; the house-martin to collect mud or clay and construct a cup against the side of a cliff or a house.

In a not dissimilar way, the bird which is in the physiological state of broodiness will have the violent urge to sit on eggs, or, if no eggs are available, it will often take something else. Crows have been known to brood golf-balls, gulls to sit on tobacco-tins substituted for their eggs; and the majestic emperor penguin, if it loses its egg or chick, will even brood lumps of ice in its inhospitable Antarctic home.

This fobbing off of a natural urge with an unnatural substitute is doubtless unintelligent; but we may ask whether it is more unintelligent than the behavior of elderly maiden ladies who spend their maternal impulses upon lapdogs or canaries, or that of disappointed old bachelors who turn their energies into a useless hobby.

In all probability, however, the birds' behavior *is* more unintelligent; for undoubtedly it does not even rationalize as we do, or seek

to find reasons for its behavior. How unhumanly a bird regards the
central facts of its life is seen in many of its relations to its offspring.
Birds undoubtedly have a strong emotional concern over their eggs
and young, but it is an instinctive, irrational concern, not an instinct
entwined, as is the human parents' concern, with reason, memory,
personal affection, and foresight. A pair of birds is robbed of their
whole brood; the parental instinct finds itself frustrated, and they
will show great agitation. But if one or more of the nestlings die before they are fledged — a frequent and in some species a normal
occurrence — the old birds show no signs of sorrow or even agitation,
but merely throw the corpse out of the nest as if it were a stick or a
piece of dirt. And while a chick is, to our eyes, obviously failing, the
old birds, far from making special efforts to restore it, as would human parents, definitely neglect it. The fact seems to be that the
bird parent feels parental only when stimulated by some activity on
the part of its children. When they gape and squawk, this is a stimulus to the parent to feed and tend them assiduously; when the
stimulus fails, the parental feeling is no longer aroused, the bird is
no longer impelled to parental actions.

This same incapacity to experience things as men and women
would experience them is shown by the fact that if you remove
young birds from a nest, as Mr. Kearton did with some starlings,
and substitute some eggs, the mother, after a moment's apparent
surprise, may accept the situation with equanimity, and respond to
the new stimulus in the proper way, by sitting on the eggs. There
was no trace of the distraction and grief which a human mother
would have felt.

But perhaps the familiar cuckoo provides us with the completest
proof, over the widest field, of the dissimilarity of birds' minds with
our own. The young cuckoo, having been deposited as an egg in the
nest of some quite other species of bird — a meadow-pipit, say, or a
hedge-sparrow; and having hatched out in double-quick time, the
rate of its embryonic development being adjusted to its parasitic
habits, so that it shall not lag behind its foster-brothers, next proceeds to evict all the rest of the contents of the nest, be these eggs
or young birds. It is provided with a flat and indeed slightly hollow
back; and, hoisting its victim onto this, it crawls backward up the
side of the nest, to pitch the object outside. This it continues to do
until the nest is empty.

What cruelty, you will say, and what unpleasant ingenuity! But
you will be wrong. The nestling cuckoo is not cruel, nor does he
know why he is murdering his fellow nest-mates. He acts blindly,
because he is a machine constructed to act thus and not otherwise.
Not only is his back slightly concave, but this concavity is highly

irritable and oversensitive; the touch of any object there drives him frantic, and if it is continued, it releases the impulse to walk upward and backward until he has reached the edge of whatever he is walking on, and then to tilt the object overboard. He will behave in just the same way to marbles or hazelnuts or any other small object. Indeed, if you think of it, he *cannot* know what he is doing. For he will act thus immediately he is hatched, before his eyes are open; even if he could be taught, his parents have never been near him, and his foster-parents are hardly likely to instruct him in this particular! No, the whole train of actions is the outcome of a marvelous piece of machinery with which he is endowed by heredity, just as he is endowed with the equally marvelous adaptive mechanism of his feathers. The machinery consists in the shape of the back, its hyper-sensitiveness, and the intricate pattern of nervous connections in the brain and spinal cord which set the particular muscles into action. The act in fact is purely instinctive, just as instinctive and automatic as sneezing or coughing in ourselves. And, like coughing, it has been brought into being by the long unconscious process of natural selection, not by any foresight or conscious will.

Once the foster-brothers are outside, we shall get another surprising peep into bird mind. When the foster-mother comes home, she does not seem in the least distressed by the absence of all but one of her brood, but at once sets about feeding the changeling. What is more, she pays no attention to her own offspring, even should some of these be dangling just outside the nest. As long as there is something in the nest which appeals to her parental instincts, it seems that young birds outside the nest, even if they be her own, are treated as so many foreign objects.

Then the young cuckoo begins to grow. It grows into a creature entirely different from its foster-parents, and eventually becomes several times bulkier than they, so that they have to perch on its head to drop food into its mouth! But they are not in the least disconcerted, as would human parents if their children began growing into giants, and giants of quite a different appearance from themselves. They are built to respond to the stimulus of appeals for food from any nestling that starts life in their nest, and they continue their response, whether the nestling is their own or a cuckoo.

At last the young cuckoo is ready to fly, leaves his foster-parents, and very soon must leave the country on migration. So far as we know, all the old cuckoos have before this time left the country for the south, so that it is again without any teaching or any knowledge that the young ones must obey the migration urge.

Some very interesting experiments by Professor Rowan of Alberta have thrown a good deal of light on this mysterious question of the impulse to migrate. In autumn, he caught a number of birds which usually leave the regions of an Alberta winter for the south (crows and the little finches called juncos were the kind he used), and kept them in unheated aviaries. So long as they were supplied with plenty of food, they remained perfectly healthy and happy, even with the temperature many degrees below zero. One lot were simply kept thus as "controls" for the experiment: but another lot, in place of being exposed to the natural shortening of the days in early winter, had their days artificially lengthened by electric light, a little more every evening. In midwinter, Rowan liberated a number of birds. The controls made no attempt to migrate southward, but just hung about the place. The birds whose day had been lengthened, however, for the most part did move away — but apparently most of them moved north and not south!

Other birds were killed and examined: all the controls, as was expected, had their reproductive organs shrunken to the tiny size characteristic of birds in winter; but the long-day birds showed reproductive organs which were enlarging like those of ordinary wild birds in early spring about the time of northward migration.

The view held by Rowan — and though it cannot yet be regarded as completely proved, it certainly seems probable — is as follows. The extra length of day caused the birds to spend more of their time in activity, less in sleep; this, by some mechanism we do not yet understand, caused the reproductive organs to begin to grow instead of shrinking; and the secretions of the reproductive organs control the migratory urge. When they are shrinking in early autumn, the changed secretion in the blood impels the birds to move south. When they are tiny and inactive, as normally in the dead of winter, there is no impulse to migrate at all; and when they are growing again, the secretion impels to northward movement, even if the bird be already in the most wintry and inhospitable conditions.

Whatever the precise interpretation, it is at least clear that the impulse to migrate is a strange blind urge, controlled and set in motion by the chemical agency of the reproductive secretions, and wholly unrelated to reason, or to any consciously envisaged destination.

Then again there is the well-known "broken-wing trick" practiced by so many birds when their young are threatened. Most writers of natural history books set this down as a remarkable example of intelligence: — the bird, seeing its offspring in danger, deliberately invents a ruse, and acts its part with consummate skill to draw the intruder away. All the evidence, however, points to this too being merely instinctive, a trick not invented by the individual bird, but patented by the species. If it were the fruit of intelligent reflection, we should expect to find some individuals of a species practicing it, others not, and great variations in the efficacy of the performance; but in species like the purple sandpiper or the arctic skua, every individual seems to be a good performer, and this without any previous training. The trick, in fact, is on a par with the purely automatic "shamming dead" which many insects practice: it is the inevitable outcome of the animal's nervous machinery when this machinery is stimulated in a particular way.

Besides instinctive actions, we could multiply instances of un-intelligent behavior among birds. If a strange egg is put among a bird's own eggs, the mother may accept it through uncritical instinct, or may intelligently turn it out of the nest and continue to sit. But a quite common reaction is for it to turn the strange egg out, and *then* to desert its nest — a most decidedly illogical procedure! Again, Mr. St. Quentin had two hens and one cock of a kind of sand-grouse in his aviary. This is a bird in which the hens normally sit by day, the cock by night. One year, both the hens laid at the same time. The cock tried his best, sitting part of the night on one clutch, part on another, but of course the eggs came to nothing. If the birds had had any intelligence, they would have divided up the twenty-four hours so that the eggs were always brooded; but the day-brooding of the hens and the night-brooding of the cock are mechanical instinct, and intelligence neither enters into them in normal, nor modifies them in abnormal circumstances.

But because birds are mainly instinctive and not intelligent in their actions, it does not follow that their minds are lacking in intensity or variety: so far as we can judge, they must be experiencing a wide range of powerful emotions.

A bird clearly finds an intense satisfaction in fulfilling its brooding impulse or the impulse to feed its young, even though the impulse may be, for want of intelligence, what we should call a strangely blind one: and when the young birds are threatened with danger, the parents clearly are suffering very real distress, just as birds suffer very real fear when cornered by an enemy. In song, too, the bird, besides expressing a certain general well-being, is giving vent to a deep current of feeling, even if it does not understand the feeling or reflect upon it, as would a human poet or musician. For the moment, they *are* that feeling. Some birds are so obsessed by their emotions during their courtship display that they become oblivious of danger. The males of that huge bird of the grouse tribe, the capercaillie, have an extraordinary courtship ceremony which they carry out at daybreak in the branches of a favorite tree. While they are in the ecstasy of this passionate performance a man can easily creep up within range; and it is by this method that in certain countries many are shot.

Again, birds seem as subject as men to the emotion of jealousy. Rival cocks may fight to the death. One remarkable case with captive parakeets is quite human in its incidents. Two cocks and a hen were in one cage. After much squabbling, one night one of the cocks killed the other: upon which the hen, who had hitherto rather favored this bird, turned upon him and might have killed him too if they had not been separated.

The bird-mind has sufficient subtlety to indulge in play. Dr. Gill of Capetown records seeing a hooded crow fly up into the air, drop a small object it was carrying, swoop after it, croaking loudly, catch it in mid air, and repeat the performance over and over again with the greatest evidence of enjoyment. And tame ravens often display what seems a real sense of humor, though it must be admitted humor of rather a low order. A pair of them will combine to tease a cat or dog, one occupying its attention from the front, while the other steals round behind to tweak its tail and hop off with loud and delighted squawkings. They will play tricks on each other; in an aviary, one raven of a pair has been seen to slink up from behind when its mate was sitting on a low perch, and then reach up to knock the perching bird's foot from under it, with evident malicious enjoyment.

But in all these varied manifestations of emotions, birds still differ in a fundamental way from ourselves. Being without the power of conceptual thought, their emotion, while occupying their life with a completeness which is perhaps rarer with us, is not linked up with the future or the past as in a human mind. Their fear is just fear: it is not the fear of death, nor can it anticipate pain, nor become an ingredient of a lasting "complex." They cannot worry or torment themselves. When the fear-situation is past, the fear just disappears. So, as we have seen, with their maternal instincts. The bird mother is not concerned with the fate of an individual offspring, as a human mother would be concerned about Johnny's career or Tommy's poor health. She is concerned just to give vent to her instincts impersonally, as it were; and when the young grow up and her inner physiology changes, there is no intellectual framework making a continuing personal or individual interest possible.

That indeed is the greatest difference between the bird and ourselves. We, whether we want to or not, cannot help living within the framework of a continuing life. Our powers of thought and imagination bind up the present with the future and the past: the bird's life is almost wholly a patchwork, a series of self-sufficing moments.

A Storm Is Born

GEORGE R. STEWART

FIRST DAY

ENVELOPED in the gaseous film of the atmosphere, half covered by a skim of water forming the oceans — the great sphere of the earth spun upon its axis and moved inflexibly in its course around the sun. Continuously, in the succession of day and night, season and season, year and year, the earth had received heat from the sun, and again lost into space that same amount of heat. But this balance of the entire sphere did not hold for its individual parts. The equatorial belt received yearly much more heat than it radiated off, and the polar regions lost much more heat than they received. Nevertheless the one was not growing hotter while the others sank toward absolute zero. Instead, at once tempering cosmic extremes and maintaining equilibrium with the sun, by a gigantic and complex circulation, the poles constantly cooled the tropics and the tropics reciprocally warmed the poles.

In this process, cold currents bore icebergs toward the equator, and warm currents moved poleward. But even these vast rivers of the oceans achieved only a small part of the necessary whole.

In the stupendous work of transport the paramount agent was the atmosphere, thin and insignificant though it was in comparison with the monstrous earth itself. Within the atmosphere the chief equalizers of heat were the great winds — the trades and anti-trades, the monsoons, the tropical hurricanes, the polar easterlies, and (most notable of all) the gigantic whirling storms of the temperate zones, which in the stateliest of earthly processions moved ever along their sinuous paths, across ocean and continent, from the setting toward the rising sun.

2

Early in November, had come "Election Day rains." Chilling after the warmth of October, low-lying clouds blew in from the southwest, thick with moisture from the Pacific. The golden-brown hills of the Coast Ranges grew darker beneath the downpour. In the Great Valley summer-dry creeks again ran water. Upon the Sierra the snow fell steadily. The six-month dry season was over.

Between drenching showers the sun shone brightly, warming the earth. Thousands of hillsides were suddenly green with the sprouted grass. In the valleys, overnight, the square miles of summer fallow became fields of new wheat and barley. Stockmen talked jovially to one another — a good year! Farmers in irrigated districts thought comfortably of rising water tables and filling reservoirs. In the towns the merchants gave larger orders to wholesale houses.

November ended with two weeks of good growing weather. The grass and the grain sucked moisture from the soil, and spread lush blades in the sunshine.

December came in — days still warm and sunny, nights clear, with a touch of frost in the valleys and on the higher hills. Farmers began to look more often to the south — but there were no clouds. Stockmen no longer went about slapping one another on the back; instead, they went secretly and inquired the price of cottonseed meal at the Fresno mills. As the weeks passed, storekeepers grew chary about granting credit.

By Christmas, the green of the pasture lands and the wide grain fields showed a faint cast of yellow. In favored spots the grass was six inches tall; but the blades were curled a little, and at the edges were brownish red. Where cattle had grazed, the ragged ends still showed.

The city folk went about congratulating themselves on the fine weather. The tourist trade was flourishing. On New Year's Day the sports experts broadcasting the football games talked almost as much about the fine weather as about the passes.

But just after the first of the year pessimistic crop reports from California helped send the price of barley up a half cent on the Chicago exchange. That same day, six great trucks with trailers, heavy-laden with cottonseed meal, plugged up the highway from Fresno; the richer stockmen had started to buy feed.

So, in the first weeks of the new year a winter drought lay tense upon the land.

3

From Siberia the wide torrent of air was sweeping southward — from death-cold Verkhoyansk, from the frigid basin of the Lena, from thick-frozen Lake Baikal. The great wind poured over the Desert of Gobi. Even the hardy nomads winced; the long-haired northern camels stirred uneasily; the rough-coated ponies shivered; all sound of running water was hushed. High in the air swirled the dust blown up from the desert. Over the mountain-jagged rim of the tableland the wind poured forth; through all the gaps and passes of the Khingan Mountains, down the gorge of the Hwang-ho. As in centuries past, it stormed across the Great Wall, asking no emperor's leave. Swifter than Tartar, more terrible than Mongol, more pitiless than Manchu, it swept down upon the plains of China.

Descending from the plateau and entering a warmer region, the air lost some of its arctic coldness; nonetheless, in the ancient northern capital the chill struck into men's blood. By day, a sun like tarnished brass shone without warmth through clouds of yellow dust. By night, the eyes saw nothing, but the dryness and smell of dust pinched the nostrils. The fur-coated foreigners (as was their birthright) blasphemed at the weather; the thin-clad, shivering coolies moved stoically about their business. Nightly in hovel and doorway, huddling in corners, some scores of the poor froze slowly to death.

Southward along the coast of China ran that river of air. Among the hills of Shantung it was still an iron-cold blast, but on the plain of the Yangtze its power was less. In Nanking and Shanghai the ice formed only in quieter, shallower pools.

The air at last swung away from the coast, and moved out over the sea; with every mile of passage across the water it grew more moist and temperate. Through a thinning yellow haze the sun pierced more warmly. Now the wind was no longer a gale, scarcely even a strong breeze. The polar fury was spent. But still, east by south, the river of air flowed on across the China Sea toward the far reaches of the Pacific.

4

In mid-afternoon the front of the Siberian air mass was pushing slowly across the island-studded ocean which lies east of China and south of Japan. Its cold heavy air clung close to the surface of the water. Advancing thus as a northeasterly breeze, it forced backward the warmer, lighter air ahead of it, and occasionally pushed beneath this air vigorously enough to cause a shower.

This opposing and retreating air had lain, some days previous, over the tropical ocean near the Philippine Islands. A storm had taken it northeast, shedding rain, clear to the Japanese coast; it had then moved slowly back before the pressure of the cold wave. By this northern foray it had lost its extreme humidity and warmth, and become temperate rather than tropical. Nevertheless it still remained warmer and more moist than the air which had swept down from Siberia.

The advance of the northern air and corresponding retreat of the southern were related, like all movements in the atmosphere, to conditions existing concurrently over the whole earth. The conditions of this particular day were such that the advance was losing its vigor and becoming slower.

An hour before sunset, one section of the front reached a small island — a mere mountain peak above the ocean. A dead-tired man may stumble over a pebble and fall; but his weariness, rather than the pebble, is the cause. Similarly, a vigorously advancing front would simply have swept over and around the island, but now the obstruction caused an appreciable break, and a hesitant eddy, about a mile in diameter, began to form — weakened — took shape again. At one point the southern air no longer yielded passively to the northern, but actively flowed up its slope, as up a gradual hill. Rising, this air grew cooler, and from it a fine drizzle began to fall. This condensation of water in turn further warmed the air, and caused it to press up the slope more steadily with still further condensation. The process thus became self-perpetuating and self-strengthening.

The movement of this advancing warm air was now a little southwest breeze, where previously all the flow of air had been from the northeast. With this new breeze, air which was still warmer and more moist moved in from the south along the nearby section of the original front, renewing its vigor and causing a little shower. All these new and renewed activities — winds, drizzle, and shower — were now arranged in complex but orderly fashion around a single point.

As from the union of two opposite germ cells begins a life, so from the contact of northern and southern air had sprung something which before had not been. As a new life, a focus of activity, begins to develop after its kind and grow by what it feeds on, so in the air that complex of forces began to develop and grow strong. A new storm had been born.

5

The ship's course lay almost due west. Her position was about three hundred miles southeast of Yokohama, but her port was Foochow on the coast of China, still fourteen hundred miles distant.

At seven that evening when the radio operator came on deck, he found that the weather had changed. He noted breaks in the high cloud-deck beneath which the ship had been moving for several days. The air seemed both cool and dry, in comparison with the former half-tropical suavity. Automatically, he looked at the smoke wisp trailing behind; knowing the ship's course, he estimated that in the last hour the wind had veered from about two points south of west to an equal angle north of west.

Since one of his duties was to read the instruments and report to shore stations, the radio operator felt more than the usual seafaring man's interest in the weather. He stepped in to look at the barometer; it had fallen slightly, but not enough to matter. In January a typhoon was unlikely; and besides, the international reports showed no disturbance in the region which they were now traversing.

Nevertheless, about eight o'clock a light drizzle began. This increased to a steady gentle rain; but the air was warmer than before. The light wind had backed sharply, and was now from the southwest. The smoke rose almost vertically. After a few minutes the rain ceased, but the ship still moved beneath the low cloud-deck. The air was again warm and oppressive as it had been on preceding days.

A quarter of an hour later, the weather changed again. A gust of wind, not enough to be called a squall, raised a few whitecaps. Along with it but scarcely of ten seconds' duration, a sudden shower spattered the deck with large raindrops. The temperature seemed to drop immediately at least ten degrees.

"Queer weather!" remarked the radio operator to the second officer, at the same time noticing the smoke. It was trailing off to port, again indicating a northerly wind; moreover, instead of rising, the smoke lay close to the surface of the ocean.

"Something getting ready to begin," said the second officer. "Hope it's not for us."

There was, however, no further marked change. At nine o'clock — noon by Greenwich time — the radio operator began to make his observations, preparatory to reporting to the nearest shore station. He recorded the barometer at 1011, slightly higher than at the time of the shower. He noted the Fahrenheit temperature at 55, fourteen degrees cooler than on the preceding evening. The wind was a steady breeze from the northwest. The cloud-deck was breaking, and a new moon, low in the west, shone over the ocean surface.

West toward the Chinese coast the ship plowed on steadily. "Whatever we ran through back there," said the radio operator, "we're done with it." Then he sniffed curiously. "Funny thing — hundreds of miles at sea, and I'd swear I smell dust!"

6

The new Junior Meteorologist ($2,000 a year) was working at his table. The telephone rang and he answered it mechanically. "Weather Bureau. . . . Fair tonight and Wednesday; no change in temperature; moderate northwest winds. . . . You're welcome." He clicked down the receiver with unnecessary vigor, showing his irritation. In the five weeks since he had come to work in the Bureau, the weather had been inane. Sometimes he wanted to take up the telephone and shout into it: "Blizzards, lightning, and hurricanes!" But as he bent over his table again, irritation oozed away. Instead, there swelled up within him the joy of the workman, of the scientist, even of the artist. For, as he often told himself, his present task was the only one of his daily assignments over which he could work with some degree of calm and detachment. It was not like the hurried preparation of the early morning map upon which the forecasts were based. His present work had its uses, but they were a little removed from the immediate present.

On the table lay a large map which he had almost finished preparing. It was large not only by its own dimensions but also by its coverage of about one half the northern hemisphere. At its top were the Arctic regions; from these the two continents slanted down — to the right, North America, to the left, the eastern portion of Asia. In the center of the map stretched the great spaces of the North Pacific Ocean. The outline of land and sea, the parallels and meridians, the names and numbers of weather stations formed the printed background. Upon this the Junior Meteorologist had entered the current weather data as they had been reported by radio and telegraph, internationally, some hours earlier.

Visitors to the Weather Bureau found such a map confused and unintelligible. But to its maker it was simple, beautiful, and inspiring. Now he was giving it the final revision; with the care of a poet polishing a quatrain, he erased an inch of one line and redrew it with slightly altered curve.

He laid aside his eraser and colored pencils, and sat back to look at the work. Involuntarily, he breathed a little more deeply. To him, as to some archangel hovering in the ninth heaven, the weather lay revealed. Suppose that the telephone should ring and some voice inquire the weather in Kamchatka, upon Laysan Island, or at Akla-vik in the frozen delta of the Mackenzie. He could reply not only as to what the weather actually was but also with fair assurance as to what it would most likely be in the near future.

The first sweeping glance assured him that nothing exceptional or unforeseen had happened in the twenty-four hours since he had prepared the last similar map. Antonia had moved about as he had expected. Cornelia and the others were developing normally. Not at any price would the Junior Meteorologist have revealed to the Chief that he was bestowing names — and girls' names — upon those great moving low-pressure areas. But he justified the senti-mental vagary by explaining mentally that each storm was really an individual and that he could more easily say (to himself, of course) "Antonia" than "the low-pressure center which was yesterday in lati-tude one-seventy-five East, longitude forty-two North."

The game, nevertheless, was beginning to play out. At first he had christened each newborn storm after some girl he had known — Ruth, Lucy, Katherine. Then he had watched eagerly, hoping in turn that each of these little storms might develop in proper fashion to bring the rain. But one after another they had failed him. Of late the supply of names had run short, and he had been relying chiefly upon long ones ending in *-ia* which suggested actresses or heroines of books rather than girls he had ever known.

Upon the present map four such storms stood out boldly — con-centricities of black-pencil curves about centers marked LOW, the curves sharpening to angles as they crossed certain red, blue, or purple lines. Sylvia was a vigorous storm now centering over Bos-ton; it — or she — had just brought heavy snowfall to the north-eastern states and was now moving out to sea, leaving a cold snap behind. Felicia was a weak disturbance over Manitoba; she had little past and probably not much future. Cornelia was a large ma-ture storm centering four hundred miles at sea southeast of Dutch Harbor. Antonia, young and still growing, was moving out into mid-ocean some two thousand miles behind Cornelia. In spite of their distances apart, the storms overlapped, and a curved belt of dis-turbed weather thus extended from Nova Scotia clear across to Japan.

In the western United States, however, and over the adjacent part of the Pacific Ocean the black curves nowhere crossed colored lines or sharpened to angles; they lay far apart and were drawn about points marked HIGH. To the Junior Meteorologist these were all obvious signs of clear calm weather. In the jargon of his trade, this region was covered by "the semi-permanent Pacific High." He looked at it malignantly. Then he smiled, for he noticed that the

High had today accidentally assumed the shape of a gigantic dog's head. Rising from the Pacific waters it looked out stupidly across the continent. The blunt nose just touched Denver; the top of the head was in British Columbia. A small circle over southern Idaho supplied an eye; three concentric ovals pointing southwest from the California coast furnished a passable ear.

Dog's head or not — the Pacific High was no laughing matter for California. While it remained, every storm advancing in boldly from the Pacific would sheer off northeastward. A drenching rain would pour down upon the south Alaskan coast and Vancouver Island; a steady drizzle in Seattle and Portland. But San Francisco and the Great Valley would have only cloud, while still farther south Los Angeles would continue to bake in the sunshine. In its actuality, invisible to man's eye, the Pacific High lay upon the map as clearly as a mountain range — and not less important than the Sierra Nevada itself in its effects upon the people of California.

For away from the American coast, in the upper left-hand corner of the map, long lines which were close together and almost parallel ran from the interior of Asia southward to China and then curved eastward into the Pacific. To the Junior Meteorologist this too was a commonplace — the visible sign of that great river of wind, the winter monsoon, at work pouring out the cold air from Siberia. He noted in passing that the temperature at Peiping was eight below zero Fahrenheit. With more professional interest he let his eyes follow along those curving lines which ran into the Pacific.

Here and there in this region as elsewhere in the ocean he saw a little cluster of notations representing the weather reports furnished by radio from some vessel. Over one of these he paused. The ship, three hundred miles southeast of Yokohama, had reported a barometric pressure of 1011, but by its position on the map it should have reported about 1012. A difference of one millibar, he realized, was inconsiderable and might easily result from an inaccurate barometer or from a careless reading of the instrument. For these reasons he had at first permitted himself to neglect this particular report. But now he reconsidered.

The ship's position was about halfway between the island weather stations of Hatidyosima to the north and Titijima to the south, about two hundred miles distant from each. But the temperature of the air at the ship was only two degrees warmer than at Hatidyosima, whereas it was twelve degrees colder than at Titijima. This was clear indication that the ship had already been engulfed in the cooler air which was sweeping out with the monsoon, and that somewhere between the ship and the southern island the cooler air which had come from the north would be pushing

against the warmer southern air. He himself had already recognized
this fact by drawing a blue line, indicative of a "cold front," from the
center of Antonia westward and southward clear to the Chinese
coast. Along such a boundary between cool and warm air a new
storm was almost certain to form somewhere.

No other ships reported from that vicinity. Glancing at the wind
arrows of the two island stations, he saw that they tended to contra-
dict rather than confirm the reading of the ship's barometer. Hatidyosima had a northeast wind instead of northwest; Titijima a west
wind instead of south or southwest. Practically, he realized, the
whole matter was of no importance, but he felt the twinge of scientific curiosity and the challenge of a difficult problem.

Methodically, he checked back over the maps of the last ten
days, and determined that there had never before been an occasion
to doubt the accuracy of the reports from this particular ship. He
paused a moment with eraser held above the blue line. The ship's
barometer reading, he considered, along with the general probability of the whole situation indicated an incipient storm. The failure
of the island reports to confirm would mean only that the disturbance was as yet too small to have affected them. This in itself lent a
piquancy, for seldom was it possible to spot a storm so close to its
beginning.

He erased a little section of the blue line, and drew in a red line
at such an angle as to indicate a shallow wave. Then around the
crest of the wave as center he drew a black line in the shape of a
tiny football; this he labeled 1011, and inside it he printed, in minute letters, LOW. So much accomplished, he again surveyed his
work, and smiled.

As a baby possesses the parts of the adult, so the baby storm
displayed as in caricature the features of a mature storm. The red
line symbolized the "warm front" along which the southern air was
advancing and sliding over the northern; the blue line symbolized
the "cold front" where the northern air was advancing and pushing
beneath the southern. The black line shaped like a football was
an isobar, indicating a barometric pressure of 1011 around the center of low pressure, symbolizing also the complete circuit of winds
around that point. As a baby is without teeth, so also the storm was
lacking in some attributes of maturity. But just as surely as a baby is
a human being, so also was his new discovery a storm in charming
miniature — provided always that he had rightly analyzed the situation.

For a moment he looked contentedly at his creation, and then
glanced over the Pacific, considering the future. The general setup
seemed to indicate that in the next twenty-four hours the new storm

would move rapidly eastward. As it moved, it could grow both in area and in intensity; its winds becoming stronger, its rains heavier.

Suddenly his fingers itched for a slide-rule. He remembered his training under professors who considered weather a branch of physics; his own thesis — almost entirely complicated equations — had won him High Honors. Such equations now flashed into his mind with photographic exactitude; they dealt with velocities and accelerations, with the Coriolis force, and frictionless horizontal rectilinear flow. They contained such delightful terms as $\frac{1}{2}A_i t^2$, $\triangle T^{0,0}$, and $2mv_\omega \sin \phi$. To a well-trained mathematical meteorologist they were more beautiful than Grecian urns.

He shrugged his shoulders. The local Weather Bureau had to deal in immediate practicality; there was little need and no time for mathematical abstractions. And besides — he was forced to admit — with data supplied by a single ship and by weather stations two hundred miles from the center of activity, the application of highly refined methods was hardly warranted.

With resignation he again turned his attention to the map, and considered the lonely cluster of notations in the ocean. That particular ship, he presumed, had just passed through the area of disturbance. In a few hours it had probably crossed the boundary between warm and cold air more than once, and had experienced changeable but not very pronounced weather. The ship was moving west; the storm, like all such storms, was moving easterly. Ship and storm would not meet again, and yet for a moment the two lingered together in his thoughts. Doubtless the ship would be of interest to sailors, but to him it seemed wholly dull and mechanical. It might be one of twenty built to the same specifications, indistinguishable from the others unless you were close enough to read the name. But the storm! He felt the sudden rise of feeling along his spine. A storm lived and grew; no two were ever the same.

This one — this incipient little whorl, come into being southeast of Japan — would live its own life, for good or for bad, just as much as some human child born the same hour. With the luck of favorable conditions it would grow and prosper to a fine old age for a storm; just as possibly it might languish, or be suddenly annihilated.

There remained one other detail, and this called for no marks on the map. He must name the baby. He considered a moment for more names in -ia, and thought of Maria. It was more homely than Antonia or Cornelia; it did not even sound like them. But it was a name. And, as if he had been a minister who had just christened a baby, he found himself smiling and benign, inchoately wishing it joy and prosperity. Good luck, Maria!

The Plains of Patagonia

W. H. HUDSON

I SPENT the greater part of one winter at a point on the Rio Negro, seventy or eighty miles from the sea, where the valley on my side of the water was about five miles wide. The valley alone was habitable, where there was water for man and beast, and a thin soil producing grass and grain; it is perfectly level, and ends abruptly at the foot of the bank or terrace-like formation of the higher barren plateau. It was my custom to go out every morning on horseback with my gun, and, followed by one dog, to ride away from the valley; and no sooner would I climb the terrace and plunge into the gray universal thicket, than I would find myself as completely alone and cut off from all sight and sound of human occupancy as if five hundred instead of only five miles separated me from the hidden green valley and river. So wild and solitary and remote seemed that gray waste, stretching away into infinitude, a waste untrodden by man, and where the wild animals are so few that they have made no discoverable path in the wilderness of thorns. There I might have dropped down and died, and my flesh been devoured by birds and my bones bleached white in sun and wind, and no person would have found them, and it would have been forgotten that one had ridden forth in the morning and had not returned. Or if, like the few wild animals there — puma, huanaco, and hare-like *Dolichotis*, or Darwin's rhea and the crested tinamou among the birds — I had been able to exist without water, I might have made myself a hermitage of brushwood or dugout in the side of a cliff, and dwelt there until I had grown gray as the stones and trees around me, and no human foot would have stumbled on my hiding place.

Not once, nor twice, nor thrice, but day after day I returned to this solitude, going to it in the morning as if to attend a festival, and leaving it only when hunger and thirst and the westering sun compelled me. And yet I had no object in going — no motive which could be put into words; for although I carried a gun, there was nothing to shoot — the shooting was all left behind in the valley. Sometimes a *Dolichotis*, starting up at my approach, flashed for one moment on my sight, to vanish the next moment in the continuous thicket; or a covey of tinamous sprang rocketlike into the air, and

From *Idle Days in Patagonia* by W. H. Hudson. Published by E. P. Dutton & Co., Inc., and reprinted with their permission. Canadian reprint rights granted by The Royal Society for the Protection of Birds and The Society of Authors.

fled away with long wailing notes and loud whur of wings; or on some distant hillside a bright patch of yellow, of a deer that was watching me, appeared and remained motionless for two or three minutes. But the animals were few, and sometimes I would pass an entire day without seeing one mammal, and perhaps not more than a dozen birds of any size. The weather at that time was cheerless, generally with a gray film of cloud spread over the sky, and a bleak wind, often cold enough to make my bridle hand feel quite numb. Moreover, it was not possible to enjoy a canter; the bushes grew so close together that it was as much as one could do to pass through at a walk without brushing against them; and at this slow pace, which would have seemed intolerable in other circumstances, I would ride about for hours at a stretch. In the scene itself there was nothing to delight the eye. Everywhere through the light, gray mold, gray as ashes and formed by the ashes of myriads of generations of dead trees, where the wind had blown on it, or the rain had washed it away, the underlying yellow sand appeared, and the old ocean-polished pebbles, dull red, and gray, and green, and yellow. On arriving at a hill, I would slowly ride to its summit, and stand there to survey the prospect. On every side it stretched away in great undulations; but the undulations were wild and irregular; the hills were rounded and cone-shaped, they were solitary and in groups and ranges; some sloped gently, others were ridgelike and stretched away in league-long terraces, with other terraces beyond; and all alike were clothed in the gray everlasting thorny vegetation. How gray it all was! hardly less so near at hand than on the haze-wrapped horizon, where the hills were dim and the outline blurred by distance. Sometimes I would see the large eaglelike, white-breasted buzzard, *Buteo erythronotus*, perched on the summit of a bush half a mile away; and so long as it would continue stationed motionless before me, my eyes would remain involuntarily fixed on it, just as one keeps his eyes on a bright light shining in the gloom; for the whiteness of the hawk seemed to exercise a fascinating power on the vision, so surpassingly bright was it by contrast in the midst of that universal unrelieved grayness. Descending from my lookout, I would take up my aimless wanderings again, and visit other elevations to gaze on the same landscape from another point; and so on for hours, and at noon I would dismount and sit or lie on my folded poncho for an hour or longer. One day, in these rambles, I discovered a small grove composed of twenty to thirty trees, about eighteen feet high, and taller than the surrounding trees. They were growing at a convenient distance apart, and evidently had been resorted to by a herd of deer or other wild animals for a long time, for the boles were polished to a glassy smoothness with much rubbing, and the ground beneath was trodden to a floor of clean, loose yellow sand. This grove was on a hill differing in shape from other hills in its neighborhood, so that it was easy for me to find it on other occasions; and after a time I made a point of finding and using it as a resting place every day at noon. I did not ask myself why I made choice of that one spot, sometimes going miles out of my way to sit there, instead of sitting down under any one of the millions of trees and bushes covering the country, on any other hillside. I thought nothing at all about it, but acted unconsciously; only afterward, when revolving the subject, it seemed to me that after having rested there once, each time I wished to rest again the wish came associated with the image of that particular clump of trees, with polished stems and clean bed of sand beneath; and in a short time I formed the habit of returning, animal-like, to repose at that same spot.

It was perhaps a mistake to say that I would sit down and rest, since I was never tired: and yet without being tired, that noonday pause, during which I sat for an hour without moving, was strangely grateful. All day the silence seemed grateful, it was very perfect, very profound. There were no insects, and the only bird sound — a feeble chirp of alarm emitted by a small skulking wren-like species — was not heard oftener than two or three times an hour. The only sounds as I rode were the muffled hoof-strokes of my horse, scratching of twigs against my boot or saddle flap, and the low panting of the dog. And it seemed to be a relief to escape even from these sounds when I dismounted and sat down: for in a few moments the dog would stretch his head out on his paws and go to sleep, and then there would be no sound, not even the rustle of a leaf. For unless the wind blows strong there is no fluttering motion and no whisper in the small stiff undeciduous leaves; and the bushes stand unmoving as if carved out of stone. One day while *listening* to the silence, it occurred to my mind to wonder what the effect would be if I were to shout aloud. This seemed at the time a horrible suggestion of fancy, a "lawless and uncertain thought" which almost made me shudder, and I was anxious to dismiss it quickly from my mind. But during those solitary days it was a rare thing for any thought to cross my mind; animal forms did not cross my vision or bird voices assail my hearing more rarely. In that novel state of mind I was in, thought had become impossible. Elsewhere I had always been able to think most freely on horseback; and on the pampas, even in the most lonely places, my mind was always most active when I traveled at a swinging gallop. This was doubtless habit; but now, with a horse under me, I had become incapable of reflection; my mind had suddenly transformed itself from a thinking machine into a machine for some other unknown purpose. To think was like setting in motion a noisy engine in my brain; and there was something there which bade me be still, and I was forced to obey. My state was one of *suspense* and *watchfulness:* yet I had no expectation of meeting with an adventure, and felt as free from apprehension as I feel now when sitting in a room in London. The change in me was just as great and wonderful as if I had changed my identity for that of another man or animal; but at the time I was powerless to wonder at or speculate about it; the state seemed familiar rather than strange, and although accompanied by a strong feeling of elation, I did not know it — did not know that something had come between me and my intellect — until I lost it and returned to my former self — to thinking, and the old insipid existence.

Polar Night

RICHARD E. BYRD

APRIL 12

. . . IT HAS BEEN CRYSTAL CLEAR, with a temperature of about 50° below zero, and a whispering southerly wind that sets fire to the skin. Each day more light drains from the sky. The storm-blue bulge of darkness pushing out from the South Pole is now nearly overhead at noon. The sun rose this morning at about 9:30 o'clock, but never really left the horizon. Huge and red and solemn, it rolled like a wheel along the Barrier edge for about two and a half hours, when the sunrise met the sunset at noon. For another two and a half hours it rolled along the horizon, gradually sinking past it until nothing was left but a blood-red incandescence. The whole effect was something like that witnessed during an eclipse. An unearthly twilight spread over the Barrier, lit by flames thrown up as from a vast pit, and the snow flamed with liquid color.

At home I am used to seeing the sun leap straight out of the east, cross the sky overhead, and set in a line perpendicular to the west-

From *Alone* by Admiral Richard E. Byrd, copyright 1938 by Richard E. Byrd. Published by G. P. Putnam's Sons.

ern horizon. Here the sun swings to a different law. It lives by extremes. In the spring it rises for the first time at noon, and for the last time at midnight. As in the fall, it rises and sets daily for a month and a half. Then for four months and a half it never sets at all, never crosses directly overhead, but instead wheels around the horizon, nearly parallel to it and never rising higher than 33½°. In the fall it sets for the first time at midnight, and sets for good at noon. Then for four and a half months it does not rise at all, but instead sinks gradually below the horizon to a depth of 13½° before it begins to lift again. This is the period I am approaching now; a period when the day seems to be holding its breath.

Thus the coming of the polar night is not the spectacular rush that some imagine it to be. The day is not abruptly walled off; the night does not drop suddenly. Rather the effect is a gradual accumulation, like that of an infinitely prolonged tide. Each day the darkness, which is the tide, washes in a little farther and stays a little longer; each time the day, which is a beach, contracts a little more, until at last it is covered. The onlooker is not conscious of haste. On the contrary, he is sensible of something of incalculable importance being accomplished with timeless patience. The going of the day is a gradual process, modulated by the intervention of twilight. You look up, and it is gone. But not completely. Long after the horizon has interposed itself, the sun continues to cast up a pale and dwindling imitation of the day. You can trace its progress by the glow thrown up as it makes its round just below the horizon.

These are the best times, the times when neglected senses expand to an exquisite sensitivity. You stand on the Barrier, and simply look and listen and feel. The morning may be compounded of an unfathomable, tantalizing fog in which you stumble over sastrugi you can't see, and detour past obstructions that don't exist, and take your bearings from tiny bamboo markers that loom as big as telephone poles and hang suspended in space. On such a day, I could swear that the instrument shelter was as big as an ocean liner. On one such day I saw the blank northeastern sky become filled with the most magnificent Barrier coast I have ever seen, true in every line and faced with cliffs several thousand feet tall. A mirage, of course. Yet, a man who had never seen such things would have taken oath that it was real. The afternoon may be so clear that you dare not make a sound, lest it fall in pieces. And on such a day I have seen the sky shatter like a broken goblet, and dissolve into iridescent tipsy fragments — ice crystals falling across the face of the sun. And once in the golden downpour a slender column of platinum leaped up from the horizon, clean through the sun's core; a second luminous shadow formed horizontally through the sun, making a perfect cross. Presently two miniature suns, green and yellow in color, flipped simultaneously to the ends of each arm. These are parhelia, the most dramatic of all refraction phenomena; nothing is lovelier.

APRIL 14

. . . Took my daily walk at 4 P.M. today, in 89° of frost. The sun had dropped below the horizon, and a blue — of a richness I've never seen anywhere else — flooded in, extinguishing all but the dying embers of the sunset.

Due west, halfway to the zenith, Venus was an unblinking diamond; and opposite her, in the eastern sky, was a brilliant twinkling star set off exquisitely, as was Venus, in the sea of blue. In the northeast a silver-green serpentine aurora pulsed and quivered gently. In places the Barrier's whiteness had the appearance of dull platinum. It was all delicate and illusive. The colors were subdued and not numerous; the jewels few; the setting simple. But the way these things went together showed a master's touch.

I paused to listen to the silence. My breath, crystallized as it passed my cheeks, drifted on a breeze gentler than a whisper. The wind vane pointed toward the South Pole. Presently the wind cups ceased their gentle turning as the cold killed the breeze. My frozen breath hung like a cloud overhead.

The day was dying, the night being born — but with great peace. Here were the imponderable processes and forces of the cosmos, harmonious and soundless. Harmony, that was it! That was what came out of the silence — a gentle rhythm, the strain of a perfect chord, the music of the spheres, perhaps.

It was enough to catch that rhythm, momentarily to be myself a part of it. In that instant I could feel no doubt of man's oneness with the universe. The conviction came that that rhythm was too orderly, too harmonious, too perfect to be a product of blind chance — that, therefore, there must be purpose in the whole and that man was part of that whole and not an accidental offshoot. It was a feeling that transcended reason; that went to the heart of man's despair and found it groundless. The universe was a cosmos, not a chaos; man was as rightfully a part of that cosmos as were the day and night. . . .

APRIL 30

Today came in fine and clear. So bright was the moonlight at the beginning of my walk that I could read the second hand on the wrist watch. The whole sky was bathed with light, and the Barrier seemed to exhale a soft internal luminescence of its own. At first there was not a cloud anywhere, and the stars glittered with an unnatural brightness. Overhead, in the shape of a great ellipse, was a brilliant aurora. It ran across the sky from north to south. The short diameter of the ellipse ran east and west from where I stood, and the eastern segment of the curve was at my zenith. Waves of light pulsed rapidly through the structure. Beyond the south end of the ellipse, scintillating in the sky, was what appeared to be a drapery hanging over the South Pole. It hung in folds, like a gigantic curtain, and was composed of brilliant light rays.

The snow was different shades of silver gray (not white as one would suppose) with the brightest gray making a pathway to the moon. And to the eastward was another faint patch of aurora.

The wind blew gently from the pole, and the temperature was between 40° and 50° below. When Antarctica displays her beauty, she seems to give pause to the winds, which at such times are always still.

Overhead the aurora began to change its shape and became a great, lustrous serpent moving slowly across the zenith. The small patch in the eastern sky now expanded and grew brighter; and almost at the same instant the folds in the curtain over the pole began to undulate, as if stirred by a celestial presence.

Star after star disappeared as the serpentine folds covered them. It was like witnessing a tragedy on a cosmic scale; the serpent, representing the forces of evil, was annihilating beauty.

Suddenly the serpent disappeared. Where it had been only a moment before, the sky was once more clear; the stars showed as if they had never been dimmed. When I looked for the luminous patch in the eastern sky, it, too, was gone; and the curtain was lifting over the pole, as if parted by the wind which at that instant came throbbing over the Barrier. I was left with the tingling feeling that I had witnessed a scene denied to all other mortal men. . . .

Yet, this harmony was mostly of the mind: a temporary peace won by a physically occupied body. But the glory of the celestial is one, and the glory of the terrestrial is another. Even in my most exalted moods I never quite lost the feeling of being poised over an undermined footing, like a man negotiating a precipice who pauses to admire the sunset, but takes care where he places his feet. There were few days, even in April, that did not produce a reminder of the varied hazards of isolation. . . .

As I saw it, three risks stood out before all the others. One was fire. Another was getting lost on the Barrier. And the third was being incapacitated, either by injury or illness. Of the three, the last was the most difficult to anticipate and prepare for. Yet, the possibilities were authentic enough, and I had carefully taken them into account. My health was sound. A thoroughgoing medical examination, before I left New Zealand, had confirmed that fact. From disease I had little to fear. Antarctica is a paradise in that respect. It is the germless continent. Vast oceans, frozen most of the time, seal it from the germ-laden civilization to the north; and the refrigerating temperatures of an active Ice Age, which even in the summer — and then only for a few hours — rarely rise from freezing, have reduced the surviving micro-organisms to a largely encysted existence. The only germs are those you bring. In the bitter cold I've seen men shake to the periodic gusts of malarial fever contracted in the tropics; and once, in the winter night, flu laid half of Little America low — the result, according to the doctor, of opening a box of old clothing. I believe that, if any germs did survive at Advance Base, the temperature even in the hut never became warm enough for them to become active.

With the help of a doctor friend, I had equipped the Base with a medical library, containing, among other books, a medical dictionary, Gray's *Anatomy*, and Strumpell's *Practice of Medicine*. With these, if I thumbed far enough, I could recognize the symptoms of anything from AAA (a form of hookworm) to caries. A small supply of narcotics and anesthetics (such as novocaine), plus hypodermic needles, was available. These were stored on a shelf in the food tunnel, next to the surgical instruments, of which I had a fairly complete set — complete enough, in all events, for any operation up to a leg amputation. God knows, I had no desire to use these instruments, and only the vaguest idea what each one was for; but there they were, shiny and sharp.

But I did not expect anything serious to happen. A man never does. My preparations were of a piece with the methodical, impersonal preparations which I had learned in flying. For example, in taking fuel for the stove, I made a practice of drawing upon the drums at the distant end of the tunnel. Thus, in the event of my ever being crippled to such an extent that I might not be able to move very far or do much carrying, I should be able to struggle along with the nearby drums at the tunnel entrance. Fire was a serious hazard, and one very much on my mind. I had plenty of liquid fire bombs; but the cold had cracked most of them; and I was afraid that, if the hut ever caught fire, nothing could save it. Stowed at the far end of the fuel tunnel, I had in reserve a complete trail outfit, including tent, sleeping bag, cooker, and primus stove, also a flare and even a kite for signaling. If I ever lost the shack, I could gouge the tunnel a little wider, pitch the tent inside, and get by. But I was careful that this necessity should never arise. Going for a walk, I always shut down the stove before leaving the shack; and at night I put it out before getting into the sleeping bag, knowing the drowsiness that came with books and the temptation to let the fire run until morning.

This filling of cracks and chinks, this constant watchfulness, used to remind me of how my brothers Harry and Tom and I used to play war as children. Although Harry was just old enough to be somewhat contemptuous of games, Tom and I were always building forts. Not just "pretend" forts, flimsy box structures to be brushed away as soon as the game palled, but elaborate earthworks and bastions which transformed the Byrd grounds into an armed city. . . .

Except that I was now alone, Advance Base was something like this. It, too, was a fort, whose enemies were likewise invisible and often, I suppose, no less imaginary. The daily business of inspecting the defenses, and prying the ice out of the ventilators with a long stick armed with a sharp nail, and storing the scientific records in a safe place in the tunnels, sometimes seemed a ridiculous game. Yet, it was a game I played with deadly seriousness, even in the simple matter of my daily walks. North and south of the shack I marked a path about one hundred yards long, which I called the hurricane deck. Every three paces a two-foot bamboo stick was driven into the crust, and along these poles I ultimately strung a life line. By running my hand over this, blindman fashion, I could feel my way back and forth in the worst weather; and many were the times I did it when the air was so thick with drift that I could not see past the cowling on my windproof, and the line was a thin cord through chaos.

On clear days I could extend my path in any direction. Then I'd tuck a bundle of split bamboo sticks under my arms; and every thirty yards or so, as I went along, I'd prick one of these sticks into the surface. When the bundle was used up, I'd retrace my steps, picking up the sticks on the way, the last stick fetching me hard by my path. The sticks weighed very little, and I could easily carry enough to mark a path a quarter of a mile long. Although I varied the route often, the change really made no difference. No matter which quarter I faced, an identical sameness met the view. I could have walked 175 miles northeast to the Rockefeller Mountains, or 300 miles south to the Queen Mauds, or 400 miles west to the mountains of South Victoria Land, and not seen anything different.

Yet, I could, with a little imagination, make every walk *seem* different. One day I would imagine that my path was the Esplanade, on the water side of Beacon Hill in Boston, where, in my mind's eye, I often walked with my wife. I would meet people I knew along the bank, and drink in the perfection of a Boston spring. There was no need for the path's ever becoming a rut. Like a rubber band, it could be stretched to suit my mood; and I could move it forward and backward in time and space, as when, in the midst of reading Yul's *Travels of Marco Polo*, I divided the path into stages of that miraculous journey, and in six days and eighteen miles wandered from Venice to China, seeing everything that Marco Polo saw. And on occasion the path led back down the eons, while I watched the slow pulsations of the Ice Age, which today grips the once semi-tropical Antarctic Continent even as it once gripped North America.

By speeding up the centuries I could visualize a tidal wave of ice flooding down from the Arctic and crushing everything before it. I could see it surging forward until the advancing edge made a zig-zag line from what is now New York to what is now California, blotting out everything but the peaks of the mountains, and forming towering barriers on the margins of the sea. I could see bottomless chasms and enormous ridges thrown up by pressure, and blocks of ice strewn about in endless confusion. And for centuries I could see nothing but the obliterating ice, hear nothing but the wind, and feel nothing but the rigidity of death. But, finally, I could see the ice imperceptibly sinking; and the ocean rising as the ice melted; and the land resurrecting under the sun, with the mountains scoured and planed, and the rivers pushed into new courses. And along the edges of the land in Europe and Asia I could see men with primitive tools laying the foundations of history.

Thus it was in the Northern Hemisphere, and so it will some day be in the Antarctic, where the ice still holds mastery over the land. Except, I used to tell myself, that long before the ice rolls back, excursion boats will be steaming down from Sandy Hook and every moraine will have its tourist hotel.

All this was fun. But, if I wasn't careful, it could also be dangerous, as an experience which I went through just about this time will testify. Being in a particularly fine mood, I had decided to take a longer walk than usual. It was drifting a bit, and the Barrier was pretty dark, but that didn't bother me. After parading up and down for half an hour, I turned to go back. The line of bamboo sticks was nowhere in sight! In my abstraction, I had walked completely past and beyond it; and now, wondering which way to turn, I was overwhelmed by the realization that I had no idea of how far I had walked, nor the direction in which I was heading. On the chance that my footsteps would show, I scanned the Barrier with a flashlight; but my boots had left no marks on the hard sastrugi. It was scary. The first impulse was to run. I quelled that, and soberly took stock of my predicament.

Since it was the one fact that I had to work with, I again pulled the flashlight up out of my pants, where I carried it to keep it from freezing, and scratched into the snow with the butt end an arrow in the direction whence I had come. I remembered also, from having glanced at the wind vane as I started, that the wind was in the south. It was then on my left cheek and was still on the same cheek, but that meant little. For the wind might have changed, and subconsciously I might have veered with it. I was lost, and I was sick inside.

In order to keep from wandering still farther from the shack, I made a reference point. I broke off pieces of sastrugi with my heel and heaped them into a little beacon about eighteen inches high at the butt of the arrow. This took quite a little while. Straightening up and consulting the sky, I discovered two stars which were in line with the direction in which I had been walking when I stopped. This was a lucky break, as the sky had been overcast until now and had only cleared in a couple of places. In the navigator's phrase, the stars gave me a range and the beacon a departure. So, taking careful steps, and with my eyes on the stars, I started forward; after 100 paces I stopped. I swung the flashlight all around and could see nothing but blank Barrier.

Not daring to go farther for fear of losing the snow beacon, I started back, glancing over my shoulder at the two stars to hold my line. At the end of a hundred steps I failed to fetch the beacon. For an instant I was on the edge of panic. Then the flashlight beam picked it up about twenty feet or so on my left hand. That miserable pile of snow was nothing to rejoice over, but at least it kept me from feeling that I was stabbing blindfolded. On the next sortie, I swung the course 30° to the left. And as before, after a hundred steps, I saw nothing.

You're lost now, I told myself. I was appalled. I realized that I should have to lengthen my radius from the beacon; and in lengthening it I might never be able to find the way back to the one certainty. However, there was no alternative unless I preferred to freeze to death, and I could do that just as thoroughly 1,000 yards from the hut as 500. So now I decided to take 30 steps more in the same direction, after scraping a little heap of snow together to mark the 100-pace point. On the 29th step, I picked up the first of the bamboo sticks, not more than 30 feet away. No shipwrecked mariner, sighting a distant sail, could have been more overjoyed.

◇◇◇◇◇◇◇◇◇◇◇◇◇◇◇◇◇◇◇◇◇◇◇◇◇◇◇◇◇◇◇◇◇◇◇◇

A Jaunt to the Limits of the Universe

LLOYD MOTZ

THE TEMPO of scientific and technological development has been so rapid in the last two decades that we may soon greet each announcement of a new discovery with as much or as little excitement as we feel reading daily stock market quotations or the latest unemployment figures. Only occasionally are we jolted out of our sophisticated complacency by a scientific event because it brings promise of drastic changes in our way of life. The advent of man-made satellites aroused another kind of excitement as well: the kind that Columbus and all other great explorers must have experienced as they set out to discover new lands. Very few of us living today will actually travel out into space, but most of us will certainly live to see others taking such trips — and returning.

Even now, though still earth-bound, we can anticipate what the space-traveler of the future will see as he flies at very great speeds through the solar system and to the stars beyond. But before we consider what is in store for the interstellar tourist, let us consider some of the technical problems that must be solved before space travel becomes a reality. And after that, a few of the theoretical problems to which space travel will offer solutions.

We shall soon be sending unmanned rockets to the moon and back. But before any people leave on such trips, it will be necessary to construct a system of space platforms circling the earth at greater and greater distances above its surface. In fact, the initial phase of this important work has been done: since we have established the fact that a satellite can be put into an orbit, the construction of a space station becomes simply a matter of improving our satellite launching techniques.

We must now learn to project into the same orbit all the material that will be required to construct and maintain a space station. It will hardly be possible to do this in a single launching because of the enormous mass of material involved — the work must be done piecemeal. Picture, then, the space a few thousand miles above the earth's surface swarming with hundreds of containers, each filled with parts of lathes, electrical equipment, storage batteries, chemicals, food, etc. When all of these have been put into orbit, scientists,

Reprinted from the *Columbia University Forum*, Volume 2, No. 1. Copyrighted 1958 by Columbia University. By permission of the author.

engineers, technicians, and laborers will be sent aloft to construct a station and to man it.

The actual construction of the station will be relatively easy because everything associated with it will be in what physicists and engineers call "free fall." In other words, everything will be weightless; there will be no structural strains such as we have to worry about in buildings here on the earth. This means that the station can be constructed of the lightest kind of plastic pieces glued or welded together. The dome of the platform may be made of tough transparent plastic sheeting that can withstand pressures of a few atmospheres. The station can then be inflated to one atmosphere of pressure by pumping into it oxygen and nitrogen in the same proportion as that which obtains in our own atmosphere.

Since all of the people working with the space station will be orbiting right along with it, there will be no such thing as "falling off" as one might fall off the wing of an airplane. If a person were to step away from the space station in any direction, he would, because of his inertia, continue moving with constant speed in a straight line away from the platform; but he would also move in the same direction as the station moves while it circles the earth. Each member of the crew will therefore have to carry with him some kind of propulsion device, a small jet of some sort, to enable him to alter his direction of motion relative to the platform whenever he wants to.

Inside the station the absence of gravitational forces could produce complications; but such forces can be simulated if the entire of an atmosphere surrounding the station will enable men to view the sky continuously. The sky will appear pitch black, and the stars will be visible at all times, shining with a sharpness and untwinkling clarity quite unimaginable here on earth. Of course, night platform is made to rotate fast enough about an axis.

A space platform of the sort I have just described will be of tremendous importance for astronomical research, since the absence and day and our earth time-reckoning, with its twenty-four-hour period, will have no significance for the observers on a space station or for those on an interplanetary journey.

Artificial satellites and space stations will make possible experiments to verify some predictions of the theory of relativity, which, as we shall see later, will have an extraordinary effect upon tourists on interstellar trips.

One of the most profound consequences of the theory of relativity is that space and time can no longer be considered as absolute concepts in the Newtonian sense, but rather as sections of a space-time continuum which have different aspects for different observers moving in relation to one another. What this means is that our universe cannot be represented by a sequence of events having a unique separation in space and a unique order in time. Each observer in the wide universe, depending upon his state of motion, will find different distances between objects and different time intervals between events; concepts such as simultaneity and length lose their absolute meanings.

We may illustrate this by considering the results obtained by two observers moving past each other if they were to measure the distance between the same two points. Take as our two subjects a man in a moving train and another one standing on the railroad bank. Suppose that each of them measures the length of the car in which the man in the train is riding. The theory of relativity teaches us that the results of the two measurements will not be the same. The length of the car as measured by the man in the train will be greater than that obtained by the man on the railroad bank, and the difference between the two results will increase if the speed of the train increases. In other words, the observed dimension of a moving body parallel to the direction of its motion, as measured by a fixed observer, shrinks more and more as its speed increases, and approaches zero as the speed of the object approaches the speed of light.

Just as the length of a moving body changes with its speed, so too, according to relativity, does the rate of a moving clock. If the man on the side of the track were able to compare his watch quite accurately with a watch in the moving train, he would find that the moving watch was running slow compared to his watch. The faster the train moves, the slower will be the rate of the moving watch, finally approaching zero as the speed of the train approaches the speed of light.

A space platform will enable us to test this consequence of the theory of relativity: we now have clocks, such as the MASER clock (Microwave Amplification by Stimulated Emission of Radiation) developed by Professor Charles Townes of the Columbia University physics department, which are accurate to one part in a billion. If such a clock were placed in a satellite or on a space platform traveling at 18,000 miles per hour, then, according to the theory of relativity, it should, after one day, lag behind a similar clock on the earth by about one twenty-thousandth of a second.

Professor Leon Lederman of Columbia is one of several scientists who have obtained direct evidence supporting this time dilatation (as scientists call it) in studying the lifetime of mesons. These ephemeral particles, with masses a few hundred times that of an electron, are born during energetic collisions of protons and neutrons with nuclei of atoms. In general, mesons have very short lives, living for no more than a few one-hundred-millionths of a second; but Professor Lederman has observed that the lifetimes of mesons increase, in accordance with relativity theory, as the speeds which they have at birth increase. In other words, if two mesons are created during two different collisions, the one that is moving faster through space is observed to live longer as a meson than the other one.

Once we get to the moon, the MASER clock will enable us to check a prediction of the general theory of relativity concerning the effect of a gravitational field on a clock. According to the theory, a clock in a strong gravitational field should lag behind one in a weaker gravitational field. Since the surface gravity on the moon is only one-sixth of that on the earth (a person on the moon will weigh only one-sixth of what he does on the earth), a clock on the moon should run ahead of an identical clock on the surface of the earth. This prediction can be tested by placing a MASER on the moon.

Now a rocket that lands on the moon should, of course, carry enough fuel to take off again and return to the earth. Since the speed needed to escape from the moon is less than one-fourth that required to escape from the earth (because the force of gravity is less), a rocket need only carry additional fuel amounting to less than one-sixteenth the quantity necessary to escape from the earth.

Professor Jan Schilt, director of Columbia's Rutherford Observatory, has suggested that a trip may be even more readily managed to and from one of the two moons of Mars. If we landed on Deimos, which is 14,000 miles from the center of Mars, we would require very little fuel to take off again for the earth, since we would have to acquire a speed of only 4,000 miles per hour relative to Mars. Our space ship would already be moving at almost this speed, since Deimos moves at about 3,000 miles per hour relative to Mars. And the mass of Deimos is so tiny that it has practically no gravitational field of its own to be overcome.

Once interplanetary trips have become usual, the next step in space travel will be to the stars. Here problems of an entirely different order of magnitude will have to be solved, because of the vast distances to be crossed. The star nearest to us, Alpha Centauri, is so far away — about 26 trillion miles — that it takes light four and a half years to traverse the distance. This means that if interstellar navigators are to journey to the stars and back in times that are conveniently short within their own lifetimes, they must travel at speeds approaching the speed of light. If such speeds can be achieved by man, the relativistic time dilatation discussed above will have an extraordinary effect. To a crew in a space ship traveling at four-fifths the speed of light, a ten-year journey into space and back again, as measured by a clock here on the earth, will last only six years as measured by a clock on the ship; at nine-tenths the speed of light the duration of the trip will be only slightly more than four years.

It should not be supposed, by the way, that this difference in the duration of the trip as measured by an observer on the earth and by one on the space ship means that the travelers will detect any change in their metabolism or in any other biological or psychological processes. As far as our travelers are concerned, the four or six years they spend in transit will be the same as any other four or six years spent here on the earth; the aging process will go on as usual, and only on their return to earth will they be aware of the difference in times. They will return to an earth which is ten years older.

In principle, there is no reason why trips to remote galaxies may not be possible if man can achieve speeds close enough to the speed of light. But in practice it is doubtful that mankind will go very far beyond the nearest stars within the next few centuries.

Still, let us suppose for the remainder of this article that a space traveler could achieve the speed of light — an impossible speed for a body of finite mass. Let us consider what such an imaginary traveler might see as he explored all corners of the universe. The times referred to in what follows will be those measured by a clock on earth, *not* a clock moving with the traveler.

Our imaginary traveler will reach the moon in less than two *earth-time* seconds. After he sweeps past this lifeless sphere, it will take him another eight and a half minutes to reach the sun. He will have to be very careful to avoid being vaporized by the intense radiation pouring out of its 5500° C. surface, but a few more minutes of travel will take him well beyond the danger zone. Lifeless Mercury, the planet closest to the sun, with one face in perpetual light and the other in eternal darkness, will rush quickly past, to be followed immediately by the mysterious Venus, with her veil of everlasting clouds completely obscuring the planet's surface from the earth. So similar to the earth is Venus in its geometrical features that scientists feel it is the likeliest site for another advanced form of life.

Our traveler will stop only a moment at Mars to convince himself that the green coloration in its equatorial region is indeed due to a low form of vegetation. He will then rush on to the largest and most massive of all the planets, Jupiter. With its atmosphere composed of noxious gases like ammonia and methane, and with its 15,000-mile-thick surface layer of ice, this forbidding king of the planets will present all kinds of hazards to explorers from earth. Ours moves on.

Five and a half hours after leaving the earth, the space ship will have traveled about four million miles, passing the planet Pluto at the very outskirts of our solar system and heading toward Alpha Centauri, the star nearest to the earth. But so empty is space, and so vast the distances between the stars in the neighborhood of the sun, that four and a half years, as measured by a clock on the earth, will elapse before this star is reached. If the ship heads toward the very densest part of the Milky Way in the direction of the constellation Sagittarius, our traveler will find after some 15,000 years (earth-time) that the stars become much more numerous and also undergo a change in character.

By this time he will be leaving the outer spiral arm of our galaxy and entering the nucleus. He will have passed many millions of stars, most of them redder and fainter than the sun, but many others tens — and even thousands — of times more luminous than the sun. Among these will be the very hot blue-white stars to be found only in the spiral arms of the Milky Way. These stars are probably no more than a few million years old, the infants of our galaxy, born just recently of the dust and gas expelled by the dying gasps of the very oldest stars, those which were formed about seven billion years ago from the primordial hydrogen. Our tourist will meet only these very old stars during the 30,000 years it takes his ship to move through the dust-free nucleus by earth time. At the very center of the nucleus, which is 30,000 light-years away from us, he will find the stars so crowded that were he living in that neighborhood, he would receive as much light from these stars at night as we might receive here on earth from three hundred full moons.

After the ship has passed through the nucleus, it will spend another 25,000 years rushing through the dusty spiral arms on the other side of the nucleus, and it will then proceed to the galaxies (the so-called spiral nebulae) that lie beyond. Our explorer will find that these galaxies, which are spaced millions of light-years apart, look in many respects like his own Milky Way. Most of them contain many billions of stars and have the same dusty spiral arms swirling around a densely populated nucleus. Like our own galaxy, they are thousands of light-years across, with the very old stars extending out from the nuclei to form the bulk of the stellar population, and with the younger second- and third-generation stars like our sun scattered along the spiral arms. He will observe that the galaxies do not live in isolation but belong to huge clusters, some of which contain thousands of members, all moving together through space. So numerous and closely spaced are the galaxies in many of these clusters that collisions between two such galaxies are quite frequent. These titanic collisions release vast amounts of energy which come to the earth in the form of cosmic rays and radio waves.

Our traveler will discover that it is not the individual galaxy that is the fundamental cosmological unit of matter but rather the cluster of galaxies. These clusters extend uniformly out into space as far as our telescopes can see, and, by the radiation that we receive from them, we know that they are rushing away from us with speeds that increase as their distances from us increase. We must not suppose, however, that this means that our Milky Way occupies a central spot in the universe from which all things are receding; we would find the same thing to be true no matter which galaxy our solar system belonged to. For in fact all of these clusters of galaxies are receding from *one another* as if they were remnants of a huge explosion that occurred billions of years ago. It is this feature of the motion of the galaxy clusters that we refer to when we speak of the theory of the expanding universe.

According to this theory, about seven billion years ago all the matter in the universe was in a highly compressed state concentrated in a sphere not many times larger than the sun. This unstable condensed universe gave way to an explosive state in which the expanding gases (principally hydrogen and neutrons) broke up into huge turbulences which became clusters of galaxies.

This conception of the expanding universe is a direct consequence of the general theory of relativity, but it is not the only possible conception. As Fred Hoyle, the British astrophysicist, has shown, it is possible to obtain a steady-state model of the universe from the theory of relativity by postulating that matter is being continuously created. As the galaxies rush away from us, and ultimately disappear, the Hoyle theory requires that one proton be born in each gallon of space every billion years to keep constant the total amount of matter in the observable part of our universe. These protons ultimately collect into huge clouds which then become new clusters of galaxies, only to rush away from each other and disappear.

The most recent data on the recession of the galaxies, gathered with the 200-inch telescope at Mount Palomar, seem to favor the evolving universe (the model expanding from an initial condensed state) as against the steady-state model of Hoyle. In fact, it appears that our universe is in the expanding phase of a pulsating motion, so that we may expect the expansion that is now going on to be replaced by a contraction, which will then be followed by another expansion, and so on ad infinitum.

This conclusion is supported by the recent observations made at Mount Palomar that the most distant observable galaxies (almost two billion light-years away from us) are receding faster than they ought to be if the universe were simply expanding at a constant rate. In other words, the expansion of the universe two billion years ago was proceeding faster than it is now, which means that a slowing down in the expansion has taken place since then. From this it follows that in about fifteen billion years the expansion will come to a halt altogether and the universe will begin to collapse and finally reach a highly condensed state again. Then another expansion will begin, in which all the changes in the universe which are now taking place will recur in precisely the same order.

Such a pulsating universe follows from the general theory of relativity and has important consequences for our imaginary traveler, whom we left wandering among the galaxies. A pulsating universe is necessarily one in which space is curved and completely closed back upon itself — finite but boundless, so that our space tourist will ultimately find himself back again at the point from which he started if he continues traveling in what he takes to be a straight line. Since billions of years as measured on the earth will have elapsed by that time, he will certainly not find the earth as he left it. But he will have had a fairly memorable — though still, alas, impractical — trip in the interim.

"THE PROPER STUDY OF MANKIND . . ."

<<<<<<<<<<<<<<<<<<<<<<<<<<<<<<<<<<<<<<<<<<<<<<<<

The People of Tierra del Fuego

CHARLES DARWIN

HAVING NOW FINISHED with Patagonia and the Falkland Islands, we doubled Cape St. Diego, and entered the famous strait of Le Maire. We kept close to the Fuegian shore, but the outline of the rugged, inhospitable Staten-land was visible amidst the clouds. In the afternoon we anchored in the Bay of Good Success. While entering we were saluted in a manner becoming the inhabitants of this savage land. A group of Fuegians partly concealed by the entangled forest, were perched on a wild point overhanging the sea; and as we passed by, they sprang up and waving their tattered cloaks sent forth a loud and sonorous shout. The savages followed the ship, and just before dark we saw their fire, and again heard their wild cry. . . .

In the morning the Captain sent a party to communicate with the Fuegians. When we came within hail, one of the four natives who were present advanced to receive us, and began to shout most vehemently, wishing to direct us where to land. When we were on shore the party looked rather alarmed, but continued talking and making gestures with great rapidity. It was without exception the most curious and interesting spectacle I ever beheld: I could not have believed how wide was the difference between savage and civilized man: it is greater than between a wild and domesticated animal, inasmuch as in man there is a greater power of improvement. The chief spokesman was old, and appeared to be the head of the family; the three others were powerful young men, about six feet high. The women and children had been sent away. These Fuegians are a very different race from the stunted, miserable wretches farther westward; and they seem closely allied to the famous Patagonians of the Strait of Magellan. Their only garment consists of a mantle made of guanaco skin, with the wool outside; this they wear just

From *The Diary of the Voyage of H.M.S. Beagle* by Charles Darwin, edited by Nora Barlow. Reprinted by permission of Cambridge University Press.

thrown over their shoulders, leaving their persons as often exposed as covered. Their skin is of a dirty coppery red color.

The old man had a fillet of white feathers tied round his head, which partly confined his black, coarse and entangled hair. His face was crossed by two broad transverse bars; one, painted bright red, reached from ear to ear and included the upper lip; the other, white like chalk, extended above and parallel to the first, so that even his eyelids were thus colored. The other two men were ornamented by streaks of black powder, made of charcoal. The party altogether closely resembled the devils which come on the stage in plays like *Der Freischütz.*

Their very attitudes were abject, and the expression of their countenances distrustful, surprised, and startled. After we had presented them with some scarlet cloth, which they immediately tied round their necks, they became good friends. This was shown by the old man patting our breasts, and making a chuckling kind of noise, as people do when feeding chickens. I walked with the old man, and this demonstration of friendship was repeated several times; it was concluded by three hard slaps, which were given me on the breast and back at the same time. He then bared his bosom for me to return the compliment, which being done, he seemed highly pleased. The language of these people, according to our notions, scarcely deserves to be called articulate. Captain Cook has compared it to a man clearing his throat, but certainly no European ever cleared his throat with so many hoarse, guttural and clicking sounds.

They are excellent mimics; as often as we coughed or yawned, or made any odd motion, they immediately imitated us. Some of our party began to squint and look awry; but one of the young Fuegians (whose whole face was painted black, excepting a white band across his eyes), succeeded in making far more hideous grimaces. They could repeat with perfect correctness each word in any sentence we addressed them, and they remembered such words for some time. Yet we Europeans all know how difficult it is to distinguish apart the sounds in a foreign language. Which of us, for instance, could follow an American Indian through a sentence of more than three words? All savages appear to possess, to an uncommon degree, this power of mimicry. I was told, almost in the same words, of the same ludicrous habit among the Caffres: the Australians, likewise, have long been notorious for being able to imitate and describe the gait of any man, so that he may be recognized. How can this faculty be explained? Is it a consequence of the more practiced habits of perception and keener senses, or common to all men in a savage state, as compared with those long civilized?

When a song was struck up by our party, I thought the Fuegians would have fallen down with astonishment. With equal surprise they viewed our dancing; but one of the young men, when asked, had no objection to a little waltzing. Little accustomed to Europeans as they appeared to be, yet they knew and dreaded our firearms; nothing would tempt them to take a gun in their hands. They begged for knives, calling them by the Spanish word "*cuchilla*." They explained also what they wanted, by acting as if they had a piece of blubber in their mouths, and then pretending to cut instead of tear it.

I have not as yet noticed the Fuegians whom we had on board. During the former voyage of the *Adventurer* and *Beagle* in 1826 to 1830, Captain FitzRoy seized on a party of natives, as hostages for the loss of a boat, which had been stolen, to the great jeopardy of a party employed on the survey; and some of these natives, as well as a child whom he bought for a pearl button, he took with him to England, determining to educate them and instruct them in religion at his own expense. To settle these natives in their own country, was one chief inducement to Captain FitzRoy to undertake our present voyage; and before the Admiralty had resolved to send out this expedition, Captain FitzRoy had generously chartered a vessel, and would himself have taken them back. . . . Two men, one of whom died in England of the smallpox, a boy and a little girl, were originally taken; and we had now on board, York Minster, Jemmy Button (whose name expresses his purchase-money), and Fuegia Basket. York Minster was a full-grown, short, thick, powerful man: his disposition was reserved, taciturn, morose, and when excited violently passionate; his affections were very strong toward a few friends on board; his intellect good. Jemmy Button was a universal favorite, but likewise passionate; the expression of his face at once showed his nice disposition. He was merry and often laughed, and was remarkably sympathetic with anyone in pain: when the water was rough, I was often a little seasick, and he used to come to me and say in a plaintive voice, "Poor, poor fellow!" but the notion, after his aquatic life, of a man being seasick, was too ludicrous, and he was generally obliged to turn on one side to hide a smile or laugh, and then he would repeat his "Poor, poor fellow!" He was of a patriotic disposition; and he liked to praise his own tribe and country, in which he truly said there were "plenty of trees," and he abused all the other tribes: he stoutly declared that there was no Devil in his land. Jemmy was short, thick, and fat, but vain of his personal appearance; he used always to wear gloves, his hair was neatly cut, and he was distressed if his well-polished shoes were dirtied. He was fond of admiring himself in a looking-glass; and a merry-faced little Indian boy from the Rio Negro, whom we had for some months on board, soon perceived this, and used to mock him: Jemmy, who was always rather jealous of the attention paid to this little boy, did not at all like this, and used to say, with rather a contemptuous twist of his head, "Too much skylark." It seems yet wonderful to me, when I think over all his many good qualities, that he could have been of the same race, and doubtless partaken of the same character, with the miserable, degraded savages whom we first met here. Lastly, Fuegia Basket was a nice, modest, reserved young girl, with a rather pleasing but sometimes sullen expression, and very quick in learning anything, especially languages. This she showed in picking up some Portuguese and Spanish, when left on shore for only a short time at Rio de Janeiro and Montevideo, and in her knowledge of English. York Minster was very jealous of any attention paid to her; for it was clear he determined to marry her as soon as they were settled on shore.

Although all three could both speak and understand a good deal of English, it was singularly difficult to obtain much information from them, concerning the habits of their countrymen: this was partly owing to their apparent difficulty in understanding the simplest alternative. Every one accustomed to very young children, knows how seldom one can get an answer even to so simple a question as whether a thing is black *or* white; the idea of black or white seems alternately to fill their minds. So it was with these Fuegians, and hence it was generally impossible to find out, by cross-questioning, whether one had rightly understood anything which they had asserted. Their sight was remarkably acute: it is well known that sailors, from long practice, can make out a distant object much better than a landsman; but both York and Jemmy were much superior to any sailor on board: several times they have declared what some distant object has been, and though doubted by everyone, they have proved right, when it has been examined through a telescope. They were quite conscious of this power; and Jemmy, when he had any little quarrel with the officer on watch, would say, "me see ship, me no tell."

It was interesting to watch the conduct of the savages, when we landed, toward Jemmy Button: they immediately perceived the difference between him and ourselves, and held much conversation one with another on the subject. The old man addressed a long harangue to Jemmy, which it seems was to invite him to stay with them. But Jemmy understood very little of their language, and was, moreover, thoroughly ashamed of his countrymen. When York Minster afterward came on shore, they noticed him in the same way, and told him he ought to shave; yet he had not twenty dwarf hairs on his face, whilst we all wore our untrimmed beards. They examined the color of his skin, and compared it with ours. One of our arms being bared, they expressed the liveliest surprise and admiration at its whiteness, just in the same way in which I have seen the orang-outang do at the Zoological Gardens. We thought that they mistook two or three of the officers, who were rather shorter and fairer, though adorned with large beards, for the ladies of our party. The tallest amongst the Fuegians was evidently much pleased at his height being noticed. When placed back to back with the tallest of the boat's crew, he tried his best to edge on higher ground, and to stand on tiptoe. He opened his mouth to show his teeth, and turned his face for a side view; and all this was done with such alacrity, that I dare say he thought himself the handsomest man in Tierra del Fuego. After our first feeling of grave astonishment was over, nothing could be more ludicrous than the odd mixture of surprise and imitation which these savages every moment exhibited. . . .

The Fuegian wigwam resembles, in size and dimensions, a haycock. It merely consists of a few broken branches stuck in the ground, and very imperfectly thatched on one side with a few tufts of grass and rushes. The whole cannot be the work of an hour, and it is only used for a few days. At Goeree Roads I saw a place where one of these naked men had slept, which absolutely offered no more cover than the form of a hare. The man was evidently living by himself, and York Minster said he was "very bad man," and that probably he had stolen something. On the west coast, however, the wigwams are rather better, for they are covered with seal-skins. We were detained here several days by the bad weather. The climate is certainly wretched: the summer solstice was now passed, yet every day snow fell on the hills, and in the valleys there was rain, accompanied by sleet. The thermometer generally stood about 45°, but in the night fell to 38° or 40°. From the damp and boisterous state of the atmosphere, not cheered by a gleam of sunshine, one fancied the climate even worse than it really was.

While going one day on shore near Wollaston Island, we pulled alongside a canoe with six Fuegians. These were the most abject and miserable creatures I have anywhere beheld. On the east coast, the natives, as we have seen, have guanaco cloaks, and on the west, they possess seal-skins. Amongst these central tribes the men generally have an otter-skin, or some small scrap about as large as a pocket-handkerchief, which is barely sufficient to cover their backs as low down as their loins. It is laced across the breast by strings, and according as the wind blows, it is shifted from side to side. But these Fuegians in the canoe were quite naked, and even one full-grown woman was absolutely so. It was raining heavily, and the fresh water, together with the spray, trickled down her body. In another harbor not far distant, a woman, who was suckling a recently-born child, came one day alongside the vessel, and remained there out of mere curiosity, whilst the sleet fell and thawed on her naked bosom, and on the skin of her naked baby! These poor wretches were stunted in their growth, their hideous faces bedaubed with white paint, their skins filthy and greasy, their hair entangled, their voices discordant, and their gestures violent. Viewing such men, one can hardly make oneself believe that they are fellow-creatures, and inhabitants of the same world. It is a common subject of conjecture what pleasure in life some of the lower animals can enjoy: how much more reasonably the same question may be asked with respect to these barbarians! At night, five or six human beings, naked and scarcely protected from the wind and rain of this tempestuous climate, sleep on the wet ground coiled up like animals. Whenever it is low water, winter or summer, night or day, they must rise to pick shell-fish from the rocks; and the women either dive to collect sea-eggs, or sit patiently in their canoes, and with a baited hair-line without any hook, jerk out little fish. If a seal is killed, or the floating carcass of a putrid whale discovered, it is a feast; and such miserable food is assisted by a few tasteless berries and fungi.

They often suffer from famine: I heard Mr. Low, a sealing master intimately acquainted with the natives of this country, give a curious account of the state of a party of one hundred and fifty natives on the west coast, who were very thin and in great distress. A succession of gales prevented the women from getting shell-fish on the rocks, and they could not go out in their canoes to catch seal. A small party of these men one morning set out, and the other Indians explained to him, that they were going a four days' journey for food: on their return, Low went to meet them, and he found them excessively tired, each man carrying a great square piece of putrid whale-blubber with a hole in the middle, through which they put their heads, like the Gauchos do through their ponchos or cloaks. As soon as the blubber was brought into a wigwam, an old man cut off thin slices, and muttering over them, broiled them for a minute, and distributed them to the famished party, who during this time preserved a profound silence. Mr. Low believes that whenever a whale is cast on shore, the natives bury large pieces of it in the sand, as a resource in time of famine; and a native boy, whom he had on board, once found a stock thus buried. The different tribes when at war are cannibals. From the concurrent, but quite independent evidence of the boy taken by Mr. Low, and of Jemmy Button, it is certainly true, that when pressed in winter by hunger, they kill and devour their old women before they kill their dogs: the boy, being asked by Mr. Low why they did this, answered, "Doggies catch otters, old women no." This boy described the manner in which they are killed by being held over smoke and thus choked; he imitated their screams as a joke, and described the parts of their bodies which are considered best to eat. Horrid as such a death by the hands of their friends and relatives must be, the fears of the old women, when hunger begins to press, are more painful to think of; we were told that they then often run away into the mountains, but that they are pursued by the men and brought back to the slaughterhouse at their own firesides!

The different tribes have no government or chief; yet each is surrounded by other hostile tribes, speaking different dialects, and separated from each other only by a deserted border or neutral territory: the cause of their warfare appears to be the means of subsistence. Their country is a broken mass of wild rocks, lofty hills, and useless forests: and these are viewed through mists and endless storms. The habitable land is reduced to the stones on the beach; in search of food they are compelled unceasingly to wander from spot to spot, and so steep is the coast, that they can only move about in their wretched canoes. They cannot know the feeling of having a home, and still less that of domestic affection; for the husband is to the wife a brutal master to a laborious slave. Was a more horrid deed ever perpetrated than was witnessed on the west coast by Byron, who saw a wretched mother pick up her bleeding dying infant boy, whom her husband had mercilessly dashed on the stones for dropping a basket of sea-eggs! How little can the higher powers of the mind be brought into play; what is there for imagination to picture, for reason to compare, for judgment to decide upon? To knock a limpet from the rock does not require even cunning, that lowest power of the mind. Their skill in some respects may be compared to the instinct of animals; for it is not improved by experience: the canoe, their most ingenious work, poor as it is, has remained the same, as we know from Drake, for the last two hundred and fifty years.

Whilst beholding these savages, one asks, whence have they come? What could have tempted, or what change compelled a tribe of men, to leave the fine regions of the north, to travel down the Cordillera or backbone of America, to invent and build canoes, which are not used by the tribes of Chile, Peru, and Brazil, and then to enter on one of the most inhospitable countries within the limits of the globe? Although such reflections must at first seize on the mind, yet we may feel sure that they are partly erroneous. There is no reason to believe that the Fuegians decrease in number; therefore we must suppose that they enjoy a sufficient share of happiness, of whatever kind it may be, to render life worth having. Nature by making habit omnipotent, and its effects hereditary, has fitted the Fuegian to the climate and the productions of his miserable country.

◇◇

Patterns of Culture: The Dance

RUTH BENEDICT

ANTHROPOLOGY is the study of human beings as creatures of society. It fastens its attention upon those physical characteristics and industrial techniques, those conventions and values, which distinguish one community from all others that belong to a different tradition.

The distinguishing mark of anthropology among the social sciences is that it includes for serious study other societies than our own. For its purposes any social regulation of mating and reproduction is as significant as our own, though it may be that of the Sea Dyaks, and have no possible historical relation to that of our civilization. To the anthropologist, our customs and those of a New Guinea tribe are two possible social schemes for dealing with a common problem, and in so far as he remains an anthropologist he is bound to avoid any weighting of one in favor of the other. He is interested in human behavior, not as it is shaped by one tradition, our own, but as it has been shaped by any tradition whatsoever. He is interested in the great gamut of custom that is found in various cultures, and his object is to understand the way in which these cultures change and differentiate, the different forms through which they express themselves, and the manner in which the customs of any peoples function in the lives of the individuals who compose them. . . .

Anthropology was by definition impossible as long as these distinctions between ourselves and the primitive, ourselves and the barbarian, ourselves and the pagan, held sway over people's minds. It was necessary first to arrive at that degree of sophistication where we no longer set our own belief over against our neighbor's superstition. It was necessary to recognize that these institutions which are based on the same premises, let us say the supernatural, must be considered together, our own among the rest.

In the first half of the nineteenth century this elementary postulate of anthropology could not occur to the most enlightened person of Western civilization. Man, all down his history, has defended his uniqueness like a point of honor. In Copernicus' time this claim to supremacy was so inclusive that it took in even the earth on which we live, and the fourteenth century refused with passion to have this planet subordinated to a place in the solar scheme. By Darwin's time, having granted the solar system to the enemy, man fought with all the weapons at his command for the uniqueness of the soul, an unknowable attribute given by God to man in such a manner that it disproved man's ancestry in the animal kingdom. No lack of continuity in the argument, no doubts of the nature of this "soul," not even the fact that the nineteenth century did not care in the least to defend its brotherhood with any group of aliens — none of these facts counted against the first-rate excitement that raged on account of the indignity evolution proposed against the notion of man's uniqueness.

Both these battles we may fairly count as won — if not yet, then soon; but the fighting has only massed itself upon another front. We are quite willing to admit now that the revolution of the earth about the sun, or the animal ancestry of man, has next to nothing to do with the uniqueness of our human achievements. If we inhabit one chance planet out of a myriad solar systems, so much the greater glory, and if all the ill-assorted human races are linked by evolution with the animal, the provable differences between ourselves and them are the more extreme and the uniqueness of our institutions the more remarkable. But *our* achievements, *our* institutions are unique; they are of a different order from those of lesser races and must be protected at all costs. So that today, whether it is a question of imperialism, or of race prejudice, or of a comparison between Christianity and paganism, we are still preoccupied with the uniqueness, not of the human institutions of the world at large, which no one has ever cared about anyway, but of our own institutions and achievements, our own civilization.

. . . . It is one of the philosophical justifications for the study of primitive peoples that the facts of simpler cultures may make clear social facts that are otherwise baffling and not open to demonstration. This is nowhere more true than in the matter of the fundamental and distinctive cultural configurations that pattern existence and condition the thoughts and emotions of the individuals who participate in those cultures. The whole problem of the formation of the individual's habit-patterns under the influence of traditional custom can best be understood at the present time through the study of simpler peoples. This does not mean that the facts and processes we can discover in this way are limited in their application to primitive civilizations. Cultural configurations are as compelling and as significant in the highest and most complex societies of which we have knowledge. But the material is too intricate and too close to our eyes for us to cope with it successfully.

The understanding we need of our own cultural processes can most economically be arrived at by a detour. When the historical relations of human beings and their immediate forebears in the animal kingdom were too involved to use in establishing the fact of biological evolution, Darwin made use instead of the structure of beetles, and the process, which in the complex physical organization of the human is confused, in the simpler material was transparent in its cogency. It is the same in the study of cultural mechanisms. We need all the enlightenment we can obtain from the study of thought and behavior as it is organized in the less complicated groups. . . .

The basic contrast between the Pueblos and the other cultures of North America is the contrast that is named and described by Nietzsche in his studies of Greek tragedy. He discusses two diametrically opposed ways of arriving at the values of existence. The Dionysian pursues them through "the annihilation of the ordinary bounds and limits of existence"; he seeks to attain in his most valued moments escape from the boundaries imposed upon him by his five senses, to break through into another order of experience. The desire of the Dionysian, in personal experience or in ritual, is to press through it toward a certain psychological state, to achieve excess. The closest analogy to the emotions he seeks is drunkenness, and he values the illuminations of frenzy. With Blake, he believes "the path of excess leads to the palace of wisdom." The Apollonian distrusts all this, and has often little idea of the nature of such experiences. He finds means to outlaw them from his conscious life. He "knows but one law, measure in the Hellenic sense." He keeps the middle of the road, stays within the known map, does not meddle with disruptive psychological states. In Nietzsche's fine phrase, even in the exaltation of the dance he "remains what he is, and retains his civic name."

The Southwest Pueblos are Apollonian. . . . Perhaps no people
in North America spend more time in the dance than the Southwest
Pueblos. But their object in it never is to attain self-oblivion. It is by
the frenzy of the dance that the Greek cult of Dionysus was best
known, and it recurs over and over in North America. The Ghost
Dance of the Indians that swept the country in the 1870s was a
round dance danced monotonously till the dancers, one after the
other, fell rigid, prostrate on the ground. During their seizure they
had visions of deliverance from the whites, and meanwhile the
dance continued and others fell. It was the custom in most of the
dozens of tribes to which it penetrated to hold the dance every Sunday. There were other and older dances also that were thoroughly
Dionysian. The tribes of northern Mexico danced, frothing at the
mouth, upon the altar. The shamans' dances of California required
a cataleptic seizure. The Maidu used to hold shamans' contests in
which that one was victor who danced down the others; that is, who
did not succumb to the hypnotic suggestions of the dance. On the
Northwest Coast the whole winter ceremonial was thought of as
being designed to tame the man who had returned mad and possessed by the spirits. The initiates played out their rôle with the
frenzy that was expected of them. They danced like Siberian shamans, tethered by four ropes strung to the four directions so that
they could be controlled if they ran into harm to themselves or
others.

Of all this there is no suggestion in all the dance occasions of
Zuñi. The dance, like their ritual poetry, is a monotonous compulsion of natural forces by reiteration. The tireless pounding of their
feet draws together the mist in the sky and heaps it into the piled
rain clouds. It forces out the rain upon the earth. They are bent not
at all upon an ecstatic experience, but upon so thoroughgoing an
identification with nature that the forces of nature will swing to
their purposes. This intent dictates the form and spirit of Pueblo
dances. There is nothing wild about them. It is the cumulative force
of the rhythm, the perfection of forty men moving as one, that
makes them effective.

No one has conveyed this quality of Pueblo dancing more precisely than D. H. Lawrence. "All the men sing in unison, as they
move with the soft, yet heavy bird tread which is the whole of the
dance, with bodies bent a little forward, shoulders and heads loose
and heavy, feet powerful but soft, the men tread the rhythm into
the centre of the earth. The drums keep up the pulsating heart beat
and for hours, hours, it goes on." Sometimes they are dancing the
sprouting corn up out of the earth, sometimes they are calling the
game animals by the tramp of their feet, sometimes they are con-

straining the white cumulus clouds that are slowly piling up the sky on a desert afternoon. Even the presence of these in the sky, whether or not they vouchsafe rain, is a blessing from the supernaturals upon the dance, a sign that their rite is accepted. If rain comes, that is the sign and seal of the power of their dance. It is the answer. They dance on through the swift Southwest downpour, their feathers wet and heavy, their embroidered kilts and mantles drenched. But they have been favored by the gods. The clowns make merry in the deep adobe mud, sliding at full length in the puddles and paddling in the half-liquid earth. It is their recognition that their feet in the dance have the compulsion of natural forces upon the storm clouds and have been powerful to bring the rain.

Even where the Pueblos share with their near neighbors dance patterns the very forms of which are instinct with Dionysian meaning, they are used among the Pueblos with complete sobriety. The Cora of northern Mexico have a whirling dance, like so many other tribes of that part of the country, and the climax of it comes when the dancer, having reached the greatest velocity and obliviousness of which he is capable, whirls back and back and upon the very ground altar itself. At any other moment, on any other occasion, this is sacrilege. But of such things the highest Dionysian values are made. In his madness the altar is destroyed, trampled into the sand again. At the end the dancer falls upon the destroyed altar.

In the sets of dances in the underground kiva chamber in the Hopi Snake Dance they also dance upon the altar. But there is no frenzy. It is prescribed, like a movement of a Virginia Reel. One of the commonest formal dance patterns of the Pueblos is built up of the alternation of two dance groups who in each set vary a similar theme, appearing from alternate sides of the dancing space. Finally for the last set the two come out simultaneously from both directions. In this kiva snake dance, the Antelope Society dancers are opposed to the Snake dancers. In the first set the Antelope priest dances, squatting, the circuit of the altar, and retires. The Snake priest repeats. In the second set Antelope receives a vine in his mouth and dances before the initiates, trailing it over their knees. He retires. Snake follows, receiving a live rattlesnake in his mouth in the same fashion and trailing it over the initiates' knees. In the final set Antelope and Snake come out together, still in the squatting position, and dance not the circuit of the altar but upon it, ending the dance. It is a formal sequence like that of a Morris dance, and it is danced in complete sobriety.

Nor is the dancing with snakes a courting of the dangerous and the terrible in Hopi. There is current in our civilization so common a horror of snakes that we misread the Snake Dance. We readily attribute to the dancers the emotions we should feel in like case. But snakes are not often regarded with horror by the American Indians. They are often reverenced, and occasionally their holiness makes them dangerous, as anything may be that is sacred or *manitou*. But our unreasoned repulsion is no part of their reaction. Nor are snakes especially feared for their attack. There are Indian folktales that end, "and that is why the rattlesnake is not dangerous." The habits of the rattlesnake make it easy to subdue and Indians readily cope with it. The feeling tone of the dancers toward the snakes in the Snake Dance is not that of unholy dread or repulsion, but that of cult members toward their animal patron. Moreover, it has been repeatedly verified that the poison sacs of the rattlesnakes are removed for the dance. They are bruised or pinched out, and when the snakes are released after the dance, the sacs grow again and fill with poison as before. But for the period of the dance the snakes are harmless. The situation, therefore, in the mind of the Hopi dancer is not Dionysian either in its secular or in its supernatural aspect. It is an excellent example of the fact that the same objective behavior may be according to inculcated ideas, either a Dionysian courting of dangerous and repulsive experience, or a sober and formal ceremonial.

Whether by the use of drugs, of alcohol, of fasting, of torture, or of the dance, no experiences are sought or tolerated among the Pueblos that are outside of ordinary sensory routine. The Pueblos will have nothing to do with disruptive individual experiences of this type. The love of moderation to which their civilization is committed has no place for them.

On Being the Right Size

J. B. S. HALDANE

THE MOST OBVIOUS DIFFERENCES between different animals are differences of size, but for some reason the zoologists have paid singularly little attention to them. In a large textbook of zoology before me I find no indication that the eagle is larger than the sparrow, or the hippopotamus bigger than the hare, though some grudging admissions are made in the case of the mouse and the whale. But yet it is easy to show that a hare could not be as large as a hippopotamus, or a whale as small as a herring. For every type of animal there is a most convenient size, and a large change in size inevitably carries with it a change of form.

Let us take the most obvious of possible cases, and consider a giant man sixty feet high — about the height of Giant Pope and Giant Pagan in the illustrated *Pilgrim's Progress* of my childhood. These monsters were not only ten times as high as Christian, but ten times as wide and ten times as thick, so that their total weight was a thousand times his, or about eighty to ninety tons. Unfortunately the cross sections of their bones were only a hundred times those of Christian, so that every square inch of giant bone had to support ten times the weight borne by a square inch of human bone. As the human thigh-bone breaks under about ten times the human weight, Pope and Pagan would have broken their thighs every time they took a step. This was doubtless why they were sitting down in the picture I remember. But it lessens one's respect for Christian and Jack the Giant Killer.

To turn to zoology, suppose that a gazelle, a graceful little creature with long thin legs, is to become large, it will break its bones unless it does one of two things. It may make its legs short and thick, like the rhinoceros, so that every pound of weight has still about the same area of bone to support it. Or it can compress its body and stretch out its legs obliquely to gain stability, like the giraffe. I mention these two beasts because they happen to belong to the same order as the gazelle, and both are quite successful mechanically, being remarkably fast runners.

Gravity, a mere nuisance to Christian, was a terror to Pope, Pagan, and Despair. To the mouse and any smaller animal it presents practically no dangers. You can drop a mouse down a thousand-yard mine shaft; and, on arriving at the bottom, it gets a slight shock and walks away, provided that the ground is fairly soft. A rat is killed, a man is broken, a horse splashes. For the resistance presented to movement by the air is proportional to the surface of the moving object. Divide an animal's length, breadth, and height each by ten; its weight is reduced to a thousandth, but its surface only to a hundredth. So the resistance to falling in the case of the small animal is relatively ten times greater than the driving force.

An insect, therefore, is not afraid of gravity; it can fall without danger, and can cling to the ceiling with remarkably little trouble. It can go in for elegant and fantastic forms of support like that of the daddy-longlegs. But there is a force which is as formidable to an insect as gravitation to a mammal. This is surface tension. A man coming out of a bath carries with him a film of water of about one-fiftieth of an inch in thickness. This weighs roughly a pound. A wet mouse has to carry about its own weight of water. A wet fly has to lift many times its own weight and, as everyone knows, a fly once wetted by water or any other liquid is in a very serious position indeed. An insect going for a drink is in as great danger as a man leaning out over a precipice in search of food. If it once falls into the grip of the surface tension of the water — that is to say, gets wet — it is likely to remain so until it drowns. A few insects, such as water-beetles, contrive to be unwettable; the majority keep well away from their drink by means of a long proboscis.

Of course tall land animals have other difficulties. They have to pump their blood to greater heights than a man, and therefore, require a larger blood pressure and tougher blood vessels. A great many men die from burst arteries, especially in the brain, and this danger is presumably still greater for an elephant or a giraffe. But animals of all kinds find difficulties in size for the following reason. A typical small animal, say a microscopic worm or rotifer, has a smooth skin through which all the oxygen it requires can soak in, a straight gut with sufficient surface to absorb its food, and a single kidney. Increase its dimensions tenfold in every direction, and its weight is increased a thousand times, so that if it is to use its muscles as efficiently as its miniature counterpart, it will need a thousand times as much food and oxygen per day and will excrete a thousand times as much of waste products.

Now if its shape is unaltered its surface will be increased only a hundredfold, and ten times as much oxygen must enter per minute through each square millimeter of skin, ten times as much food through each square millimeter of intestine. When a limit is reached to their absorptive powers their surface has to be increased by some special device. For example, a part of the skin may be drawn out into tufts to make gills or pushed in to make lungs, thus increasing the oxygen-absorbing surface in proportion to the animal's bulk. A man, for example, has a hundred square yards of lung. Similarly, the gut, instead of being smooth and straight, becomes coiled and develops a velvety surface, and other organs increase in complication. The higher animals are not larger than the lower because they are more complicated. They are more complicated because they are larger. Just the same is true of plants. The simplest plants, such as the green algae growing in stagnant water or on the bark of trees, are mere round cells. The higher plants increase their surface by putting out leaves and roots. Comparative anatomy is largely the story of the struggle to increase surface in proportion to volume.

Some of the methods of increasing the surface are useful up to a point, but not capable of a very wide adaptation. For example, while vertebrates carry the oxygen from the gills or lungs all over the body in the blood, insects take air directly to every part of their body by tiny blind tubes called tracheae which open to the surface at many different points. Now, although by their breathing movements they can renew the air in the outer part of the tracheal system, the oxygen has to penetrate the finer branches by means of diffusion. Gases can diffuse easily through very small distances, not many times larger than the average length traveled by a gas molecule between collisions with other molecules. But when such vast journeys — from the point of view of a molecule — as a quarter of an inch have to be made, the process becomes slow. So the portions of an insect's body more than a quarter of an inch from the air would always be short of oxygen. In consequence hardly any insects are much more than half an inch thick. Land crabs are built on the same general plan as insects, but are much clumsier. Yet like ourselves they carry oxygen around in their blood, and are therefore able to grow far larger than any insects. If the insects had hit on a plan for driving air through their tissues instead of letting it soak in, they might well have become as large as lobsters, though other considerations would have prevented them from becoming as large as man.

Exactly the same difficulties attach to flying. It is an elementary principle of aeronautics that the minimum speed needed to keep an aeroplane of a given shape in the air varies as the square root of its length. If its linear dimensions are increased four times, it must fly twice as fast. Now the power needed for the minimum speed increases more rapidly than the weight of the machine. So the larger aeroplane, which weighs sixty-four times as much as the smaller, needs one hundred and twenty-eight times its horsepower to keep up. Applying the same principles to the birds, we find that the limit to their size is soon reached. An angel whose muscles developed no more power weight for weight than those of an eagle or a pigeon would require a breast projecting for about four feet to house the muscles engaged in working its wings, while to economize in weight, its legs would have to be reduced to mere stilts. Actually a large bird such as an eagle or kite does not keep in the air mainly by moving its wings. It is generally to be seen soaring, that is to say balanced on a rising column of air. And even soaring becomes more and more difficult with increasing size. Were this not the case eagles might be as large as tigers and as formidable to man as hostile aeroplanes.

But it is time that we pass to some of the advantages of size. One of the most obvious is that it enables one to keep warm. All warm-blooded animals at rest lose the same amount of heat from a unit area of skin, for which purpose they need a food supply proportional to their surface and not to their weight. Five thousand mice weigh as much as a man. Their combined surface and food or oxygen consumption are about seventeen times a man's. In fact a mouse eats about one quarter its own weight of food every day, which is mainly used in keeping it warm. For the same reason small animals cannot live in cold countries. In the arctic regions there are no reptiles or amphibians, and no small mammals. The smallest mammal in Spitzbergen is the fox. The small birds fly away in winter, while the insects die, though their eggs can survive six months or more of frost. The most successful mammals are bears, seals, and walruses.

Similarly, the eye is a rather inefficient organ until it reaches a large size. The back of the human eye on which an image of the outside world is thrown, and which corresponds to the film of a camera, is composed of a mosaic of "rods and cones" whose diameter is little more than a length of an average light wave. Each eye has about a half a million, and for two objects to be distinguishable their images must fall on separate rods or cones. It is obvious that with fewer but larger rods and cones we should see less distinctly. If they were twice as broad two points would have to be twice as far apart before we could distinguish them at a given distance. But if their size were diminished and their number increased we should see no better. For it is impossible to form a definite image smaller than a wave-length of light. Hence a mouse's eye is not a small-scale model of a human eye. Its rods and cones are not much smaller than ours, and therefore there are far fewer of them. A mouse could not distinguish one human face from another six feet away. In order that they should be of any use at all the eyes of small animals have to be much larger in proportion to their bodies than our own. Large animals on the other hand only require relatively small eyes, and those of the whale and elephant are little larger than our own.

For rather more recondite reasons the same general principle holds true of the brain. If we compare the brain-weights of a set of very similar animals such as the cat, cheetah, leopard, and tiger, we find that as we quadruple the body-weight the brain-weight is only doubled. The larger animal with proportionately larger bones can economize on brain, eyes, and certain other organs.

Such are a very few of the considerations which show that for every type of animal there is an optimum size. Yet although Galileo demonstrated the contrary more than three hundred years ago, people still believe that if a flea were as large as a man it could jump a thousand feet into the air. As a matter of fact the height to which an animal can jump is more nearly independent of its size than proportional to it. A flea can jump about two feet, a man about five. To jump a given height, if we neglect the resistance of the air, requires an expenditure of energy proportional to the jumper's weight. But if the jumping muscles form a constant fraction of the animal's body, the energy developed per ounce of muscle is independent of the size, provided it can be developed quickly enough in the small animal. As a matter of fact an insect's muscles, although they can contract more quickly than our own, appear to be less efficient; as otherwise a flea or grasshopper could rise six feet into the air.

The Neurosis Wears a Mask

LAWRENCE S. KUBIE

NOT LONG AGO I was on a platform with a distinguished friend, Sidney Lovett, the Chaplain of Yale University. He was a lamb among the psychiatric wolves who were present. Yet he looked very happy. I could not quite understand this until he explained that for years the padres had been taking it on the chin, all the jokes being at their expense. "That never happens any more," he said. "Now they are all on the psychiatrists and I have begun to enjoy life again."

I am somewhat overwhelmed at the task I have undertaken. It is a peculiarly difficult one to me because I have to try not merely to describe a phenomenon, the process of inner illumination as we encounter it in psychotherapy, but also to give you some idea of how we relate it to the process of religious revelation, and finally how we attempt to explain it, in so far as we have succeeded in advancing even any partial explanations.

From *Moments of Personal Discovery*, R. M. MacIver, editor. Copyright 1952. By permission of Harper and Brothers. [Originally delivered as a lecture at The Institute for Religious and Social Studies of the Jewish Theological Seminary.]

I feel like that famous old French mathematician who was about to address the French Academy. He reached the podium, gazed around, and said, "I have changed my mind," and went home. Whenever I have bitten off more than I can chew, I feel that way; and that is how I feel at this moment. You know how it is. When you promise to give a talk like this you hope that your wisdom will somehow grow enough, so that by the time the fatal day comes, you may know enough to be able to talk about what you have promised to discuss.

Nonetheless, there is a deeper reason why I am here: a reason which goes back to the devout atmosphere of my childhood home, to my own concern with religious matters when I was young, and to the processes of change that went on in me whereby that early interest became channeled into the direction of general science, and from the start particularly in the direction of psychiatry. It was in the midst of my years as an undergraduate at Harvard that I decided that I was not going to be the lawyer that I had gone to college to become; but to study medicine so as to become a psychiatrist. There has never seemed to me to be any discontinuity in this sequence of events. The interest with which I had originally started as a youngster went through various transformations into a transitory interest in the law — I think largely because I was argumentative anyway — to concentrate finally on the field of activity which has occupied me ever since.

Undoubtedly certain youthful personality problems influenced my development in this direction, notably the uneasiness, self-consciousness, and confusion in human relationships which characterized my childhood and adolescence. There were also a certain number of facts about the world and the people around me which attracted my attention. Long before I had words with which to characterize those observations, they began to make a difference in my own purposes. I began to see that human personality as such contained enormously powerful forces: so that each individual human being shaped and molded his faith at least as much as his faith actively shaped and molded him. Furthermore, I observed that many different kinds of human beings become lawyers, artists, poets, scientists, and ministers of the gospel: and that among those who were devout, there were divergences in personalities as wide as those to be found among people without religious devotion. This made me realize that there must be forces at work in human nature which operated on some level other than the level of faith, forces which determined what men did with their faith, forces which human beings must learn to understand and to control if they were going to be able to make effective use of their own devoted feelings.

I had friends among different groups within the Jewish community, both Orthodox and Reform, because parts of my family with whom I had close personal ties were affiliated with both groups. Through other friends I saw a great deal of a large number of members of the Society of Friends, again both Orthodox and Reform, and so on through a broad variety of faiths and forms. And wherever I looked, I saw that each human being made of his faith what he had to, not by conscious voluntary choice, but by reason of some powerful inner forces which had the power to determine his behavior, his way of living and feeling and believing and preaching, his way of standing for what he believes; just as these same inner forces determined the quality of human relationships both in the home and out of it. This extraordinary variety of temperaments, and the power which these temperaments displayed, gradually made me realize that one cannot deal effectively with any aspect of life without taking unconscious psychological processes into account as well as the conscious forces which shape human personality. In turn this led me to a conviction that there were no short cuts, no easy formulas by which a human being could purge himself of dross, of the unwanted primitive elements in his own nature. All of my later training proved that this process of change involves man in a slow and difficult and painful toil.

As years went on those early primitive observations — partly on myself and partly on others — led to clinical studies and to the study of the techniques of psychotherapy by which the moments of discovery are achieved. Therefore, at this point I have to take time to describe some of the more technical aspects of this process. I will not go deeply into technical formulations, only far enough to make understandable a point of view in approaching this problem which is common to us all. It is worthwhile to do this, because so frequently the psychiatrist is misunderstood. Indeed, some religious teachers seem to believe that their goals and mine are dissimilar: whereas it is only in our paths to the goal and in our attitude to the obstacles in that path that we may differ.

I can summarize what I have to say by pointing out that what we have learned about human nature in these past fifty years is that in all human nature there is a universal masked neurotic component. This neurotic component in human nature occurs even in the most normal of us. It has its origins in our earliest years. Moreover these origins are linked to the development of those very capacities which are essential also to our highest endowment, i.e., the capacity for thinking and feeling in symbolic terms. Without these there could be no art or literature or science or religion. Thus man's highest spiritual and cultural attainments and his neurotic ability to get into trouble, arise out of this same capacity to make abstractions and condensations from experience, and then to represent those abstractions and condensations in symbolic form. This capacity for symbolic psychic process is highly vulnerable, however, and starts getting in trouble quite early in life. When I say early, I mean almost as soon as the infant develops his first primitive language sounds. The human race is not yet wise enough to know how to cultivate the spiritually creative aspects of the symbolic process while avoiding the destructive neurotic distortions. Indeed, all of our hopes to discover a way to prevent the neurotic distortion of human personality depend upon our learning more about how this distortion of symbolic feeling and thinking occurs so early in life, and how to avoid it.

The ultimate goal of the psychiatrist is exactly the same as yours. This is something we have in common, namely, the goal of a good life. Also in the effort to achieve the good life the experience that is sought in psychiatry is precisely the experience which is sought in religion, i.e., the experience of an essential inner change in the human personality, achieved through a succession of moments of deeply moving and often painful discovery of truths about oneself. This is always close to the process of conversion. It is what William James described many times in *The Varieties of Religious Experiences;* and it is something that we see repeatedly in any successful effort at psychotherapy. When psychotherapy succeeds, one watches subtle, deeply moving, slow increments of change in a personality, each marked by these cumulative moments of discovery. These go on step by step throughout the process of treatment. Sometimes they occur only after long periods of baffling frustration, in which one wanders through the wilderness, not unlike *Pilgrim's Progress* or Dante's *Inferno.* There may be long periods of struggle without any sign of change, taxing equally the courage and the patience of analyst and of patient; but it will be rewarded in the course of time, by those deeply moving moments of discovery and of consequent change to which I have referred.

Before coming to that, however, we must talk for a moment about the devil. For the psychiatrist, of course, the devil is within us. He is the pride which makes everybody want to be freed from pain without paying the price of learning how to be a different kind of person. Everyone wants to get rid of his toothache; but no one wants to change. This is true both in the struggle for religious conversion and in that process of conversion which is an essential component in any deeply penetrating form of psychotherapy. Many a patient comes saying, "Yes, I would like to get rid of my painful symptoms, but I don't want to be different. Don't tamper with *me.*"

This is the stiff-necked, self-willed, self-proud quality against which every kind of spiritual growth has constantly to contend. Personally I believe it to be one of the obstacles to effective psychotherapy which we have not yet solved effectively.

I would like to stress the fact that here again we are on common grounds. We psychiatrists recognize that in order to get well the human being must change deeply, and that this means that he must first *want* to change; but that at the same time merely wanting to be different is not enough. It requires the humility of purpose plus a complex technique. Furthermore, we know that the technique is not enough without the humility of goal. Moreover, the psychiatrist recognizes that illness can distort even this spiritual humility, and that the need to change can be as misguided as is the stiff-necked resistance to changing, that we can be neurotically dissatisfied with things that are all right about us, just as we can be neurotically complacent over things that are all wrong. All of this arises, as I have indicated, because we bring forward from our earliest years something damaged in our personalities. Furthermore I want to stress that this happens universally, in every stratum of society. It happens under the most favorable as well as under the most unfavorable economic, cultural, educational, and spiritual circumstances. In other words, the problem that we are discussing here today is truly universal and has to do with the earliest formative steps in the development of human nature.

Again we have in common the recognition of the fact that man does not find it easy to achieve the good life. He can define the goal, more easily than he can reach it. As a matter of fact, the mere task of being a human being seems to be more than most of us are up to. The human race has not yet grown up to human stature; and in struggling with this basic problem we are struggling on common grounds; and with supplementary but not antithetical techniques.

I do not want to gloss over actual differences of opinion and feeling. These exist. For instance, the ancient issue of original sin comes up for thought. I am not going into that problem here, although if we are to be inclusive in our thinking we must recognize that it has to be considered. Whenever I consider that vexed problem, I turn back to St. Augustine with considerable comfort, because he was a really wise psychiatrist. You all know his famous saying that the innocence of childhood is due less to the purity of their hearts than to the weakness of their limbs. Freud himself could not have put more succinctly. What psychiatry adds to that is the effort to discover why that is true and how to deal with it both preventively and curatively.

This issue confronted me recently in a moving, perplexing, and illuminating situation. I was visiting a school which does a magnificent job with youngsters who have gotten into serious trouble. At the end of the day I sat around with the director and the faculty of the school, and with the Protestant and Catholic chaplains. I showed them a psychiatric film called "Angry Boy." It was an accurate documentary. It showed a youngster who had gotten into trouble, and had done some stealing. It gave you a glimpse of his background, of how this arose, of the stormy inner rages which he was expressing and of the resentments and jealousies which played into his blind grabbing at things that he did not really need. Then it gave a glimpse of the process of therapy, condensed and simplified, yet as true as a picture of that kind can be.

In the end it was a happy little picture, and both young chaplains were much moved. More than one nose was blown surreptitiously; and the young Catholic priest was among those who felt its lesson most keenly. We proceeded to talk about some of the implications of the film for the therapeutic techniques of this particular school. Suddenly the Catholic chaplain turned to me and, with genuine perplexity and alarm and almost with some indignation, said: "But no one said anything about sin!"

I answered that this youngster was sick, that he acted out his sickness in a way which in our mores is sinful, and that certain manipulations helped him to unburden himself of feelings which had been inaccessible to him before, so that as time went on he no longer felt unhappy, no longer mean or full of rage and hate and envy and jealousy. Thereupon he had stopped stealing. True, nobody had said anything to him about sin. Yet the change that was evoked was precisely the change that we would be seeking for if we had first made him feel ashamed and sinful. The essential question is which is the surer and the more lasting road to the permanent change, which renders the Good Life attainable.

In other words, the same mountain had been climbed. I was not there to say which would always be the better way to climb that mountain. Nor was I ready to say that there is always only one good way to climb a mountain. Maybe there are some mountains that have to be climbed one way and other mountains that have to be climbed another way, and maybe what we have to do is to sit down together, to compare actual case notes, so as to find out how lasting is the change of heart in different kinds of disturbance of the human spirit when these changes of heart are achieved by the technical processes which comprise modern psychotherapy or by processes which are more familiar to us in religion.

Here again our goal is the same. Our areas of possible divergence are chiefly over the paths to that goal.

What then about the moments of discovery which come in the course of such therapy? I would stress first the fact that they usually come in small increments. You will understand, therefore, why I cannot talk to you about sudden moments of vast revelation. These do happen, but only rarely in our attack on these problems. We are accustomed to achieving change by inches. The struggles are long and painful: and it is amazing how frequently that moment of illumination concerns something which seems minute. Indeed, as soon as it is put into words, it may seem trite and banal, and obvious to everybody except to the patient.

Patients often become chagrined after describing to some friend the insight into themselves which they gained through weeks or months of painful struggle, insights which seemed to them to be extraordinary and surprising and profound, until the friend says, "Why, I could have told you that before you ever started. You did not have to go to a psychiatrist for all that time, spending all that money, just to discover that. I could have told you that before you ever started."

Of course the friend could have. The things that are wrong with us are often quite obvious to everybody around us. But what other people see in us is one thing; our ability to see ourselves as others see us is quite another. What the friend misses is the fact that the essential change which has happened is not just that the patient now understands that 2 and 2 make 4, but that certain inner blinders have disappeared, blinders which made it impossible for him to see the obvious and which have made him try to prove that 2 and 2 make 3 or 5 instead. It is the elimination of the blinders of distortions in vision, the badly refracted spiritual lenses, which is the essential process of therapy in psychiatry. The moving discoveries which then occur are usually due to the fact that suddenly the same individual can see the truth directly.

I think of a woman of destructive fury: a fury which shook her relationship to husband, child, and neighbors. With the elimination of certain of these inner blinders, it suddenly became clear that a wholly different person was hidden behind this façade of hostility and rage and hatred and meanness. This discovery occurred without any preaching to her that she must be different. The words in which she described her new insight indicated that subtle changes had occurred in all of the unconscious forces which had made her behave like one of the ancient furies, and which had made her always justify and rationalize and defend conduct which she had always known to be destructive.

The first man who ever taught me anything about psychotherapy was a very wise man, William Alanson White of Washington, then the head of the St. Elizabeth Hospital. He gave an informal lecture in the psychiatric clinic of the Johns Hopkins Hospital, where I was studying. In it he said, "You know, there is no use in telling a patient that 2 and 2 are 4. If he does not see that for himself, there must be some reason why he cannot see it. While you are talking to him he may be very polite and say, 'Yes, Doctor, I understand that 2 plus 2 make 4.' But the next day he is not going to agree so readily, and two days later he will have forgotten that he ever agreed with you. When you discover with him *why* he has to believe that 2 and 2 are 3 or 5, you never need tell him that 2 and 2 are 4. His own direct sense will then be free to carry him to the truth."

There is in that fundamentally true statement a profound optimism about the human spirit. I emphasize this because psychiatry is accused so often of being pessimistic, when in fact it is quite the opposite. Its basic premise is that if you can eliminate the blind spots and the distorting lenses which we acquire early in life, then for the most part human beings will see truly for themselves.

It will be helpful to think of the different forms of psychotherapy as a spectrum. At one end is that form which consists of an effort to alter the environment in which people suffer, to lessen the external stresses which play on the patient. Here the tacit assumption is that it is the social milieu which is ill rather than the individual. Not infrequently this is true: and when it is the case, all such external aids are an important contribution to human welfare. To do this takes heart and skill and imagination and human sympathy. Much of the magnificent structure of psychiatric and medical social work is a formal implementation of the skill. Similarly the drive to reform in economics and in politics is infused with this same hope: namely, the hope that if you cure the social ills, individual ills will heal themselves. In fact when the situation is sick but not the man, this can actually happen: but there are many people whose illnesses are of such a nature that they persist in spite even of ideal external and environmental circumstances. When this is true, we psychiatrists have to attempt to change the individual himself. This can first be attempted by relatively superficial devices: you encourage him; you give him hope; you train him and educate him, and find him a new job; you give him the support of art and literature and music; you rest him with vacations; you argue with him, plead with him, try to gain his loyalty. You use every conscious intellectual and emotional force which can alter a human being's conscious feelings and allegiances, his conscious thinking and reasoning. A certain proportion of human beings receive great help from this. Yet there is still a residue which remains ill in spite of all such efforts. These men and women have to be helped through a deeper insight, an insight which penetrates below the surface to the unconscious forces which operate on them, unconscious forces which they cannot see for themselves, such as the unconscious fears, hatreds, rivalries, and envies which distort their behavior. With these patients, the psychiatrist adjusts his therapy to what he sees below the surface of the patient's conscious personality. He may or may not try to make the patient understand his own unconscious problems. Where the psychiatrist is not content to understand the patient's unconscious struggles, but asks the patient to achieve an equally unsparing insight into himself, we make as heroic a demand on the human spirit as can be made. This is always difficult to achieve; and the mere fact that it ever is attained, is a tribute to what the human spirit is capable of.

I do not know of anything which is more moving or dramatic or more humbling than to see the change that occurs in a human being whose insights have finally broken through all of the self-protective, self-defending barriers, all of the false fronts, behind which we begin to hide ourselves almost from the moment we start to talk. Now for the first time a man begins to see himself truly, with all of his frailties, all of his false gods, as he really is. Thereupon, and this is the encouraging part of it, as he begins to see himself truly, he begins also to see other people in the world around him more truly. Out of this grows an extraordinarily creative identification with the struggles of the human spirit toward a good life.

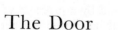

The Door

E. B. WHITE

EVERYTHING (he kept saying) is something it isn't. And everybody is always somewhere else. Maybe it was the city, being in the city, that made him feel how queer everything was and that it was something else. Maybe (he kept thinking) it was the names of the

From *The Second Tree from the Corner* by E. B. White. Copyright 1939 by E. B. White. Harper and Brothers, New York.

things. The names were tex and frequently koid. Or they were flex and oid or they were duroid (sani) or flexsan (duro), but everything was glass (but not quite glass) and the thing that you touched (the surface, washable, crease-resistant) was rubber, only it wasn't quite rubber and you didn't quite touch it but almost. The wall, which was glass but thrutex, turned out on being approached not to be a wall, it was something else, it was an opening or door-way — and the doorway (through which he saw himself approaching) turned out to be something else, it was a wall. And what he had eaten not having agreed with him.

He was in a washable house, but he wasn't sure. Now about those rats, he kept saying to himself. He meant the rats that the Professor had driven crazy by forcing them to deal with problems which were beyond the scope of rats, the insoluble problems. He meant the rats that had been trained to jump at the square card with the circle in the middle, and the card (because it was something it wasn't) would give way and let the rat into a place where the food was, but then one day it would be a trick played on the rat, and the card would be changed, and the rat would jump but the card wouldn't give way, and it was an impossible situation (for a rat) and the rat would go insane and into its eyes would come the unspeakably bright imploring look of the frustrated, and after the convulsions were over and the frantic racing around, then the passive stage would set in and the willingness to let anything be done to it, even if it was something else.

He didn't know which door (or wall) or opening in the house to jump at, to get through, because one was an opening that wasn't an opening, it was a sanitary cupboard of the same color. He caught a glimpse of his eyes staring into his eyes, in the thrutex, and in them was the expression he had seen in the picture of the rats — weary after convulsions and the frantic racing around, when they were willing and did not mind having anything done to them. More and more (he kept saying) I am confronted by a problem which is incapable of solution (for this time even if he chose the right door, there would be no food behind it) and that is what madness is, and things seeming different from what they are. He heard, in the house where he was, in the city to which he had gone (as toward a door which might, or might not, give way), a noise — not a loud noise but more of a low prefabricated humming. It came from a place in the base of the wall (or stat) where the flue carrying the filterable air was, and not far from the Minipiano, which was made of the same material nailbrushes are made of, and which was under the stairs. "This, too, has been tested," she said, pointing, but not at it, "and found viable." It wasn't a loud noise, he kept thinking, sorry that he had seen his eyes, even though it was through his own eyes that he had seen them.

First will come the convulsions (he said), then the exhaustion, then the willingness to let anything be done. "And you better believe it *will* be."

All his life he had been confronted by situations which were incapable of being solved, and there was a deliberateness behind all this, behind this changing of the card (or door), because they would always wait till you had learned to jump at the certain card (or door) — the one with the circle — and then they would change it on you. There have been so many doors changed on me, he said, in the last twenty years, but it is now becoming clear that it is an impossible situation, and the question is whether to jump again, even though they ruffle you in the rump with a blast of air — to make you jump. He wished he wasn't standing by the Minipiano. First they would teach you the prayers and the Psalms, and that would be the right door (the one with the circle), and the long sweet words with the holy sound, and that would be the one to jump at to get where the food was. Then one day you jumped and it didn't give way, so that all you got was the bump on the nose, and the first bewilderment, the first young bewilderment.

I don't know whether to tell her about the door they substituted or not, he said, the one with the equation on it and the picture of the amoeba reproducing itself by division. Or the one with the photostatic copy of the check for thirty-two dollars and fifty cents. But the jumping was so long ago, although the bump is . . . how those old wounds hurt! Being crazy this way wouldn't be so bad if only, if only. If only when you put your foot forward to take a step, the ground wouldn't come up to meet your foot the way it does. And the same way in the street (only I may never get back to the street unless I jump at the right door), the curb coming up to meet your foot, anticipating ever so delicately the weight of the body, which is somewhere else. "We could take your name," she said, "and send it to you." And it wouldn't be so bad if only you could read a sentence all the way through without jumping (your eye) to something else on the same page; and then (he kept thinking) there was that man out in Jersey, the one who started to chop his trees down, one by one, the man who began talking about how he would take his house to pieces, brick by brick, because he faced a problem incapable of solution, probably, so he began to hack at the trees in the yard, began to pluck with trembling fingers at the bricks in the house. Even if a house is not washable, it is worth taking down. It is not till later that the exhaustion sets in.

But it is inevitable that they will keep changing the doors

on you, he said, because that is what they are for; and the thing is
to get used to it and not let it unsettle the mind. But that would
mean not jumping, and you can't. Nobody can not jump. There will
be no not-jumping. Among rats, perhaps, but among people never.
Everybody has to keep jumping at a door (the one with the circle
on it) because that is the way everybody is, specially some people.
You wouldn't want me, standing here, to tell you, would you, about
my friend the poet (deceased) who said, "My heart has followed
all my days something I cannot name"? (It had the circle on it.)
And like many poets, although few so beloved, he is gone. It killed
him, the jumping. First, of course, there were the preliminary
bouts, the convulsions, and the calm and the willingness.

I remember the door with the picture of the girl on it (only it
was spring), her arms outstretched in loveliness, her dress (it was
the one with the circle on it) uncaught, beginning the slow, clear,
blinding cascade — and I guess we would all like to try that door
again, for it seemed like the way and for a while it was the way, the
door would open and you would go through winged and exalted
(like any rat) and the food would be there, the way the Professor
had it arranged, everything O.K., and you had chosen the right
door for the world was young. The time they changed that door on
me, my nose bled for a hundred hours — how do you like that,
Madam? Or would you prefer to show me further through this so
strange house, or you could take my name and send it to me, for
although my heart has followed all my days something I cannot
name, I am tired of the jumping and I do not know which way to
go, Madam, and I am not even sure that I am not tried beyond the
endurance of man (rat, if you will) and have taken leave of sanity.
What are you following these days, old friend, after your recovery
from the last bump? What is the name, or is it something you cannot name? The rats have a name for it by this time, perhaps, but I
don't know what they call it. I call it plexikoid and it comes in
sheets, something like insulating board, unattainable and ugli-
proof.

And there was the man out in Jersey, because I keep thinking
about his terrible necessity and the passion and trouble he had
gone to all those years in the indescribable abundance of a house-
holder's detail, building the estate and the planting of the trees and
in spring the lawn-dressing and in fall the bulbs for the spring
burgeoning, and the watering of the grass on the long light evenings in summer and the gravel for the driveway (all had to be
thought out, planned) and the decorative borders, probably, the
perennials and the bug spray, and the building of the house from
plans of the architect, first the sills, then the studs, then the full corn

in the ear, the floors laid on the floor timbers, smoothed, and then the carpets upon the smooth floors and the curtains and the rods therefor. And then, almost without warning, he would be jumping at the same old door and it wouldn't give: they had changed it on him, making life no longer supportable under the elms in the elm shade, under the maples in the maple shade.

"Here you have the maximum of openness in a small room."

It was impossible to say (maybe it was the city) what made him feel the way he did, and I am not the only one either, he kept thinking — ask any doctor if I am. The doctors, they know how many there are, they even know where the trouble is only they don't like to tell you about the prefrontal lobe because that means making a hole in your skull and removing the work of centuries. It took so long coming, this lobe, so many, many years. (Is it something you read in the paper, perhaps?) And now, the strain being so great, the door having been changed by the Professor once too often . . . but it only means a whiff of ether, a few deft strokes, and the higher animal becomes a little easier in his mind and more like the lower one. From now on, you see, that's the way it will be, the ones with the small prefrontal lobes will win because the other ones are hurt too much by this incessant bumping. They can stand just so much, eh, Doctor? (And what is that, pray, that you have in your hand?) Still, you never can tell, eh, Madam?

He crossed (carefully) the room, the thick carpet under him softly, and went toward the door carefully, which was glass and he could see himself in it, and which, at his approach, opened to allow him to pass through; and beyond he half expected to find one of the old doors that he had known, perhaps the one with the circle, the one with the girl her arms outstretched in loveliness and beauty before him. But he saw instead a moving stairway, and descended in light (he kept thinking) to the street below and to the other people. As he stepped off, the ground came up slightly, to meet his foot.

◇◇◇◇◇◇◇◇◇◇◇◇◇◇◇◇◇◇◇◇◇◇◇◇◇◇◇◇◇◇◇◇◇◇◇

The Colloid and the Crystal

JOSEPH WOOD KRUTCH

THE FIRST REAL SNOW was soon followed by a second. Over the radio the weatherman talked lengthily about cold masses and warm masses, about what was moving out to sea and what wasn't.

Did Benjamin Franklin, I wondered, know what he was starting when it first occurred to him to trace by correspondence the course of storms? From my stationary position the most reasonable explanation seemed to be simply that winter had not quite liked the looks of the landscape as she first made it up. She was changing her sheets.

Another forty-eight hours brought one of those nights ideal for frosting the panes. When I came down to breakfast, two of the windows were almost opaque and the others were etched with graceful, fernlike sprays of ice which looked rather like the impressions left in rocks by some of the antediluvian plants, and they were almost as beautiful as anything which the living can achieve. Nothing else which has never lived looks so much as though it were actually informed with life.

I resisted, I am proud to say, the almost universal impulse to scratch my initials into one of the surfaces. The effect, I knew, would not be an improvement. But so, of course, do those less virtuous than I. That indeed is precisely why they scratch. The impulse to mar and to destroy is as ancient and almost as nearly universal as the impulse to create. The one is an easier way than the other of demonstrating power. Why else should anyone not hungry prefer a dead rabbit to a live one? Not even those horrible Dutch painters of bloody still — or shall we say stilled? — lifes can have really believed that their subjects were more beautiful dead.

Indoors it so happened that a Christmas cactus had chosen this moment to bloom. Its lush blossoms, fuchsia-shaped but pure red rather than magenta, hung at the drooping ends of strange, thick stems and outlined themselves in blood against the glistening background of the frosty pane — jungle flower against frostflower; the warm beauty that breathes and lives and dies competing with the cold beauty that burgeons, not because it wants to, but merely because it is obeying the laws of physics which require that crystals shall take the shape they have always taken since the world began. The effect of red flower against white tracery was almost too theatrical, not quite in good taste perhaps. My eye recoiled in shock and sought through a clear area of the glass the more normal out-of-doors.

On the snow-capped summit of my bird-feeder a chickadee pecked at the new-fallen snow and swallowed a few of the flakes which serve him in lieu of the water he sometimes sadly lacks when there is nothing except ice too solid to be picked at. A downy wood-pecker was hammering at a lump of suet and at the coconut full of peanut butter. One nuthatch was dining while the mate waited his — or was it her? — turn. The woodpecker announces the fact that he is a male by the bright red spot on the back of his neck, but to me, at least, the sexes of the nuthatch are indistinguishable. I shall never know whether it is the male or the female who eats first. And that is a pity. If I knew, I could say, like the Ugly Duchess, "and the moral of that is . . ."

But I soon realized that at the moment the frosted windows were what interested me most — especially the fact that there is no other natural phenomenon in which the lifeless mocks so closely the living. One might almost think that the frostflower had got the idea from the leaf and the branch if one did not know how inconceivably more ancient the first is. No wonder that enthusiastic biologists in the nineteenth century, anxious to conclude that there was no quali-tative difference between life and chemical processes, tried to be-lieve that the crystal furnished the link, that its growth was actually the same as the growth of a living organism. But excusable though the fancy was, no one, I think, believes anything of the sort today. Protoplasm is a colloid and the colloids are fundamentally different from the crystalline substances. Instead of crystallizing they jell, and life in its simplest known form is a shapeless blob of rebellious jelly rather than a crystal eternally obeying the most ancient law.

No man ever saw a dinosaur. The last of these giant reptiles was dead eons before the most dubious halfman surveyed the world about him. Not even the dinosaurs ever cast their dim eyes upon many of the still earlier creatures which preceded them. Life changes so rapidly that its later phases know nothing of those which preceded them. But the frostflower is older than the dinosaur, older than the protozoan, older no doubt than the enzyme or the ferment. Yet it is precisely what it has always been. Millions of years before there were any eyes to see it, millions of years before any life existed, it grew in its own special way, crystallized along its preor-dained lines of cleavage, stretched out its pseudo-branches and pseudo-leaves. It was beautiful before beauty itself existed.

We find it difficult to conceive a world except in terms of pur-pose, of will, or of intention. At the thought of the something with-out beginning and presumably without end, of something which is, nevertheless, regular though blind, and organized without any end in view, the mind reels. Constituted as we are it is easier to conceive how the slime floating upon the waters might become in time Homo sapiens than it is to imagine how so complex a thing as a crystal

could have always been and can always remain just what it is —
complicated and perfect but without any meaning, even for itself.
How can the lifeless even obey a law?

To a mathematical physicist I once confessed somewhat shame-
facedly that I had never been able to understand how inanimate nature managed to follow so invariably and so promptly her own laws.
If I flip a coin across a table, it will come to rest at a certain point.
But before it stops at just that point, many factors must be taken
into consideration. There is the question of the strength of the initial impulse, of the exact amount of resistance offered by the friction
of that particular table top, and of the density of the air at the moment. It would take a physicist a long time to work out the problem
and he could achieve only an approximation at that. Yet presumably
the coin will stop exactly where it should. Some very rapid calculations have to be made before it can do so, and they are, presumably,
always accurate.

And then, just as I was blushing at what I supposed he must regard as my folly, the mathematician came to my rescue by informing me that Laplace had been puzzled by exactly the same fact.
"Nature laughs at the difficulties of integration," he remarked —
and by "integration" he meant, of course, the mathematician's word
for the process involved when a man solves one of the differential
equations to which he has reduced the laws of motion.

When my Christmas cactus blooms so theatrically a few inches
in front of the frost-covered pane, it also is obeying laws but obeying
them much less rigidly and in a different way. It blooms at about
Christmastime because it has got into the habit of doing so, because,
one is tempted to say, it wants to. As a matter of fact it was, this year,
not a Christmas cactus but a New Year's cactus, and because of this
unpredictability I would like to call it "he," not "it." His flowers assume their accustomed shape and take on their accustomed color.
But not as the frostflowers follow their predestined pattern. Like
me, the cactus has a history which stretches back over a long past
full of changes and developments. He has not always been merely
obeying fixed laws. He has resisted and rebelled; he has attempted
novelties, passed through many phases. Like all living things he has
had a will of his own. He has made laws, not merely obeyed them.

"Life," so the platitudinarian is fond of saying, "is strange." But
from our standpoint it is not really so strange as those things which
have no life and yet nevertheless move in their predestined orbits
and "act" though they do not "behave." At the very least one ought
to say that if life is strange there is nothing about it more strange
than the fact that it has its being in a universe so astonishingly
shared on the one hand by "things" and on the other by "creatures,"

that man himself is both a "thing" which obeys the laws of chemistry or physics and a "creature" who to some extent defies them. No other contrast, certainly not the contrast between the human being and the animal, or the animal and the plant, or even the spirit and the body, is so tremendous as this contrast between what lives and what does not.

To think of the lifeless as merely inert, to make the contrast merely in terms of a negative, is to miss the real strangeness. Not the shapeless stone which seems to be merely waiting to be acted upon but the snowflake or the frostflower is the true representative of the lifeless universe as opposed to ours. They represent plainly, as the stone does not, the fixed and perfect system of organization which includes the sun and its planets, includes therefore this earth itself, but against which life has set up its seemingly puny opposition. Order and obedience are the primary characteristics of that which is not alive. The snowflake eternally obeys its one and only law: "Be thou six pointed"; the planets their one and only: "Travel thou in an ellipse." The astronomer can tell where the North Star will be ten thousand years hence; the botanist cannot tell where the dandelion will bloom tomorrow.

Life is rebellious and anarchical, always testing the supposed immutability of the rules which the nonliving changelessly accepts. Because the snowflake goes on doing as it was told, its story up to the end of time was finished when it first assumed the form which it has kept ever since. But the story of every living thing is still in the telling. It may hope and it may try. Moreover, though it may succeed or fail, it will certainly change. No form of frostflower ever became extinct. Such, if you like, is its glory. But such also is the fact which makes it alien. It may melt but it cannot die.

If I wanted to contemplate what is to me the deepest of all mysteries, I should choose as my object lesson a snowflake under a lens and an amoeba under the microscope. To a detached observer — if one can possibly imagine any observer who *could* be detached when faced with such an ultimate choice — the snowflake would certainly seem the "higher" of the two. Against its intricate glistening perfection one would have to place a shapeless, slightly turbid glob, perpetually oozing out in this direction or that but not suggesting so strongly as the snowflake does, intelligence and plan. Crystal and colloid, the chemist would call them, but what an inconceivable contrast those neutral terms imply! Like the star, the snowflake seems to declare the glory of God, while the promise of the amoeba, given only perhaps to itself, seems only contemptible. But its jelly holds, nevertheless, not only its promise but ours also, while the snowflake represents some achievement which we cannot possibly share. After the passage of billions of years, one can see and be aware of the other, but the relationship can never be reciprocal. Even after these billions of years no aggregate of colloids can be as beautiful as the crystal always was, but it can know, as the crystal cannot, what beauty is.

Even to admire too much or too exclusively the alien kind of beauty is dangerous. Much as I love and am moved by the grand, inanimate forms of nature, I am always shocked and a little frightened by those of her professed lovers to whom landscape is the most important thing, and to whom landscape is merely a matter of forms and colors. If they see or are moved by an animal or flower, it is to them merely a matter of a picturesque completion and their fellow creatures are no more than decorative details. But without some continuous awareness of the two great realms of the inanimate and the animate there can be no love of nature as I understand it, and what is worse, there must be a sort of disloyalty to our cause, to us who are colloid, not crystal. The pantheist who feels the oneness of all living things, I can understand; perhaps indeed he and I are in essential agreement. But the ultimate All is not one thing, but two. And because the alien half is in its way as proud and confident and successful as our half, its fundamental difference may not be disregarded with impunity. Of us and all we stand for, the enemy is not so much death as the not-living, or rather that great system which succeeds without ever having had the need to be alive. The frostflower is not merely a wonder; it is also a threat and a warning. How admirable, it seems to say, not living can be! What triumphs mere immutable law can achieve!

Some of Charles Peirce's strange speculations about the possibility that "natural law" is not law at all but merely a set of habits fixed more firmly than any habits we know anything about ourselves or in the animals suggest the possibility that the snowflake was not, after all, always inanimate, that it merely surrendered at some time impossibly remote the life which once achieved its perfect organization. Yet even if we can imagine such a thing to be true, it serves only to warn us all the more strongly against the possibility that what we call the living might in the end succumb also to the seduction of the immutably fixed.

No student of the anthill has ever failed to be astonished either into admiration or horror by what is sometimes called the perfection of its society. Though even the anthill can change its ways, though even ant individuals — ridiculous as the conjunction of the two words may seem — can sometimes make choices, the perfection of the techniques, the regularity of the habits almost suggest the possibility that the insect is on its way back to inanition, that, vast as the difference still is, an anthill crystallizes somewhat as a snowflake does. But not even the anthill, nothing else indeed in the whole known universe is so perfectly planned as one of these same snowflakes. Would, then, the ultimately planned society be, like the anthill, one in which no one makes plans, any more than a snowflake does? From the cradle in which it is not really born to the grave where it is only a little deader than it always was, the ant-citizen follows a plan to the making of which he no longer contributes anything.

Perhaps we men represent the ultimate to which the rebellion, begun so long ago in some amoeba-like jelly, can go. And perhaps the inanimate is beginning the slow process of subduing us again. Certainly the psychologist and the philosopher are tending more and more to think of us as creatures who obey laws rather than as creatures of will and responsibility. We are, they say, "conditioned" by this or by that. Even the greatest heroes are studied on the assumption that they can be "accounted for" by something outside themselves. They are, it is explained, "the product of forces." All the emphasis is placed, not upon that power to resist and rebel which we were once supposed to have, but upon the "influences" which "formed us." Men are made by society, not society by men. History as well as character "obeys laws." In their view, we crystallize in obedience to some dictate from without instead of moving in conformity with something within.

And so my eye goes questioningly back to the frosted pane. While I slept the graceful pseudo-fronds crept across the glass, assuming, as life itself does, an intricate organization. "Why live," they seem to say, "when we can be beautiful, complicated, and orderly without the uncertainty and effort required of a living thing? Once we were all that was. Perhaps some day we shall be all that is. Why not join us?"

Last summer no clod or no stone would have been heard if it had asked such a question. The hundreds of things which walked and sang, the millions which crawled and twined were all having their day. What was dead seemed to exist only in order that the living might live upon it. The plants were busy turning the inorganic into green life and the animals were busy turning that green into red. When we moved, we walked mostly upon grass. Our preeminence was unchallenged.

On this winter day nothing seems so successful as the frostflower. It thrives on the very thing which has driven some of us indoors or underground and which has been fatal to many. It is having now its hour of triumph, as we before had ours. Like the cactus flower itself, I am a hothouse plant. Even my cats gaze dreamily out of the window at a universe which is no longer theirs.

How are we to resist, if resist we can? This house into which I have withdrawn is merely an expedient and it serves only my mere physical existence. What mental or spiritual convictions, what will to maintain to my own kind of existence can I assert? For me it is not enough merely to say, as I do say, that I shall resist the invitation to submerge myself into a crystalline society and to stop planning in order that I may be planned for. Neither is it enough to go further, as I do go, and to insist that the most important thing about a man is not that part of him which is "the product of forces" but that part, however small it may be, which enables him to become something other than what the most accomplished sociologist, working in conjunction with the most accomplished psychologist, could predict that he would be.

I need, so I am told, a faith, something outside myself to which I can be loyal. And with that I agree, in my own way. I am on what I call "our side," and I know, though vaguely, what I think that is. Wordsworth's God had his dwelling in the light of setting suns. But the God who dwells there seems to me most probably the God of the atom, the star, and the crystal. Mine, if I have one, reveals Himself in another class of phenomena. He makes the grass green and the blood red.

THE MIND REELS!

◇◇◇◇◇◇◇◇◇◇◇◇◇◇◇◇◇◇◇◇◇◇◇◇◇◇◇◇◇◇

Common Sense and the Universe

STEPHEN LEACOCK

. . . WHEN THE MEDIEVAL SUPERSTITION was replaced by the new learning, mathematics, astronomy, and physics were the first sciences to get organized and definite. By the opening of the nineteenth century they were well set; the solar system was humming away so drowsily that Laplace was able to assure Napoleon that he didn't need God to watch over it. Gravitation worked like clockwork, and clockwork worked like gravitation. Chemistry, which, like electricity, was nothing but a set of experiments in Benjamin Franklin's time, turned into a science after Lavoisier had discovered that fire was not a thing but a process, something happening to things — an idea so far above the common thought that they guillotined him for it in 1794. Dalton followed and showed that all things could be broken up into a set of very, very small atoms, grouped into molecules all acting according to plan. With Faraday and Maxwell, electricity, which turned out to be the same as magnetism, or interchangeable with it, fell into its place in the new order of science.

By about 1880 it seemed as if the world of science was fairly well explained. Metaphysics still talked in its sleep. Theology still preached sermons. It took issue with much of the new science, especially with geology and the new evolutionary science of life that went with the new physical world. But science paid little attention.

For the whole thing was so amazingly simple. There you had your space and time, two things too obvious to explain. Here you had your matter, made up of solid little atoms, infinitely small but really just like birdseed. All this was set going by and with the Law of Gravitation. Once started, the nebulous world condensed into suns, the suns threw off planets, the planets cooled, life resulted and presently became conscious, conscious life got higher up and higher

up till you had apes, then Bishop Wilberforce, and then Professor
Huxley.

A few little mysteries remained, such as the question of what
space and matter and time and life and consciousness really were.
But all this was conveniently called by Herbert Spencer the *Unknowable,* and then locked in a cupboard and left there.

Everything was thus reduced to a sort of Dead Certainty. Just
one awkward skeleton remained in the cupboard. And that was the
peculiar, mysterious aspect of electricity, which was not exactly a
thing and yet was more than an idea. There was also, and electricity
only helped to make it worse, the old puzzle about "action at a distance." How does gravitation pull all the way from here to the sun?
And if there is *nothing* in space, how does light get across from
the sun in eight minutes, and even all the way from Sirius in eight
years?

Even the invention of "ether" as a sort of universal jelly that
could have ripples shaken across it proved a little unconvincing.

Then, just at the turn of the century, the whole structure began
to crumble.

The first note of warning that something was going wrong came
with the discovery of X rays. Sir William Crookes, accidentally
leaving around tubes of rarefied gas, stumbled on "radiant matter,"
or "matter in the fourth state," as accidentally as Columbus discovered America. The British Government knighted him at once
(1897), but it was too late. The thing had started. Then came
Guglielmo Marconi with the revelation of more waves, and universal at that. Light, the world had learned to accept, because we
can see it, but this was fun in the dark.

There followed the researches of the radioactivity school and,
above all, those of Ernest Rutherford which revolutionized the
theory of matter. I knew Rutherford well as we were colleagues at
McGill for seven years. I am quite sure that he had no original intention of upsetting the foundations of the universe. Yet that is what
he did, and he was in due course very properly raised to the peerage
for it.

When Rutherford was done with the atom, all the solidity was
pretty well knocked out of it.

Till these researches began, people commonly thought of atoms
as something like birdseed — little round, solid particles, ever so
little, billions to an inch. They were small. But they were there. You
could weigh them. You could apply to them all the laws of Isaac
Newton about weight and velocity and mass and gravitation — in
other words, the whole of first-year physics.

Let us try to show what Rutherford did to the atom. Imagine to yourself an Irishman whirling a shillelagh around his head with the rapidity and dexterity known only in Tipperary or Donegal. If you come anywhere near, you'll get hit with the shillelagh. Now make it go faster; faster still; get it going so fast that you can't tell which is Irishman and which is shillelagh. The whole combination has turned into a green blur. If you shoot a bullet at it, it will probably go through, as there is mostly nothing there. Yet if you go up against it, it won't hit you now, because the shillelagh is going so fast that you will seem to come against a solid surface. Now make the Irishman smaller and the shillelagh longer. In fact, you don't need the Irishman at all; just his force, his Irish determination, so to speak. Just keep that, the *disturbance.* And you don't need the shillelagh either, just the *field of force* that it sweeps. There! Now put in two Irishmen and two shillelaghs and reduce them in the same way to one solid body — at least it seems solid but you can shoot bullets through it anywhere now. What you have now is a hydrogen atom — one proton and one electron flying around as a *disturbance* in space. Put in more Irishmen and more shillelaghs — or, rather, more protons and electrons — and you get other kinds of atoms. Put in a whole lot — eleven protons, eleven electrons; that is a sodium atom. Bunch the atoms together into combinations called molecules, themselves flying round — and there you are! That's solid matter, and nothing in it at all except disturbance. You're standing on it right now: the molecules are beating against your feet. But there is nothing there, and nothing in your feet. This may help you to understand how "waves," ripples of disturbance — for instance, the disturbance you call radio — go right through all matter, indeed right through *you,* as if you weren't there. You see, you aren't.

The peculiar thing about this atomic theory was that whatever the atoms were, birdseed or disturbance, it made no difference in the way they acted. They followed all the laws of mechanics and motion, or they seemed to. There was no need to change any idea of space or time because of them. Matter was their forte, like wax figures with Artemus Ward.

One must not confuse Rutherford's work on atoms with Einstein's theories of space and time. Rutherford worked all his life without reference to Einstein. Even in his later days at the Cavendish Laboratory at Cambridge when he began, ungratefully, to smash up the atom that had made him, he needed nothing from Einstein. I once asked Rutherford — it was at the height of the popular interest in Einstein in 1923 — what he thought of Einstein's relativity. "Oh, that stuff!" he said. "We never bother with that in our work!" His admirable biographer, Professor A. S. Eve, tells us that when the German physicist, Wien, told Rutherford that no Anglo-Saxon could understand relativity, Rutherford answered, "No, they have too much sense."

But it was Einstein who made the real trouble. He announced in 1905 that there was no such thing as absolute rest. After that there never was. But it was not till just after the Great War that the reading public caught on to Einstein and that little books on "Relativity" covered the bookstalls.

Einstein knocked out space and time, as Rutherford knocked out matter. The general viewpoint of relativity toward space is very simple. Einstein explains that there is no such place as *here*. "But," you answer, "I'm here; here is where I am right now." But you're moving, you're spinning around as the earth spins; and you and the earth are both spinning around the sun, and the sun is rushing through space toward a distant galaxy, and the galaxy itself is beating it away at 26,000 miles a second. Now, where is that spot that is here! How did you mark it? You remember the story of the two idiots who were out fishing, and one said, "We should have marked that place where we got all the fish," and the other said, "I did; I marked it on the boat." Well, that's it. That's *here*.

You can see it better still if you imagine the universe swept absolutely empty: nothing in it, not even *you*. Now put a *point* in it, just one point. Where is it? Why, obviously it's nowhere. If you say it's right there, where do you mean by there? In which direction is there? In *that* direction? Oh! Hold on, you're sticking yourself in to make a direction. It's in *no* direction; there aren't any directions. Now put in another point. Which is which? You can't tell. They *both* are. One is on the right, you say, and one on the left. You keep out of that space! There's no right and no left. Join the points with a line. Now you think you've got something, and I admit this is the nearest you have come to it. But is the line long or short? How long is it? Length soon vanishes into a purely relative term. One thing is longer than another: that's all.

There's no harm in all this, so far. To many people it's as obvious as it is harmless. But that's only the beginning. Leave space alone for a moment and take on time and then things begin to thicken. If there is no such place as here, a similar line of thought will show that there's no such time as now — not absolutely now. Empty the universe again as you did before, with not a speck in it, and now ask, What time is it? God bless me, how peculiar! It isn't any time. It can't be; there's nothing to tell the time by. You say you can feel it go; oh, but you're not there. There will be no *time* until you put something into space with dimensions to it — and then there'll be time, but only as connected somehow — no knowing how — with things in space. But just as there is no such thing as absolute top or bottom in space, so there is a similar difficulty as to time backward and time forward.

The relativity theory undertakes to explain both space and time by putting them together, since they are meaningless without one another, into a compound called "space-time continuum." Time thus becomes, they say, the fourth dimension of space. Until just recently it was claimed further that to fit these relationships together, to harmonize space and time, space must have a curve, or curvature. This was put over to the common mind by comparing what happens in space with what happens to a fly walking on a sphere (a globe). The fly walks and walks and never gets to the end. It's curved. The joke is on the fly. So was the joke long ago on the medieval people who thought the world was flat. "What happened to the theory of the earth," writes Eddington, "has happened also to the world of space and time."

The idea was made plainer for us by comparing space-time to an onion skin, or rather to an infinite number of onion skins. If you have enough, you can fill all space. The universe is your onion, as it was Shakespeare's oyster.

The discovery by Einstein of this curvature of space was greeted by the physicists with the burst of applause that greets a winning home run at baseball. That brilliant writer just mentioned, Sir Arthur Eddington, who can handle space and time with the imagery of a poet, and even infiltrate humor into gravitation — as when he says that a man in an elevator falling twenty stories has an ideal opportunity to study gravitation — is loud in his acclaim. Without this curve, it appears, things won't fit into their place. The fly on the globe, as long as he thinks it flat (like Mercator's map), finds things shifted, as by some unaccountable demon, to all sorts of wrong distances. Once he gets the idea of a sphere, everything comes straight. So with our space. The mystery of gravitation puzzles us, except those who have the luck to fall in an elevator, and even for them knowledge comes too late. They weren't falling at all: just curving. "Admit a curvature of the world," wrote Eddington in his Gifford Lectures of 1927, "and the mysterious agency disappears. Einstein has exorcised this demon."

But it appears now, fourteen years later, that Einstein doesn't care if space is curved or not. He can take it either way. A prominent physicist of today, head of the department in one of the greatest universities of the world, wrote me on this point: "Einstein had stronger hopes that a general theory which involved the assumption of a property of space, akin to what is ordinarily called curvature, would be more useful than he now believes to be the case." Plain talk for a professor. Most people just say Einstein has given up curved space. It's as if Sir Isaac Newton years after had said, with a yawn, "Oh, about that apple — perhaps it wasn't falling."

Now with the curve knocked out of it, the space-time continuum, with these so-called four dimensions, becomes really a very simple matter; in fact, only a very pretentious name for a very obvious fact. It just means that information about an occurrence is not complete unless we know both where it happened and when it happened. It is no use telling me that Diogenes is dead if I didn't know that he was alive.

Obviously "time-when" or "place-where" are bound together and coexist with one another. If there were no space — just emptiness — there could be no time. It wouldn't count itself. And if there were no time, there could be no space. Start it and it would flicker out again in no time — like an electric bulb on a wobble-plug. Space-time continuum is just a pretentious name for this consequence of consciousness. We can't get behind it. We begin life with it, as the chicken out of the egg begins with its cell memory. All the mathematics based on "space-time continuum" gets no further, as far as concerns the search for reality. . . .

◇◇

The Universe and Me
or
How to
Understand the Wonders of Science

JACK GOODMAN AND
ALAN GREEN

A BUSY, inquiring mind like mine can't remain idle these long winter evenings. Phyllis refuses to let me play any more bridge because of her narrow-minded obsession with the budget. Gilbert

From *How to Do Practically Anything* by permission of Simon and Schuster, publishers. Copyright © 1942 by Jack Goodman and Alan Green.

refuses to allow me to develop pictures in the bathroom because he likes sleeping on the bath mat, and since he's a great Dane the room isn't big enough for both of us. So I have been forced to seek some new hobby.

I've found it, and all because of the provocative discussion I had with my friend Professor Johnson at lunch a few weeks ago. He is an astrophysicist who speaks with his mouth full.

"A fine specimen of twentieth-century human being you are!" he muttered between mouthfuls of a lamb chop.

This hostile remark was probably inspired by the fact that I had happened, a few moments before, to push his soup in his lap while attempting to mop up the water from a glass I had chanced to overturn as a result of dabbing quickly at his coat to remove a live cigarette ash of mine that had fallen on it.

"Just suppose," he continued, "that you were suddenly transported back to the tenth century — you'd be a fine representative of this one, wouldn't you? Could you hasten human progress by one iota? No. Could you, for instance, show them how to make an automobile? No, you can't even change a tire on your own. Could you convince them that the earth was round — explain what gravity is — show them how to make a simple steam engine? No — you wouldn't be there for ten minutes before getting your finger caught in one of their crossbows."

"Ah, shut up," I parried.

This exchange started me thinking. Tossing in bed late that night, I conceded to myself that I hadn't had the best of it, and that there was a certain amount of justice in Johnson's remarks. I could think of only a few things which I might teach tenth-century people. The response to an opening two-no-trump bid, for instance. The odds against filling an inside straight and the folly of using a brassie in a cuppy lie. The fact that you should take aspirin if you had a headache. It didn't add up to much, especially when there was no bridge, poker, or golf in those days and consequently no headaches.

I decided then and there to do something about it, to learn about the world around me. After all, meek little professors who wouldn't go out in a drizzle without their galoshes are manufacturing lightning bolts and playing catch with them. Austere gentlemen who haven't been out on a date in years are trying to create artificial life out of a couple of electrons and the yolk of an old egg. Why shouldn't I too know something of the mysteries of the universe?

I started to find out. I read articles galore and ransacked libraries of books on popular science. As a result, I am now a mass of information, able to talk the ear off any tenth-century scholar, if given half a chance. And the following findings, which I have translated from scientific jargon to clear language anyone can understand, should be invaluable to all who feel that there is the slightest likelihood of their being transported back to the tenth century.

Let us first consider how oblivious we all are to the wonders about us in everyday life. When your phone rings at three in the morning and a guttural voice says, "Hullo — Acme Laundry? Lemme speak to Gus," do you stop for a moment and ponder the pretty play of physical forces that makes this modern miracle possible?

No, you don't. Yet we have here a perfect illustration of the phenomenon of Sound. There is the sound the voice makes. There is the sound you make. There is the further sound you make as, trying to replace the receiver in the dark, you drop it on your foot. There are the sounds you hear all around you for the rest of the night as you lie staring at the ceiling, trying to get to sleep. While you do this it may be comforting to ponder the fact that all these sounds are nothing but oodles and oodles of little waves of air, all dashing about at a speed of 1087.13 feet per second — much faster than you could run away from them.

Now let's consider another wonder. Let's consider that you do what I did the other day, which was to drop my fountain pen into a bowl of water, reach for it swearing, and then suddenly realize that the shimmering object I was observing through the water was my expensive new wrist watch.

Would you pause and consider the marvel of physics which makes the wrist watch appear even more distorted to the eye than does the face of the owner to an observer? Neither did I, but that is beside the point.

What is that wrist watch doing? I ask you.

Costing money, you perhaps answer.

No, no, this is not the scientific attitude. The important fact is that the wrist watch looks distorted because the light that has entered the water is "refracted." This means that it bounces off the water at the same angle at which it strikes. It was doing this all the time before we saw the wrist watch in the water and nobody noticed it. Science claims that this is why light distorts wrist watches under water and is probably right. So we see now that the repair work on a wrist watch is little to pay for the important principle we have learned.

All right. We now understand Sound and Light and can get on to the really tough stuff. Now we go off to the foot of Mount Everest and see how absurdly simple it is to explain the laws of Physics and Relativity.

Next to us is a large boulder weighing about eighty pounds. I have with me a man named Smith. Smith will proceed to push the boulder up Mount Everest.

Smith objects, saying that people can't get up Mount Everest by themselves, let alone pushing up boulders. We dismiss this sternly as hearsay. This is not the scientific attitude.

He begins. He does splendidly for a minute. He's doing pretty well. Not so good — oop!

Smith has fallen down on us, and for that matter the boulder only missed us by inches. But we have now completed another practical experiment. The deduction we draw is: *a force can't move a mass up an incline unless it doesn't get tired.*

But wait. A scientist pops up from nowhere. He objects to our drawing conclusions just yet. He says any fool knows that one experiment doesn't prove the case — we must try several hundred identical experiments to make sure.

We concede the point, but inquire if maybe the scientist would like to make a small side bet that we're wrong. Smith gets up and says he's going home.

But the scientist continues to argue. He says that even with ten thousand experiments our law might still be wrong.

"*Up* Mount Everest indeed!" he says contemptuously. "How do you know he isn't pushing the boulder down Mount Everest? Remember," he adds crushingly, "that from the point of view of an observer in space, Mount Everest would run downhill all the way from its base to its summit. And to someone else even farther away, the man and the boulder would just be going around and around in little whorls."

"But that's silly," we protest.

"No — that's Relativity."

And so it is. So we abandon the experiment, cheering ourselves with the thought that on the top — or bottom — of Mount Everest water boils at such a low temperature that we couldn't even cook an egg if we got there. Even those most passionately lusting to climb Mount Everest concede that it has this drawback. It is because the same "atmospheric pressure" exists at the top of Mount Everest as in your house when you are in a hurry to get to work and are trying to boil some water for coffee.

"Atmospheric pressure" is merely a hoity-toity scientific term for the weight of air. As any shrewd mind can immediately perceive for itself, there's naturally less air up at the top of Mount Everest, because nobody goes there to breathe it.

Now for Gravity. Before the time of Sir Isaac Newton, if someone got hit by an apple falling from a tree, all he knew was that he had been hit by an apple falling from a tree. This shows the barbaric state the human race was in at that time. For ages upon ages people refrained from standing under apple trees, believing in their simple, savage way that it was better not to be hit by an apple. But Sir Isaac Newton, breaking through this curtain of ignorance, got hit by one, and as a result everybody knows now that the reason apples fall to earth is because a big mass like the earth attracts a little mass like an apple.

As a matter of cold fact, any two masses anywhere attract each other, whether they like it or not. A Democrat is attracted to a Republican, for instance, and he doesn't have to be falling out of a tree, either. If the Republican is a big one, the Democrat is *even more attracted* to him than he would be to a small Democrat.

So we see that the findings of Science extend even to our political lives.

Astronomy is perhaps a trifle more complex than Gravity. I will admit that, during my intensive study of scientific works about the Universe, I did occasionally get the impression that one astronomer was kneeling in back of me while another was standing in front of me and pushing. I confess that I was occasionally baffled by statements such as: "Space is like a tennis ball which has been turned inside out without breaking the cover." Or: "There really is no such number as the square root of minus one, nor could there be. We astronomers just use it to multiply other numbers by, which makes them imaginary, too. That's what we base our most important theories on."

But on the whole it is really a simple matter. It is a man's subject, though. Women — or anyway, my wife, Phyllis — do not seem to have the mental scope to grasp it.

When I told her that originally our solar system consisted of only the sun, a huge, distended, gaseous mass, it merely reminded her that I had forgotten to get the soda-mint tablets I wanted.

When I added that, ages ago, another great celestial object, hurtling through space, had passed too close to the sun, she recalled that I wouldn't have to have the car's fender fixed if I had been more careful.

When I attempted to continue, pointing out that the gravitational attraction of a passing star had pulled huge masses of material from the sun and flung them into space, causing cosmic disorder, she giggled and said that it reminded her of the time I had tried to defrost the icebox.

I gave up completely after having mentioned a piece of interesting, valuable information which might come in very handy sometime. It was that the moon appears at a different hour every night. There is no hope for mental improvement in anyone who can answer: "I'll bet *it* doesn't expect *its* dinner to be ready and hot and done just right."

I regret to say that it is Phyllis' opinion that science is a sheer waste of time. She has a black bobbie pin with which she seems able to pick locks when I lose keys and to effect all sorts of repairs around the house that my buoyant male vigor makes necessary. Although I can do none of these things, I invariably know the theory behind them and could be extremely helpful if listened to. But she places more faith in the bobbie pin.

After that session with Phyllis I wished that I could find someone to talk with about my new-found knowledge. And that very night after I got to sleep I found him.

It was an extremely vivid dream. I was back in the tenth century and I was lying on the banks of the Hudson. Everything was very peaceful. The Hudson River Dayliners were lying useless at the piers because Bear Mountain and Albany hadn't been discovered yet. Suddenly a little man with a wispy, graying beard and a pair of wrinkled chain-mail pants sauntered up to me.

"If I could only get *enough* tapioca, it would work," he said confidentially.

"What would work?" I said.

He looked at me in some surprise. "Alchemy, of course."

I asked what that was. He said it was the science of turning base metals into gold. I was amazed that this simple, economical idea had not occurred to me.

"I thought everyone knew that!" he said. "Where on earth can you be from?"

"I'm from the twentieth century."

"Couldn't you have brought along some tapioca?" he said irritably. "I've tried all the base metals and it's no go. I'm sure tapioca's the thing."

I said I was sorry. I hadn't thought of it.

"Whereabouts in the twentieth century?" he said with mild curiosity.

"New York City."

He nodded. "Oh, yes, I've heard about it."

"That," I said, "is obviously impossible."

"No, it isn't. I'm a wizard."

I apologized for not having believed him. He said it was quite all right.

Then there was a moment's embarrassed silence.

"By the way," I said. "Do you fellows around here happen to know that the world is round?"

"No, it isn't," he said. "It's flattened out a little at the poles. That's old stuff — some Greek was trying to sell it more than a thousand years ago. If you really want to tell me something, I'm curious about those mechanical wonders you have in your century. The radio, for instance. How do you work that?"

There was a moment's silence.

"I'm not very clear on that," I said, "but did you know that an express train, if it traveled at sixty miles an hour, would take an awful long time to reach the nearest star?"

"All right," he said. "But how does an express train work? *That* would be information I could use."

"It works by steam," I said proudly. He asked how. A little annoyed, I said the steam compressed, then it expanded, then it compressed again, and so forth.

"You can see how when you boil a kettle," I ended weakly. "Anyway, that's all James Watt saw and he invented the steam engine that got to be the express train."

"Hmmm," he said. He stroked his beard and looked at me quizzically. "Know anything about electricity?" he said.

"Well . . . there's this little button on the wall and you push it. Or you shuffle your feet on a carpet and then touch somebody and they get a shock. It's fun, electricity." I laughed uncertainly, but he didn't join in.

"Hmmm," he repeated. He looked at me more sharply. "Are you *sure* you're from the twentieth century?" he said.

I nodded silently.

"Here," he said sympathetically, handing me a small object, "take this back with you and see if someone won't teach you how to use it."

He shook his head sadly and walked away.

I looked at his parting gift. It was a small bobbie pin.

❖❖

Lines in Dispraise of Dispraise

OGDEN NASH

I HEREBY bequeath to the Bide-a-Wee Home all people who have
　　statistics to prove that a human
Is nothing but a combination of iron and water and potash and
　　albumen.
That may very well be the truth
But it's just like saying that a cocktail is nothing but ice and gin
　　and vermouth.
People who go around analyzing
Are indeed very tanalizing.
They always want to get at the bottom
Of everything from spring to ottom.
They can't just look at a Rembrandt or a Bartolozzi
And say, Boy! that's pretty hozzi-tozzi!
No, they have to break it up into its component parts
And reconstruct it with blueprints and charts.
My idea is that while after looking around me and even at me
I may not be proud of being a human
I object to having attention called to my iron and water and potash
　　and albumen.
In the first place, it's undignified,
And in the second place, nothing by it is signified.
Because it isn't potash etcetera that makes people Republicans or
　　Democrats or Ghibellines or Guelphs,
It's the natural perversity of the people themselfs.
No, no, you old analysts, away with the whole kit and kaboodle
　　of you.
I wouldn't even make mincemeat to give to a poodle of you.

5

The Gift of Prometheus

Science is wonder
As number is music, if we can
But read our thought back to the high listener
Whose language in us, overheard,
Creates the mind.

The Man of Science seeks truth as a remote and unknown benefactor; he cherishes and loves it in his solitude: the Poet, singing a song in which all human beings join with him, rejoices in the presence of truth as our visible friend and hourly companion. Poetry is the breath and finer spirit of all knowledge; it is the impassioned expression which is in the countenance of all Science. . . . If the labors of men of Science should ever create any material revolution, direct or indirect, in our condition, and in the impressions which we habitually receive, the Poet will sleep then no more than at present, but he will be ready to follow the steps of the man of Science, not only in those general indirect effects, but he will be at his side, carrying sensation into the midst of the objects of the Science itself. The remotest discoveries of the Chemist, the Botanist, or Mineralogist, will be as proper objects of the Poet's art as any upon which it can be employed, if the time should ever come when these things shall be familiar to us, and the relations under which they are contemplated by the followers of these perspective Sciences shall be manifestly and palpably material to us as enjoying and suffering beings.

— From WILLIAM WORDSWORTH:
Preface to *Lyrical Ballads*

◇◇

"Where Wast Thou When I Laid the Foundations of the Earth?"

From THE BOOK OF JOB

VOICE OUT OF THE WHIRLWIND. Who is this that darkeneth counsel
By words without knowledge?
Gird up now thy loins like a man;
For I will demand of thee, and declare thou unto me.
Where wast thou when I laid the foundations of the earth?
Declare, if thou hast understanding.
Who determined the measures thereof, if thou knowest?
Or who stretched the line upon it?
Whereupon were the foundations thereof fastened?
Or who laid the corner stone thereof;
When the morning stars sang together,
And all the sons of God shouted for joy?
Or who shut up the sea with doors,
When it broke forth, as if it had issued out of the womb;
When I made the cloud the garment thereof,
And thick darkness a swaddlingband for it,
And prescribed for it my decree,
And set bars and doors,
And said, "Hitherto shalt thou come, but no further;
And here shall thy proud waves be stayed"?
Hast thou commanded the morning since thy days began,
And caused the dayspring to know its place;
That it might take hold of the ends of the earth,
And the wicked be shaken out of it?
It is changed as clay under the seal;
And all things stand forth as a garment:
And from the wicked their light is withheld,
And the high arm is broken.
Hast thou entered into the springs of the sea?

From *The Bible, Designed to Be Read as Living Literature*, edited by Ernest Sutherland Bates. Copyright © 1936 by Simon and Schuster, Inc.

Or hast thou walked in the recesses of the deep?
Have the gates of death been revealed unto thee?
Or hast thou seen the gates of the shadow of death?
Hast thou comprehended the breadth of the earth?
Declare, if thou knowest it all.
Where is the way to the dwelling of light,
And as for darkness, where is the place thereof;
That thou shouldest take it to the bound thereof,
And that thou shouldest discern the paths to the house thereof?
Doubtless, thou knowest, for thou wast then born,
And the number of thy days is great!
Hast thou entered the treasuries of the snow,
Or hast thou seen the treasuries of the hail,
Which I have reserved against the time of trouble,
Against the day of battle and war?
By what is the light parted,
Or the east wind scattered upon the earth?
Who hath cleft a channel for the waterflood,
Or a way for the lightning of the thunder;
To cause it to rain on a land where no man is;
On the wilderness, wherein there is no man;
To satisfy the waste and desolate ground;
And to cause the tender grass to spring forth?
Hath the rain a father?
Or who hath begotten the drops of dew?
Out of whose womb came the ice?
And the hoary frost of heaven, who hath gendered it?
The waters are hidden as with stone,
And the face of the deep is frozen.
Canst thou bind the cluster of the Pleiades,
Or loose the bands of Orion?
Canst thou lead forth the Mazzaroth in their season?
Or canst thou guide the Bear with her train?
Knowest thou the ordinances of the heavens?
Canst thou establish the dominion thereof in the earth?
Canst thou lift up thy voice to the clouds,
That abundance of waters may cover thee?
Canst thou send forth lightnings, that they may go,
And say unto thee, "Here we are"?
Who hath put wisdom in the inward parts?
Or who hath given understanding to the mind?
Who can number the clouds by wisdom?
Or who can pour out the bottles of heaven,
When the dust runneth into a mass,

And the clods cleave fast together?
Wilt thou hunt the prey for the lioness?
Or satisfy the appetite of the young lions,
When they couch in their dens,
And abide in the covert to lie in wait?
Who provideth for the raven his food,
When his young ones cry unto God,
And wander for lack of meat?

Knowest thou the time when the wild goats of the rock bring
  forth?
Or canst thou mark when the hinds do calve?
Canst thou number the months that they fulfil?
Or knowest thou the time when they bring forth?
They bow themselves, they bring forth their young,
They cast out their sorrows.
Their young ones are in good liking, they grow up in the open field,
They go forth, and return not again.
  Who hath sent out the wild ass free?
Or who hath loosed the bands of the wild ass?
Whose house I have made the wilderness,
And the salt land his dwelling place.
He scorneth the tumult of the city,
Neither heareth he the shoutings of the driver.
The range of the mountains is his pasture,
And he searcheth after every green thing.
  Will the wild ox be content to serve thee?
Or will he abide by thy crib?
Canst thou bind the wild ox with his band in the furrow?
Or will he harrow the valleys after thee?
Wilt thou trust him, because his strength is great?
Or wilt thou leave to him thy labour?
Wilt thou confide in him, that he will bring home thy seed,
And gather the corn of thy threshing-floor?
  The wing of the ostrich rejoiceth;
But are her pinions and feathers kindly?
For she leaveth her eggs on the earth,
And warmeth them in the dust,
And forgetteth that the foot may crush them,
Or that the wild beast may trample them.
She is hardened against her young ones, as if they were not hers:
Though her labour be in vain, she is without fear;
Because God hath deprived her of wisdom,
Neither hath he imparted to her understanding.

What time she lifteth up herself on high,
She scorneth the horse and his rider.
 Hast thou given the horse his might?
Hast thou clothed his neck with the quivering mane?
Hast thou made him to leap as a locust?
The glory of his snorting is terrible.
He paweth in the valley, and rejoiceth in his strength:
He goeth out to meet the armed men.
He mocketh at fear, and is not dismayed;
Neither turneth he back from the sword.
The quiver rattleth against him,
The flashing spear and the javelin.
 He swalloweth the ground with fierceness and rage;
Neither believeth he that it is the voice of the trumpet.
As oft as the trumpet soundeth he saith, "Aha!"
And he smelleth the battle afar off,
The thunder of the captains, and the shouting.
 Doth the hawk soar by thy wisdom,
And stretch her wings toward the south?
Doth the eagle mount up at thy command,
And make her nest on high?
She dwelleth on the rock, and hath her lodging there,
Upon the crag of the rock, and the strong hold.
From thence she spieth out the prey;
Her eyes behold it afar off.
Her young ones also suck up blood:
And where the slain are, there is she.
 Shall he that cavilleth contend with the Almighty?
He that argueth with God, let him answer it.

JOB. Behold. I am of small account; what shall I answer thee?
I lay mine hand upon my mouth.
Once have I spoken, and I will not answer;
Yea twice, but I will proceed no further.
VOICE OUT OF THE WHIRLWIND. Gird up thy loins now like a man:
I will demand of thee, and declare thou unto me.
Wilt thou even disannul my judgment?
Wilt thou condemn me, that thou mayest be justified?
Or hast thou an arm like God?
And canst thou thunder with a voice like him?
Deck thyself now with excellency and dignity;
And array thyself with honour and majesty.
Pour forth the overflowings of thine anger:
And look upon every one that is proud, and abase him.

Look on every one that is proud, and bring him low;
And tread down the wicked where they stand.
Hide them in the dust together;
Bind their faces in the hidden place.
Then will I also confess of thee
That thine own right hand can save thee.
    Behold now Behemoth, which I made with thee;
He eateth grass as an ox.
Lo now, his strength is in his loins,
And his force is in the muscles of his belly.
He moveth his tail like a cedar:
The sinews of his thighs are knit together.
His bones are as tubes of brass;
His limbs are like bars of iron.
He is the chief of the ways of God:
He only that made him can make his sword to approach unto him.
Surely the mountains bring him forth food;
Where all the beasts of the field do play.
He lieth under the lotus trees,
In the covert of the reed, and the fen.
The lotus trees cover him with their shadow;
The willows of the brook compass him about.
Behold, if a river overflow, he trembleth not:
He is confident, though Jordan swell even to his mouth.
Shall any take him when he is on the watch,
Or pierce through his nose with a snare?

    Canst thou draw out Leviathan with a fishhook?
Or press down his tongue with a cord?
Canst thou put a rope into his nose?
Or pierce his jaw through with a hook?
Will he make many supplications unto thee?
Or will he speak soft words unto thee?
Will he make a covenant with thee,
That thou shouldest take him for a servant for ever?
Wilt thou play with him as with a bird?
Or wilt thou bind him for thy maidens?
Shall the bands of fishermen make traffic of him?
Shall they part him among the merchants?
Canst thou fill his skin with barbed irons,
Or his head with fish spears?
Lay thine hand upon him;
Remember the battle, and do so no more.
Behold, the hope of him is in vain:

Shall not one be cast down even at the sight of him?
None is so fierce that he dare stir him up:
Who then is he that can stand before me?
Who hath first given unto me, that I should repay him?
Whatsoever is under the whole heaven is mine.
I will not keep silence concerning his limbs,
Nor his mighty strength, nor his comely proportion.
Who can strip off his outer garment?
Who shall come within his double bridle?
Who can open the doors of his face?
Round about his teeth is terror.
His strong scales are his pride,
Shut up together as with a close seal.
One is so near to another,
That no air can come between them.
They are joined one to another;
They stick together, that they cannot be sundered.
His sneezings flash forth light,
And his eyes are like the eyelids of the morning.
Out of his mouth go burning torches,
And sparks of fire leap forth.
Out of his nostrils a smoke goeth,
As of a seething pot and burning rushes.
His breath kindleth coals,
And a flame goeth forth from his mouth.
In his neck abideth strength,
And terror danceth before him.
The flakes of his flesh are joined together:
They are firm upon him; they cannot be moved.
His heart is as firm as a stone;
Yea, firm as the nether millstone.
When he raiseth himself up, the mighty are afraid:
By reason of consternation they are beside themselves.
If one lay at him with his sword, it cannot avail;
Nor the spear, the dart, nor the pointed shaft.
He counteth iron as straw,
And brass as rotten wood.
The arrow cannot make him flee:
Slingstones are turned with him into stubble.
Clubs are counted as stubble:
He laugheth at the rushing of the javelin.
His underparts are like sharp potsherds:
He spreadeth as it were a threshing wain upon the mire.
He maketh the deep to boil like a pot:

He maketh the sea like ointment.
He maketh a path to shine after him;
One would think the deep to be hoary.
Upon earth there is not his like,
That is made without fear.
He beholdeth every thing that is high:
He is king over all the sons of pride.
JOB. I know that thou canst do all things,
And that no purpose of thine can be restrained.
"Who is this that hideth counsel without knowledge?"
Therefore have I uttered that which I understand not,
Things too wonderful for me, which I knew not.
Hear, I beseech thee, and I will speak;
I will demand of thee, and declare thou unto me.
I had heard of thee by the hearing of the ear;
But now mine eye seeth thee,
Wherefore I abhor myself, and repent
In dust and ashes.

"All Arts of Mortals from Prometheus Spring"

AESCHYLUS

PROMETHEUS speaks: But those woes of men,
List ye to them, — how they, before as babes,
By me were roused to reason, taught to think;
And this I say, not finding fault with men,
But showing my good-will in all I gave.
For first, though seeing, all in vain they saw,
And hearing, heard not rightly. But, like forms
Of phantom-dreams, throughout their life's whole length
They muddled all at random; did not know
Houses of brick that catch the sunlight's warmth,
Nor yet the work of carpentry. They dwelt

From *Prometheus Bound* (Plumptre translation).

In hollowed holes, like swarms of tiny ants,
In sunless depths of caverns; and they had
No certain signs of winter, nor of spring
Flower-laden, nor of summer with her fruits;
But without counsel fared their whole life long,
Until I showed the risings of the stars,
And settings hard to recognize. And I
Found Number for them, chief device of all,
Groupings of letters, Memory's handmaid that,
And mother of the Muses. And I first
Bound in the yoke wild steeds, submissive made
Or to the collar or men's limbs, that so
They might in man's place bear his greatest toils;
And horses trained to love the rein I yoked
To chariots, glory of wealth's pride of state;
Nor was it anyone but I that found
Sea-crossing, canvas-wingèd cars of ships:
Such rare designs inventing (wretched me!)
For mortal men, I yet have no device
By which to free myself from this my woe. . . .

Hearing what yet remains thou'lt wonder more,
What arts and what resources I devised:
And this the chief: if any one fell ill,
There was no help for him, nor healing food,
Nor unguent, nor yet potion; but for want
Of drugs they wasted, till I showed to them
The blendings of all mild medicaments,
Wherewith they ward the attacks of sickness sore. . . .

And 'neath the earth the hidden boons for men,
Bronze, iron, silver, gold, who else could say
That he, ere I did, found them? None, I know,
Unless he fain would babble idle words.
In one short word, then, learn the truth condensed, —
All arts of mortals from Prometheus spring.

"All Things Flow"

LUCRETIUS

No single thing abides; but all things flow.
Fragment to fragment clings — the things thus grow
Until we know and name them. By degrees
They melt, and are no more the things we know.

Globed from the atoms falling slow or swift
I see the suns, I see the systems lift
Their forms; and even the systems and the suns
Shall go back slowly to the eternal drift.

Thou, too, oh earth — thine empires, lands, and seas —
Least, with thy stars, of all the galaxies,
Globed from the drift like these, like these thou too
Shalt go. Thou art going, hour by hour, like these.

Nothing abides. Thy seas in delicate haze
Go off; those moonèd sands forsake their place;
And where they are, shall other seas in turn
Mow with their scythes of whiteness other bays. . . .

This bowl of milk, the pitch on yonder jar,
Are strange and far-bound travelers come from far.
This is a snowflake that was once a flame —
The flame was once the fragment of a star. . . .

Round, angular, soft, brittle, dry, cold, warm,
Things *are* their qualities: things *are* their form —
And these in combination, even as bees,
Not singly but combined, make up the swarm:

And when the qualities like bees on wing,
Having a moment clustered, cease to cling,
As the thing dies without its qualities,
So die the qualities without the thing.

Quoted from *Lucretius on Life and Death* by William H. Mallock. Reprinted
by kind permission of A. and C. Black, Ltd., London.

Where is the coolness when no cool winds blow?
Where is the music when the lute lies low?
Are not the redness and the red rose one,
And the snow's whiteness one thing with the snow?

Even so, now mark me, here we reach the goal
Of Science, and in little have the whole —
Even as the redness and the rose are one,
So with the body one thing is the soul. . . .

The seeds that once were we take flight and fly,
Winnowed to earth, or whirled along the sky,
Not lost but disunited. Life lives on.
It is the lives, the lives, the lives, that die.

They go beyond recapture and recall,
Lost in the all-indissoluble All: —
Gone like the rainbow from the fountain's foam,
Gone like the spindrift shuddering down the squall. . . .

Oh, Science, lift aloud thy voice that stills
The pulse of fear, and through the conscience thrills —
Thrills through the conscience the news of peace —
How beautiful thy feet are on the hills!

SCIENCE: PROMETHEAN OR MEPHISTOPHELEAN

◇◇

St. Augustine, a man of real learning in his generation, and one of the greatest of all Christian philosophers quite apart from his compelling literary force, could write: "Whatever knowledge man has acquired outside Holy Writ, if it be harmful is there condemned; if it be wholesome it is there contained." There we have almost the words which tradition ascribes, rightly or wrongly, to Caliph Omar, condemning to flames that Library of Alexandria which had no equal in the world before it, and was destined to have no rival, even at an immense distance, for the rest of the Middle Ages. "If all those volumes" (so his words are reported) "contain that which is written in the Koran, then they are superfluous; if anything contrary, then they are mischievous: burn them all."

— G. C. COULTON: *Medieval Panorama*

⊂⊅ *NATURE REHABILITATED*

BASIL WILLEY

THE NOTION of a "forbidden" knowledge is ingrained deeply in the human race; but widely different views have been held as to which kind of knowledge was the forbidden kind. Broadly it may be guessed that the knowledge which in any age is "forbidden," is always that which presents itself as a distraction or seducement from what is then considered the main purpose of living. At the very outset of *The Advancement of Learning* Bacon is confronted with the medieval conception of natural science as the forbidden knowledge. It is objected, he says, by divines, that "knowledge puffeth up," that it "hath somewhat of the serpent," that (in a word) it was the original cause of the Fall of Man. Marlowe's *Faustus* had

From *The Seventeenth Century Background* by Basil Willey. Reprinted by kind permission of the publishers, Chatto and Windus, Ltd.

appeared not long before *The Advancement of Learning*, and the
Faustus legend testifies to the strength of the fascinated dread with
which the Middle Ages had thought of natural science. From the
earliest days of man there had of course been evil forces in Nature
to be feared and propitiated; but during the Christian centuries
"Nature" had, in quite a special sense, been consigned to the Satanic
order. Both the myth-making instinct of paganism and the Stoic
yearning for the Universe as the City of God were checked by the
Pauline and Augustinian theology, which represented Nature (including man) as depraved since the Fall, and as groaning under
the divine malediction. The divine order, the order of Grace, was
felt to be wholly separate from, and in a sense opposed to, "Nature."
The sense which above all marks the Christian consciousness, of sin
in man and of imperfection in Nature, expressed itself in a virtual
dualism, the Satanic forces being as real as the divine, if less powerful. The "beggarly elements" of Nature, as St. Paul calls them, were
handed over to the Prince of the Air and his fallen angels, who were
soon identified with the dethroned divinities of the heathen pan-
theons. At the Nativity of Christ, in Milton's Ode:

> "Nature in awe to Him
> Had doff't her gaudy trim,"

and

> "woos the gentle Air
> To hide her guilty front with innocent snow,
> And on her naked shame,
> Pollute with sinful blame,
>   The saintly veil of maiden white to throw;
> Confounded, that her Maker's eyes
> Should look so near upon her foul deformities."

To escape upward from this Satan-ridden earth, and the body of this
death, beyond the planetary spheres with their disastrous influences,
into the divine empyrean — this was the purpose of living, this
the effort of the believer; and only by divine grace supernaturally
mediated was success possible. Whatever diverted attention from
this supreme object would be liable to rank as "forbidden." Even
the female sex was held by some theologians to belong to the Satanic
order, Chrysostom calling woman a "desirable calamity." How much
more sinful, then, to interest oneself in Nature's ungodly secrets!
Since earth, water, air and fire were the allotted spheres of the
several hierarchies of evil spirits, to study nature meant to repeat

the original sin of Adam; it meant a compact with the devil and the death of the soul. Astrology, alchemy and black magic are the (popular) medieval names for science, just as "heresy" was the name for any trust, such as Pelagius showed, in the natural virtue of man.

On the other hand, that it had at any rate once been possible to think of science quite differently, the Prometheus myth was there to testify. The purveyor of knowledge and civilization might be the friend, and not the Adversary, of man. Bacon's task, it may be said, was to prove that natural science was Promethean and not Mephistophelean. . . .

This recrudescence of confidence in Nature was immensely strengthened by the scientific movement of the Renaissance, which reclaimed the physical world from its traditional association with Satan. In the *Utopia* of Sir Thomas More, natural philosophy is considered, not as "conjuring," involving a pact like that of Faust and Mephistopheles, but as something acceptable to God, and even as part of religious duty. The strength of the "Faust" tradition is attested by the fact that Bacon concerns himself, at the outset of his great work, to show that whatever the forbidden knowledge may be, it is not natural science. Bacon's argument is of great importance, because it furnished the scientists of the following two centuries with a technique for reconciling science with religion, and gave a first impulse to the movement toward scientific deism. Bacon's purpose requires that Nature should be established as divine instead of Satanic, and this he secures by arguing that God has revealed himself to man by means of *two* scriptures: first, of course, through the written word, but also, secondly, through his handiwork, the created universe. To study nature, therefore, cannot be contrary to religion; indeed, it is part of the duty we owe to the great Artificer of the world. "It was not," he says, "the pure knowledge of nature and universality, a knowledge by the light whereof man did give names unto other creatures in Paradise, as they were brought before him, according to their proprieties, which gave the occasion to the fall"; it was not, that is to say, natural science. It was "the proud knowledge of good and evil, with an intent in man to give law unto himself, and to depend no more on God's commandments, which was the form of the temptation."

To Bacon the logic-spinning of the schoolmen was a kind of forbidden knowledge; it was a presumptuous attempt to read the secret purposes of God, and to force his works into conformity with the laws of the human mind. This was for him the real *hubris*, this metaphysical arrogance, which "disdains to dwell upon particulars,"

and confidently explains all things by syllogism. The true humility is
the attribute of the Baconian scientist, who is content to come
forth into the light of things, and let nature be his teacher. "Nor
could we hope to succeed, if we arrogantly searched for the sciences
in the narrow cells of the human understanding, and not submis-
sively in the wider world." Access to the kingdom of man, which is
founded on the sciences, resembles "that to the kingdom of heaven,
where no admission is conceded except to children."

◇◇◇

From Dr. Faustus

CHRISTOPHER MARLOWE

Enter CHORUS.

CHORUS. Not marching now in fields of Thrasymene
Where Mars did mate the Carthaginians,
Nor sporting in the dalliance of love
In courts of kings where state is overturned,
Nor in the pomp of proud audacious deeds
Intends our Muse to daunt his heavenly verse:
Only this, Gentlemen, we must perform,
The form of Faustus' fortunes good or bad.
To patient judgments we appeal our plaud
And speak for Faustus in his infancy.
Now is he born, his parents base of stock,
In Germany within a town called Rhodes;
Of riper years to Wittenberg he went
Whereas his kinsmen chiefly brought him up;
So soon he profits in divinity,
The fruitful plot of scholarism graced,
That shortly he was graced with Doctor's name,
Excelling all whose sweet delight disputes
In heavenly matters of theology,
Till swollen with cunning, of a self-conceit,
His waxen wings did mount above his reach

From *Tragical History of Doctor Faustus* (abridged).

And melting heavens conspired his overthrow.
For, falling to a devilish exercise
And glutted more with learning's golden gifts,
He surfeits upon cursed necromancy.
Nothing so sweet as magic is to him,
Which he prefers before his chiefest bliss —
And this the man that in his study sits. *Exit.*

Enter FAUSTUS *in his Study.*

FAUSTUS. Settle thy studies, Faustus, and begin
To sound the depth of that thou wilt profess.
Having commenced, be a divine in show,
Yet level at the end of every art
And live and die in Aristotle's works:
Sweet Analytics, 'tis thou hast ravished me! [*Reads.*]
Bene disserere est finis logicis —
Is to dispute well logic's chiefest end?
Affords this art no greater miracle?
Then read no more; thou hast attained the end.
A greater subject fitteth Faustus' wit:
Bid ὸν καὶ μὴ ὸν farewell, Galen come,
Seeing *ubi desinit philosophus, ibi incipit medicus;*
Be a physician, Faustus, heap up gold
And be eternized for some wondrous cure. [*Reads.*]
Summum bonum medicinae sanitas —
The end of physic is our bodies' health:
Why, Faustus, hast thou not attained that end?
Is not thy common talk sound aphorisms?
Are not thy bills hung up as monuments
Whereby whole cities have escaped the plague
And thousand desperate maladies been eased?
Yet art thou still but Faustus, and a man.
Couldst thou make men to live eternally
Or, being dead, raise them to life again,
Then this profession were to be esteemed.
Physic, farewell. Where is Justinian? [*Reads.*]
Si una eademque res legatur duobus,
Alter rem, alter valorem rei, etc. —
A pretty case of paltry legacies!
Exhaereditare filium non potest pater nisi —
Such is the subject of the Institute
And universal body of the law.
His study fits a mercenary drudge

Who aims at nothing but external trash,
Too servile and illiberal for me.
When all is done, divinity is best.
Jerome's Bible, Faustus, view it well: [*Reads.*]
Stipendium peccati mors est — Ha! *Stipendium, etc.*
The reward of sin is death. That's hard.
Si pecasse negamus, fallimur, et nulla est in nobis veri-
          tas —
If we say that we have no sin
We deceive ourselves, and there's no truth in us.
Why then belike
We must sin and so consequently die,
Ay, we must die an everlasting death.
What doctrine call you this, *Che sera, sera:*
What will be, shall be? Divinity, adieu!
These metaphysics of magicians
And necromantic books are heavenly:
Lines, circles, signs, letters and characters —
Ay, these are those that Faustus most desires.
O what a world of profit and delight,
Of power, of honor, of omnipotence,
Is promised to the studious artisan!
All things that move between the quiet poles
Shall be at my command. Emperors and kings
Are but obeyed in their several provinces,
Nor can they raise the wind or rend the clouds;
But his dominion that exceeds in this
Stretcheth as far as doth the mind of man.
A sound magician is a mighty god:
Here, Faustus, try thy brains to gain a deity!

          Enter WAGNER.

Wagner, commend me to my dearest friends,
The German Valdes and Cornelius;
Request them earnestly to visit me.
          WAGNER. I will, sir.   *Exit.*
FAUST. Their conference will be a greater help to me
Than all my labors, plod I ne'er so fast.

          Enter the GOOD ANGEL *and the* EVIL ANGEL.

     G. ANG. O Faustus, lay that damned book aside
And gaze not on it, lest it tempt thy soul

And heap God's heavy wrath upon thy head.
Read, read the Scriptures! That is blasphemy.
 E. ANG. Go forward, Faustus, in that famous art
Wherein all nature's treasury is contained:
Be thou on earth, as Jove is in the sky,
Lord and commander of these elements.

         Exeunt ANGELS.

 FAUST. How am I glutted with conceit of this!
Shall I make spirits fetch me what I please,
Resolve me of all ambiguities,
Perform what desperate enterprise I will?
I'll have them fly to India for gold,
Ransack the océan for orient pearl,
And search all corners of the new-found world
For pleasant fruits and princely delicates;
I'll have them read me strange philosophy
And tell the secrets of all foreign kings;
I'll have them wall all Germany with brass
And make swift Rhine circle fair Wittenberg;
I'll have them fill the public schools with silk
Wherewith the students shall be bravely clad;
I'll levy soldiers with the coin they bring,
And chase the Prince of Parma from our land
And reign sole king of all our provinces;
Yea, stranger engines for the brunt of war
Than was the fiery keel at Antwerp's bridge
I'll make my servile spirits to invent!

   Enter VALDES *and* CORNELIUS.

Come, German Valdes and Cornelius,
And make me blest with your sage conference.
Valdes, sweet Valdes and Cornelius,
Know that your words have won me at the last
To practise magic and concealéd arts;
Yet not your words only, but mine own fantasy
That will receive no object for my head
But ruminates on necromantic skill.
Philosophy is odious and obscure,
Both law and physic are for petty wits,
Divinity is basest of the three,
Unpleasant, harsh, contemptible and vile;
'Tis magic, magic, that hath ravished me!
Then, gentle friends, aid me in this attempt,

And I that have with concise syllogisms
Gravelled the pastors of the German church,
And made the flowering pride of Wittenberg
Swarm to my problems as the infernal spirits
On sweet Musaeus when he came to hell,
Will be as cunning as Agrippa was
Whose shadows made all Europe honor him.

    VALD. Faustus, these books, thy wit and our experience
Shall make all nations to canonize us.
As Indian Moors obey their Spanish lords
So shall the subjects of every element
Be always serviceable to us three:
Like lions shall they guard us when we please,
Like Almain rutters with their horsemen's staves,
Or Lapland giants trotting by our sides;
Sometimes like women, or unwedded maids,
Shadowing more beauty in their airy brows
Than has the white breasts of the queen of love;
From Venice shall they drag huge argosies
And from America the golden fleece
That yearly stuffs old Philip's treasury,
If learned Faustus will be resolute.

    FAUST. Valdes, as resolute am I in this
As thou to live; therefore object it not.

    CORN. The miracles that magic will perform
Will make thee vow to study nothing else.
He that is grounded in astrology,
Enriched with tongues, well seen in minerals,
Hath all the principles magic doth require.
Then doubt not, Faustus, but to be renowned
And more frequented for this mystery
Than heretofore the Delphian oracle.
The spirits tell me they can dry the sea
And fetch the treasure of all foreign wrecks —
Ay, all the wealth that our forefathers hid
Within the massy entrails of the earth.
Then tell me, Faustus, what shall we three want?

    FAUST. Nothing, Cornelius. O this cheers my soul!
Come, show me some demonstrations magical
That I may conjure in some lusty grove
And have these joys in full possessión.

    VALD. Then haste thee to some solitary grove
And bear wise Bacon's and Albanus' works,
The Hebrew Psalter and new Testament;

And whatsoever else is requisite
We will inform thee ere our conference cease.
   CORN. Valdes, first let him know the words of art,
And then, all other ceremonies learned,
Faustus may try his cunning by himself.
   VALD. First I'll instruct thee in the rudiments,
And then wilt thou be perfecter than I.
   FAUST. Then come and dine with me, and after meat
We'll canvas every quiddity thereof;
For ere I sleep I'll try what I can do:
This night I'll conjure though I die therefore.   *Exeunt.*

*   *   *

   Enter again FAUSTUS *and* MEPHISTOPHILIS.

MEPH. Hold, take this book: peruse it thoroughly.
The iterating of these lines brings gold,
The framing of this circle on the ground
Brings whirlwinds, tempests, thunder and lightning;
Pronounce this thrice devoutly to thyself
And men in armor shall appear to thee,
Ready to execute what thou desirest.
   FAUST. Thanks, Mephistophilis, yet fain would I have a
book wherein I might behold all spells and incantations,
that I might raise up spirits when I please.
   MEPH. Here they are in this book.
                             There turn to them.
   FAUST. Now would I have a book where I might see all
characters and planets of the heavens, that I might know
their motions and dispositions.
   MEPH. Here they are too.   *Turn to them.*
   FAUST. Nay, let me have one book more, and then I
have done, wherein I might see all plants, herbs, and trees
that grow upon the earth.
   MEPH. Here they be.
   FAUST. O thou art deceived!
   MEPH. Tut, I warrant thee. . . .   *Turn to them.*

*   *   *

   FAUST. Come, Mephistophilis, let us dispute again
And argue of divine astrology.
Tell me, are there many heavens above the moon?
Are all celestial bodies but one globe

As is the substance of this centric earth?

MEPH. As are the elements, such are the spheres,
Mutually folded in each other's orb;
And jointly move upon one axletree
Whose terminine is termed the world's wide pole;
Nor are the names of Saturn, Mars, or Jupiter
Feigned, but are erring stars.

FAUST. But tell me, have they all one motion, both *situ
et tempore?*

MEPH. All jointly move from East to West in 24 hours
upon the poles of the world, but differ in their motion
upon the poles of the zodiac.

FAUST. Tush,
These slender trifles Wagner can decide.
Hath Mephistophilis no greater skill?
Who knows not the double motion of the planets?
The first is finished in a natural day;
The second thus, as Saturn in 30 years, Jupiter in 12,
Mars in 4, the Sun, Venus, and Mercury in a year, the
Moon in 28 days. Tush, these are freshmen's supposi-
tions. But tell me, hath every sphere a dominion or *Intel-
ligentia?*

MEPH. Ay.

FAUST. How many heavens or spheres are there?

MEPH. Nine: the seven planets, the firmament, and the
empyreal heaven.

FAUST. But is there not *coelum igneum, et crystalli-
num?*

MEPH. No, Faustus, they be but fables.

FAUST. Well, resolve me in this question: why have
we not conjunctions, oppositions, aspects, eclipses, all at
one time, but in some years we have more, in some less?

MEPH. *Per inequalem motum respectu totius.*

FAUST. Well, I am answered. Tell me, who made the
world?

MEPH. I will not.

FAUST. Sweet Mephistophilis, tell me.

MEPH. Move me not, for I will not tell thee.

FAUST. Villain, have I not bound thee to tell me anything?

MEPH. Ay, that is not against our kingdom; but this is.
Think thou on hell, Faustus, for thou art damned. . . .

Enter WAGNER *solus, as* CHORUS.

WAG. Learned Faustus,
To know the secrets of astronomy
Graven in the book of Jove's high firmament,
Did mount himself to scale Olympus' top.
Being seated in a chariot burning bright
Drawn by the strength of yokéd dragons' necks,
He views the clouds, the planets, and the stars,
The tropic zones and quarters of the sky
From the bright circle of the horned moon
Even to the height of *Primum Mobile;*
And whirling round with this circumference
Within the concave compass of the pole,
From east to west his dragons swiftly glide
And in eight days did bring him home again.
Not long he stayed within his quiet house
To rest his bones after his weary toil
But new exploits do hale him out again;
And mounted then upon a dragon's back
That with his wings did part the subtle air,
He now is gone to prove cosmography
That measures coasts and kingdoms of the earth: . . .

* * *

The clock strikes eleven.

FAUST. Ah, Faustus,
Now hast thou but one bare hour to live
And then thou must be damned perpetually!
Stand still, you ever-moving spheres of heaven,
That time may cease and midnight never come;
Fair Nature's eye, rise, rise again, and make
Perpetual day; or let this hour be but
A year, a month, a week, a natural day,
That Faustus may repent and save his soul!
O lente lente currite noctis equi.
The stars move still, time runs, the clock will strike,
The devil will come, and Faustus must be damned.
O I'll leap up to my God! Who pulls me down?
See, see, where Christ's blood streams in the firma-
    ment! —
One drop would save my soul — half a drop! ah, my
    Christ!
Ah, rend not my heart for naming of my Christ;
Yet will I call on him — Oh, spare me, Lucifer!

Where is it now? 'Tis gone; and see where God
Stretcheth out his arm and bends his ireful brows.
Mountains and hills, come, come and fall on me
And hide me from the heavy wrath of God,
That when you vomit forth into the air
My limbs may issue from your smoky mouths,
So that my soul may but ascend to heaven.
No, no —
Then will I headlong run into the earth:
Earth, gape! O no, it will not harbor me.
You stars that reigned at my nativity,
Whose influence hath allotted death and hell,
Now draw up Faustus like a foggy mist
Into the entrails of yon laboring cloud
So that my soul may but ascend to heaven.

                                        The watch strikes.

Ah, half the hour is past; 'twill all be past anon.
O God,
If thou wilt not have mercy on my soul,
Yet for Christ's sake whose blood hath ransomed me
Impose some end to my incessant pain:
Let Faustus live in hell a thousand years,
A hundred thousand, and at last be saved!
O, no end is limited to damned souls.
Why wert thou not a creature wanting soul?
Or why is this immortal that thou hast?
Ah, Pythagoras' *metempsychosis* — were that true,
This soul should fly from me, and I be changed
Unto some brutish beast. All beasts are happy,
For when they die
Their souls are soon dissolved in elements,
But mine must live still to be plagued in hell.
Cursed be the parents that engendered me!
No, Faustus, curse thyself, curse Lucifer
That hath deprived thee of the joys of heaven.

                                        The clock strikes twelve.

O it strikes, it strikes! Now, body, turn to air
Or Lucifer will bear thee quick to hell.

                                        Thunder and lightning.

O soul, be changed into little water drops
And fall into the ocean, ne'er be found.
My God, my God, look not so fierce on me!

[*Thunder.*] *Enter* DEVILS.

Adders and serpents, let me breathe awhile!
Ugly hell, gape not — come not, Lucifer —
I'll burn my books — ah, Mephistophilis!

Exeunt with him.

Enter CHORUS.

CHORUS. Cut is the branch that might have grown full
    straight,
And burnéd is Apollo's laurel bough
That sometime grew within this learned man.
Faustus is gone: regard his hellish fall,
Whose fiendful fortune may exhort the wise
Only to wonder at unlawful things
Whose deepness doth entice such forward wits
To practise more than heavenly power permits.

[*Exit.*]

Terminat hora diem, terminat author opus.

"Knowledge Infinite"

CHRISTOPHER MARLOWE

Nature that framed us of four elements,
Warring within our breasts for regiment,
Doth teach us all to have aspiring minds:
Our souls, whose faculties can comprehend
The wondrous architecture of the world
And measure every wandering planet's course,
Still climbing after knowledge infinite,
And always moving as the restless spheres,
Will us to wear ourselves, and never rest . . .

From *Tamburlane.*

The Ordered Universe

WILLIAM SHAKESPEARE

The heavens themselves, the planets, and this centre
Observe degree, priority, and place,
Insisture, course, proportion, season, form,
Office and custom, in all line of order:
And therefore is the glorious planet Sol
In noble eminence enthron'd and spher'd
Amidst the other; whose med'cinable eye
Corrects the ill aspects of planets evil,
And posts, like the commandment of a king,
Sans check, to good and bad: but when the planets
In evil mixture to disorder wander,
What plagues, and what portents, what mutiny,
What raging of the sea, shaking of earth,
Commotion in the winds, frights, changes, horrors,
Divert and crack, rend and deracinate
The unity and married calm of states
Quite from their fixture! O! when degree is shak'd
Which is the ladder to all high designs,
The enterprise is sick. How could communities,
Degrees in schools, and brotherhoods in cities,
Peaceful commerce from dividable shores,
The primogeniture and due of birth,
Prerogative of age, crowns, sceptres, laurels,
But by degree, stand in authentic place?
Take but degree away, untune that string,
And, hark! what discord follows; each thing meets
In mere oppugnancy: the bounded waters
Should lift their bosoms higher than the shores,
And make a sop of all this solid globe:
Strength should be lord of imbecility,
And the rude son should strike his father dead:
Force should be right; or rather, right and wrong —
Between whose endless jar justice resides —
Should lose their names, and so should justice too.
Then every thing includes itself in power,
Power into will, will into appetite;
And appetite, a universal wolf,

From *Troilus and Cressida*.

So doubly seconded with will and power,
Must make perforce a universal prey,
And last eat up himself.

"The New Philosophy Calls All in Doubt"

JOHN DONNE

[*new philosophy: science*]

And new Philosophy calls all in doubt,
The element of fire is quite put out;
The Sun is lost, and th'earth, and no man's wit
Can well direct him where to looke for it.
And freely men confesse that this world's spent,
When in the Planets, and the Firmament
They seeke so many new; they see that this
Is crumbled out againe to his Atomies.
'Tis all in peeces, all cohaerence gone;
All just supply, and all Relation:
Prince, Subject, Father, Sonne, are things forgot,
For every man alone thinkes he hath got
To be a Phoenix, and that there can bee
None of that kinde, of which he is, but hee. . . .

We thinke the heavens enjoy their Sphericall,
Their round proportion embracing all.
But yet their various and perplexed course,
Observ'd in divers ages, doth enforce
Men to finde out so many Eccentrique parts,
Such divers downe-right lines, such overthwarts,
As disproportion that pure forme: It teares
The Firmament in eight and forty sheires,

From "An Anatomie of the World. Wherein, By occasion of the untimely death
of Mistris Elizabeth Drury, the frailty and the decay of this whole World is
represented."

And in these Constellations then arise
New starres, and old doe vanish from our eyes: . . .

Man hath weav'd out a net, and this net throwne
Upon the Heavens, and now they are his owne.
Loth to goe up the hill, or labour thus
To goe to heaven, we make heaven come to us.
We spur, we reine the starres, and in their race
They're diversely content t'obey our pace.
But keepes the earth her round proportion still?

Solomon's House

FRANCIS BACON

[Bacon's dream institute for scientific research.]

"GOD BLESS THEE, my son; I will give thee the greatest jewel I have. For I will impart unto thee, for the love of God and men, a relation of the true state of Solomon's House. Son, to make you know the true state of Solomon's House, I will keep this order. First, I will set forth unto you the end of our foundation: Secondly, the preparations and instruments we have for our works. Thirdly, the several employments and functions whereto our fellows are assigned. And fourthly, the ordinances and rites which we observe.

"The end of our foundation is the knowledge of causes, and secret motions of things; and the enlarging of the bounds of human empire, to the effecting of all things possible.

"The preparations and instruments are these. We have large and deep caves of several depths: the deepest are sunk six hundred fathoms; and some of them are digged and made under great hills and mountains; so that if you reckon together the depth of the hill, and the depth of the cave, they are, some of them, above three miles deep. For we find that the depth of a hill, and the depth of a cave from the flat, is the same thing; both remote alike from the sun and heaven's beams, and from the open air. These caves we call the lower region,

From *The New Atlantis*.

and we use them for all coagulations, indurations, refrigerations, and conservations of bodies. We use them likewise for the imitation of natural mines, and the producing also of new artificial metals, by compositions and materials which we use and lay there for many years. We use them also sometimes (which may seem strange) for curing of some diseases, and for prolongation of life, in some hermits that choose to live there, well accommodated of all things necessary, and indeed live very long; by whom also we learn many things.

"We have burials in several earths, where we put divers cements, as the Chinese do their porcelain. But we have them in greater variety, and some of them more fine. We also have great variety of composts and soils, for the making of the earth fruitful.

"We have high towers, the highest about half a mile in height, and some of them likewise set upon high mountains, so that the vantage of the hill, with the tower, is in the highest of them three miles at least. And these places we call the upper region, accounting the air between the high places and the low as a middle region. We use these towers, according to their several heights and situations, for insolation, refrigeration, conservation, and for the view of divers meteors — as winds, rain, snow, hail; and some of the fiery meteors also. And upon them, in some places, are dwellings of hermits, whom we visit sometimes, and instruct what to observe.

"We have great lakes, both salt and fresh, whereof we have use for the fish and fowl. We use them also for burials of some natural bodies, for we find a difference in things buried on earth, or in air below the earth, and things buried in water. We have also pools, of which some do strain fresh water out of salt, and others by art do turn fresh water into salt. We have also some rocks in the midst of the sea, and some bays upon the shore for some works, wherein is required the air and vapor of the sea. We have likewise violent streams and cataracts, which serve us for many motions; and likewise engines for multiplying and enforcing of winds to set also on divers motions.

"We have also a number of artificial wells and fountains, made in imitation of the natural sources and baths, as tincted upon vitriol, sulphur, steel, brass, lead, nitre, and other minerals; and again, we have little wells for infusions of many things, where the waters take the virtue quicker and better than in vessels or basins. And amongst them we have a water, which we call Water of Paradise, being by that we do to it made very sovereign for health and prolongation of life.

"We have also great and spacious houses, where we imitate and demonstrate meteors — as snow, hail, rain, some artificial rains of bodies, and not of water, thunders, lightnings; also generations of bodies in air — as frogs, flies, and divers others.

"We have also certain chambers, which we call chambers of health, where we qualify the air as we think good and proper for the cure of divers diseases, and preservation of health.

"We have also fair and large baths, of several mixtures, for the cure of diseases, and the restoring of man's body from arefaction; and others for the confirming of it in strength of sinews, vital parts, and the very juice and substance of the body.

"We have also large and various orchards and gardens, wherein we do not so much respect beauty as variety of ground and soil, proper for divers trees and herbs, and some very spacious, where trees and berries are set, whereof we make divers kinds of drinks, besides the vineyards. In these we practise likewise all conclusions of grafting and inoculating, as well of wild-trees as fruit-trees, which produceth many effects. And we make by art, in the same orchards and gardens, trees and flowers to come earlier or later than their seasons, and to come up and bear more speedily than by their natural course they do. We make them also by art greater much than their nature; and their fruit greater and sweeter, and of differing taste, smell, color, and figure, from their nature. And many of them we so order as they become of medicinal use.

"We have also means to make divers plants rise by mixtures of earths, without seeds, and likewise to make divers new plants, differing from the vulgar, and to make one tree or plant turn into another.

"We have also parks, and enclosures of all sorts, of beasts and birds; which we use not only for view or rareness, but likewise for dissections and trials, that thereby we may take light what may be wrought upon the body of man. Wherein we find many strange effects: as continuing life in them, though divers parts, which you account vital, be perished and taken forth; resuscitating of some that seem dead in appearance, and the like. We try also all poisons, and other medicines upon them, as well of chirurgery as physic. By art likewise we make them greater or taller than their kind is, and contrariwise dwarf them and stay their growth; we make them more fruitful and bearing than their kind is, and contrariwise barren and not generative. Also we make them differ in color, shape, activity, many ways. We find means to make commixtures and copulations of divers kinds, which have produced many new kinds, and them not barren, as the general opinion is. We make a number of kinds, of serpents, worms, flies, fishes, of putrefaction, whereof some are advanced (in effect) to be perfect creatures, like beasts or birds, and have sexes, and do propagate. Neither do we this by chance, but we know beforehand of what matter and commixture, what kind of those creatures will arise.

"We have also particular pools where we make trials upon fishes, as we have said before of beasts and birds.

"We have also places for breed and generation of those kinds of worms and flies which are of special use; such as are with you your silkworms and bees.

"I will not hold you long with recounting of our brew-houses, bake-houses, and kitchens, where are made divers drinks, breads, and meats, rare and of special effects. Wines we have of grapes, and drinks of other juice, of fruits, of grains, and of roots, and of mixtures with honey, sugar, manna, and fruits dried and decocted; also of the tears or woundings of trees, and of the pulp of canes. And these drinks are of several ages, some to the age or last of forty years. We have drinks also brewed with several herbs, and roots and spices; yea, with several fleshes and white-meats; whereof some of the drinks are such as they are in effect meat and drink both, so that divers, especially in age, do desire to live with them with little or no meat or bread. And above all we strive to have drinks of extreme thin parts, to insinuate into the body, and yet without all biting, sharpness, or fretting; insomuch as some of them, put upon the back of your hand, will with a little stay pass through to the palm, and taste yet mild to the mouth. We have also waters, which we ripen in that fashion, as they become nourishing, so that they are indeed excellent drinks, and many will use no other. Bread we have of several grains, roots, and kernels; yea, and some of flesh, and fish, dried; with divers kinds of leavenings and seasonings; so that some do extremely move appetites, some do nourish so, as divers do live of them, without any other meat, who live very long. So for meats, we have some of them so beaten, and made tender, and mortified, yet without all corrupting, as a weak heat of the stomach will turn them into good chilus, as well as a strong heat would meat otherwise prepared. We have some meats also, and breads, and drinks, which taken by men, enable them to fast long after; and some other, that used make the very flesh of men's bodies sensibly more hard and tough, and their strength far greater than otherwise it would be.

"We have dispensatories or shops of medicines; wherein you may easily think, if we have such variety of plants, and living creatures, more than you have in Europe (for we know what you have), the simples, drugs and ingredients of medicines, must likewise be in so much the greater variety. We have them likewise of divers ages, and long fermentations. And for their preparations, we have not only all manner of exquisite distillations and separations, and especially by gentle heats, and percolations through divers strainers, yea, and substances; but also exact forms of composition, whereby they incorporate almost as they were natural simples.

"We have also divers mechanical arts, which you have not; and stuffs made by them, as papers, linen, silks, tissues, dainty works of feathers of wonderful lustre, excellent dyes, and many others: and shops likewise, as well for such as are not brought into vulgar use amongst us, as for those that are. For you must know, that of the things before recited, many of them are grown into use throughout the kingdom, but yet, if they did flow from our invention, we have of them also for patterns and principles.

"We have also furnaces of great diversities, and that keep great diversity of heats: fierce and quick, strong and constant, soft and mild; blown, quiet, dry, moist, and the like. But above all we have heats, in imitation of the sun's and heavenly bodies' heats, that pass divers inequalities, and (as it were) orbs, progresses, and returns, whereby we produce admirable effects. Besides, we have heats of dungs, and of bellies and maws of living creatures and of their bloods and bodies, and of hays and herbs laid up moist, of lime unquenched, and such like. Instruments also which generate heat only by motion. And farther, places for strong insulations; and again, places under the earth, which by nature or art yield heat. These divers heats we use as the nature of the operation which we intend requireth.

"We have also perspective houses, where we make demonstrations of all lights and radiations, and of all colors; and out of things uncolored and transparent, we can represent unto you all several colors, not in rainbows (as it is in gems and prisms), but of themselves single. We represent also all multiplications of light, which we carry to great distance, and make so sharp, as to discern small points and lines. Also all colorations of light; all delusions and deceits of the sight, in figures, magnitudes, motions, colors; all demonstrations of shadows. We find also divers means yet unknown to you of producing of light, originally from divers bodies. We procure means of seeing objects afar off, as in the heaven and remote places; and represent things near as afar off, and things afar off as near; making feigned distances. We have also helps for the sight, far above spectacles and glasses in use. We have also glasses and means to see small and minute bodies, perfectly and distinctly; as the shapes and colors of small flies and worms, grains, and flaws in gems which cannot otherwise be seen, observations in urine and blood not otherwise to be seen. We make artificial rainbows, halos, and circles about light. We represent also all manner of reflections, refractions, and multiplications of visual beams of objects.

"We have also precious stones of all kinds, many of them of great beauty and to you unknown; crystals likewise, and glasses of divers kinds; and amongst them some of metals vitrificated, and other materials, besides those of which you make glass. Also a number of fossils and imperfect minerals, which you have not. Likewise load-stones of prodigious virtue: and other rare stones, both natural and artificial.

"We have also sound-houses, where we practise and demonstrate all sounds and their generation. We have harmonies which you have not, of quarter-sounds and lesser slides of sounds. Divers instruments of music likewise to you unknown, some sweeter than any you have; together with bells and rings that are dainty and sweet. We represent small sounds as great and deep; likewise great sounds, extenuate and sharp; we make divers tremblings and warblings of sounds, which in their original are entire. We represent and imitate all articulate sounds and letters, and the voices and notes of beasts and birds. We have certain helps which set to the ear do further the hearing greatly. We have also divers strange and artificial echoes, reflecting the voice many times, and as it were tossing it; and some that give back the voice louder than it came, some shriller and some deeper: yea, some rendering the voice, differing in the letters or articulate sound from that they receive. We have also means to convey sounds in trunks and pipes, in strange lines and distances.

"We have also perfume-houses, wherewith we join also practices of taste. We multiply smells, which may seem strange: we imitate smells, making all smells to breathe out of other mixtures than those that give them. We make divers imitations of taste likewise, so that they will deceive any man's taste. And in this house we contain also a confiture-house, where we make all sweetmeats, dry and moist, and divers pleasant wines, milks, broths, and salads, far in greater variety than you have.

"We have also engine-houses, where are prepared engines and instruments for all sorts of motions. There we imitate and practise to make swifter motions than any you have, either out of your muskets or any engine that you have; and to make them and multiply them more easily and with small force, by wheels and other means, and to make them stronger and more violent than yours are, exceeding your greatest cannons and basilisks. We represent also ordnance and instruments of war and engines of all kinds; and likewise new mixtures and compositions of gunpowder, wildfires burning in water and unquenchable, also fire-works of all variety, both for pleasure and use. We imitate also flights of birds; we have some degrees of flying in the air. We have ships and boats for going under water and brooking of seas, also swimming-girdles and supporters. We have divers curious clocks, and other like motions of return, and some perpetual motions. We imitate also motions of living creatures by images of men, beasts, birds, fishes, and serpents; we have also a great number of other various motions, strange for equality, fineness, and subtlety.

"We have also a mathematical-house, where are represented all instruments, as well of geometry as astronomy, exquisitely made.

"We have also houses of deceits of the senses, where we represent all manner of feats of juggling, false apparitions, impostures and illusions, and their fallacies. And surely you will easily believe that we, that have so many things truly natural which induce admiration, could in a world of particulars deceive the senses if we would disguise those things, and labor to make them seem more miraculous. But we do hate all impostures and lies, insomuch as we have severely forbidden it to all our fellows, under pain of ignominy and fines, that they do not show any natural work or thing adorned or swelling, but only pure as it is, and without all affectation of strangeness.

"These are, my son, the riches of Solomon's House.

"For the several employments and offices of our fellows, we have twelve that sail into foreign countries under the names of other nations (for our own we conceal), who bring us the books and abstracts, and patterns of experiments of all other parts. These we call merchants of light.

"We have three that collect the experiments which are in all books. These we call Depredators.

"We have three that collect the experiments of all mechanical arts, and also of liberal sciences, and also of practices which are not brought into arts. These we call Mystery-men.

"We have three that try new experiments, such as themselves think good. These we call Pioneers or Miners.

"We have three that draw the experiments of the former four into titles and tables, to give the better light for the drawing of observations and axioms out of them. These we call Compilers.

"We have three that bend themselves, looking into the experiments of their fellows, and cast about how to draw out of them things of use and practice for man's life and knowledge, as well for works as for plain demonstration of causes, means of natural divinations, and the easy and clear discovery of the virtues and parts of bodies. These we call Dowry-men or Benefactors.

"Then after divers meetings and consults of our whole number, to consider of the former labors and collections, we have three that take care out of them to direct new experiments, of a higher light, more penetrating into nature than the former. These we call Lamps.

"We have three others that do execute the experiments so directed, and report them. These we call Inoculators.

"Lastly, we have three that raise the former discoveries by experiments into greater observations, axioms, and aphorisms. These we call Interpreters of Nature.

"We have also, as you must think, novices and apprentices, that the succession of the former employed men do not fail; besides a great number of servants and attendants, men and women. And this we do also: we have consultations, which of the inventions and experiences which we have discovered shall be published, and which not: and take all an oath of secrecy for the concealing of those which we think fit to keep secret: though some of those we do reveal sometimes to the state, and some not.

"For our ordinances and rites, we have two very long and fair galleries: in one of these we place patterns and samples of all manner of the more rare and excellent inventions: in the other we place the statues of all principal inventors. There we have the statue of your Columbus, that discovered the West Indies: also the inventor of ships: your monk that was the inventor of ordnance and of gunpowder: the inventor of music: the inventor of letters: the inventor of printing: the inventor of observations of astronomy: the inventor of works in metal: the inventor of glass: the inventor of silk of the worm: the inventor of wine: the inventor of corn and bread: the inventor of sugars: and all these by more certain tradition than you have. Then we have divers inventors of our own, of excellent works, which since you have not seen, it were too long to make descriptions of them; and besides, in the right understanding of those descriptions you might easily err. For upon every invention of value we erect a statue to the inventor, and give him a liberal and honorable reward. These statues are some of brass, some of marble and touchstone, some of cedar and other special woods gilt and adorned; some of iron, some of silver, some of gold.

"We have certain hymns and services, which we say daily, of laud and thanks to God for his marvellous works. And forms of prayer, imploring his aid and blessing for the illumination of our labors, and the turning of them into good and holy uses.

"Lastly, we have circuits or visits, of divers principal cities of the kingdom; where, as it cometh to pass, we do publish such new profitable inventions as we think good. And we do also declare natural divinations of diseases, plagues, swarms of hurtful creatures, scarcity, tempests, earthquakes, great inundations, comets, temperature of the year, and divers other things; and we give counsel thereupon, what the people shall do for the prevention and remedy of them."

And when he had said this he stood up; and I, as I had been taught, knelt down; and he laid his right hand upon my head, and said, "God bless thee, my son, and God bless this relation which I have made. I give thee leave to publish it, for the good of other nations; for we here are in God's bosom, a land unknown." And so he left me; having assigned a value of about two thousand ducats for a bounty to me and my fellows. For they give great largesses, where they come, upon all occasions.

The rest was not perfected.

The Book of God

JOHN MILTON

[Adam has asked Raphael how it is that the earth, small as it is, appears to be served by the sun and the other planets. Raphael replies:]

> To ask or search I blame thee not; for Heaven
> Is as the Book of God before thee set,
> Wherein to read his wondrous works, and learn
> His seasons, hours, or days, or months, or years.
> This to attain, whether Heaven move or Earth
> Imports not, if thou reckon right; the rest
> From Man or Angel the great Architect
> Did wisely to conceal, and not divulge
> His secrets, to be scanned by them who ought
> Rather admire. Or, if they list to try
> Conjecture, He His fabric of the Heavens
> Hath left to their disputes — perhaps to move
> His laughter at their quaint opinions wide
> Hereafter, when they come to model Heaven,
> And calculate the stars; how they will wield
> The mighty frame; how build, unbuild, contrive
> To save appearances; how gird the Sphere

From *Paradise Lost*, Book VIII.

With Centric and Eccentric scribbled o'er,
Cycle and Epicycle, Orb in Orb.
Already by thy reasoning this I guess,
Who art to lead thy offspring, and supposest
That bodies bright and greater should not serve
The less not bright, nor Heaven such journeys run,
Earth sitting still, when she alone receives
The benefit. . . .

       What if the Sun
Be centre to the World, and other Stars,
By his attractive virtue and their own
Incited, dance about him various rounds?
Their wandering course, now high, now low, then hid,
Progressive, retrograde, or standing still,
In six thou seest; and what if, seventh to these,
The planet Earth, so steadfast though she seem,
Insensibly three different motions move? . . .

But whether thus these things, or whether not —
Whether the Sun, predominant in heaven,
Rise on the Earth, or Earth rise on the Sun;
He from the east his flaming road begin,
Or she from west her silent course advance
With inoffensive pace that spinning sleeps
On her soft axle, while she paces even,
And bears thee soft with the smooth air along —
Solicit not thy thoughts with matters hid:
Leave them to God above; him serve and fear.

◇◇◇◇◇◇◇◇◇◇◇◇◇◇◇◇◇◇◇◇◇◇◇◇◇◇◇◇◇◇◇◇◇◇◇◇◇◇

▣ *SCIENCE ADORED: SCIENCE MOCKED*

The Spacious Firmament

JOSEPH ADDISON

The spacious firmament on high,
With all the blue ethereal sky,
And spangled heavens, a shining frame,

Their great Original proclaim:
The unwearied sun from day to day
Does his Creator's power display,
And publishes to every land
The work of an Almighty hand.

Soon as the evening shades prevail,
The moon takes up the wondrous tale,
And nightly to the listening earth
Repeats the story of her birth;
Whilst all the stars that round her burn,
And all the planets, in their turn,
Confirm the tidings as they roll,
And spread the truth from pole to pole.

What though, in solemn silence, all
Move round the dark terrestrial ball?
What though nor real voice nor sound
Amid their radiant orbs be found?
In reason's ear they all rejoice
And utter forth a glorious voice,
For ever singing, as they shine,
The hand that made us is Divine.

"Of God Above or Man Below . . ."

ALEXANDER POPE

Say first, of God above, or Man below,
What can we reason, but from what we know?
Of Man, what see we but his station here,
From which to reason, or to which refer?
Through worlds unnumbered though the God be known,
'Tis ours to trace him only in our own.
He, who through vast immensity can pierce,
See worlds on worlds compose one universe,

From *Essay on Man*, Epistle I.

Observe how system into system runs,
What other planets circle other suns,
What varied Being peoples every star,
May tell why Heaven has made us as we are. . . .

Ask for what end the heavenly bodies shine,
Earth for whose use? Pride answers, " 'Tis for mine:
For me kind Nature wakes her genial power,
Suckles each herb, and spreads out every flower;
Annual for me, the grape, the rose renew
The juice nectareous, and the balmy dew;
For me, the mine a thousand treasures brings;
For me, health gushes from a thousand springs;
Seas roll to waft me, suns to light me rise;
My footstool earth, my canopy the skies."
But errs not Nature from this gracious end,
From burning suns when livid deaths descend,
When earthquakes swallow, or when tempests sweep
Towns to one grave, whole nations to the deep?
"No," ('tis replied) "the first Almighty Cause
Acts not by partial, but by general laws;
Th'exceptions few; some change since all began:
And what created perfect?" Why then Man?
If the great end be human Happiness,
Then Nature deviates; and can Man do less? . . .

Submit. — In this, or any other sphere,
Secure to be as blest as thou canst bear:
Safe in the hand of one disposing Power,
Or in the natal, or the mortal hour.
All nature is but Art, unknown to thee;
All Chance, Direction, which thou canst not see;
All Discord, Harmony not understood;
All partial Evil, universal Good:
And spite of Pride, in erring Reason's spite,
One truth is clear, WHATEVER IS, IS RIGHT.

The Proper Study of Mankind

ALEXANDER POPE

Know then thyself, presume not God to scan;
The proper study of Mankind is Man.
Placed on this isthmus of a middle state,
A Being darkly wise, and rudely great:
With too much knowledge for the Sceptic side,
With too much weakness for the Stoic's pride,
He hangs between; in doubt to act, or rest;
In doubt to deem himself a God, or Beast;
In doubt his Mind or Body to prefer;
Born but to die, and reasoning but to err;
Alike in ignorance, his reason such,
Whether he thinks too little, or too much:
Chaos of Thought and Passion, all confused;
Still by himself abused, or disabused;
Created half to rise, and half to fall;
Great lord of all things, yet a prey to all;
Sole judge of Truth, in endless Error hurled:
The glory, jest, and riddle of the world!
    Go, wondrous creature! mount where Science guides,
Go, measure earth, weigh air, and state the tides;
Instruct the planets in what orbs to run,
Correct old Time, and regulate the Sun;
Go, soar with Plato to th'empyreal sphere,
To the first good, first perfect, and first fair;
Or tread the mazy round his followers trod,
And quitting sense call imitating God;
As Eastern priests in giddy circles run,
And turn their heads to imitate the Sun.
Go, teach Eternal Wisdom how to rule —
Then drop into thyself, and be a fool!
    Superior beings, when of late they saw
A mortal man unfold all Nature's law,
Admired such wisdom in an earthly shape,
And showed a NEWTON as we show an Ape.
    Could he, whose rules the rapid Comet bind,
Describe or fix one movement of his Mind?

From *Essay on Man*, Epistle II.

Who saw its fires here rise, and there descend,
Explain his own beginning, or his end?
Alas, what wonder! Man's superior part
Unchecked may rise, and climb from art to art;
But when his own great work is but begun,
What Reason weaves, by Passion is undone.
Trace Science then, with Modesty thy guide;
First strip off all her equipage of Pride;
Deduct what is but Vanity, or Dress,
Or Learning's luxury, or Idleness;
Or tricks to show the stretch of human brain,
Mere curious pleasure, or ingenious pain;
Expunge the whole, or lop th'excrescent parts
Of all our Vices have created Arts;
Then see how little the remaining sum,
Which served the past, and must the times to come!

"And Don't Go Near the Water"

THOMAS SHADWELL

[From Act II]

LONGVIL: . . . But may we not have the honor we were promised, of seeing Sir Nicholas?

LADY GIMCRACK: The truth on't is, he is within; but upon some private business. But nothing shall be reserved from such accomplished persons as you are. The truth on't is, he's learning to swim.

LONG: Is there any water hereabouts, madam?

L. GIM: He does not learn to swim in the water, sir.

BRUCE: Not in the water, madam! How then?

L. GIM: In his laboratory, a spacious room where all his instruments and fine knickknacks are.

BRUCE (*aside*): A swimming master! This is beyond all precedent. He is the most curious coxcomb breathing.

L. GIM: He has a frog in a bowl of water, tied with a packthread by his loins; which packthread Sir Nicholas holds in his

From *The Virtuoso* by Thomas Shadwell. [*virtuoso: scientist, expert.*]

teeth, lying upon his belly on a table. And as the frog strikes, he strikes; and his swimming master stands by, to tell him when he does well or ill.

LONG: This is the rarest fop that ever was heard of.

BRUCE: Few virtuosos can arrive to this pitch, madam. This is the most curious invention I ever heard of.

L. GIM: Alas! He has many such. He is a rare mechanic philosopher. The College indeed refused him; they envied him.

LONG: Were it not possible to have the favor of seeing this experiment?

L. GIM: I cannot deny anything to such persons. I'll introduce you. (*exeunt*)

Scene opens and discovers SIR NICHOLAS *learning to swim upon a table,* SIR FORMAL TRIFLE *and the* SWIMMING MASTER *standing by.*

SIR FORMAL: In earnest, this is very fine! I doubt not, sir, but in a short space of time you will arrive at that curiosity in this watery science, that not a frog breathing will exceed you. Though I confess, it is the most curious of all amphibious animals in the art, shall I say, or rather nature of swimming.

SWIM. MAST: Ah! Well struck, Sir Nicholas. That was admirable; that was as well swum as any man in England can. Observe the frog. Draw up your arms a little nearer, and then thrust 'em out strongly. Gather up your legs a little more. So, very well. Incomparable!

Enter BRUCE, LONGVIL, *and* LADY GIMCRACK.

BRUCE: Let's not interrupt them, madam, yet; but observe a little this great curiosity.

LONG: 'Tis a noble invention.

L. GIM: 'Tis a thing the College never thought of.

SIR NICH: Let me rest a little to respire. So; it is wonderful, my noble friend, to observe the agility of this pretty animal; which notwithstanding I impede its motion by the detention of this filum, or thread, within my teeth, which makes a ligature about its loins; and though by many sudden stops I cause the animal sometimes to sink or immerge, yet with indefatigable activity it rises, and keeps almost its whole body upon the superficies, or surface, of this humid element.

SIR FORM: True, noble sir. Nor do I doubt but your genius will make art equal, if not exceed, nature; nor will this or any other frog upon the face of the earth outswim you.

SIR NICH: Nay, I doubt not, sir, in a very little time to become amphibious. A man, by art, may appropriate any element to himself. You know a great many virtuosos that can fly, but I am so much advanced in the art of flying that I can already outfly that ponderous animal called a bustard; nor should any greyhound in England catch me in the calmest day, before I got upon wing. Nay, I doubt not but in a little time to improve the art so far, 'twill be as common to buy a pair of wings to fly to the world in the Moon, as to buy a pair of wax-boots to ride into Sussex with.

SIR FORM: Nay doubtless, sir, if you proceed in those swift gradations you have hitherto prospered in, there will be no difficulty in the noble enterprise, which is devoutly to be efflagitated by all ingenious persons; since the intelligence with that lunary world would be of infinite advantage to us in the improvement of our politics.

SIR NICH: Right. For the Moon being *Domina humidorum,* to wit, the governess of moist bodies, has no doubt the superior government of all islands; and its influence is the cause so many of us are delirious and lunatic in this. But having sufficiently refrigerated my lungs by way of respiration, I will return to my swimming.

SWIM. MAST: Admirably well struck! rarely swum! He shall swim with any man in Europe.

SIR FORM: Hold, Sir Nicholas. Here are those noble gentlemen and philosophers whom I invited to kiss your hands; and I am not a little proud of the honor of being the grateful and happy instrument of the necessitude and familiar communication, which is like to intervene between such excellent virtuosos.

BRUCE: We are Sir Nicholas's and your most humble servants.

LONG: We shall think ourselves much honored with the knowledge of so celebrated a virtuoso.

SIR NICH: You are right welcome into my poor laboratory. And if in aught I can serve you in the way of science, my nature is diffusive; and I shall be glad of communicating with such eminent virtuosos, as I am let to know you are.

LONG: We pretend to nothing more than to be your humble admirers.

SIR FORM: All the ingenious world are proud of Sir Nicholas for his physico-mechanical excellencies.

SIR NICH: I confess I have some felicity that way. But were I as precelling in physico-mechanical investigations as you in tropical rhetorical flourishes, I would yield to none.

LONG (*aside*): How the asses claw one another!

BRUCE: We are both your admirers! But of all quaint inventions, none ever came near this of swimming.

SIR FORM: Truly, I opine it to be a most compendious method, that in a fortnight's prosecution has advanced him to be the best swimmer of Europe. Nay, it were possible to swim with any fish of his inches.

LONG: Have you ever tried in the water, sir?

SIR NICH: No, sir; but I swim most exquisitely on land.

BRUCE: Do you intend to practise in the water, sir?

SIR NICH: Never, sir. I hate the water; I never come upon the water, sir.

LONG: Then there will be no use of swimming.

SIR NICH: I content myself with the speculative part of swimming; I care not for the practice. I seldom bring anything to use; 'tis not my way. Knowledge is my ultimate end.

Laputan Projects

JONATHAN SWIFT

THIS ACADEMY is not an entire single building, but a continuation of several houses on both sides of a street, which growing waste was purchased and applied to that use.

I was received very kindly by the Warden, and went for many days to the Academy. Every room hath in it one or more projectors, and I believe I could not be in fewer than five hundred rooms.

The first man I saw was of a meagre aspect, with sooty hands and face, his hair and beard long, ragged and singed in several places. His clothes, shirt, and skin, were all of the same colour. He had been eight years upon a project for extracting sun-beams out of cucumbers, which were to be put into vials hermetically sealed, and let out to warm the air in raw inclement summers. He told me, he did not doubt, in eight years more, he should be able to supply the Governor's gardens with sunshine at a reasonable rate; but he complained that his stock was low, and entreated me to give him something as an encouragement to ingenuity, especially since this had been a very dear season for cucumbers. I made him a small present, for my lord had furnished me with money on purpose, because he knew their practice of begging from all who go to see them. . . .

I saw another at work to calcine ice into gunpowder, who like-

From *Gulliver's Travels.*

wise showed me a treatise he had written concerning the malleability of fire, which he intended to publish.

There was a most ingenious architect who had contrived a new method for building houses, by beginning at the roof, and working downwards to the foundation, which he justified to me by the like practice of those two prudent insects, the bee and the spider.

There was a man born blind, who had several apprentices in his own condition: their employment was to mix colours for painters, which their master taught them to distinguish by feeling and smelling. It was indeed my misfortune to find them at that time not very perfect in their lessons, and the professor himself happened to be generally mistaken: this artist is much encouraged and esteemed by the whole fraternity.

In another apartment I was highly pleased with a projector, who had found a device of ploughing the ground with hogs, to save the charges of ploughs, cattle, and labour. The method is this: in an acre of ground you bury, at six inches distance and eight deep, a quantity of acorns, dates, chestnuts, and other mast or vegetables whereof these animals are fondest; then you drive six hundred or more of them into the field, where in a few days they will root up the whole ground in search of their food, and make it fit for sowing, at the same time manuring it with their dung. It is true, upon experiment they found the charge and trouble very great, and they had little or no crop. However, it is not doubted that this invention may be capable of great improvement.

I went into another room, where the walls and ceiling were all hung round with cobwebs, except a narrow passage for the artist to go in and out. At my entrance he called aloud to me not to disturb his webs. He lamented the fatal mistake the world had been so long in of using silk-worms, while we had such plenty of domestic insects, who infinitely excelled the former, because they understood how to weave as well as spin. And he proposed farther, that by employing spiders, the charge of dyeing silks should be wholly saved, whereof I was fully convinced when he showed me a vast number of flies most beautifully coloured, wherewith he fed his spiders, assuring us, that the webs would take a tincture from them; and as he had them of all hues, he hoped to fit everybody's fancy, as soon as he could find proper food for the flies, of certain gums, oils, and other glutinous matter to give a strength and consistence to the threads.

There was an astronomer who had undertaken to place a sundial upon the great weathercock on the townhouse, by adjusting the annual and diurnal motions of the earth and sun, so as to answer and coincide with all accidental turnings by the wind. . . .

I had hitherto seen only one side of the Academy, the other being appropriated to the advancers of speculative learning, of whom I shall say something when I have mentioned one illustrious person more, who is called among them *the universal artist*. He told us he had been thirty years employing his thoughts for the improvement of human life. He had two large rooms full of wonderful curiosities, and fifty men at work. Some were condensing air into a dry tangible substance, by extracting the nitre, and letting the aqueous or fluid particles percolate; others softening marble for pillows and pin-cushions; others petrifying the hoofs of a living horse to preserve them from foundering. The artist himself was at that time busy upon two great designs: the first, to sow land with chaff, wherein he affirmed the true seminal virtue to be contained, as he demon-strated by several experiments which I was not skilful enough to comprehend. The other was, by a certain composition of gums, min-erals, and vegetables outwardly applied, to prevent the growth of wool upon two young lambs; and he hoped in a reasonable time to propagate the breed of naked sheep all over the kingdom.

We crossed a walk to the other part of the Academy, where, as I have already said, the projectors in speculative learning resided.

The first professor I saw was in a very large room, with forty pupils about him. After salutation, observing me to look earnestly upon a frame, which took up the greatest part of both the length and breadth of the room, he said perhaps I might wonder to see him employed in a project for improving speculative knowledge by practical and mechanical operations. But the world would soon be sensible of its usefulness, and he flattered himself that a more noble exalted thought never sprang in any other man's head. Every one knew how laborious the usual method is of attaining to arts and sciences; whereas, by his contrivance, the most ignorant person at a reasonable charge, and with a little bodily labour, may write books, in philosophy, poetry, politics, law, mathematics, and theology, without the least assistance from genius or study. He then led me to the frame, about the sides whereof all his pupils stood in ranks. It was twenty foot square, placed in the middle of the room. The superficies was composed of several bits of wood, about the bigness of a die, but some larger than others. They were all linked together by slender wires. These bits of wood were covered on every square with paper pasted on them, and on these papers were written all the words of their language, in their several moods, tenses, and de-clensions, but without any order. The professor then desired me to observe, for he was going to set his engine at work. The pupils at his command took each of them hold of an iron handle, whereof there were forty fixed round the edges of the frame; and giving them a sudden turn, the whole disposition of the words was entirely changed. He then commanded six and thirty of the lads to read the several lines softly as they appeared upon the frame; and where they found three or four words together that might make part of a sentence, they dictated to the four remaining boys who were scribes. This work was repeated three or four times, and at every turn the engine was so contrived, that the words shifted into new places, as the square bits of wood moved upside down.

Six hours a day the young students were employed in this labour, and the professor showed me several volumes in large folio already collected, of broken sentences, which he intended to piece together, and out of those rich materials to give the world a complete body of all arts and sciences; which however might be still improved, and much expedited, if the public would raise a fund for making and employing five hundred such frames in Lagado, and oblige the managers to contribute in common their several collections. . . .

He assured me, that this invention had employed all his thoughts from his youth, that he had emptied the whole vocabulary into his frame, and made the strictest computation of the general proportion there is in books between the numbers of particles, nouns, and verbs, and other parts of speech.

I made my humblest acknowledgment to this illustrious person for his great communicativeness, and promised if ever I had the good fortune to return to my native country, that I would do him justice, as the sole inventor of this wonderful machine; the form and contrivance of which I desired leave to delineate upon paper, . . . I told him, although it were the custom of our learned in Europe to steal inventions from each other, who had thereby at least this advantage, that it became a controversy which was the right owner, yet I would take such caution, that he should have the honour entire without a rival.

We next went to the school of languages, where three professors sat in consultation upon improving that of their own country.

The first project was to shorten discourse by cutting polysyllables into one, and leaving out verbs and particles, because in reality all things imaginable are but nouns.

The other was a scheme for entirely abolishing all words whatsoever; and this was urged as a great advantage in point of health as well as brevity. For it is plain that every word we speak is in some degree a diminution of our lungs by corrosion, and consequently contributes to the shortening of our lives. An expedient was therefore offered, that since words are only names for *things*, it would be more convenient for all men to carry about them such *things* as were

necessary to express the particular business they are to discourse on.
And this invention would certainly have taken place, to the great
ease as well as health of the subject, if the women, in conjunction
with the vulgar and illiterate, had not threatened to raise a rebellion, unless they might be allowed the liberty to speak with their
tongues, after the manner of their forefathers: such constant irrec-
oncilable enemies to science are the common people. However,
many of the most learned and wise adhere to the new scheme of
expressing themselves by *things*, which hath only this inconvenience attending it, that if a man's business be very great, and of
various kinds, he must be obliged in proportion to carry a greater
bundle of *things* upon his back, unless he can afford one or two
strong servants to attend him. I have often beheld two of those
sages almost sinking under the weight of their packs, like pedlars
among us; who, when they met in the streets, would lay down their
loads, open their sacks, and hold conversation for an hour together;
then put up their implements, help each other to resume their
burthens, and take their leave.

But for short conversations a man may carry implements in his
pockets and under his arms, enough to supply him, and in his
house he cannot be at a loss. Therefore the room where company
meet who practise this art, is full of all things ready at hand, requisite to furnish matter for this kind of artificial converse.

Another great advantage proposed by this invention, was that
it would serve as an universal language to be understood in all
civilised nations, whose goods and utensils are generally of the same
kind, or nearly resembling, so that their uses might easily be comprehended. And thus ambassadors would be qualified to treat with
foreign princes or ministers of state, to whose tongues they were
utter strangers.

I was at the mathematical school, where the master taught his
pupils after a method scarce imaginable to us in Europe. The proposition and demonstration were fairly written on a thin wafer, with
ink composed of a cephalic tincture. This the student was to swallow upon a fasting stomach, and for three days following eat nothing but bread and water. As the wafer digested, the tincture
mounted to his brain, bearing the proposition along with it. But the
success hath not hitherto been answerable, partly by some error in
the *quantum* or composition, and partly by the perverseness of lads,
to whom this bolus is so nauseous, that they generally steal aside,
and discharge it upwards before it can operate; neither have they
been yet persuaded to use so long an abstinence as the prescription
requires.

TWO WAYS OF SEEING

*May God us keep
From Single Vision and Newton's Sleep!*

— WILLIAM BLAKE

NEW MYTHS, NEW SYMBOLS

LEWIS MUMFORD

SCIENCE had something other to contribute to the arts than the notion that the machine was an absolute. It contributed, through its effects upon invention and mechanization, a new type of order to the environment: an order in which power, economy, objectivity, the collective will play a more decisive part than they had played before even in such absolute forms of dominion as in the royal priesthood — and engineers — of Egypt or Babylon. The sensitive apprehension of this new environment, its translation into terms which involve human affections and feelings, and that bring into play once more the full personality, became part of the mission of the artist: and the great spirits of the nineteenth century, who first fully greeted this altered environment, were not indifferent to it. Turner and Tennyson, Emily Dickinson and Thoreau, Whitman and Emerson, all saluted with admiration the locomotive, that symbol of the new order in Western society. They were conscious of the fact that new instruments were changing the dimensions and to some extent therefore the very qualities of experience; these facts were just as clear to Thoreau as to Samuel Smiles; to Kipling as to H. G. Wells. The telegraph wire, the locomotive, the ocean steamship, the very shafts and pistons and switches that conveyed and canalized or controlled the new power, could awaken emotion as well as the harp and the war-horse: the hand at the throttle or the switch was no less regal than the hand that had once held a scepter.

The second contribution of the scientific attitude was a limiting one: it tended to destroy the lingering mythologies of Greek goddesses and Christian heroes and saints; or rather, it prevented a naïve and repetitious use of these symbols. But at the same time, it disclosed new universal symbols, and widened the very domain of the symbol itself. This process took place in all the arts: it affected poetry as well as architecture. The pursuit of science, however, suggested new myths. The transformation of the medieval folk-legend of Doctor Faustus from Marlowe to Goethe, with Faust ending up as a builder of canals and a drainer of swamps and finding the meaning of life in sheer activity, the transformation of the Prometheus myth in Melville's *Moby Dick*, testify not to the destruction of myths by positive knowledge but to their more pregnant application. I can only repeat here what I have said in another place: "What the scientific spirit has actually done has been to exercise the imagination in finer ways than the autistic wish — the wish of the infant possessed of the illusions of power and domination — was able to express." Faraday's ability to conceive the lines of force in a magnetic field was quite as great a triumph as the ability to conceive of fairies dancing in a ring: and, as Mr. A. N. Whitehead has shown, the poets who sympathized with this new sort of imagination, poets like Shelley, Wordsworth, Whitman, Melville, did not feel themselves robbed of their specific powers, but rather found them enlarged and refreshed.

One of the finest love poems in the nineteenth century, Whitman's "Out of the Cradle Endlessly Rocking," is expressed in such an image as Darwin or Audubon might have used, were the scientist as capable of expressing his inner feelings as of noting "external" events: the poet haunting the seashore and observing the mating of the birds, day after day following their life, could scarcely have existed before the nineteenth century. In the early seventeenth century such a poet would have remained in the garden and written about a literary ghost, Philomel, and not about an actual pair of birds; in Pope's time the poet would have remained in the library and written about the birds on a lady's fan. Almost all the important works of the nineteenth century were cast in this mode and expressed the new imaginative range: they respect the fact: they are replete with observation: they project an ideal realm in and through, not transcendentally over, the landscape of actuality. *Notre Dame* might have been written by an historian, *War and Peace* by a sociologist, *The Idiot* might have been created by a psychiatrist, and *Salammbô* might have been the work of an archaeologist. I do not say that these books were scientific by intention, or that they might be replaced by a work of science without grave loss; far from it. I merely point out that they were conceived in the same spirit; that they belong to a similar plane of consciousness.

Three Rainbows

Meantime, refracted from yon eastern cloud,
Bestriding earth, the grand ethereal now
Shoots up immense, and every hue unfolds,
In fair proportion running from the red
To where the violet fades into the sky.
Here, awful Newton, the dissolving clouds
Form, fronting on the sun, thy shadowy prism;
And to the sage-instructed eye unfold
The various twine of light, by thee disclosed
From the white mingling blaze.

— JAMES THOMSON: *The Seasons*

My heart leaps up when I behold
    A rainbow in the sky:
So was it when my life began;
So is it now I am a man;
So be it when I shall grow old,
    Or let me die!
The Child is father of the Man;
And I could wish my days to be
Bound each to each by natural piety.

— WILLIAM WORDSWORTH

Do not all charms fly
At the mere touch of cold philosophy?
There was an awful rainbow once in heaven:
We know her woof, her texture: she is given
In the dull catalogue of common things.
Philosophy will clip an Angel's wings,
Conquer all mysteries by rule and line,
Empty the haunted air, and gnomed mine —
Unweave a rainbow . . .

— JOHN KEATS: *Lamia*

⊂≣ *SEEING INTO THE LIFE OF THINGS*

Mock On, Mock On!

WILLIAM BLAKE

Mock on, mock on, Voltaire, Rousseau:
Mock on, mock on; 'tis all in vain!
You throw the sand against the wind,
And the wind blows it back again.

And every sand becomes a gem
Reflected in the beams divine;
Blown back they blind the mocking eye,
But still in Israel's paths they shine.

The atoms of Democritus
And Newton's particles of light
Are sands upon the Red Sea shore,
Where Israel's tents do shine so bright.

A New Jerusalem

WILLIAM BLAKE

And did those feet in ancient time
Walk upon England's mountains green?
And was the holy Lamb of God
On England's pleasant pastures seen?

And did the countenance divine
Shine forth upon our clouded hills?
And was Jerusalem builded here
Among these dark Satanic mills?

Bring me my bow of burning gold!
Bring me my arrows of desire!
Bring me my spear! O clouds unfold!
Bring me my chariot of fire!

I will not cease from mental fight,
Nor shall my sword sleep in my hand,
Till we have built Jerusalem
In England's green and pleasant land.

Lines Composed a Few Miles Above Tintern Abbey

[*abridged*]

WILLIAM WORDSWORTH

Five years have passed; five summers with the length
Of five long winters; and again I hear
These waters, rolling from their mountain-springs
With a soft inland murmur. — Once again
Do I behold these steep and lofty cliffs,
That on a wild secluded scene impress
Thoughts of more deep seclusion; and connect
The landscape with the quiet of the sky. . . .
⠀⠀⠀⠀⠀⠀⠀⠀These beauteous forms,
Through a long absence, have not been to me
As is a landscape to a blind man's eye:
But oft, in lonely rooms, and 'mid the din
Of towns and cities, I have owed to them
In hours of weariness, sensations sweet,
Felt in the blood, and felt along the heart;
And passing even into my purer mind,
With tranquil restoration: — feelings, too
Of unremembered pleasure: such, perhaps,
As have no slight or trivial influence
On that best portion of a good man's life,

His little, nameless, unremembered acts
Of kindness and of love. Nor less, I trust,
To them I may have owed another gift,
Of aspect more sublime; that blessed mood,
In which the burthen of the mystery,
In which the heavy and the weary weight
Of all this unintelligible world,
Is lightened: — that serene and blessed mood,
In which the affections gently lead us on, —
Until, the breath of this corporeal frame
And even the motion of our human blood
Almost suspended, we are laid asleep
In body, and become a living soul:
While with an eye made quiet by the power
Of harmony, and the deep power of joy,
We see into the life of things.
                                    If this
Be but a vain belief, yet, oh! — how oft —
In darkness and amid the many shapes
Of joyless daylight; when the fretful stir
Unprofitable, and the fever of the world,
Have hung upon the beatings of my heart —
How oft, in spirit, have I turned to thee,
O sylvan Wye! thou wanderer through the woods,
How often has my spirit turned to thee!
   And now, with gleams of half-extinguished thought,
With many recognitions dim and faint,
And somewhat of a sad perplexity,
The picture of the mind revives again;
While here I stand, not only with the sense
Of present pleasure, but with pleasing thoughts
That in this moment there is life and food
For future years. And so I dare to hope,
Though changed, no doubt, from what I was when first
I came among these hills; when like a roe
I bounded o'er the mountains, by the sides
Of the deep rivers, and the lonely streams,
Wherever nature led: more like a man
Flying from something that he dreads, than one
Who sought the thing he loved. For nature then
(The coarser pleasures of my boyish days,
And their glad animal movements all gone by)
To me was all in all. — I cannot paint
What then I was. The sounding cataract

Haunted me like a passion: the tall rock,
The mountain, and the deep and gloomy wood,
Their colours and their forms, were then to me
An appetite; a feeling and a love,
That had no need of a remoter charm,
By thought supplied, nor any interest
Unborrowed from the eye. — That time is past,
And all its aching joys are now no more,
And all its dizzy raptures. Not for this
Faint I, nor mourn nor murmur; other gifts
Have followed; for such loss, I would believe,
Abundant recompense. For I have learned
To look on nature, not as in the hour
Of thoughtless youth; but hearing oftentimes
The still, sad music of humanity,
Nor harsh nor grating, though of ample power
To chasten and subdue. And I have felt
A presence that disturbs me with the joy
Of elevated thoughts; a sense sublime
Of something far more deeply interfused,
Whose dwelling is the light of setting suns,
And the round ocean, and the living air,
And the blue sky, and in the mind of man;
A motion and a spirit, that impels
All thinking things, all objects of all thought,
And rolls through all things. Therefore am I still
A lover of the meadows and the woods,
And mountains; and of all that we behold
From this green earth, of all the mighty world
Of eye, and ear, — both what they half create,
And what perceive; well pleased to recognize
In nature and the language of the sense,
The anchor of my purest thoughts, the nurse,
The guide, the guardian of my heart, and soul
Of all my moral being. . . .

                 . . . and this prayer I make,
Knowing that Nature never did betray
The heart that loved her; 'tis her privilege,
Through all the years of this our life, to lead
From joy to joy: for she can so inform
The mind that is within us, so impress
With quietness and beauty, and so feed
With lofty thoughts, that neither evil tongues,

Rash judgments, nor the sneers of selfish men,
Nor greetings where no kindness is, nor all
The dreary intercourse of daily life,
Shall e'er prevail against us, or disturb
Our cheerful faith that all which we behold
Is full of blessings. Therefore let the moon
Shine on thee in thy solitary walk;
And let the misty mountain-winds be free
To blow against thee: and, in after years,
When these wild ecstasies shall be matured
Into a sober pleasure; when thy mind
Shall be a mansion for all lovely forms,
Thy memory be as a dwelling-place
For all sweet sounds and harmonies; oh! then,
If solitude, or fear, or pain, or grief,
Should be thy portion, with what healing thoughts
Of tender joy wilt thou remember me,
And these my exhortations! Nor, perchance —
If I should be where I no more can hear
Thy voice, nor catch from thy wild eyes these gleams
Of past existence — wilt thou then forget
That on the banks of this delightful stream
We stood together; and that I, so long
A worshipper of Nature, hither came
Unwearied in that service: rather say
With warmer love — oh! with far deeper zeal
Of holier love. Nor wilt thou then forget,
That after many wanderings, many years
Of absence, these steep woods and lofty cliffs,
And this green pastoral landscape, were to me
More dear, both for themselves and for thy sake!

"Immortal Drink"

JOHN KEATS

A thing of beauty is a joy for ever:
Its loveliness increases; it will never
Pass into nothingness; but still will keep

A bower quiet for us, and a sleep
Full of sweet dreams, and health, and quiet breathing.
Therefore, on every morrow, are we wreathing
A flowery band to bind us to the earth,
Spite of despondence, of the inhuman dearth
Of noble natures, of the gloomy days,
Of all the unhealthy and o'er-darkened ways
Made for our searching: yes, in spite of all,
Some shape of beauty moves away the pall
From our dark spirits. Such the sun, the moon,
Trees old and young, sprouting a shady boon
For simple sheep: and such are daffodils
With the green world they live in; and clear rills
That for themselves a cooling covert make
'Gainst the hot season; the mid-forest brake,
Rich with a sprinkling of fair musk-rose blooms:
And such too is the grandeur of the dooms
We have imagined for the mighty dead;
All lovely tales that we have heard or read:
An endless fountain of immortal drink,
Pouring unto us from the heaven's brink.

— JOHN KEATS: *Endymion*, Book I.

Proem to *Endymion*.

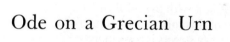

Ode on a Grecian Urn

JOHN KEATS

Thou still unravish'd bride of quietness,
    Thou foster-child of silence and slow time,
Sylvan historian, who canst thus express
    A flowery tale more sweetly than our rhyme:
What leaf-fringed legend haunts about thy shape
    Of deities or mortals, or of both,
        In Tempé or the dales of Arcady?
What men or gods are these? What maidens loth?

What mad pursuit? What struggle to escape?
What pipes and timbrels? What wild ecstasy?

Heard melodies are sweet, but those unheard
    Are sweeter; therefore, ye soft pipes, play on;
Not to the sensual ear, but, more endear'd,
    Pipe to the spirit ditties of no tone:
Fair youth, beneath the trees, thou canst not leave
    Thy song, nor ever can those trees be bare;
        Bold Lover, never, never canst thou kiss,
Though winning near the goal — yet, do not grieve;
    She cannot fade, though thou hast not thy bliss,
        Forever wilt thou love, and she be fair!

Ah, happy, happy boughs! that cannot shed
    Your leaves, nor ever bid the Spring adieu;
And, happy melodist, unweariéd,
    Forever piping songs forever new;
More happy love! more happy, happy love!
    Forever warm and still to be enjoy'd,
        Forever panting, and forever young;
All breathing human passion far above,
    That leaves a heart high-sorrowful and cloy'd,
        A burning forehead, and a parching tongue.

Who are these coming to the sacrifice?
    To what green altar, O mysterious priest,
Lead'st thou that heifer lowing at the skies,
    And all her silken flanks with garlands drest?
What little town by river or seashore,
    Or mountain-built with peaceful citadel,
        Is emptied of this folk, this pious morn?
And, little town, thy streets forevermore
    Will silent be; and not a soul to tell
        Why thou art desolate, can e'er return.

O Attic shape! Fair attitude! with brede
    Of marble men and maidens overwrought,
With forest branches and the trodden weed;
    Thou, silent form, dost tease us out of thought
As doth eternity: Cold Pastoral!
    When old age shall this generation waste,
        Thou shalt remain, in midst of other woe
Than ours, a friend to man, to whom thou say'st,

"Beauty is truth, truth beauty," — that is all
Ye know on earth, and all ye need to know.

◇◇

☞ SHELLEY: "A NEWTON AMONG POETS"

The Dance of Matter

SIR HUMPHRY DAVY

MATTER MAY ULTIMATELY BE FOUND to be the same in essence, differing only in the arrangement of its particles; or two or three simple substances may produce all the varieties of compound bodies.

Whether matter consists of individual corpuscles, or physical points endowed with attraction and repulsion, still the same conclusions may be formed concerning the powers by which they act, and the quantities in which they combine, and the powers seem capable of being measured by their electrical relations, and the quantities on which they act of being expressed by numbers.

Since all matter may be made to fill a smaller volume by cooling, it is evident that the particles of matter must have space between them; and since every body can communicate the power of expansion to a body of lower temperature, that is, can give an expansive motion to its particles, it is a probable inference that its own particles are possessed of motion; but as there is no change in the position of its parts as long as its temperature is uniform, the motion if it exists, must be vibratory or undulatory motion, or a motion of the particles round their axes, or a motion of particles round each other.

This is the dance of matter, incessant in motion, a microcosm of involved orbits, yet seemingly at rest.

◇◇

The Dance of Matter:
The Motion of the Spheres

And from the other opening in the wood
Rushes, with loud and whirlwind harmony,
A sphere, which is as many thousand spheres,
Solid as crystal, yet through all its mass
Flow, as through empty space, music and light:
Ten thousand orbs involving and involved,
Purple and azure, white, and green, and golden,
Sphere within sphere; and every space between
Peopled with unimaginable shapes,
Such as ghosts dream dwell in the lampless deep,
Yet each inter-transpicuous, and they whirl
Over each other with a thousand motions,
Upon a thousand sightless axles spinning,
And with the force of self-destroying swiftness,
Intensely, slowly, solemnly roll on,
Kindling with mingled sounds, and many tones,
Intelligible words and music wild.
With mighty whirl the multitudinous orb
Grinds the bright brook into an azure mist
Of elemental subtlety, like light;
And the wild odor of the forest flowers,
The music of the living grass and air,
The emerald light of leaf-entangled beams
Round its intense yet self-conflicting speed,
Seem kneaded into one aerial mass
Which drowns the sense. Within the orb itself . . .

The Spirit of the Earth is laid asleep . . .
And from a star upon its forehead, shoot,
Like swords of azure fire, or golden spears
With tyrant-quelling myrtle overtwined,
Embleming heaven and earth united now,
Vast beams like spokes of some invisible wheel
Which whirl as the orb whirls, swifter than thought,
Filling the abyss with sun-like lightnings,
And perpendicular now, and now transverse,

Pierce the dark soil, and as they pierce and pass,
Make bare the secrets of the earth's deep heart. . . .

— PERCY BYSSHE SHELLEY: *Prometheus
Unbound*, Act IV.

◇◇◇◇◇◇◇◇◇◇◇◇◇◇◇◇◇◇◇◇◇◇◇◇◇◇◇◇◇◇◇◇◇◇

The Dance of Light:
The Cycle of the Waters

I bring fresh showers for the thirsting flowers,
   From the seas and the streams;
I bear light shade for the leaves when laid
   In their noonday dreams.
From my wings are shaken the dews that waken
   The sweet buds every one,
When rocked to rest on their mother's breast,
   As she dances about the sun.
I wield the flail of the lashing hail,
   And whiten the green plains under,
And then again I dissolve it in rain,
   And laugh as I pass in thunder.

I sift the snow on the mountains below,
   And their great pines groan aghast,
And all the night 'tis my pillow white,
   While I sleep in the arms of the blast.
Sublime on the towers of my skiey bowers,
   Lightning, my pilot, sits,
In a cavern under is fettered the thunder,
   It struggles and howls at fits;
Over earth and ocean, with gentle motion,
   This pilot is guiding me,
Lured by the love of the genii that move
   In the depths of the purple sea;
Over the rills, and the crags, and the hills,
   Over the lakes and the plains,

Wherever he dream, under mountain or stream,
  The Spirit he loves remains;
And I all the while bask in heaven's blue smile,
  Whilst he is dissolving in rains.

The sanguine sunrise, with his meteor eyes,
  And his burning plumes outspread,
Leaps on the back of my sailing rack,
  When the morning star shines dead,
As on the jag of a mountain crag,
  Which an earthquake rocks and swings,
An eagle alit one moment may sit
  In the light of its golden wings.
And when sunset may breathe, from the lit sea beneath,
  Its ardours of rest and of love,
And the crimson pall of eve may fall
  From the depth of heaven above,
With wings folded I rest, on mine airy nest,
  As still as a brooding dove.

That orbèd maiden with white fire laden,
  Whom mortals call the moon,
Glides glimmering o'er my fleece-like floor,
  By the midnight breezes strewn:
And wherever the beat of her unseen feet,
  Which only the angels hear,
May have broken the woof of my tent's thin roof,
  The stars peep behind her and peer;
And I laugh to see them whirl and flee,
  Like a swarm of golden bees,
When I widen the rent in my wind-built tent,
  Till the calm rivers, lakes, and seas,
Like strips of the sky fallen through me on high,
  Are each paved with the moon and these.

I bind the sun's throne with a burning zone,
  And the moon's with a girdle of pearl;
The volcanoes are dim, and the stars reel and swim,
  When the whirlwinds my banner unfurl.
From cape to cape, with a bridge-like shape,
  Over a torrent sea,
Sunbeam-proof, I hang like a roof,
  The mountains its columns be.

The triumphal arch through which I march
   With hurricane, fire, and snow,
When the powers of the air are chained to my chair,
   Is the million-coloured bow;
The sphere-fire above its soft colours wove,
   While the moist earth was laughing below.

I am the daughter of earth and water,
   And the nursling of the sky;
I pass through the pores of the ocean and shores;
   I change, but I cannot die.
For after the rain, when with never a stain
   The pavilion of heaven is bare,
And the winds and sunbeams, with their convex gleams,
   Build up the blue dome of air,
I silently laugh at my own cenotaph,
   And out of the caverns of rain,
Like a child from the womb, like a ghost from the tomb,
   I arise and unbuild it again.

     — PERCY BYSSHE SHELLEY: *The Cloud*

The Dance of Mind: New Reading of Ancient Myth

. . . There was the Heaven and Earth at first,
And Light and Love; then Saturn, from whose throne
Time fell, an envious shadow; such the state
Of the earth's primal spirits beneath his sway,
As the calm joy of flowers and living leaves
Before the wind or sun has withered them
And semivital worms; but he refused
The birthright of their being, knowledge, power,
The skill which wields the elements, the thought
Which pierces this dim universe like light,
Self-empire, and the majesty of love;
For thirst of which they fainted. Then Prometheus

Gave wisdom, which is strength, to Jupiter,
And with this law alone, "Let man be free,"
Clothed him with the dominion of wide Heaven.
To know nor faith, nor love, nor law, to be
Omnipotent but friendless, is to reign;
And Jove now reigned; for, on the race of man
First famine, and then toil, and then disease,
Strife, wounds, and ghastly death unseen before,
Fell; and the unseasonable seasons drove,
With alternating shafts of frost and fire,
Their shelterless, pale tribes to mountain caves;
And in their desert hearts fierce wants he sent,
And mad disquietudes, and shadows idle
Of unreal good, which levied mutual war,
So ruining the lair wherein they raged.

Prometheus saw, and waked the legioned hopes
Which sleep within folded Elysian flowers,
Nepenthe, Moly, Amaranth, fadeless blooms,
That they might hide with thin and rainbow wings
The shape of Death; and Love he sent to bind
The disunited tendrils of that vine
Which bears the wine of life, the human heart;
And he tamed fire which, like some beast of prey,
Most terrible, but lovely, played beneath
The frown of man; and tortured to his will
Iron and gold, the slaves and signs of power,
And gems and poisons, and all subtlest forms
Hidden beneath the mountains and the waves.
He gave man speech, and speech created thought,
Which is the measure of the universe;
And Science struck the thrones of earth and heaven,
Which shook, but fell not; and the harmonious mind
Poured itself forth in all-prophetic song;
And music lifted up the listening spirit
Until it walked, exempt from mortal care,
Godlike, o'er the clear billows of sweet sound;
And human hands first mimicked and then mocked,
With molded limbs more lovely than its own,
The human form, till marble grew divine;
And mothers, gazing, drank the love men see
Reflected in their race, behold, and perish.
He told the hidden power of herbs and springs,
And Disease drank and slept. Death grew like sleep.

He taught the implicated orbits woven
Of the wide-wandering stars; and how the sun
Changes his lair, and by what secret spell
The pale moon is transformed, when her broad eye
Gazes not on the interlunar sea.
He taught to rule, as life directs the limbs,
The tempest-winged chariots of the Ocean,
And the Celt knew the Indian. Cities then
Were built, and through their snow-like columns flowed
The warm winds, and the azure ether shone,
And the blue sea and shadowy hills were seen.
Such, the alleviations of his state,
Prometheus gave to man . . .

[For this daring act of giving science to man, Prometheus is punished by Jupiter by being chained to a rock
where he is tortured through the ages by the Furies, who
show him his gift to mankind corrupted and made an
instrument of destruction.]

FURY: He yet defies the deepest power of Hell.
FURY: Tear the veil!
ANOTHER FURY: It is torn.
CHORUS: The pale stars of the morn
Shine on a misery, dire to be borne.
Dost thou faint, mighty Titan? We laugh thee to scorn.
Dost thou boast the clear knowledge thou waken'dst
      for man?
Then was kindled within him a thirst which outran
Those perishing waters; a thirst of fierce fever,
Hope, love, doubt, desire, which consume him forever.

One came forth of gentle worth,
Smiling on the sanguine earth;
His words outlived him, like swift poison
   Withering up truth, peace, and pity.
Look! where round the wide horizon
   Many a million-peopled city
Vomits smoke in the bright air!
Mark that outcry of despair!
'Tis his mild and gentle ghost
   Wailing for the faith he kindled.
Look again! the flames almost
   To a glow-worm's lamp have dwindled;

The survivors round the embers
Gather in dread.
Joy, joy, joy!
Past ages crowd on thee, but each one remembers.
And the future is dark, and the present is spread
Like a pillow of thorns for thy slumberless head.

Semichorus I

Drops of bloody agony flow
From his white and quivering brow.
Grant a little respite now;
See! a disenchanted nation
Springs like day from desolation;
To Truth its state is dedicate,
And Freedom leads it forth, her mate;
A legioned band of linked brothers,
Whom Love calls children —

Semichorus II
'Tis another's.
See how kindred murder kin!
'Tis the vintage-time for Death and Sin;
Blood like new wine bubbles within
Till Despair smothers
The struggling world, which slaves and tyrants
win. . . .

IONE: What didst thou see?
PANTHEA: A woful sight: a youth
With patient looks nailed to a crucifix . . .
FURY: Behold an emblem: those who do endure
Deep wrongs for man, and scorn, and chains,
      but heap
Thousandfold torment on themselves and him.
PROMETHEUS: Remit the anguish of that lighted stare;
Close those wan lips; let that thorn-wounded brow
Stream not with blood; it mingles with thy tears!
Fix, fix those tortured orbs in peace and death,
So thy sick throes shake not that crucifix,
So those pale fingers play not with thy gore.
O, horrible! Thy name I will not speak,
It hath become a curse. I see, I see
The wise, the mild, the lofty and the just,
Whom thy slaves hate for being like to thee

Some hunted by foul lies from their heart's home,
An early-chosen, late-lamented home;
As hooded ounces cling to the driven hind;
Some linked to corpses in unwholesome cells:
Some — Hear I not the multitude laugh loud? —
Impaled in lingering fire: and mighty realms
Float by my feet, like sea-uprooted isles,
Whose sons are kneaded down in common blood
By the red light of their own burning homes.

FURY: Blood thou canst see, and fire; and canst hear groans;
Worse things, unheard, unseen, remain behind.

PROMETHEUS: Worse?

FURY: In each human heart terror survives
The ruin it has gorged: the loftiest fear
All that they would disdain to think were true:
Hypocrisy and custom make their minds
The fanes of many a worship, now outworn.
They dare not devise good for man's estate,
And yet they know not that they do not dare.
The good want power, but to weep barren tears.
The powerful goodness want: worse need for them.
The wise want love; and those who love want wisdom;
And all best things are thus confused to ill.
Many are strong and rich, and would be just,
But live among their suffering fellow-men
As if none felt: they know not what they do.

PROMETHEUS: Thy words are like a cloud of winged snakes;
And yet I pity those they torture not.

FURY: Thou pitiest them? I speak no more! (*Vanishes*)

[At the close of the play, Shelley expresses his faith that love and intelligence, ultimately transmuting the evils that have seemed to spring from Prometheus' gift, will eventually set man free.]

This is the day, which down the void abysm
At the Earth-born's spell yawns for Heaven's despotism,
    And Conquest is dragged captive through the deep:
Love, from its awful throne of patient power
In the wise heart, from the last giddy hour
    Of dread endurance, from the slippery, steep,
And narrow verge of crag-like agony, springs
And folds over the world its healing wings.

Gentleness, Virtue, Wisdom, and Endurance,
These are the seals of that most firm assurance
   Which bars the pit over Destruction's strength;
And if, with infirm hand, Eternity,
Mother of many acts and hours, should free
   The serpent that would clasp her with its length;
These are the spells by which to re-assume
An empire o'er the disentangled doom.

To suffer woes which Hope thinks infinite;
To forgive wrongs darker than death or night;
   To defy Power, which seems omnipotent;
To love, and bear; to hope till Hope creates
From its own wreck the thing it contemplates;
   Neither to change, nor falter, nor repent;
This, like thy glory, Titan, is to be
Good, great and joyous, beautiful and free;
This is alone Life, Joy, Empire, and Victory.

      — PERCY BYSSHE SHELLEY: *Prometheus Unbound*

FAITH AND UNFAITH: ADVANCING SCIENCE CHALLENGES ESTABLISHED CREED

◇◇◇◇◇◇◇◇◇◇◇◇◇◇◇◇◇◇◇◇◇◇◇◇◇◇◇◇◇◇◇◇◇

⊂⊒ *"CLASH BY NIGHT"*

Dover Beach

MATTHEW ARNOLD

The sea is calm to-night.
The tide is full, the moon lies fair
Upon the straits — on the French coast the light
Gleams and is gone; the cliffs of England stand,
Glimmering and vast, out in the tranquil bay.
Come to the window; sweet is the night air!
Only, from the long line of spray
Where the sea meets the moon-blanched land,
Listen! you hear the grating roar
Of pebbles which the waves draw back, and fling,
At their return, up the high strand,
Begin, and cease, and then again begin,
With tremulous cadence slow, and bring
The eternal note of sadness in.

Sophocles long ago
Heard it on the Ægæan, and it brought
Into his mind the turbid ebb and flow
Of human misery; we
Find also in the sound a thought,
Hearing it by this distant northern sea.

The Sea of Faith
Was once, too, at the full, and round earth's shore
Lay like the folds of a bright girdle furled.
But now I only hear
Its melancholy, long, withdrawing roar,

Retreating, to the breath
Of the night wind, down the vast edges drear
And naked shingles of the world.

Ah, love, let us be true
To one another! for the world, which seems
To lie before us like a land of dreams,
So various, so beautiful, so new,
Hath really neither joy, nor love, nor light,
Nor certitude, nor peace, nor help for pain;
And we are here as on a darkling plain
Swept with confused alarms of struggle and flight
Where ignorant armies clash by night.

Ah, Yet Consider It Again

ARTHUR HUGH CLOUGH

'Old things need not be therefore true,'
  O brother men, nor yet the new;
Ah, still awhile the old thought retain,
  And yet consider it again!

The souls of now two thousand years,
  Have laid up here their toils and fears,
And all the earnings of their pain, —
  Ah, yet consider it again!

We! what do we see? each a space
  Of some few yards before his face;
Does that the whole wide plan explain?
  Ah, yet consider it again.

Alas! the great world goes its way,
  And takes its truth from each new day;
They do not quit, nor can retain,
  Far less consider it again.

With Whom Is No Variableness

ARTHUR HUGH CLOUGH

It fortifies my soul to know
That, though I perish, Truth is so:
That, howsoe'er I stray and range,
Whate'er I do, Thou dost not change.
I steadier step when I recall
That, if I slip Thou dost not fall.

◇◇◇◇◇◇◇◇◇◇◇◇◇◇◇◇◇◇◇◇◇◇◇◇◇◇◇◇◇◇◇◇◇

The Latest Decalogue

ARTHUR HUGH CLOUGH

Thou shalt have one God only; who
Would be at the expense of two?
No graven images may be
Worshipped, except the currency;
Swear not at all, for, for thy curse
Thine enemy is none the worse;
At church on Sunday to attend
Will serve to keep the world thy friend;
Honor thy parents: that is, all
From whom advancement may befall;
Thou shalt not kill; but need'st not strive
Officiously to keep alive;
Do not adultery commit;
Advantage rarely comes of it;
Thou shalt not steal; an empty feat,
When it's so lucrative to cheat;
Bear not false witness; let the lie
Have time on its own wings to fly.
Thou shalt not covet; but tradition
Approves all forms of competition.

"TRUTHS THAT NEVER CAN BE PROVED"

From In Memoriam A. H. H.

ALFRED, LORD TENNYSON

. . . *"Is this an hour*
For private sorrow's barren song,
When more and more the people throng
The chairs and thrones of civil power?

"A time to sicken and to swoon,
When Science reaches forth her arms
To feel from world to world, and charms
Her secret from the latest moon?"

O, yet we trust that somehow good
Will be the final goal of ill,
To pangs of nature, sins of will,
Defects of doubt, and taints of blood;

That nothing walks with aimless feet;
That not one life shall be destroy'd.
Or cast as rubbish to the void,
When God hath made the pile complete;

That not a worm is cloven in vain;
That not a moth with vain desire
Is shrivell'd in a fruitless fire,
Or but subserves another's gain.

Behold, we know not anything;
I can but trust that good shall fall
At last — far off — at last, to all,
And every winter change to spring.

So runs my dream; but what am I?
An infant crying in the night;

An infant crying for the light,
And with no language but a cry.

The wish, that of the living whole
　No life may fail beyond the grave,
　Derives it not from what we have
The likest God within the soul?

Are God and Nature then at strife,
　That Nature lends such evil dreams?
　So careful of the type she seems,
So careless of the single life,

That I, considering everywhere
　Her secret meaning in her deeds,
　And finding that of fifty seeds
She often brings but one to bear,

I falter where I firmly trod,
　And falling with my weight of cares
　Upon the great world's altar-stairs
That slope thro' darkness up to God,

I stretch lame hands of faith, and grope,
　And gather dust and chaff, and call
　To what I feel is Lord of all,
And faintly trust the larger hope.

"So careful of the type?" but no.
　From scarped cliff and quarried stone
　She cries, "A thousand types are gone;
I care for nothing, all shall go.

"Thou makest thine appeal to me:
　I bring to life, I bring to death;
　The spirit does but mean the breath:
I know no more." And he, shall he,

Man, her last work, who seem'd so fair,
　Such splendid purpose in his eyes,
　Who roll'd the psalm to wintry skies,
Who built him fanes of fruitless prayer,

Who trusted God was love indeed
  And love Creation's final law —
  Tho' Nature, red in tooth and claw
With ravin, shriek'd against his creed —

Who loved, who suffer'd countless ills,
  Who battled for the True, the Just,
  Be blown about the desert dust,
Or seal'd within the iron hills?

No more? A monster then, a dream,
  A discord. Dragons of the prime,
  That tare each other in their slime,
Were mellow music match'd with him.

O life as futile, then, as frail!
  O for thy voice to soothe and bless!
  What hope of answer, or redress?
Behind the veil, behind the veil.

————

Contemplate all this work of Time,
  The giant laboring in his youth;
  Nor dream of human love and truth,
As dying Nature's earth and lime;

But trust that those we call the dead
  Are breathers of an ampler day
  For ever nobler ends. They say,
The solid earth whereon we tread

In tracts of fluent heat began,
  And grew to seeming-random forms,
  The seeming prey of cyclic storms,
Till at the last arose the man;

Who throve and branch'd from clime to clime,
  The herald of a higher race,
  And of himself in higher place,
If so he type this work of time

Within himself, from more to more;
  Or, crown'd with attributes of woe

Like glories, move his course, and show
That life is not as idle ore,

But iron dug from central gloom,
    And heated hot with burning fears,
    And dipt in baths of hissing tears,
And batter'd with the shocks of doom

To shape and use. Arise and fly
    The reeling Faun, the sensual feast;
    Move upward, working out the beast,
And let the ape and tiger die.

I trust I have not wasted breath:
    I think we are not wholly brain,
    Magnetic mockeries; not in vain,
Like Paul with beasts, I fought with Death;

Not only cunning casts in clay:
    Let Science prove we are, and then
    What matters Science unto men,
At least to me? I would not stay.

Let him, the wiser man who springs
    Hereafter, up from childhood shape
    His action like the greater ape,
But I was *born* to other things.

There rolls the deep where grew the tree.
    O earth, what changes hast thou seen!
    There where the long street roars hath been
The stillness of the central sea.

The hills are shadows, and they flow
    From form to form, and nothing stands;
    They melt like mist, the solid lands,
Like clouds they shape themselves and go.

But in my spirit will I dwell,
    And dream my dream, and hold it true;
    For tho' my lips may breathe adieu,
I cannot think the thing farewell.

O living will that shalt endure
   When all that seems shall suffer shock,
   Rise in the spiritual rock,
Flow through our deeds and make them pure,

That we may lift from out of dust
   A voice as unto him that hears,
   A cry above the conquer'd years
To one that with us works, and trust,

With faith that comes of self-control,
   The truths that never can be proved
   Until we close with all we loved,
And all we flow from, soul in soul.

By an Evolutionist

ALFRED, LORD TENNYSON

The Lord let the house of a brute to the soul of a man,
   And the man said "Am I your debtor?"
And the Lord — "Not yet: but make it as clean as you can,
   And then I will let you a better."

I

If my body come from brutes, my soul uncertain, or a fable,
   Why not bask amid the senses while the sun of morning shines,
I, the finer brute rejoicing in my hounds, and in my stable,
   Youth and health, and birth and wealth, and choice of women and
      of wines?

II

What hast thou done for me, grim Old Age, save breaking my bones
      on the rack?
   Would I had past in the morning that looks so bright from afar!

OLD AGE

Done for thee? starved the wild beast that was linkt with thee eighty
    years back.
Less weight now for the ladder-of-heaven that hangs on a star.

I

If my body come from brutes, tho' somewhat finer than their own,
    I am heir, and this my kingdom. Shall the royal voice be mute?
No, but if the rebel subject seek to drag me from the throne,
    Hold the sceptre, Human Soul, and rule thy Province of the brute.

II

I have climbed to the snows of Age, and I gaze at a field in the Past,
    Where I sank with the body at times in the sloughs of a low
        desire,
But I hear no yelp of the beast, and the Man is quiet at last
    As he stands on the heights of his life with a glimpse of a height
        that is higher.

Flower in the Crannied Wall

ALFRED, LORD TENNYSON

Flower in the crannied wall,
I pluck you out of the crannies,
I hold you here, root and all, in my hand,
Little flower — but *if* I could understand
What you are, root and all, and all in all,
I should know what God and man is.

Crossing the Bar

ALFRED, LORD TENNYSON

Sunset and evening star,
　And one clear call for me!
And may there be no moaning of the bar,
　When I put out to sea,

But such a tide as moving seems asleep,
　Too full for sound and foam,
When that which drew from out the boundless deep
　Turns again home.

Twilight and evening bell,
　And after that the dark!
And may there be no sadness of farewell,
　When I embark;

For though, from out our bourne of Time and Place
　The flood may bear me far,
I hope to see my Pilot face to face
　When I have crost the bar.

Rubáiyát of Omar Khayyám

EDWARD FITZGERALD

Alike for those who for TODAY prepare,
And those that after some TOMORROW stare,
　A Muezzín from the Tower of Darkness cries,
"Fools! your Reward is neither Here nor There."

Why, all the Saints and Sages who discuss'd
Of the Two Worlds so wisely — they art thrust
   Like foolish Prophets forth; their Words to Scorn
Are scatter'd, and their Mouths are stopt with Dust.

Myself when young did eagerly frequent
Doctor and Saint, and heard great argument
   About it and about: but evermore
Came out by the same door where in I went.

With them the seed of Wisdom did I sow,
And with mine own hand wrought to make it grow;
   And this was all the Harvest that I reap'd —
"I came like Water, and like Wind I go."

Into this Universe, and *Why* not knowing
Nor *Whence*, like Water willy-nilly flowing;
   And out of it, as Wind along the Waste,
I know not *Whither*, willy-nilly, blowing.

What, without asking, hither hurried *Whence?*
And, without asking, *Whither* hurried hence?
   Oh, many a Cup of this forbidden Wine
Must drown the memory of that insolence!

Up from Earth's Centre through the Seventh Gate
I rose, and on the Throne of Saturn sate,
   And many a Knot unravell'd by the Road;
But not the Master-knot of Human Fate.

There was the Door to which I found no Key;
There was the Veil through which I might not see:

Some little talk awhile of ME and THEE
There was — and then no more of THEE and ME.

◇◇◇◇◇◇◇◇◇◇◇◇◇◇◇◇◇◇◇◇◇◇◇◇◇◇◇◇◇◇◇◇◇◇◇◇◇◇

☞ "UNALTERABLE LAW"

Nature Without Check

WALT WHITMAN

Creeds and schools in abeyance,
Retiring back awhile sufficed at what they are, but never forgotten,
I harbor for good or bad, I permit to speak at every hazard
Nature without check with original energy.

◇◇◇◇◇◇◇◇◇◇◇◇◇◇◇◇◇◇◇◇◇◇◇◇◇◇◇◇◇◇◇◇◇◇◇◇◇◇

When I Heard the Learn'd Astronomer

WALT WHITMAN

When I heard the learn'd astronomer,
When the proofs, the figures, were ranged in columns before me,
When I was shown the charts and diagrams, to add, divide, and
    measure them,
When I sitting heard the astronomer where he lectured with much
    applause in the lecture room,
How soon unaccountable I became tired and sick,
Till rising and gliding out I wandered off by myself,
In the mystical moist night air, and from time to time,
Looked up in perfect silence at the stars.

◇◇◇◇◇◇◇◇◇◇◇◇◇◇◇◇◇◇◇◇◇◇◇◇◇◇◇◇◇◇◇◇◇◇◇◇◇◇

Miracles

WALT WHITMAN

Why, who makes much of a miracle?
As to me I know of nothing else but miracles,
Whether I walk the streets of Manhattan,
Or dart my sight over the roofs of houses toward the sky,
Or wade with naked feet along the beach just in the edge of the
    water,
Or stand under trees in the woods,
Or talk by day with anyone I love, or sleep in the bed at night with
    anyone I love,
Or sit at table at dinner with the rest,
Or look at strangers opposite me riding in the car,
Or watch honeybees busy around the hive of a summer forenoon,
Or animals feeding in the fields,
Or birds, or the wonderfulness of insects in the air,
Or the wonderfulness of the sundown, or of stars shining so quiet
    and bright,
Or the exquisite delicate curve of the new moon in spring;
These with the rest, one and all, are to me miracles,
The whole referring, yet each distinct and in its place.

To me every hour of the night and dark is a miracle,
Every cubic inch of space is a miracle,
Every square yard of the surface of the earth is spread with the
    same,
Every foot of the interior swarms with the same.

To me the sea is a continual miracle,
The fishes that swim — the rocks — the motion of the waves — the
    ships with men in them,
What stranger miracles are there?

Lucifer in Starlight

GEORGE MEREDITH

On a starred night Prince Lucifer uprose.
Tired of his dark dominion swung the fiend
Above the rolling ball in cloud part screened,
Where sinners hug their specter of repose.
Poor prey to his hot fit of pride were those.
And now upon his western wing he leaned,
Now his huge bulk o'er Afric's sands careened,
Now the black planet shadowed Arctic snows.
Soaring through wider zones that pricked his scars
With memories of the old revolt from Awe,
He reached a middle height, and at the stars,
Which are the brain of heaven, he looked, and sank.
Around the ancient track marched, rank on rank,
The army of unalterable law.

O World

GEORGE SANTAYANA

O world, thou choosest not the better part!
It is not wisdom to be only wise,
And on the inward vision close the eyes,
But it is wisdom to believe the heart.
Columbus found a world, and had no chart,
Save one that faith deciphered in the skies;
To trust the soul's invincible surmise
Was all his science and his only art.
Our knowledge is a torch of smoky pine
That lights the pathway but one step ahead

Reprinted from *Poems* by George Santayana with the permission of Charles Scribner's Sons.

Across a void of mystery and dread.
Bid, then, the tender light of faith to shine
By which alone the mortal heart is led
Unto the thinking of the thought divine.

Each in His Own Tongue

WILLIAM HERBERT CARRUTH

A fire mist and a planet,
A crystal and a cell,
A jellyfish and a saurian,
And caves where cavemen dwell.

Then a sense of law and beauty,
And a face turned from the clod.
Some call it evolution,
And others call it God.

The Far-Seeing Eye

TEMPLE RICE HOLLCROFT

The great eye turns, and suddenly we see
Far stellar systems as they used to be
Before man was — now his to view and know
Worlds as they were a billion years ago.

Reprinted by permission from the *Scientific Monthly*, February 1951.

We hear the psalmist in his wonder say,
"A thousand years to him is but a day!"
Now, once a distant nebula has beckoned,
A thousand million years is but a second.

◇◇◇◇◇◇◇◇◇◇◇◇◇◇◇◇◇◇◇◇◇◇◇◇◇◇◇◇◇◇◇◇◇◇◇◇◇◇

"OUR PLACE AMONG THE INFINITIES"

◇◇

⊂⊋ *PULVIS ET UMBRA*

ROBERT LOUIS STEVENSON

WE LOOK for some reward of our endeavors and are disappointed; not success, not happiness, not even peace of conscience, crowns our ineffectual efforts to do well. Our frailities are invincible, our virtues barren; the battle goes sore against us to the going down of the sun. The canting moralist tells us of right and wrong; and we look abroad, even on the face of our small earth, and find them changed with every climate, and no country where some action is not honored for a virtue and none where it is not branded for a vice; and we look in our experience, and find no vital congruity in the wisest rules, but at the best a municipal fitness. It is not strange if we are tempted to despair of good. We ask too much. Our religions and moralities have been trimmed to flatter us, till they are all emasculate and sentimentalized, and only please and weaken. Truth is of a rougher strain. In the harsh face of life, faith can read a bracing gospel. The human race is a thing more ancient than the Ten Commandments; and the bones and revolutions of the Kosmos, in whose joints we are but moss and fungus, more ancient still.

I

Of the Kosmos in the last resort, science reports many doubtful things and all of them appalling. There seems no substance to this solid globe on which we stamp: nothing but symbols and ratios. Symbols and ratios carry us and bring us forth and beat us down; gravity that swings the incommensurable suns and worlds through space is but a figment varying inversely as the squares of distances; and the suns and worlds themselves, imponderable figures of abstraction, NH_3 and H_2O. Consideration dares not dwell upon this view; that way madness lies; science carries us into zones of speculation, where there is no habitable city for the mind of man.

But take the Kosmos with a grosser faith, as our senses give it us. We behold space sown with rotatory islands, suns and worlds and

From *Across the Plains*, 1892.

the shards and wrecks of systems: some, like the sun, still blazing; some rotting, like the earth; others, like the moon, stable in desolation. All of these we take to be made of something we call matter: a thing which no analysis can help us to conceive; to whose incredible properties no familiarities can reconcile our minds. This stuff, when not purified by the lustration of fire, rots uncleanly into something we call life; seized through all its atoms with a pediculous malady; swelling in tumors that become independent, sometimes even (by an abhorrent prodigy) locomotory; one splitting into millions, millions cohering into one, as the malady proceeds through varying stages. This vital putrescence of the dust, used as we are to it, yet strikes us with occasional disgust, and the profusion of worms in a piece of ancient turf, or the air of a marsh darkened with insects, will sometimes check our breathing so that we aspire for cleaner places. But none is clean: the moving sand is infected with lice; the pure spring, where it bursts out of the mountain, is a mere issue of worms; even in the hard rock the crystal is forming.

In two main shapes this eruption covers the countenance of the earth: the animal and the vegetable: one in some degree the inversion of the other: the second rooted to the spot; the first coming detached out of its natal mud, and scurrying abroad with the myriad feet of insects or towering into the heavens on the wings of birds: a thing so incomprehensible that, if it be well considered, the heart stops. To what passes with the anchored vermin, we have little clue: doubtless they have their joys and sorrows, their delights and killing agonies: it appears not how. But of the locomotory, to which we ourselves belong, we can tell more. These share with us a thousand miracles: the miracles of sight, of hearing, of the projection of sound, things that bridge space; the miracles of memory and reason, by which the present is conceived, and when it is gone, its image kept living in the brains of man and brute; the miracle of reproduction, with its imperious desires and staggering consequences. And to put the last touch upon this mountain mass of the revolting and the inconceivable, all these prey upon each other, lives tearing other lives in pieces, cramming them inside themselves, and by that summary process, growing fat: the vegetarian, the whale, perhaps the tree, not less than the lion of the desert; for the vegetarian is only the eater of the dumb.

Meanwhile our rotatory island loaded with predatory life, and more drenched with blood, both animal and vegetable, than ever mutinied ship, scuds through space with unimaginable speed, and turns alternate cheeks to the reverberation of a blazing world, ninety million miles away.

II

What a monstrous specter is this man, the disease of the agglutinated dust, lifting alternate feet or lying drugged with slumber; killing, feeding, growing, bringing forth small copies of himself; grown upon with hair like grass, fitted with eyes that move and glitter in his face; a thing to set children screaming; — and yet looked at nearlier, known as his fellows know him, how surprising are his attributes! Poor soul, here for so little, cast among so many hardships, filled with desires so incommensurate and so inconsistent, savagely surrounded, savagely descended, irremediably condemned to prey upon his fellow lives: who should have blamed him had he been of a piece with his destiny and a being merely barbarous? And we look and behold him instead filled with imperfect virtues: infinitely childish, often admirably valiant, often touchingly kind; sitting down, amidst his momentary life, to debate of right and wrong and the attributes of the deity; rising up to do battle for an egg or die for an idea; singling out his friends and his mate with cordial affection; bringing forth in pain, rearing with long-suffering solicitude, his young. To touch the heart of his mystery, we find in him one thought, strange to the point of lunacy: the thought of duty; the thought of something owing to himself, to his neighbor, to his God; an ideal of decency, to which he would rise if it were possible; a limit of shame below which, if it be possible, he will not stoop. The design in most men is one of conformity; here and there, in picked natures, it transcends itself and soars on the other side, arming martyrs with independence; but in all, in their degrees, it is a bosom thought: — Not in man alone, for we trace it in dogs and cats whom we know fairly well, and doubtless some similar point of honor sways the elephant, the oyster, and the louse, of whom we know so little: — But in man, at least, it sways with so complete an empire that merely selfish things come second, even with the selfish: that appetites are starved, fears are conquered, pains supported; that almost the dullest shrinks from the reproof of a glance, although it were a child's; and all but the most cowardly stand amid the risks of war; and the more noble, having strongly conceived an act as due to their ideal, affront and embrace death. Strange enough if, with their singular origin and perverted practice, they think they are to be rewarded in some future life: stranger still, if they are persuaded of the contrary, and think this blow, which they solicit, will strike them senseless for eternity. I shall be reminded what a tragedy of misconception and misconduct man at large presents: of organized injustice, cowardly violence, and treacherous crime; and of the damning imperfections of the best. They cannot be too darkly drawn. Man is indeed marked for failure in his efforts to do right. But where the best consistently miscarry, how tenfold more remarkable that all should continue to strive; and surely we should find it both touching and inspiriting, that in a field from which success is banished, our race should not cease to labor.

If the first view of this creature, stalking in his rotatory isle, be a thing to shake the courage of the stoutest, on this nearer sight, he startles us with an admiring wonder. It matters not where we look, under what climate we observe him, in what stage of society, in what depth of ignorance, burthened with what erroneous morality; by camp-fires in Assiniboia, the snow powdering his shoulders, the wind plucking his blanket, as he sits, passing the ceremonial calumet and uttering his grave opinions like a Roman senator; in ships at sea, a man inured to hardship and vile pleasures, his brightest hope a fiddle in a tavern and a bedizened trull who sells herself to rob him, and he for all that simple, innocent, cheerful, kindly like a child, constant to toil, brave to drown, for others; in the slums of cities, moving among indifferent millions to mechanical employments, without hope of change in the future, with scarce a pleasure in the present, and yet true to his virtues, honest up to his lights, kind to his neighbors, tempted perhaps in vain by the bright gin-palace, per-haps long-suffering with the drunken wife that ruins him; in India (a woman this time) kneeling with broken cries and streaming tears, as she drowns her child in the sacred river; in the brothel, the dis-card of society, living mainly on strong drink, fed with affronts, a fool, a thief, the comrade of thieves, and even here keeping the point of honor and the touch of pity, often repaying the world's scorn with service, often standing firm upon a scruple, and at a cer-tain cost, rejecting riches: — everywhere some virtue cherished or affected, everywhere some decency of thought and carriage, every-where the ensign of man's ineffectual goodness: — ah! if I could show you this! If I could show you these men and women, all the world over, in every stage of history, under every abuse of error, under every circumstance of failure, without hope, without help, without thanks, still obscurely fighting the lost fight of virtue, still clinging, in the brothel or on the scaffold, to some rag of honor, the poor jewel of their souls! They may seek to escape, and yet they cannot; it is not alone their privilege and glory, but their doom; they are condemned to some nobility; all their lives long, the desire of good is at their heels, the implacable hunter.

Of all earth's meteors, here at least is the most strange and con-soling: that this ennobled lemur, this hair-crowned bubble of the dust, this inheritor of a few years and sorrows, should yet deny himself his rare delights, and add to his frequent pains, and live for an ideal, however misconceived. Nor can we stop with man. A new doctrine, received with screams a little while ago by canting moralists, and still not properly worked into the body of our thoughts, lights us a step farther into the heart of this rough but noble universe. For nowadays the pride of man denies in vain his kinship with the original dust. He stands no longer like a thing apart. Close at his heels we see the dog, prince of another genus: and in him too, we see dumbly testified the same cultus of an unattainable ideal, the same constancy in failure. Does it stop with the dog? We look at our feet where the ground is blackened with the swarming ant: a creature so small, so far from us in the hierarchy of brutes, that we can scarce trace and scarce comprehend his doings; and here also, in his ordered polities and rigorous justice, we see confessed the law of duty and the fact of individual sin. Does it stop, then, with the ant? Rather this desire of well-doing and this doom of frailty run through all the grades of life: rather is this earth, from the frosty top of Everest to the next margin of the internal fire, one stage of ineffectual virtues and one temple of pious tears and perseverance. The whole creation groaneth and travaileth together. It is the common and the god-like law of life. The browsers, the biters, the barkers, the hairy coats of field and forest, the squirrel in the oak, the thousand-footed creeper in the dust, as they share with us the gift of life, share with us the love of an ideal: strive like us — like us are tempted to grow weary of the struggle — to do well; like us receive at times unmerited refreshment, visitings of support, returns of courage; and are condemned like us to be crucified between that double law of the members and the will. Are they like us, I wonder, in the timid hope of some reward, some sugar with the drug? do they, too, stand aghast at unrewarded virtues, at the sufferings of those whom, in our partiality, we take to be just, and the prosperity of such as, in our blindness, we call wicked? It may be, and yet God knows what they should look for. Even while they look, even while they repent, the foot of man treads them by thousands in the dust, the yelping hounds burst upon their trail, the bullet speeds, the knives are heating in the den of the vivisectionist; or the dew falls, and the generation of a day is blotted out. For these are creatures, compared with whom our weakness is strength, our ignorance wisdom, our brief span eternity.

And as we dwell, we living things, in our isle of terror and under the imminent hand of death, God forbid it should be man the erected, the reasoner, the wise in his own eyes — God forbid it should be man that wearies in well-doing, that despairs of unrewarded effort, or utters the language of complaint. Let it be enough for faith, that the whole creation groans in mortal frailty, strives with unconquerable constancy: surely not all in vain.

⊂⊒ <u>MAN'S FATE</u>

BERTRAND RUSSELL

[Mephistopheles, telling Faustus the story of Creation, represents it as a drama which God has caused to be performed because he was weary of the praises of the archangels; finding the play good, He sends another sun through the sky, which crashes into Man's sun; all returns then to nebulae, so that the play may again be performed.]

SUCH, in outline, but even more purposeless, more void of meaning is the world which Science presents for our belief. Amid such a world, if anywhere, our ideals henceforward must find a home. That man is the product of causes which had no prevision of the end they were achieving; that his origin, his growth, his hopes and fears, his loves and beliefs, are but the outcome of accidental collocations of atoms; that no fire, no heroism, no intensity of thought and feeling, can preserve an individual life beyond the grave; that all the labors of the ages, all the devotion, all the inspiration, all the noonday brightness of human genius, are destined to extinction in the vast death of the solar system, and that the whole temple of Man's achievement must inevitably be buried beneath the debris of a universe in ruins — all these things, if not quite beyond dispute, are yet so nearly certain, that no philosophy which rejects them can hope to stand. Only within the scaffolding of these truths, only on the firm foundation of unyielding despair, can the soul's habitation henceforth be safely built.

How, in such an alien and inhuman world, can so powerless a creature as Man preserve his aspirations untarnished? A strange mystery it is that Nature, omnipotent but blind, in the revolutions

From "A Free Man's Worship" in *Mysticism and Logic* by Bertrand Russell. Reprinted by permission of George Allen and Unwin, Ltd., publishers.

of her secular hurryings through the abysses of space, has brought forth at last a child, subject still to her power, but gifted with sight, with knowledge of good and evil, with the capacity of judging all the works of his unthinking Mother. In spite of Death, the mark and seal of the parental control, Man is yet free, during his brief years, to examine, to criticize, to know and in imagination to create. To him alone, in the world with which he is acquainted, this freedom belongs; and in this lies his superiority to the resistless forces that control his outward life. . . .

Brief and powerless is Man's life; on him and all his race the slow, sure doom falls pitiless and dark. Blind to good and evil, reckless of destruction, omnipotent matter rolls on its relentless way; for Man, condemned today to lose his dearest, tomorrow himself to pass through the gate of darkness, it remains only to cherish, ere yet the blow falls, the lofty thoughts that ennoble his little day: disdaining the coward terrors of the slave of Fate, to worship at the shrine that his own hands have built; undismayed by the empire of chance, to preserve a mind free from the wanton tyranny that rules his outward life; proudly defiant of the irresistible forces that tolerate, for a moment, his knowledge and his condemnation, to sustain alone, a weary but unyielding Atlas, the world that his own ideals have fashioned despite the trampling march of unconscious power.

◖ *VOICES OF PROPHECY*

"What Is the Meaning of This City?"

T. S. ELIOT

The Word of the Lord came unto me, saying:
O miserable cities of designing men,
O wretched generations of enlightened men,
Betrayed in the mazes of your ingenuities,
Sold by the proceeds of your proper inventions:

I have given you hands which you turn from worship,
I have given you speech, for endless palaver,
I have given you my Law, and you set up commissions,
I have given you lips, to express friendly sentiments,
I have given you hearts, for reciprocal distrust.
I have given you power of choice, and you only alternate
Between futile speculation, and unconsidered action.
Many are engaged in writing books and printing them,
Many desire to see their names in print,
Many read nothing but the race reports.
Much is your reading, but not the Word of God,
Much is your building, but not the House of God.
Will you build me a house of plaster, with corrugated roofing,
To be filled with a litter of Sunday newspapers?

1ST MALE VOICE: A Cry from the East:
    What shall be done to the shore of smoky ships?
    Will you leave my people forgetful and forgotten
    To idleness, labor, and delirious stupor?
    There shall be left the broken chimney,
    The peeled hull, a pile of rusty iron,
    In a street of scattered brick where the goat climbs,
    Where my Word is unspoken.

2ND MALE VOICE: A Cry from the North, from the West and from
        the South
    Whence thousands travel daily to the timekept City;
    Where my Word is unspoken,
    In the land of lobelias and tennis flannels
    The rabbit shall burrow and the thorn revisit,
    The nettle shall flourish on the gravel court,
    And the wind shall say: "Here were decent godless people:
    Their only monument the asphalt road
    And a thousand lost golf balls."

CHORUS: We build in vain unless the LORD build with us.
    Can you keep the City that the LORD keeps not with you?
    A thousand policemen directing the traffic
    Cannot tell you why you come or where you go.
    A colony of cavies or a horde of active marmots
    Build better than they that build without the LORD.
    Shall we lift up our feet among perpetual ruins?
    I have loved the beauty of Thy House, the peace of Thy sanc-
        tuary,

I have swept the floors and garnished the altars.
Where there is no temple there shall be no homes,
Though you have shelters and institutions,
Precarious lodgings while the rent is paid,
Subsiding basements where the rat breeds
Or sanitary dwellings with numbered doors
Or a house a little better than your neighbor's;
When the Stranger says: "What is the meaning of this city?
Do you huddle close together because you love each other?"
What will you answer? "We all dwell together
To make money from each other"? or "This is a community"?
And the Stranger will depart and return to the desert.
O my soul, be prepared for the coming of the Stranger,
Be prepared for him who knows how to ask questions.

O weariness of men who turn from GOD
To the grandeur of your mind and the glory of your action,
To arts and inventions and daring enterprises,
To schemes of human greatness thoroughly discredited,
Binding the earth and the water to your service,
Exploiting the seas and developing the mountains,
Dividing the stars into common and preferred,
Engaged in devising the perfect refrigerator,
Engaged in working out a rational morality,
Engaged in printing as many books as possible,
Plotting of happiness and flinging empty bottles,
Turning from your vacancy to fevered enthusiasm
For nation or race or what you call humanity;
Though you forget the way to the Temple,
There is one who remembers the way to your door:
Life you may evade, but Death you shall not.
You shall not deny the Stranger.

Mother Goose's Garland

ARCHIBALD MACLEISH

Around, around the sun we go:
The moon goes round the earth.
We do not die of death:
We die of vertigo.

◇◇

Seafarer

ARCHIBALD MACLEISH

And learn O voyager to walk
The roll of earth, the pitch and fall
That swings across these trees those stars:
That swings the sunlight up the wall.

And learn upon these narrow beds
To sleep in spite of sea, in spite
Of sound the rushing planet makes:
And learn to sleep against the ground.

◇◇

Lines for a Prologue

ARCHIBALD MACLEISH

These alternate nights and days, these seasons
Somehow fail to convince me. It seems
I have the sense of infinity!

(In your dreams, O crew of Columbus,
O listeners over the sea
For the surf that breaks upon Nothing —)

Once I was waked by the nightingales in the garden.
I thought, What time is it? I thought,
Time — Is it Time still? — Now is it Time?

(Tell me your dreams, O sailors:
Tell me, in sleep did you climb
The tall masts, and before you —)

At night the stillness of old trees
Is a leaning over and the inertness
Of hills is a kind of waiting.

(In sleep, in a dream, did you see
The world's end? Did the water
Break — and no shore — Did you see?)

Strange faces come through the streets to me
Like messengers: and I have been warned
By the moving slowly of hands at a window.

O, I have the sense of infinity —
But the world, sailors, is round.
They say there is no end to it.

You, Andrew Marvell

ARCHIBALD MACLEISH

And here face down beneath the sun
And here upon earth's noonward height
To feel the always coming on
The always rising of the night

To feel creep up the curving east
The earthly chill of dusk and slow
Upon those under lands the vast
And ever-climbing shadow grow

And strange at Ecbatan the trees
Take leaf by leaf the evening strange
The flooding dark about their knees
The mountains over Persia change

And now at Kermanshah the gate
Dark empty and the withered grass
And through the twilight now the late
Few travelers in the westward pass

And Baghdad darken and the bridge
Across the silent river gone
And through Arabia the edge
Of evening widen and steal on

And deepen on Palmyra's street
The wheel rut in the ruined stone
And Lebanon fade out and Crete
High through the clouds and overblown

And over Sicily the air
Still flashing with the landward gulls
And loom and slowly disappear
The sails above the shadowy hulls

And Spain go under and the shore
Of Africa the gilded sand

And evening vanish and no more
The low pale light across that land

Nor now the long light on the sea —

And here face downward in the sun
To feel how swift how secretly
The shadow of the night comes on. . . .

◇◇◇◇◇◇◇◇◇◇◇◇◇◇◇◇◇◇◇◇◇◇◇◇◇◇◇◇◇◇◇◇◇◇◇◇◇◇◇

Epistle to Be Left in the Earth

ARCHIBALD MACLEISH

. . . It is colder now
                    there are many stars
                                        we are drifting
North by the Great Bear
                        the leaves are falling
The water is stone in the scooped rocks
                                        to southward
Red sun gray air
                the crows are
Slow on their crooked wings
                                        the jays have left us
Long since we passed the flares of Orion
Each man believes in his heart he will die
Many have written last thoughts and last letters
None know if our deaths are now or forever
None know if this wandering earth will be found

We lie down and the snow covers our garments
I pray you
            you (if any open this writing)
Make in your mouths the words that were our names
I will tell you all we have learned
                                    I will tell you everything
The earth is round

                              there are springs under the orchards
The loam cuts with a blunt knife
                                        beware of
Elms in thunder
                        the lights in the sky are stars
We think they do not see
                                we think also
The trees do not know nor the leaves of the grasses
                                                        hear us

The birds too are ignorant
                                Do not listen
Do not stand at dark in the open windows
We before you have heard this
                                they are voices
They are not words at all but the wind rising
Also none among us has seen God
(. . . We have thought often
The flaws of sun in the late and driving weather
Pointed to one tree but it was not so)
As for the nights I warn you the nights are dangerous
The wind changes at night and the dreams come

It is very cold
                        there are strange stars near Arcturus

Voices are crying an unknown name in the sky

Star Splitter

ROBERT FROST

"You know Orion always comes up sideways.
Throwing a leg up over our fence of mountains,
And rising on his hands, he looks in on me
Busy outdoors by lantern-light with something
I should have done by daylight, and indeed,
After the ground is frozen, I should have done

From *Collected Poems* of Robert Frost. Reprinted by permission of Henry Holt and Company, Inc., publishers.

Before it froze, and a gust flings a handful
Of waste leaves at my smoky lantern chimney
To make fun of my way of doing things,
Or else fun of Orion's having caught me.
Has a man, I should like to ask, no rights
These forces are obliged to pay respect to?"
So Brad McLaughlin mingled reckless talk
Of heavenly stars with hugger-mugger farming,
Till having failed at hugger-mugger farming,
He burned the house down for the fire insurance
And spent the proceeds on a telescope
To satisfy a life-long curiosity
About our place among the infinities.

"What do you want with one of those blame things?"
I asked him well beforehand. "Don't you get one!"
"Don't call it blamed; there isn't anything
More blameless in the sense of being less
A weapon in our human fight," he said.
"I'll have one if I sell my farm to buy it."
There where he moved the rocks to plow the ground
And plowed between the rocks he couldn't move,
Few farms changed hands; so rather than spend years
Trying to sell his farm and then not selling,
He burned his house down for the fire insurance
And bought the telescope with what it came to.
He had been heard to say by several:
"The best thing that we're put here for's to see;
The strongest thing that's given us to see with's
A telescope. Someone in every town
Seems to me owes it to the town to keep one.
In Littleton it may as well be me."
After such loose talk it was no surprise
When he did what he did and burned his house **down.**

Mean laughter went about the town that day
To let him know we weren't the least imposed on,
And he could wait — we'd see to him tomorrow.
But the first thing next morning we reflected
If one by one we counted people out
For the least sin, it wouldn't take us long
To get so we had no one left to live with.
For to be social is to be forgiving.
Our thief, the one who does the stealing from us,

We don't cut off from coming to church suppers,
But what we miss we go to him and ask for.
He promptly gives it back, that is if still
Uneaten, unworn out, or undisposed of.
It wouldn't do to be too hard on Brad
About his telescope. Beyond the age
Of being given one's gift for Christmas,
He had to take the best way he knew how
To find himself in one. Well, all we said was
He took a strange thing to be roguish over.
Some sympathy was wasted on the house,
A good old-timer dating back along;
But a house isn't sentient; the house
Didn't feel anything. And if it did,
Why not regard it as a sacrifice,
And an old-fashioned sacrifice by fire,
Instead of a new-fashioned one at auction?

Out of a house and so out of a farm
At one stroke (of a match), Brad had to turn
To earn a living on the Concord railroad,
As under-ticket-agent at a station
Where his job, when he wasn't selling tickets,
Was setting out up track and down, not plants
As on a farm, but planets, evening stars
That varied in their hue from red to green.

He got a good glass for six hundred dollars.
His new job gave him leisure for star-gazing.
Often he bid me come and have a look
Up the brass barrel, velvet black inside,
At a star quaking in the other end.
I recollect a night of broken clouds
And underfoot snow melted down to ice,
And melting further in the wind to mud.
Bradford and I had out the telescope.
We spread our two legs as we spread its three,
Pointed our thoughts the way we pointed it,
And standing at our leisure till the day broke,
Said some of the best things we ever said.
That telescope was christened the Star-splitter,
Because it didn't do a thing but split
A star in two or three the way you split
A globule of quicksilver in your hand

With one stroke of your finger in the middle.
It's a star-splitter if there ever was one
And ought to do some good if splitting stars
'S a thing to be compared with splitting wood.
We've looked and looked, but after all where are we?
Do we know any better where we are,
And how it stands between the night tonight
And a man with a smoky lantern chimney?
How different from the way it ever stood?

Riders

ROBERT FROST

The surest thing there is is we are riders,
And though none too successful at it, guiders,
Through everything presented, land and tide
And now the very air, of what we ride.

What is this talked-of mystery of birth
But being mounted bareback on the earth?
We can just see the infant up astride,
His small fist buried in the bushy hide.

There is our wildest mount — a headless horse.
But though it runs unbridled off its course,
And all our blandishments would seem defied,
We have ideas yet that we haven't tried.

Desert Places

ROBERT FROST

Snow falling and night falling fast oh fast
In a field I looked into going past,
And the ground almost covered smooth in snow,
But a few weeds and stubble showing last.

The woods around it have it — it is theirs.
All animals are smothered in their lairs.
I am too absent-spirited to count;
The loneliness includes me unawares.

And lonely as it is that loneliness
Will be more lonely ere it will be less —
A blanker whiteness of benighted snow
With no expression, nothing to express.

They cannot scare me with their empty spaces
Between stars — on stars where no human race is.
I have it in me so much nearer home
To scare myself with my own desert places.

Fire and Ice

ROBERT FROST

Some say the world will end in fire,
Some say in ice.
From what I've tasted of desire
I hold with those who favor fire.
But if it had to perish twice,
I think I know enough of hate

To say that for destruction ice
Is also great
And would suffice.

A Considerable Speck

(*Microscopic*)

ROBERT FROST

A speck that would have been beneath my sight
On any but a paper sheet so white
Set off across what I had written there.
And I had idly poised my pen in air
To stop it with a period of ink
When something strange about it made me think.
This was no dust speck by my breathing blown,
But unmistakably a living mite
With inclinations it could call its own.
It paused as with suspicion of my pen,
And then came racing wildly on again
To where my manuscript was not yet dry;
Then paused again and either drank or smelt —
With loathing, for again it turned to fly.
Plainly with an intelligence I dealt.
It seemed too tiny to have room for feet,
Yet must have had a set of them complete
To express how much it didn't want to die.
It ran with terror and with cunning crept.
It faltered; I could see it hesitate;
Then in the middle of the open sheet
Cower down in desperation to accept
Whatever I accorded it of fate.

I have none of the tenderer-than-thou
Collectivistic regimenting love
With which the modern world is being swept.
But this poor microscopic item now!

Since it was nothing I knew evil of
I let it lie there till I hoped it slept.

I have a mind myself and recognize
Mind when I meet with it in any guise.
No one can know how glad I am to find
On any sheet the least display of mind.

◇◇

A Loose Mountain

(*Telescopic*)

ROBERT FROST

Did you stay up last night (the Magi did)
To see the star shower known as Leonid
That once a year by hand or apparatus
Is so mysteriously pelted at us?
It is but fiery puffs of dust and pebbles,
No doubt directed at our heads as rebels
In having taken artificial light
Against the ancient sovereignty of night.
A fusillade of blanks and empty flashes,
It never reaches forth except as ashes
Of which you feel no least touch on your face
Nor find in dew the slightest cloudy trace.
Nevertheless it constitutes a hint
That the loose mountain lately seen to glint
In sunlight near us in momentous swing
Is something in a Balearic sling
The heartless and enormous Outer Black
Is still withholding in the Zodiac
But from irresolution in his back
About when best to have us in our orbit,
So we won't simply take it and absorb it.

◇◇

6

◇◇◇

The World We Make

Evolution: At the Mind's Cinema

I turn the handle and the story starts:
Reel after reel is all astronomy,
Till life, enkindled in a niche of sky,
Leaps on the stage to play a million parts.

Life leaves the slime, and through all ocean darts;
She conquers earth, and raises wings to fly;
The spirit blooms, and learns how not to die, —
Nesting beyond the grave in others' hearts.

— I turn the handle: other men like me
Have made the film: and now I sit and look
In quiet, privileged like Divinity
To read the roaring world as in a book.
If this thy past, where shall thy future climb,
O Spirit, built of Elements and Time?

— JULIAN HUXLEY

From Julian Huxley: *The Captive Shrew and Other Poems of a Biologist.* Reprinted by permission of Basil Blackwell and Motte, Ltd., publishers.

Taming the Elements

THOMAS JEFFERSON

INDEED, we need look back but half a century, to times which many now living remember well, and see the wonderful advances in the sciences and arts which have been made within that period. Some of these have rendered the elements themselves subservient to the purposes of man, have harnessed them to the yoke of his labors, and effected the great blessings of moderating his own, of accomplishing what was beyond his feeble force, and extending the comforts of life to a much enlarged circle, to those who had before known its necessaries only. That these are not the vain dreams of sanguine hope, we have before our eyes real and living examples. What, but education, has advanced us beyond the condition of our indigenous neighbors? And what chains them to their present state of barbarism and wretchedness, but a bigoted veneration for the supposed superlative wisdom of their fathers, and the preposterous idea that they are to look backward for better things, and not forward, longing, as it should seem, to return to the days of eating acorns and roots, rather than indulge in the degeneracies of civilization? And how much more encouraging to the achievements of science and improvement is this, than the desponding view that the condition of man cannot be ameliorated, that what has been must ever be, and that to secure ourselves where we are, we must tread with awful reverence in the footsteps of our fathers.

On the Advisableness of Improving Natural Knowledge

THOMAS HENRY HUXLEY

THIS TIME two hundred years ago — in the beginning of January, 1666 — those of our forefathers who inhabited this great and ancient city [London], took breath between the shocks of two fearful calamities: one not quite past, although its fury had abated; the other to come.

Within a few yards of the very spot on which we are assembled, so the tradition runs, that painful and deadly malady, the plague, appeared in the latter months of 1664; and, though no new visitor, smote the people of England, and especially of her capital, with a violence unknown before, in the course of the following year. The hand of a master has pictured what happened in those dismal months; and in that truest of fictions, *The History of the Plague Year*, Defoe shows death, with every accompaniment of pain and terror, stalking through the narrow streets of old London, and changing their busy hum into a silence broken only by the wailing of the mourners of fifty thousand dead; by the woeful denunciations and mad prayers of fanatics; and by the madder yells of despairing profligates.

But, about this time in 1666, the death-rate had sunk to nearly its ordinary amount; a case of plague occurred only here and there, and the richer citizens who had flown from the pest had returned to their dwellings. The remnant of the people began to toil at the accustomed round of duty, or of pleasure; and the stream of city life bid fair to flow back along its old bed, with renewed and uninterrupted vigor.

The newly kindled hope was deceitful. The great plague, indeed, returned no more; but what it had done for the Londoners, the great fire, which broke out in the autumn of 1666, did for London; and, in September of that year, a heap of ashes and the indestructible energy of the people were all that remained of the glory of five-sixths of the city within the walls.

Our forefathers had their own ways of accounting for each of these calamities. They submitted to the plague in humility and in penitence, for they believed it to be the judgment of God. But,

From *Methods and Results, Collected Essays*, 1894.

toward the fire they were furiously indignant, interpreting it as the effect of the malice of man — as the work of the Republicans, or of the Papists, according as their prepossessions ran in favor of loyalty or of Puritanism.

It would, I fancy, have fared but ill with one who, standing where I now stand, in what was then a thickly peopled and fashionable part of London, should have broached to our ancestors the doctrine which I now propound to you — that all their hypotheses were alike wrong; that the plague was no more, in their sense, Divine judgment, than the fire was the work of any political, or of any religious, sect; but that they were themselves the authors of both plague and fire, and that they must look to themselves to prevent the recurrence of calamities, to all appearances so peculiarly beyond the reach of human control — so evidently the result of the wrath of God, or of the craft and subtlety of an enemy.

And one may picture to oneself how harmoniously the holy cursing of the Puritan of that day would have chimed in with the unholy cursing and the crackling wit of the Rochesters and Sedleys, and with the revilings of the political fanatics, if my imaginary plain dealer had gone on to say that, if the return of such misfortunes were ever rendered impossible, it would not be in virtue of the victory of the faith of Laud, or of that of Milton; and, as little, by the triumph of republicanism, as by that of monarchy. But that the one thing needful for compassing this end was, that the people of England should second the efforts of an insignificant corporation, the establishment of which, a few years before the epoch of the great plague and the great fire, had been as little noticed, as they were conspicuous.

Some twenty years before the outbreak of the plague a few calm and thoughtful students banded themselves together for the purpose, as they phrased it, of "improving natural knowledge." The ends they proposed to attain cannot be stated more clearly than in the words of one of the founders of the organization: —

Our business was (precluding matters of theology and state affairs) to discourse and consider of philosophical enquiries, and such as related thereunto: — as Physick, Anatomy, Geometry, Astronomy, Navigation, Staticks, Magneticks, Chymicks, Mechanicks, and Natural Experiments; with the state of these studies and their cultivation at home and abroad. We then discoursed of the circulation of the blood, the valves in the veins, the venæ lacteæ, the lymphatic vessels, the Copernican hypothesis, the nature of comets and new stars, the satellites of Jupiter, the oval

shape (as it then appeared) of Saturn, the spots on the sun and
its turning on its own axis, the inequalities and selenography of
the moon, the several phases of Venus and Mercury, the improvement of telescopes and grinding of glasses for that purpose,
the weight of air, the possibility or impossibility of vacuities and
nature's abhorrence thereof, the Torricellian experiment in
quicksilver, the descent of heavy bodies and the degree of acceleration therein, with divers other things of like nature, some
of which were then but new discoveries, and others not so generally known and embraced as now they are; with other things ap-
pertaining to what hath been called the New Philosophy, which,
from the times of Galileo at Florence and Sir Francis Bacon
(Lord Verulam) in England, hath been much cultivated in
Italy, France, Germany, and other parts abroad, as well as with
us in England.

The learned Dr. Wallis, writing in 1696, narrates, in these words,
what happened half a century before, or about 1645. The associates met at Oxford, in the rooms of Dr. Wilkins, who was destined
to become a bishop; and subsequently coming together in London,
they attracted the notice of the king. And it is a strange evidence of
the taste for knowledge which the most obviously worthless of the
Stuarts shared with his father and grandfather, that Charles the
Second was not content with saying witty things about his philosophers, but did wise things with regard to them. For he not only bestowed upon them such attention as he could spare from his poodles
and his mistresses, but, being in his usual state of impecuniosity,
begged for them of the Duke of Ormond; and, that step being without effect, gave them Chelsea College, a charter, and a mace:
crowning his favors in the best way they could be crowned, by
burdening them no further with royal patronage or state interference.

Thus it was that the half-dozen young men, studious of the "New
Philosophy," who met in one another's lodgings in Oxford or in London, in the middle of the seventeenth century, grew in numerical
and in real strength, until, in its latter part, the "Royal Society for
the Improvement of Natural Knowledge" had already become
famous, and had acquired a claim upon the veneration of Englishmen which it has ever since retained, as the principal focus of scientific activity in our islands, and the chief champion of the cause it
was formed to support.

It was by the aid of the Royal Society that Newton published his
Principia. If all the books in the world except the *Philosophical*

Transactions were destroyed, it is safe to say that the foundations of physical science would remain unshaken, and that the vast intellectual progress of the last two centuries would be largely, though incompletely, recorded. Nor have any signs of halting or of decrepitude manifested themselves in our own times. As in Dr. Wallis' days, so in these, "our business is, precluding theology and state affairs, to discourse and consider of philosophical enquiries." But our "Mathematick" is one which Newton would have to go to school to learn; our "Staticks, Mechanicks, Magneticks, Chymicks, and Natural Experiments" constitute a mass of physical and chemical knowledge, a glimpse at which would compensate Galileo for the doings of a score of inquisitorial cardinals; our "Physick" and "Anatomy" have embraced such infinite varieties of being, have laid open such new worlds in time and space, have grappled, not unsuccessfully, with such complex problems, that the eyes of Vesalius and of Harvey might be dazzled by the sight of the tree that has grown out of their grain of mustard seed.

The fact is perhaps rather too much, than too little, forced upon one's notice, nowadays, that all this marvelous intellectual growth has a no less wonderful expression in practical life; and that, in this respect, if in no other, the movement symbolized by the progress of the Royal Society stands without a parallel in the history of mankind.

A series of volumes as bulky as the *Transactions of the Royal Society* might possibly be filled with the subtle speculations of the Schoolmen; not improbably, the obtaining a mastery over the products of medieval thought might necessitate an even greater expenditure of time and of energy than the acquirement of the "New Philosophy"; but though such work engrossed the best intellects of Europe for a longer time than has elapsed since the great fire, its effects were "writ in water," so far as our social state is concerned.

On the other hand, if the noble first President of the Royal Society could revisit the upper air and once more gladden his eyes with a sight of the familiar mace, he would find himself in the midst of a material civilization more different from that of his day, than that of the seventeenth was from that of the first century. And if Lord Brouncker's native sagacity had not deserted his ghost, he would need no long reflection to discover that all these great ships, these railways, these telegraphs, these factories, these printing presses, without which the whole fabric of modern English society would collapse into a mass of stagnant and starving pauperism — that all these pillars of our State are but the ripples and the bubbles upon the surface of that great spiritual stream, the springs

of which, only, he and his fellows were privileged to see; and seeing, to recognize as that which it behooved them above all things to
keep pure and undefiled.

It may not be too great a flight of imagination to conceive our
noble *revenant* not forgetful of the great troubles of his own day,
and anxious to know how often London had been burned down
since his time, and how often the plague had carried off its thousands. He would have to learn that, although London contains tenfold the inflammable matter that it did in 1666; though, not content with filling our rooms with woodwork and light draperies, we
must needs lead inflammable and explosive gases into every corner
of our streets and houses, we never allow even a street to burn
down. And if he asked how this had come about, we should have to
explain that the improvement of natural knowledge has furnished us
with dozens of machines for throwing water upon fires, any one of
which would have furnished the ingenious Mr. Hooke, the first
"curator and experimenter" of the Royal Society, with ample materials for discourse before half a dozen meetings of that body; and
that, to say truth, except for the progress of natural knowledge, we
should not have been able to make even the tools by which these
machines are constructed. And, further, it would be necessary to
add, that although severe fires sometimes occur and inflict great
damage, the loss is very generally compensated by societies, the
operations of which have been rendered possible only by the progress of natural knowledge in the direction of mathematics, and the
accumulation of wealth in virtue of other natural knowledge.

But the plague? My Lord Brouncker's observation would not, I
fear, lead him to think that Englishmen of the nineteenth century
are purer in life, or more fervent in religious faith, than the generation which could produce a Boyle, an Evelyn, and a Milton. He
might find the mud of society at the bottom, instead of at the top,
but I fear that the sum total would be as deserving of swift judgment as at the time of the Restoration. And it would be our duty to
explain once more, and this time not without shame, that we have
no reason to believe that it is the improvement of our faith, nor that
of our morals, which keeps the plague from our city; but, again,
that it is the improvement of our natural knowledge.

We have learned that pestilences will only take up their abode
among those who have prepared unswept and ungarnished resi-
dences for them. Their cities must have narrow, unwatered streets,
foul with accumulated garbage. Their houses must be ill-drained,
ill-lighted, ill-ventilated. Their subjects must be ill-washed, ill-fed,
ill-clothed. The London of 1665 was such a city. The cities of the
East, where plague has an enduring dwelling, are such cities. We,

in later times, have learned somewhat of Nature, and partly obey her. Because of this partial improvement of our natural knowledge and of that fractional obedience, we have no plague; because that knowledge is still very imperfect and that obedience yet incomplete, typhus is our companion and cholera our visitor. But it is not presumptuous to express the belief that, when our knowledge is more complete and our obedience the expression of our knowledge, London will count her centuries of freedom from typhus and cholera, as she now gratefully reckons her two hundred years of ignorance of that plague which swooped upon her thrice in the first half of the seventeenth century.

Surely, there is nothing in these explanations which is not fully borne out by the facts? Surely, the principles involved in them are now admitted among the fixed beliefs of all thinking men? Surely, it is true that our countrymen are less subject to fire, famine, pestilence, and all the evils which result from a want of command over and due anticipation of the course of Nature, than were the countrymen of Milton; and health, wealth, and well-being are more abundant with us than with them? But no less certainly is the difference due to the improvement of our knowledge of Nature, and the extent to which that improved knowledge has been incorporated with the household words of men, and has supplied the springs of their daily actions.

Granting for a moment, then, the truth of that which the depreciators of natural knowledge are so fond of urging, that its improvement can only add to the resources of our material civilization; admitting it to be possible that the founders of the Royal Society themselves looked for no other reward than this, I cannot confess that I was guilty of exaggeration when I hinted, that to him who had the gift of distinguishing between prominent events and important events, the origin of a combined effort on the part of mankind to improve natural knowledge might have loomed larger than the Plague and have outshone the glare of the Fire; as a something fraught with a wealth of beneficence to mankind, in comparison with which the damage done by those ghastly evils would shrink into insignificance.

It is very certain that for every victim slain by the plague, hundreds of mankind exist and find a fair share of happiness in the world, by the aid of the spinning jenny. And the great fire, at its worst, could not have burned the supply of coal, the daily working of which, in the bowels of the earth, made possible by the steam pump, gives rise to an amount of wealth to which the millions lost in old London are but as an old song.

But spinning jenny and steam pump are, after all, but toys, possessing an accidental value; and natural knowledge creates multitudes of more subtle contrivances, the praises of which do not happen to be sung because they are not directly convertible into instruments for creating wealth. When I contemplate natural knowledge squandering such gifts among men, the only appropriate comparison I can find for her is, to liken her to such a peasant woman as one sees in the Alps, striding ever upward, heavily burdened, and with mind bent only on her home; but yet, without effort and without thought, knitting for her children. Now stockings are good and comfortable things, and the children will undoubtedly be much the better for them; but surely it would be shortsighted, to say the least of it, to depreciate this toiling mother as a mere stocking-machine — a mere provider of physical comforts?

However, there are blind leaders of the blind, and not a few of them, who take this view of natural knowledge, and can see nothing in the bountiful mother of humanity but a sort of comfort-grinding machine. According to them, the improvement of natural knowledge always has been, and always must be, synonymous with no more than the improvement of the material resources and the increase of the gratifications of men.

Natural knowledge is, in their eyes, no real mother of mankind, bringing them up with kindness, and, if need be, with sternness, in the way they should go, and instructing them in all things needful for their welfare; but a sort of fairy godmother, ready to furnish her pets with shoes of swiftness, swords of sharpness, and omnipotent Aladdin's lamps, so that they may have telegraphs to Saturn, and see the other side of the moon, and thank God they are better than their benighted ancestors.

If this talk were true, I, for one, should not greatly care to toil in the service of natural knowledge. I think I would just as soon be quietly chipping my own flint ax, after the manner of my forefathers a few thousand years back, as be troubled with the endless malady of thought which now infests us all, for such reward. But I venture to say that such views are contrary alike to reason and to fact. Those who discourse in such fashion seem to me to be so intent upon trying to see what is above Nature, or what is behind her, that they are blind to what stares them in the face, in her.

I should not venture to speak thus strongly if my justification were not to be found in the simplest and most obvious facts — if it needed more than an appeal to the most notorious truths to justify my assertion, that the improvement of natural knowledge, whatever direction it has taken, and however low the aims of those who may have commenced it — has not only conferred practical benefits on men, but, in so doing, has effected a revolution in their conceptions of the universe and of themselves, and has profoundly altered their modes of thinking and their views of right and wrong. I say that natural knowledge, seeking to satisfy natural wants, has found the ideas which can alone still spiritual cravings. I say that natural knowledge, in desiring to ascertain the laws of comfort, has been driven to discover those of conduct, and to lay the foundations of a new morality.

Let us take these points separately; and, first, what great ideas has natural knowledge introduced into men's minds?

I cannot but think that the foundations of all natural knowledge were laid when the reason of man first came face to face with the facts of Nature: when the savage first learned that the fingers of one hand are fewer than those of both; that it is shorter to cross a stream than to head it; that a stone stops where it is unless it be moved, and that it drops from the hand which lets it go; that light and heat come and go with the sun; that sticks burn away in a fire; that plants and animals grow and die; that if he struck his fellow-savage a blow he would make him angry, and perhaps get a blow in return, while if he offered him a fruit he would please him, and perhaps receive a fish in exchange. When men had acquired this much knowledge, the outlines, rude though they were, of mathematics, of physics, of chemistry, of biology, of moral, economical, and political science, were sketched. Nor did the germ of religion fail when science began to bud. Listen to words which, though new, are yet three thousand years old: —

> . . . When in heaven the stars about the moon
> Look beautiful, when all the winds are laid,
> And every height comes out, and jutting peak
> And valley, and the immeasurable heavens
> Break open to their highest, and all the stars
> Shine, and the shepherd gladdens in his heart.*

If the half-savage Greek could share our feelings thus far, it is irrational to doubt that he went further, to find, as we do, that upon that brief gladness there follows a certain sorrow — the little light of awakened human intelligence shines so mere a spark amidst the abyss of the unknown and unknowable; seems so insufficient to do more than illuminate the imperfections that cannot be remedied, the aspirations that cannot be realized, of man's own nature. But

* Need it be said that this is Tennyson's English for Homer's Greek? [Huxley's note.]

in this sadness, this consciousness of the limitation of man, this sense of an open secret which he cannot penetrate, lies the essence of all religion; and the attempt to embody it in the forms furnished by the intellect is the origin of the higher theologies.

Thus it seems impossible to imagine but that the foundations of all knowledge — secular or sacred — were laid when intelligence dawned, though the superstructure remained for long ages so slight and feeble as to be compatible with the existence of almost any general view respecting the mode of governance of the universe. No doubt, from the first, there were certain phenomena which, to the rudest mind, presented a constancy of occurrence, and suggested that a fixed order ruled, at any rate, among them. I doubt if the grossest of Fetish worshipers ever imagined that a stone must have a god within it to make it fall, or that a fruit had a god within it to make it taste sweet. With regard to such matters as these, it is hardly questionable that mankind from the first took strictly positive and scientific views.

But, with respect to all the less familiar occurrences which present themselves, uncultured man, no doubt, has always taken himself as the standard of comparison, as the center and measure of the world; nor could he well avoid doing so. And finding that his apparently uncaused will has a powerful effect in giving rise to many occurrences, he naturally enough ascribed other and greater events to other and greater volitions, and came to look upon the world and all that therein is, as the product of the volitions of persons like himself, but stronger, and capable of being appeased or angered, as he himself might be soothed or irritated. Through such conceptions of the plan and working of the universe all mankind have passed, or are passing. And we may now consider, what has been the effect of the improvement of natural knowledge on the views of men who have reached this stage, and who have begun to cultivate natural knowledge with no desire but that of "increasing God's honor and bettering man's estate."

For example: what could seem wiser, from a mere material point of view, more innocent, from a theological one, to an ancient people, than that they should learn the exact succession of the seasons, as warnings for their husbandmen: or the position of the stars, as guides to their rude navigators? But what has grown out of this search for natural knowledge of so merely useful a character? You all know the reply. Astronomy — which of all sciences has filled men's minds with general ideas of a character most foreign to their daily experience, and has, more than any other, rendered it impossible for them to accept the beliefs of their fathers. Astronomy — which tells them that this so vast and seemingly solid earth is but an atom among atoms, whirling, no man knows whither, through illimitable space; which demonstrates that what we call the peaceful heaven above us, is but that space, filled by an infinitely subtle matter whose particles are seething and surging, like the waves of an angry sea; which opens up to us infinite regions where nothing is known, or ever seems to have been known, but matter and force, operating according to rigid rules; which leads us to contemplate phenomena the very nature of which demonstrates that they must have had a beginning, and that they must have an end, but the very nature of which also proves that the beginning was, to our conceptions of time, infinitely remote, and that the end is as immeasurably distant.

But it is not alone those who pursue astronomy who ask for bread and receive ideas. What more harmless than the attempt to lift and distribute water by pumping it; what more absolutely and grossly utilitarian? But out of pumps grew the discussions about Nature's abhorrence of a vacuum, and then it was discovered that Nature does not abhor a vacuum, but that air has weight; and that notion paved the way for the doctrine that all matter has weight, and that the force which produces weight is co-extensive with the universe — in short, to the theory of universal gravitation and endless force. While learning how to handle gases led to the discovery of oxygen, and to modern chemistry, and to the notion of the indestructibility of matter.

Again, what simpler, or more absolutely practical, than the attempt to keep the axle of a wheel from heating when the wheel turns round very fast? How useful for carters and gig drivers to know something about this; and how good were it, if any ingenious person would find out the cause of such phenomena, and then educe a general remedy for them. Such an ingenious person was Count Rumford; and he and his successors have landed us in the theory of the persistence, or indestructibility, of force. And in the infinitely minute, as in the infinitely great, the seekers after natural knowledge, of the kinds called physical and chemical, have everywhere found a definite order and succession of events which seem never to be infringed.

And how has it fared with "Physick" and anatomy? Have the anatomist, the physiologist, or the physician, whose business it has been to devote themselves assiduously to that eminently practical and direct end, the alleviation of the sufferings of mankind — have they been able to confine their vision more absolutely to the strictly useful? I fear they are the worst offenders of all. For if the astronomer has set before us the infinite magnitude of space, and the practical eternity of the duration of the universe; if the physical and chemical philosophers have demonstrated the infinite minuteness of its constituent parts, and the practical eternity of matter and of force; and if both have alike proclaimed the universality of a definite and predicable order and succession of events, the workers in biology have not only accepted all these, but have added more startling theses of their own. For, as the astronomers discover in the earth no center of the universe, but an eccentric speck, so the naturalists find man to be no center of the living world, but one amidst endless modifications of life; and as the astronomer observes the mark of practically endless time set upon the arrangements of the solar system so the student of life finds the records of ancient forms of existence peopling the world for ages, which, in relation to human experience, are infinite.

Furthermore, the physiologist finds life to be as dependent for its manifestation on particular molecular arrangements as any physical or chemical phenomenon; and, wherever he extends his researches, fixed order and unchanging causation reveal themselves, as plainly as in the rest of Nature.

Nor can I find that any other fate has awaited the germ of Religion. Arising, like all other kinds of knowledge, out of the action and interaction of man's mind, with that which is not man's mind, it has taken the intellectual coverings of fetishism or polytheism; of theism or atheism; of superstition or rationalism. With these, and their relative merits and demerits, I have nothing to do; but this it is needful for my purpose to say, that if the religion of the present differs from that of the past, it is because the theology of the present has become more scientific than that of the past; because it has not only renounced idols of wood and idols of stone, but begins to see the necessity of breaking in pieces the idols built up of books and traditions and fine-spun ecclesiastical cobwebs: and of cherishing the noblest and most human of man's emotions, by worship "for the most part of the silent sort" at the altar of the Unknown.

Such are a few of the new conceptions implanted in our minds by the improvement of natural knowledge. Men have acquired the ideas of the practically infinite extent of the universe and of its practical eternity; they are familiar with the conception that our earth is but an infinitesimal fragment of that part of the universe which can be seen; and that, nevertheless, its duration is, as compared with our standards of time, infinite. They have further acquired the idea that man is but one of innumerable forms of life now existing in the globe, and that the present existences are but the last of an immeasurable series of predecessors. Moreover, every step they have made in natural knowledge has tended to extend and rivet in their minds the conception of a definite order of the universe — which is embodied in what are called, by an unhappy metaphor, the laws of Nature — and to narrow the range and loosen the force of men's belief in spontaneity, or in changes other than such as arise out of that definite order itself.

Whether these ideas are well or ill founded is not the question. No one can deny that they exist, and have been the inevitable outgrowth of the improvement of natural knowledge. And if so, it cannot be doubted that they are changing the form of men's most cherished and most important convictions.

And as regards the second point — the extent to which the improvement of natural knowledge has remodeled and altered what may be termed the intellectual ethics of men — what are among the moral convictions most fondly held by barbarous and semi-barbarous people?

They are the convictions that authority is the soundest basis of belief; that merit attaches to a readiness to believe; that the doubting disposition is a bad one, and skepticism a sin; that when good authority has pronounced what is to be believed, and faith has accepted it, reason has no further duty. There are many excellent persons who yet hold by these principles, and it is not my present business, or intention, to discuss their views. All I wish to bring clearly before your minds is the unquestionable fact, that the improvement of natural knowledge is effected by methods which directly give the lie to all these convictions, and assume the exact reverse of each to be true.

The improver of natural knowledge absolutely refuses to acknowledge authority, as such. For him, skepticism is the highest of duties; blind faith the one unpardonable sin. And it cannot be otherwise, for every great advance in natural knowledge has involved the absolute rejection of authority, the cherishing of the keenest skepticism, the annihilation of the spirit of blind faith; and the most ardent votary of science holds his firmest convictions, not because the men he most venerates hold them; not because their verity is testified by portents and wonders; but because his experience teaches him that whenever he chooses to bring these convictions into contact with their primary source, Nature — whenever he thinks fit to test them by appealing to experiment and to observation — Nature will confirm them. The man of science has learned to believe in justification, not by faith, but by verification.

Thus, without for a moment pretending to despise the practical results of the improvement of natural knowledge, and its beneficial influence on material civilization, it must, I think, be admitted that the great ideas, some of which I have indicated, and the ethical

would not be honest to say — as it would be folly not to hope — that the very terror of modern weapons would in itself put an end to war; it would not even be honest to say that because of this terror the abolition of war and the maintenance of peace have become the one absolute, final objective of all political decisions. There are other things in man's life — his freedom, his decency, his sense of right and wrong — that cannot so lightly be subjected to a single end. But what we need to remember is that war today has become, and is increasingly becoming, something very different from what it was a century ago or a millennium ago. We need to recognize the new situation as new; we need to come to it with something of the same spirit as the scientist's when he has conducted an experiment and finds that the results are totally other than those that he had anticipated.

Four months before Hiroshima, in the last days of his life, President Roosevelt's thoughts turned to these questions. In the last words that he wrote, in words he did not live to speak, the President looked to the future, to the atomic age. He looked to the past, to the days of the founding of the Republic. He wrote:

"Thomas Jefferson, himself a distinguished scientist, once spoke of the 'brotherly spirit of science, which unites into one family all its votaries of whatever grade, and however widely dispersed throughout the different quarters of the globe.'

"Today science has brought all the different quarters of the globe so close together that it is impossible to isolate them one from another.

"Today we are faced with the pre-eminent fact that, if civilization is to survive, we must cultivate the science of human relationships — the ability of all peoples, of all kinds, to live together and work together, in the same world, at peace."

Science has greatly extended the range of questions in which man has a choice; it has extended man's freedom to make significant decisions. Is there anything in the methods of science itself, or in the spirit of science, which can help in the making of these decisions? To what extent is there a play on the word *science* which can mislead us and take us up false roads when we speak of this science of human relationships? Is there anything we can learn from the relevance of science to politics?

If we are to answer these questions and answer them honestly, we must recognize important and basic differences between problems of science and problems of action as they arise in personal or in political life. If we fail to recognize these differences, we shall be seeking magic solutions and not real ones. We shall delude ourselves into laying aside responsibility, which it is an essential part of man's life to bear.

In most scientific study, questions of good and evil or right and wrong play at most a minor and secondary part. For practical decisions of policy, they are basic. Without them political action would be meaningless. Practical decisions and, above all, political decisions can never quite be freed from the conflicting claims of special interest. These too are part of the meaning of a decision and of a course of action, and they must be an essential part of the force of its implementation.

Political decisions are unique acts. In politics there is little that can correspond to the scientist's repetition of an experiment. An experiment that fails in its purpose may be as good or better than one that succeeds, because it may well be more instructive. A political decision cannot be taken twice. All the factors that are relevant to it will conjoin only once. The analogies of history can provide a guide, but only a very partial one.

These are formidable differences between the problems of science and those of practice. They show that the method of science cannot be directly adapted to the solution of problems in politics and in man's spiritual life. Yet there is relevance of a more subtle but by no means trivial kind.

In trying more fully to explore this relevance, I should like to start with a text. This text is a letter written by Thomas Jefferson to a young man who had inquired of him as to the usefulness of his studies of science. It was written in the middle of the year 1799, the year in which Napoleon abolished the Directory and began to assume dictatorial power in France, the year before Thomas Jefferson was elected for the first time as President of the United States. Jefferson and the diverse brave and hopeful men who with him laid the foundations of our own government had learned much from the peoples of other nations. Many of their highest political ideals and their most powerful political instruments were built on the experience, the insight and wisdom of European scientists and philosophers. Even today we need to remember that this was so, that there may be much we can learn from others, and that we should be glad to learn, as in turn by example we should be glad to teach.

Jefferson's letter starts with a survey of the subjects in science which he believes young Munford ought to pursue. I will quote one characteristic passage which may strike a familiar and homely note for you:

". . . the science of calculation also is indispensible as far as the extraction of the square and cube roots: Algebra as far as the quadratic equation and the use of logarithms are often of value in ordinary cases: but all beyond these is but a luxury; a delicious luxury indeed; but not to be indulged in by one who is to have a profession to follow for his subsistence."

But that is not really the part of Jefferson's letter which I commend to you. Here it is:

"I am among those who think well of the human character generally. I consider man as formed for society, and endowed by nature with those dispositions which fit him for society. I believe also, with Condorcet, as mentioned in your letter, that his mind is perfectible to a degree of which we cannot as yet form any conception. It is impossible for a man who takes a survey of what is already known, not to see what an immensity in every branch of science yet remains to be discovered, and that too of articles to which our faculties seem adequate."

And later, in the same letter, still more explicitly:

". . . and it is still more certain that in the other branches of science, great fields are yet to be explored to which our faculties are equal, and that to an extent of which we cannot fix the limits. I join you therefore in branding as cowardly the idea that the human mind is incapable of further advances. This is precisely the doctrine which the present despots of the earth are inculcating, and their friends here re-echoing; and applying especially to religion and politics; 'that it is not probable that any thing better will be discovered than what was known to our fathers.' We are to look backwards then and not forwards for the improvement of science, and to find it amidst feudal barbarisms and the fires of Spital-fields. But thank heaven the American mind is already too much opened, to listen to these impostures; and while the art of printing is left to us, science can never be retrograde; what is once acquired of real knowledge can never be lost. To preserve the freedom of the human mind then and freedom of the press, every spirit should be ready to devote itself to martyrdom; for as long as we may think as we will, and speak as we think, the condition of man will proceed in improvement. The generation which is going off the stage has deserved well of mankind for the struggles it has made, and for having arrested that course of despotism which had overwhelmed the world for thousands and thousands of years. If there seems to be danger that the ground they have gained will be lost again, that danger comes from the generation your cotemporary. But that the enthusiasm which characterises youth should lift it's parracide hands against freedom and science would be such a monstrous phaenomenon as I cannot place among possible things in this age and this country."

To me there are two striking impressions which this letter of Jefferson's makes, even beyond its eloquence and its beauty. The first is that the letter is pervaded with the idea of progress, that ideal that owes so much to the development of science and that in turn has provided the great enriching human faith in which scientific discovery and invention have flourished. Jefferson is confident that an increased understanding of the world will lead to progress; he is convinced that the barbarisms of the past cannot stand up against inquiry and understanding and enlightenment; he is confident in man and sure that as men know more they will act more wisely and live better. In our contemporary expressions of hope that catastrophe can be averted and civilization yet be saved, that confidence has lost much of its robustness.

The second point is that for Jefferson there is something in the ways of science that is relevant to political life. Even in religion and politics, he holds that it is probable that things better will be discovered than what was known to our fathers. This conviction that new knowledge is possible, and that not all the answers are known, is of course the stuff of the day-to-day life of the scientist. Science itself does progress; new knowledge is possible; and new knowledge, because it does not destroy or ignore the old, can only increase our understanding. The very idea of the development of science is an example of progress, and of progress which in no true sense can ever be reversed. But this is only part of the story. It is true, as Jefferson knew, that in the large, science has flourished in conditions of human freedom, and that its growth is parallel to the growth of democratic institutions. Today, looking back on more than a century and a half of further history, we can be even more sure of this. We have seen not only the inspiring example of science and democracy flourishing together, but the tragic examples of their foundering together. We express the hope that of this tragedy we shall soon have seen the end.

What are these lessons that the spirit of science teaches us for our practical affairs? Basic to them all is that there may be no barriers to freedom of inquiry. Basic to them all is the ideal of openmindedness with regard to new knowledge, new experience and new truth. Science is not based on authority. It owes its acceptance and its universality to an appeal to intelligible, communicable evidence that any interested man can evaluate.

There is no place for dogma in science. The scientist is free to ask any question, to doubt any assertion, to seek for any evidence, to correct any error. Where science has been used in the past to erect a new dogmatism, that dogmatism has found itself incompatible with the progress of science; and in the end, the dogma has yielded, or science and freedom have perished together.

Our own political life is predicated on openness. We do not believe any group of men adequate enough or wise enough to operate without scrutiny or without criticism. We know that the only way to avoid error is to detect it, that the only way to detect it is to be free to inquire. We know that the wages of secrecy are corruption. We know that in secrecy error, undetected, will flourish and subvert.

Let me be clear. Science is not skepticism. It is not the practice of science to look for things to doubt. It was not by a deliberate attempt of skepticism that physicists were led to doubt the absolute nature of simultaneity, or to recognize that the ideas of strict causality embodied in classical physics could not be applied in the domain of atomic phenomena. There is probably no group of men who take more for granted in their daily work than the scientists. Common sense and all that flows from it are their principal basis for what they do in the laboratory and for what they make of it on paper. But for scientists it is not only honorable to doubt; it is mandatory to do that when there appears to be evidence in support of the doubt. In place of authority in science we have and we need to have only the consensus of informed opinion, only the guide of example. No scientist needs to order his colleagues to use a new technique of experiment or to enter a new field of discovery. If he has done this, it will be an invitation to his fellows to follow.

These, then, are some of the attitudes of mind, these are some of the disciplines of spirit which grow naturally in the scientist's world. They have grown there in part as a result of a humane and liberal tradition in political life and in part as a cause of that. The open mind, the reliance on example and persuasion rather than on authority — these are the heritage of the centuries in which science has altered the face of the earth. Science can help in diverse ways in preserving and extending this heritage. Its very universality speaks across frontiers to make truth manifest in lands otherwise darkened; its material applications create the preconditions — in leisure, in education, in means of communication — for the converse of men with one another. Science provides the material and the intellectual basis for a world in which example and understanding can help all men to improve their lot and fulfill their hopes. Today we need to remember that our country, founded on these practices and grown strong by their exercise, owes its strength to them. In this time of crisis, we need to cherish that strength.

And this brings me to my second wish for you. I wish you not only the joy of great discovery; I wish for you a world of confidence in man and man's humanity, a world of confidence in reason, so that as you work you may be inspired by the hope that what you find will make men freer and better — in which, working as specialists in what may be recondite parts of the intellectual life of the time, you are nevertheless contributing in a direct and basic way to the welfare of mankind.

"Forward" rang the voices then, and of the many mine was one.
Let us hush this cry of "Forward" till ten thousand years have gone.

Far among the vanished races, old Assyrian kings would flay
Captives whom they caught in battle — iron-hearted victors they.

Ages after, while in Asia, he that led the wild Moguls,
Timur built his ghastly tower of eighty thousand human skulls;

Then, and here in Edward's time, an age of noblest English names,
Christian conquerors took and flung the conquered Christian into
flames.

Love your enemy, bless your haters, said the Greatest of the great;
Christian love among the Churches looked the twin of heathen hate.

From the golden alms of Blessing man had coined himself a curse:
Rome of Caesar, Rome of Peter, which was crueler? which was
worse?

France had shown a light to all men, preached a Gospel, all men's
good;
Celtic Demos rose a Demon, shrieked and slaked the light with
blood.

Hope was ever on her mountain, watching till the day begun —
Crowned with sunlight — over darkness — from the still unrisen sun.

Have we grown at last beyond the passions of the primal clan?
"Kill your enemy, for you hate him," still, "your enemy" was a man.

Have we sunk below them? Peasants maim the helpless horse, and
drive
Innocent cattle under thatch, and burn the kindlier brutes alive.

Brutes, the brutes are not your wrongers — burned at midnight,
found at morn,
Twisted hard in mortal agony with their offspring, born-unborn,

Clinging to the silent mother! Are we devils? are we men?
Sweet Saint Francis of Assisi, would that he were here again,

He that in his Catholic wholeness used to call the very flowers
Sisters, brothers — and the beast — whose pains are hardly less than
ours!

Chaos, Cosmos! Cosmos, Chaos! who can tell how all will end?
Read the wide world's annals, you, and take their wisdom for your
    friend.

Hope the best, but hold the Present fatal daughter of the Past,
Shape your heart to front the hour, but dream not that the hour will
    last.

Aye, if dynamite and revolver leave you courage to be wise —
When was age so crammed with menace? madness? written, spoken
    lies? . . .

Heated am I? you — you wonder — well, it scarce becomes mine
    age —
Patience! let the dying actor mouth his last upon the stage.

Cries of unprogressive dotage ere the dotard fall asleep?
Noises of a current narrowing, not the music of a deep?

Aye, for doubtless I am old, and think gray thoughts, for I am gray;
After all the stormy changes shall we find a changeless May?

After madness, after massacre, Jacobinism and Jacquerie,
Some diviner force to guide us through the days I shall not see?

When the schemes and all the systems, kingdoms and republics fall,
Something kindlier, higher, holier — all for each and each for all?

All the full-brain, half-brain races, led by Justice, Love, and Truth;
All the millions one at length with all the visions of my youth?

All diseases quenched by Science, no man halt, or deaf, or blind;
Stronger ever born of weaker, lustier body, larger mind?

Earth at last a warless world, a single race, a single tongue —
I have seen her far away — for is not Earth as yet so young? —

Every tiger madness muzzled, every serpent passion killed,
Every grim ravine a garden, every blazing desert tilled,

Robed in universal harvest up to either pole she smiles,
Universal ocean softly washing all her warless isles.

Warless? when her tens are thousands, and her thousands millions,
      then —
All her harvests all too narrow — who can fancy warless men?

Warless? war will die out late then. Will it ever? late or soon?
Can it, till this outworn earth be dead as yon dead world the
      moon? . . .

Dead, but how her living glory lights the hall, the dune, the grass!
Yet the moonlight is the sunlight, and the sun himself will pass.

Venus near her! smiling downward at this earthlier earth of ours,
Closer on the sun, perhaps a world of never fading flowers.

Hesper, whom the poet called the bringer home of all good things —
All good things may move in Hesper, perfect peoples, perfect kings.

Hesper — Venus — were we native to that splendor or in Mars,
We should see the globe we groan in, fairest of their evening stars.

Could we dream of wars and carnage, craft and madness, lust and
      spite,
Roaring London, raving Paris, in that point of peaceful light?

Might we not in glancing heavenward on a star so silver-fair,
Yearn, and clasp the hands and murmur, "Would to God that we
      were there"?

Forward, backward, backward, forward, in the immeasurable sea,
Swayed by vaster ebbs and flows than can be known to you or me.

All the suns — are these but symbols of innumerable man,
Man or Mind that sees a shadow of the planner or the plan?

Is there evil but on earth? or pain in every peopled sphere?
Well, be grateful for the sounding watchword "Evolution" here,

Evolution ever climbing after some ideal good,
And Reversion ever dragging Evolution in the mud.

What are men that He should heed us? cried the king of sacred
    · song;
Insects of an hour, that hourly work their brother insect wrong,

While the silent heavens roll, and suns along their fiery way,
All their planets whirling round them, flash a million miles a day.

Many an aeon molded earth before her highest, man, was born,
Many an aeon too may pass when earth is manless and forlorn,

Earth so huge, and yet so bounded — pools of salt, and plots of
      land —
Shallow skin of green and azure — chains of mountain, grains of
      sand!

Only That which made us meant us to be mightier by and by,
Set the sphere of all the boundless heavens within the human eye,

Sent the shadow of Himself, the boundless, through the human soul;
Boundless inward in the atom, boundless outward in the Whole. . . .

Is it well that while we range with Science, glorying in the Time,
City children soak and blacken soul and sense in city slime?

There among the glooming alleys Progress halts on palsied feet,
Crime and hunger cast our maidens by the thousand on the street.

There the master scrimps his haggard sempstress of her daily bread,
There a single sordid attic holds the living and the dead.

There the smoldering fire of fever creeps across the rotted floor,
And the crowded couch of incest in the warrens of the poor.

Nay, your pardon, cry your "Forward," yours are hope and youth,
      but I —
Eighty winters leave the dog too lame to follow with the cry,

Lame and old, and past his time, and passing now into the night;
Yet I would the rising race were half as eager for the light.

Light the fading gleam of even? light the glimmer of the dawn?
Aged eyes may take the growing glimmer for the gleam withdrawn.

Far away beyond her myriad coming changes earth will be
Something other than the wildest modern guess of you and me.

Earth may reach her earthly worst, or if she gain her earthly best,
Would she find her human offspring this ideal man at rest?

Science and Society

ALBERT EINSTEIN

THERE ARE TWO WAYS in which science affects human affairs. The first is familiar to everyone: Directly, and to an even greater extent indirectly, science produces aids that have completely transformed human existence. The second way is educational in character — it works on the mind. Although it may appear less obvious to cursory examination, it is no less incisive than the first.

The most conspicuous practical effect of science is that it makes possible the contriving of things that enrich life, though they complicate it at the same time — inventions such as the steam engine, the railway, electric power and light, the telegraph, radio, automobile, airplane, dynamite, etc. To these must be added the life-preserving achievements of biology and medicine, especially the pain relievers and preservative methods of storing food. The greatest practical benefit which all these inventions confer on man I see in the fact that they liberate him from the excessive muscular drudgery that was once indispensable for the preservation of bare existence. Insofar as we may at all claim that slavery has been abolished today, we owe its abolition to the practical consequences of science.

On the other hand, technology — or applied science — has confronted mankind with problems of profound gravity. The very survival of mankind depends on a satisfactory solution of these problems. It is a matter of creating the kind of social institutions and traditions without which the new tools must inevitably bring disaster of the worst kind.

Mechanical means of production in an unorganized economy have had the result that a substantial proportion of mankind is no longer needed for the production of goods and is thus excluded from the process of economic circulation. The immediate consequences are the weakening of purchasing power and the devalua-

"mean expectancy of life" of 41.8 years, a white girl baby of 44.9. The corresponding figures for 1948, the latest year for which they are available, are 65.49 and 71.04 years.

The lights of Main Street would dazzle that citizen of the mid-nineteenth century; the absence of horses in the streets would call for comment; the automobiles that sweep silently past would astound and frighten him; the airplanes overhead would arouse wonder; a man in a telephone booth holding one end of a black instrument to his ear and talking into the other end would mystify him; motion pictures, radio broadcasting and television would entertain him but puzzle him, too, because he would not understand the underlying principle of their operation. Skyscrapers would seem fantastic and not the economic necessities that they are.

The world of 1851, out of which that resuscitated citizen came, was much more self-satisfied than ours, so far as scientific beliefs are concerned. Newton's laws were considered inviolate. Light was conveyed to us from the sun or from a candle as a series of ripples in the ether, a medium that was supposed to pervade everything and that was more tenuous than any gas, yet more rigid than steel. Atoms were the smallest indivisible units of which matter was composed. The only disturber of mental peace was Charles Darwin, whose *Origin of Species* (1859) and *Descent of Man* (1873) at first shocked the Western world but ultimately made it necessary to regard all living creatures as the warp and woof of a single fabric.

Nearly all the fundamental scientific conceptions of a century ago have been either shattered or modified, Darwin's included. Natural selection, a scythe, did not explain how new species originated, but de Vries and others who developed the mutation theory in the early part of this century did. The anthropologist of our day believes not that man is a descendant of an Old World anthropoid ape, as Darwin concluded, but that apes and men are branches of the same limb of the family tree.

As for our conception of the world around us, Albert Einstein, a young examiner in the Patent Office of Switzerland, evolved a theory of relativity in 1905 and 1915 which showed that Newton's laws did not conform with reality. He swept the ether away. Max Planck convinced physicists that light and radiation in general came not in ethereal waves but in packets called "quanta." Henri Becquerel in 1895 accidentally discovered that uranium was radioactive.

Another accident led Wilhelm Konrad Roentgen in the same year to discover that from one electrode of an evacuated tube through which an electric current passed came invisible rays that would penetrate flesh and reveal the bones of the body. In 1897 J. J. Thomson of Cambridge found that the current in such a tube the aspiration than the achievement of any hospital staff. To Dr. Klein, the experience was even salutary, and he emerged from it both unruffled and inspired. Memory revived in him with the abruptness of revelation. Early in March, he now recalled, there had been a patient at Willard Parker in whom one physician had fleetingly thought he detected indications of smallpox. Dr. Klein guided the investigators back to the files and, after some digging, produced the record of the patient he had in mind. It was that of a man named Eugene La Bar, and the case it described was morbid, chaotic, and dismaying. La Bar, an American, had lived since 1940 in Mexico City, where he had desultorily engaged in exporting leather goods. He was forty-seven years old, married, and childless. Toward the end of February, he and his wife had left Mexico City and headed for New York, traveling by bus. It was their intention to go right on to Readfield, Maine, to view a farm that Mrs. La Bar had just inherited near there, but La Bar became ill during the journey. His discomfort, which he attempted to relieve by frequent doses of aspirin, codeine, Nembutal, and phenobarbital, consisted of a headache and a severe pain in the back of the neck. By the time the couple reached New York, La Bar felt too unwell to go any farther. As far as could be ascertained from the record, he had gone at once to the clinic at Bellevue, where an examining physician, observing that he had a fever of 105° and an odd rash on his face and hands, admitted him to the hospital's dermatologic ward. The date of his admittance was March 5th, a Wednesday. Three days later, on March 8th, La Bar was transferred to Willard Parker, his condition having baffled and finally frightened the Bellevue dermatologists. He arrived there more dead than alive. The rash by then covered his entire body, and it was pustular and hemorrhagic. It was this rash that prompted one of the Willard Parker doctors to offer a half-hearted diagnosis of smallpox. It also impelled him to vaccinate Mrs. La Bar when she called at the hospital that afternoon to inquire about her husband. Then the physician dropped the theory. His reasons were plausible. A freehand analysis of material taken from the lesions did not appear to support his guess; the rash, upon closer scrutiny, was not strikingly typical of smallpox; La Bar had an old but well-developed vaccination scar; and Mrs. La Bar insisted that her husband could not possibly have been in recent contact with anybody suffering from the disease. Three other diagnoses that had also been more or less seriously considered were enumerated in the record. One, suggested by the vigor and variety of the painkillers with which La Bar had stuffed himself, was drug poisoning. Another was Kaposi's varicelliform eruption, a kind of edema complicated by pustules. The third was erythema multiforme, an acute skin infection, and this had seemed the likeliest. La Bar lay in an agony of delirium for two days. On Monday morning, March 10th, his fever suddenly vanished and he felt almost well. Late that afternoon, he died. An autopsy disclosed, among other internal dishevelments, an enlarged spleen, a friable liver, and multiple hemorrhages in the viscera and the lungs. The final entry on the record was the cause of death: "Erythema multiforme, with laryngo-tracheo-bronchitis and bronchopneumonia." It was not a deduction in which Dr. Klein and the Health Department physicians, whose wits had been sharpened by hindsight, were tempted to concur. Their persuasion was that they had just read a forceful account of an unusually virulent attack of black smallpox.

On the morning of Friday, April 4th, the report from Dr. Smadel came through. It was affirmative; both Acosta and Patricia had smallpox. (Subsequently, Dr. Smadel was able to say the same of John and several others, including the deceased La Bar; some material taken from the latter's lesions for the test made at the hospital had, it developed, fortunately been preserved.) Dr. Weinstein received the report without marked consternation. His reaction was almost one of relief. It delivered him from the misery of retaining an increasingly unreasonable doubt. It also propelled him into rapid motion. He notified the United States Public Health Service of the outbreak. Then he had a word of counsel with Dr. Bernecker. After that, he assembled the administrative officers of the Departments of Health and of Hospitals for a briefing on tactics. Next, waving Dr. Greenberg's agents out into the open, he set a full-dress investigation in motion. At two o'clock Dr. Weinstein broke the news to the press at a conference in his office. His statement included an exhortation. "It is not surprising that smallpox has reappeared in this city," he said. "The Health Department has stated many times that we are exposed to communicable diseases occurring in this and neighboring countries. The danger of a widespread epidemic is slight, because our population is for the most part protected by vaccination. Smallpox is one of the most communicable of all diseases, and the only known preventive measure is vaccination. Anyone in the city who has never been vaccinated, or who has not been vaccinated since early childhood, should get this protection at once. Smallpox is a serious disease that may cause permanent disfigurement, damage to vital organs, and even death. With vaccination, a simple and harmless procedure, available to all, there is absolutely no excuse for anyone to remain unprotected." Dr. Weinstein was aware, as he spoke, that his advice was somewhat sounder than his optimism.

The public investigation, like the plainclothes reconnaissance that had preceded it, was accompanied by a quarantine measure; the dermatologic ward at Bellevue was closed to visitors who could not give convincing assurance that they had recently been vaccinated. In addition, vaccination of the entire population of the hospital commenced — a considerable task in itself, which was entrusted to the Department of Hospitals and the Bellevue staff. The rest of the undertaking was handled, without complaint, by the Bureau of Preventable Diseases. It involved the tracking down, the vaccination, and the continued surveillance during the smallpox period of incubation of every person who was known to have been exposed to the disease. Dr. Greenberg's medical staff consists of, in addition to himself and Dr. Singer, three full-time inspectors and thirty-five part-time men. He put them all to work on the task. By nightfall on Friday, less than twelve hours after the arrival of Dr. Smadel's report, Dr. Greenberg's men had called upon, examined, and vaccinated some two hundred potential victims and were on the trail of several hundred others. These two groups comprised all the residents of the apartment buildings in which the Acostas and Patricia's family lived, everyone who had been in the Harlem clinic on the day of Patricia's visit, and everyone who had set foot in Willard Parker between March 8th and March 27th or in the Bellevue dermatologic ward between March 5th and March 8th or between March 5th and March 27th, but they did not comprise all those who might conceivably have been infected. This was no reflection on the resourcefulness of the Bureau men. Dr. Weinstein and his associates had known from the outset that the city contained innumerable possible smallpox cases who were beyond the timely reach of any investigators. They were the people among whom La Bar, on March 5th, and Patricia, on March 21st, and Acosta, on March 25th, had passed on their way to the hospital. It was largely Acosta's means of getting there that prompted Dr. Weinstein to try to stimulate in the public an orderly but general desire for vaccination. La Bar had traveled in the moderate seclusion of a cab, and Patricia had left the clinic in an ambulance. Acosta had taken the subway and a crosstown bus.

The immediate response to Dr. Weinstein's exhortation, which he quickly condensed for press and radio use into the slogan "Be Sure, Be Safe, Get Vaccinated!" was only mildly gratifying. Undismayed he instructed the Bureau of Laboratories to at once set about converting its bulk supplies of vaccine into handy, one-dose units and to make these available without charge, through drugstores, to all physicians and, directly, to all hospitals and to the city's twenty-one district health centers. He issued a public statement emphasizing that the protection he recommended was free as well as simple and harmless. Over the weekend, his meaning appeared to have been caught only by the prudent and the panicky, but on Monday, April 7th, an encouragingly widened comprehension was perceptible. There was good reason. Two new cases of suspected smallpox had turned up and been proclaimed. Acosta's wife, who was twenty-six years old and in the seventh month of pregnancy, was one of them. She had become ill at her home on Saturday night. The following morning the inspector assigned to patrol the building took one alert look at her and summoned a Willard Parker ambulance. The other was a Cuban, who, as it later turned out, had nothing worse than chicken pox, but by the time his case was correctly diagnosed, another case of smallpox had come to light. This was on Thursday, April 10th. The patient was a forty-three-year-old wanderer named Herman G——, whose condition had come to the attention of a physician in the dermatologic ward at Bellevue, where he had been confined for treatment of syphilis since March 10th. The next day, April 11th, still another victim was reported. He was a businessman of fifty-seven named Harry T——, and his case, too, was discovered in the Bellevue dermatologic ward. He had been admitted there, suffering from lymphoblastoma, on March 19th. His misfortune, as the newspapers loudly and uneasily pointed out, brought the number of smallpox cases to seven. It also had the effect of abruptly increasing to around a hundred thousand the number of people who had heeded Dr. Weinstein's admonition.

While dutifully notifying the United States Public Health Service of the outbreak and its transcontinental origin, Dr. Weinstein had expressed a normal interest in Mrs. La Bar's whereabouts and the state of her health. It was his understanding, he said, that she had continued on to Maine soon after her husband's funeral; nothing had been heard from her since, although the true cause of her husband's death had been widely publicized. As might be expected, Dr. Weinstein's curiosity concerning Mrs. La Bar was at least equaled by that of the Public Health Service. He was promised an early reply, and on Wednesday, April 9th, his day was enlivened by a report from the Service on its findings. They were numerous and in some respects reassuring, in others highly disturbing. Mrs. La Bar was at the home of a relative in East Winthrop, Maine, and in excellent health. Information obtained from her had enabled the Service to alert the health authorities in the towns at which the La Bars' bus had stopped — Laredo, San Antonio, Dallas, Tulsa, Joplin, St. Louis, Indianapolis, Cincinnati, and Pittsburgh. None had reported any local evidence of smallpox. La Bar's illness apparently hadn't reached a highly contagious stage during the journey. What distressed Dr. Weinstein was the disclosure that the La Bars had arrived in New York from Mexico City on Saturday afternoon, March 1st. This meant that they had been in the city five days before La Bar finally tottered into Bellevue. During that time, they had stayed at a hotel, which the Health Department has charitably never seen fit to identify. Fortunately, because of La Bar's unrelenting aches and pains, they seldom left their room. The only time they went outside the hotel, as far as Mrs. La Bar could recall, was on the Monday after their arrival here, when they took a stroll up Fifth Avenue and made a few trivial purchases at McCreery's, at a ten-cent store, and at the Knox hat shop. The report added that Mrs. La Bar's earlier reticence had been caused by a lifelong aversion to red tape.

A somewhat similar reticence was discovered in an assistant manager of the La Bars' hotel by a squad of Dr. Greenberg's agents who stopped by later that Wednesday. It was their intention to vaccinate all the hotel's employees and permanent residents and to gather the names and addresses of all transient guests registered there between March 1st and March 5th. The opposition that they encountered was rigid, but it was not prolonged. It vanished at a thawing murmur from Dr. Greenberg over the telephone to the effect that the full text of Mrs. La Bar's memoir could easily be substituted for the tactfully expurgated version, omitting the name of the hotel, that was then being prepared for the press. His words induced a cordiality of such intensity that the manager himself trotted out the records and asked to be the first to bare his arm. By bedtime Wednesday night, the inspectors had made a satisfying start on both their tasks, and they finished up the following day. Approximately three thousand people had spent one or more of the first five days of March under the same roof as La Bar. Nearly all were from out of town, and the names and addresses of these, who included residents of twenty-nine states, were transmitted to the health authorities of those states. Dr. Greenberg's men added what guests there had been from New York City to their already generous list of local suspects. In time, all the three thousand, except for a few dozen adventurers who had registered under spurious names, were hunted down and, as it happily turned out, given a clean bill of health.

Meanwhile, Dr. Weinstein and Dr. Greenberg had decided that there wasn't much they could do in the way of disinfecting the La Bars' month-old trail up Fifth Avenue. They tried to console themselves with the realization that private physicians and the district health centers were experiencing another substantial increase in the demand for safety and certainty. This followed the newspaper publication, on Thursday, of Mrs. La Bar's censored revelations, which contained a discomfortingly vague reference to "a midtown hotel,"

in and about which La Bar had passed five days at nearly the peak
of his contagiousness. Practically all the hotels in Manhattan at
which a transient would be likely to stop are in the midtown area.

Bright and early Saturday morning, April 12th, there was more
unpleasant news. It was relayed to Dr. Weinstein by the New York
State Department of Health, and it came from the village of Millbrook, in Dutchess County. A boy of four, Vernon L——, whose
family lived in the Bronx, had been sick there for several days with
what Dr. Smadel, in whom the state health authorities also had confidence, had just diagnosed as smallpox. The boy, an inmate of the
Cardinal Hayes Convalescent Home, on the outskirts of town, was
not, it appeared, critically ill. The source of the infection was no
mystery. Before being admitted to the Home, on March 13th,
Vernon had spent eighteen days, from February 21st to March 10th,
at Willard Parker, under treatment for scarlet fever. He was one of
a number of Willard Parker alumni no longer in the city whom the
state investigators had been asked to trace. The news of the Millbrook case was conveyed to Dr. Weinstein by telephone. The morning brought him two more agitating calls. One was from Dr. Muckenfuss and the other from Dr. Tolle. Dr. Muckenfuss reported that
the municipal supply of vaccine was going fast. Two hundred thousand units had been distributed during the past week, and no more
than that number were still on hand. Dr. Tolle called to say that
Mrs. Acosta had just died.

At one-thirty that afternoon, Dr. Weinstein, accompanied by Dr.
Bernecker and a couple of his other associates, hopped around to
Gracie Mansion for a candid chat with Mayor O'Dwyer, whom
they found enduring an instant of repose. It had been Dr. Weinstein's original and commendable determination to spare the Mayor
any direct concern with the calamity. Dr. Muckenfuss's information, on top of everything else, had compelled him to change his
mind. After Dr. Weinstein and his colleagues had successfully communicated their uneasiness to the Mayor, they divulged a more
specific reason for their visit. They asked for an appropriation of
five hundred thousand dollars. Most of this sum, which, after a little
ritualistic sparring, the Mayor agreed to wheedle out of the Board
of Estimate, would be expended for vaccine, Dr. Weinstein explained, and the rest for other extraordinary expenses of the Health
and Hospital Departments, including the hiring of a thousand doctors and a couple of hundred clerks to man additional public vaccination centers in various parts of the city. Then, also at the request
of Dr. Weinstein, the Mayor led the group down to City Hall,
where at five o'clock he met in his office with the commissioners of
all municipal departments and instructed them to see to it that no

city employee delayed an instant in getting vaccinated. Before knocking off for the day, the Mayor called in the press, invited the photographers to unlimber their cameras, and allowed Dr. Weinstein to vaccinate him. This, he pointed out, was his fifth vaccination in six years, the others having been acquired during his service in the Army, but it was better to be safe than sorry.

Over the weekend, the words and insinuating example of Mayor O'Dwyer, which were supplemented, on the air at nine o'clock Sunday evening, by a sudden, inflammatory chirp from Walter Winchell, resulted in a powerful quickening of the instinct for self-preservation, and this was still further heightened by word from the convalescent home in Millbrook that three more smallpox cases — two of them child inmates and the other an elderly nun on the staff of the institution — had been discovered there. Eighty-four thousand people, including hundreds in the remotest wastes of Staten Island, were vaccinated on Monday. On Tuesday, following the announcement of yet another case of smallpox originating at Bellevue — that of a sixty-year-old man who had been in the hospital suffering from a serious skin ailment for many months — two hundred thousand more were vaccinated. So great was the drain on the municipal reserves of vaccine that the Mayor summoned before him representatives of all the big pharmaceutical firms that have plants or offices here and extracted from them a collective promise to make available to the city an abundant and immediate supply of the preparation. Pending the fulfillment of their pledge, he arranged, over the telephone, for an interim loan of vaccine from the Army and Navy. Wednesday night, in the course of announcing that emergency clinics would be opened the following morning in all of the city's eighty-four police stations, Dr. Weinstein found an opportunity to tacitly revise his earlier description of smallpox. It was, he now declared, "the most contagious of diseases." He was rewarded on Thursday evening with word that half a million vaccinations had been performed during the day.

There was no perceptible letup in the public's desire for immunization during the remainder of the week, and on Sunday, April 20th, some additional interest was created by an announcement from Brigadier General Wallace H. Graham, the White House physician, that President Truman's preparations for a three-hour visit to New York the next day had included a brand-new vaccination. During the next week, two hundred Health Department teams, each composed of a doctor and a nurse, moved through the public elementary and high schools, vaccinating some eight hundred and eighty-nine thousand children. Toward the end of the week, Dr. Weinstein was sufficiently satisfied with the way things were going to reveal that the six surviving smallpox patients at Willard Parker and the four in Millbrook appeared to be out of danger. On Saturday, at his direction, the vaccinators were withdrawn from the police stations.

Six days later, on Friday, May 2nd, Dr. Weinstein formally announced the end of the outbreak and the completion of the biggest and fastest mass-vaccination campaign in the history of the world. Within the space of only twenty-eight days, he said, a total of at least six million three hundred and fifty thousand people had been vaccinated in the city. Practically everyone in New York was now immune. Although Dr. Weinstein had the delicacy not to say so, it was about time.

◇◇

A Whole Heart for Ramona

GLADYS DENNY SHULTZ

[A few years ago, one of the most dramatic and awe-inspiring developments in all medical history was announced: a machine to take over for a time the heart's task of circulating blood through the body, the lungs' task of oxygenating the blood. The human body's "last closed frontier," the heart, can now be breached.

"It is true that today we can mend heart defects about which we were helpless to do anything before," the eminent chest surgeon said. "I think it possible that in time we may be able to repair nearly every heart defect with which children come into the world. But I believe the public has been given a misleading impression about the ease with which an open-heart operation is performed.

"Far more is involved than a surgeon's skill. Planning must start weeks, sometimes months, in advance. Anywhere from fifteen to thirty pints of blood of the patient's blood type must be procured. The blood must be matched with more than ordinary care, to insure there are no minor factors present antagonistic to minor factors in the blood of the patient, or of one of the other donors.

"The operation itself requires a number of teams, made up of highly trained medical and technical personnel. Among the teams and team members, there must be the highest degree of co-ordination. All manner of contingencies must be anticipated, arrangements made for meeting them.

"There have been too many 'miracle' heart-operation stories. But I think the public is entitled to know what an open-heart operation is really like. If the *Journal* is interested in a story of that kind, we will be glad to co-operate."

That was the way it came about that a representative of the *Ladies' Home Journal* was present when six-and-a-half-year-old Ramona Smith, of East Northport, Long Island, was operated on by the open-heart technique. The operation took place at the Presbyterian Hospital in New York City. The medical and technical teams came from Columbia-Presbyterian Medical Center. By request of the chief surgeon, no names of professional or technical personnel are used.]

YOUR BABY was pronounced perfect at birth. You have planned and dreamed, as loving parents are bound to do. And then you learn that there *is* an imperfection. Through some accident occurring early in the pregnancy, your child's heart did not form in the way it should have. The flaw is so deep within the heart that it cannot be remedied. It will mean invalidism so long as your otherwise normal child shall live; it may mean early death, the doctor tells you. The very unexpectedness of the blow makes it the harder to bear.

How many parents have had this sorrowful experience in the past, it is impossible to say. Until very recently scant attention was paid to congenital defects in the heart itself, since most were inoperable. But now it is recognized that a rather astonishing number of persons are born with heart defects ranging from very minor to major ones; a considerable number with malformations that will prove fatal if they are not corrected. These major malformations may not always be detected in a baby's early months.

When Mr. and Mrs. Raymond Smith were told that their year-old daughter, Ramona, had been born with a defective heart, it was a long time before they could accept the verdict. Ramona had been such a strikingly beautiful baby, with her luxuriant dark hair, huge dark eyes and apple-red cheeks. Surely there could be nothing seriously wrong with her! But red cheeks are not always a sign of health, and Ramona was not growing and developing physically as she should. As months went on, she fell farther and farther behind her contemporaries in size and strength. Although advanced mentally, she was two years old before she began to walk.

There followed many visits to clinics, anxious consultations with specialists. Finally the heart defect was diagnosed as a *patent ductus*. The doctor making the diagnosis deduced that the channel which runs from the pulmonary artery to the aorta in the fetus had failed to close in Ramona's case, as it does normally by the time a baby is ready to be born. Surgeons have been correcting this condition for twenty years. When Ramona was three, she was brought to a chest surgeon to be operated on.

But the surgeon had bad news for Mr. and Mrs. Smith after he had made his own examination. Ramona's handicap was not a *patent ductus*. The defect was deep within Ramona's heart. He drew a diagram to show them. The heart is divided into four chambers, the two upper ones being called the atria, the two lower ones the ventricles. The venous blood enters through the right atrium and passes through the right ventricle to the lungs to be oxygenated and purified. The oxygenated arterial blood then enters the heart through the left upper chamber, or atrium, passes down through the left ventricle and on out to circulate through the body. In Ramona's heart there was a hole in the wall which separates the two atria. Much of the arterial blood returned from the lungs was escaping into the right atrium. The circulation in Ramona's right ventricle was being overloaded; that in the left ventricle was being deprived. This condition is known medically as a "left-to-right shunt."

Such a condition is not necessarily fatal in itself. But the impairment to circulation it causes has serious results. Children born with this defect are slowed down in physical development. By the time they reach the age of twelve or thirteen, they may be retarded in growth as much as four or five years. In times past, they have seldom lived past adolescence, for they are prone to infectious illnesses, particularly pneumonia. Blood infection is another possibility.

Yet at the time the surgeon made his diagnosis, he did not consider that the operating techniques then available were suitable in Ramona's case. All they could do was to watch over the little girl unceasingly, guard her health as best they could.

The next three years were a repetition of the first three. During the winter, Ramona would contract one infection after another. Each would drag her down still further physically. She was too frail to romp like other children. When she started to school, her doctor considered her too frail even to ride in the school bus. She had to be taken to and from school in a taxi, alone. She liked the taxi driver, but she was distressed at being set apart from the other children.

During these years, however, and years preceding them, scientists had been working on an artificial pump which would send the vital blood through the body while the heart rested. By the time Ramona was four and a half, her surgeon-doctor was himself doing open-heart operations. But in these early days the operation was very risky, the mortality rate extremely high. It was employed only as a last resort in the most desperate cases.

Then came last winter, an unusually good one in Ramona's brief life. She had fewer infections than in previous winters. With spring, the surgeon felt that she was in better physical condition than she was ever likely to be again. Now the mortality rate for the operation was no longer prohibitive. The surgeon believed the time had come to repair Ramona's heart.

There is perhaps no harder decision for parents to have to make — the immediate risk of an infinitely precious life, even though the alternative is invalidism and death in early years. But Mr. and Mrs. Smith had every confidence in the surgeon. They chose the operation.

The first step was for Ramona to go into Presbyterian Hospital, New York City, for a last, thorough diagnosis. This constituted a minor operation in itself, and was conducted under light anesthesia. For it included, besides X ray and fluoroscoping, the insertion of an exploratory catheter into the heart. (This technique, made possible by the work of Columbia Medical Center's Nobel-prize winners Dr. Dickinson W. Richards and Dr. André F. Cournand, has been an immeasurable help in surgical repair of heart defects, because of the accurate diagnosis it affords.) The exact location of the hole was determined. The operation was scheduled for April 8.

The next step was to round up the blood donors. The surgeon computed that seventeen to nineteen pints of blood would be needed. Ramona's own blood would, of course, circulate through the pump and her body. But there must be blood to prime the pump-oxygenator, and blood to replace what Ramona would lose during the operation. Twenty-odd donors must be found, to allow for some rejections after blood matching.

Mr. Smith took his problem to a woman in the Personnel Department of the Republic Aviation Corporation, where he works. "We'll call the Intercounty Blood Bank at Jamaica," she told him. Republic and some five hundred other Long Island and New York City industries and organizations belong to this blood bank; Mr. Smith himself is a member. Still, the Smiths could hardly believe their good luck when they were told the Intercounty Blood Bank would take over the entire task of finding the donors.

Some seventy telephone calls to persons with blood type A, Ramona's blood type, produced twenty-three people who said they would be glad to help. Seven were New York City firemen, a group of men always notably generous in responding to appeals for blood. Four of the volunteers had to be rejected because their blood, though of type A, contained a Kell factor (named for the person in whom this factor was first found) antagonistic to a Kell factor in Ramona's blood. Nineteen met the requirements.

Donors are entitled to receive $17.50 for each pint of blood they give. But according to Controller Grassi, of the Intercounty Blood Bank, all but four of those who gave blood to Ramona refused payment. The firemen asked credit for the New York Fire Department, a member of the Intercounty Blood Bank. Others asked for family credit, which is good indefinitely.

A week before the date set for the operation, Ramona moved into the Children's Ward of Presbyterian Hospital. The surgeon wanted to make further tests. Also, this gave Ramona a chance to get well acquainted with the special nurses who would care for her after the operation. Ramona's parents would not be able to see her until she was past the danger point, unless the operation went badly. It was important that when the little girl came out from the anesthetic there should be someone at hand whom she knew and trusted. The nurse chosen for this shift was a pediatric nurse who had had special training in the care of patients after heart surgery. She was young, pretty, vivacious. Ramona took to her at once.

Ramona understood that she would be put to sleep, and while she was asleep her surgeon friend would cure her of the wheezes with which she was afflicted. It would hurt for a while, but after that she would be as well and strong as her schoolmates. The big selling point from her standpoint, however, was that she wouldn't have to go to school by herself in a taxi any more. She would be able to ride on the school bus with the other children.

By April 7, all was in readiness for the operation which would take place the next morning. At 2:00 P.M., eleven blood donors started arriving at the hospital at half-hour intervals. They gave blood for "perfusion" — the blood that would be mixed with Ramona's in the pump-oxygenator — and "infusion" — blood to replace what Ramona would lose during the operation.

Simultaneously, Ramona's father and mother arrived in the Children's Ward for a last visit with their little girl. When visiting hours ended at 6:00 P.M., Mr. Smith returned to Long Island, to the Smiths' two younger children. Mrs. Smith tried to eat some dinner, though she had little appetite. Then she went on to Bard Hall, a residence for medical students, where she was to stay overnight.

The operation is to begin at 8:00 on Tuesday morning, April 8. But it is 5:00 A.M. when the first of the several teams an open-heart operation requires comes into the operating room. The task of this team is to install the pump-oxygenator and make sure it is in perfect working order. A surgeon is in charge, one of the three surgeons who perfected the open-heart technique as it is carried out at Columbia-Presbyterian Medical Center.

Set up on a movable steel table, the pump is a futuristic-appearing group of plastic tubes. On the left side rears up a tall tube about two inches in diameter and two to three feet high. This is the "mixing" tube. Here oxygen will be bubbled through Ramona's blood as it is drawn from her body. A wider plastic tube slants down from the top of the mixing tube. This is called the "debubbling chamber." From it, the blood will run down into the helix reservoir — a very wide plastic container inside of which are plastic coils, slanting downward. The coils are kept in a water bath in which a constant temperature is maintained. The pump proper is made of plastic rather than glass, for plastic causes less damage to the blood corpuscles and there is less likelihood of the formation of clots.

In front of the pump is its small motor, with a low steel cabinet on either side. The cabinets contain fingerlike contrivances which will wave back and forth constantly when the pump is in use. The fingers at the left of the motor will propel the blood into the vertical mixing tube as it is drawn from Ramona's body. Those at the right will propel the blood back into Ramona's body as it emerges from the coils. Perfect operation of the pump obviously is vital. When Ramona is on the pump, three surgeons and a technician will be watching it. Should the electricity go off or the motor fail, the pump can be operated by hand.

At 6:30 A.M., another team makes its appearance, bringing in the tall rack on which bottles of dextrose solution and "infusion" blood — to replace what Ramona will lose during the operation — will be suspended.

The oscilloscope, a recording machine, is rolled in. This is a steel cabinet about five feet high, with squares of yellow glass set into its front. While the operation is going on, it will display, simultaneously, an electrocardiogram and an electroencephalogram, and also the pressure in Ramona's arteries and the pressure in her veins. Before and after the operation, it will show the pressure in each of the four chambers of Ramona's heart. This will enable the surgeons to know whether or not the circulatory imbalance has been corrected.

The anesthesiology team will be responsible for following the encephalogram, which has proved to be the best indicator as to whether the brain is receiving an adequate supply of blood during the period when the machine takes over. Failure here could mean irrevocable damage to the brain if not death. A cardiologist who has been in touch with Ramona's case from the beginning will follow the cardiogram and the blood-pressure recordings.

Also at 6:30, Ramona is wakened gently by her special nurse. They make a joke together over the fact that this morning Ramona will have to go breakfastless. Ramona is given an injection. Then, happy and unafraid, the friendly nurse beside her, Ramona is taken to an anteroom of the operating theater.

7:00 A.M. The anesthesiology team arrives. It consists of four specialists and assistants. For the anesthesiologists, in addition to administering anesthesia and monitoring the encephalogram, are responsible for keeping Ramona's lungs in a proper state of expansion — both while she is using them, and during the period when the machine will be breathing for her — and for regulating the flow of infusion blood and dextrose solution.

After Ramona is sufficiently drowsy from the injection, tracheal anesthesia is started, applied through a tube inserted in her mouth and down her throat.

Promptly at 7:00, too, the day-shift nurses come on, replacing those from the night shift who had been helping to set up the machines. The day nurses begin laying out rows of instruments of all kinds, arranging in orderly fashion sterile towels, gauze pledgets, sponges, rubber gloves and the countless other objects that may be needed. In this operation, there can be no question of something forgotten for which a nurse must scurry down the hall.

And at 7:00 the eight remaining blood donors report at the hospital's blood bank. From six of these is drawn the blood that will be used to prime the pump. The two other donors will stand by until the operation is over, in case an emergency should arise and further blood should be needed.

7:30 A.M. Ramona's mother enters the hospital, goes to the lounge in the adjoining Babies' Hospital. She had planned to meet her husband here, and her parents, Mr. and Mrs. Eugene Mellevold, of Floral Park, Long Island, at 9:00 o'clock. They are to wait together. But Mrs. Smith had been unable to sleep, and had risen early. She felt that she had to get as close to Ramona as she could.

The spectators' balcony overlooking the operating theater begins to fill with doctors and nurses. Columbia-Presbyterian is a teaching hospital. The professional men engaged in the operation on Ramona are donating their services. Other professional persons are allowed to watch.

8:00 A.M. The doors of the operating theater are swung wide.

A Whole H
hours or lo:
doctor for t
by her hear
the first assi
out Columk
ond assistar
surgeon. Tv
group.

8:55 A.N
chest, at a p
she is grown
the skill wit
matic scene
face of the
and spongin
ally making
coagulates t
larger ones a
into the che
towels. Ram
ple working
sheet that is
behind her; c

9:15 A.M.
mona's lungs
is due to exp
oxygen suppl
the chest ca\
apart with a
covered with
just below th
aside, exposin

"That's a l
tors' balcony
chief surgeon
silk threads in
work the peri
they work, m
narrowing the

9:30 A.M. N
heart, nestled
expanding, co
pumping the
The chief sur

The operating table with Ramona on it is pushed in, wheeled to the center of the amphitheater, beneath a great spotlight. Lights go on behind two large X rays of Ramona s chest, in a case behind the artificial pump. Underneath Ramona is a mattress through which fluid circulates. It is important that her body temperature shall remain normal, and an electric control can make the fluid warmer or cooler as desired. Following Ramona into the theater comes an anesthesiologist with tanks of oxygen and an oxygen bag. In an open-heart operation, the right amount of oxygen at every stage is tremendously important. The oxygen will be fed through the bag. This anesthesiologist will regulate the flow by squeezing the bag with an expert hand.

Ramona lies on the table as if in a normal sleep, her dark hair spilling over the snowy sheet that covers the fluid-filled mattress. With tracheal anesthesia, no mask is necessary. The tube in Ramona's mouth does not impair the view of her pretty, childishly round face. But the round face is deceptive. Ramona's body reveals the damage done by the imperfect heart. It is pitifully small; as white, almost, as the sheet beneath it; and thin to the point of emaciation. The rib case stands out; the legs are little white sticks. One spectator feels serious qualms. Will it be possible to stand and watch while knives cut deep into this fragile structure?

But now the four surgeons of the operating team come in, gauze-masked, white-gowned. With utmost gentleness, they fasten rubber straps around Ramona's wrists and lower legs. These are to hold in place the electrodes which will convey to the oscilloscope a constant stream of messages as to the way the child is standing the operation. Her right arm is padded, then bound up out of the chief surgeon's way. Four more electrode needles are inserted gently just beneath Ramona's scalp.

Now in the theater are: four operating surgeons and two operating nurses; four anesthesiologists; two technicians at the oscilloscope; three surgeons and a technical assistant who will have charge of the pump; the cardiologist who will watch Ramona's blood pressure; an anatomist who will record Ramona's heart sounds before the operation, and record them after the operation; two circulating nurses. In an adjoining laboratory, four technicians are waiting. As the operation proceeds, they will be constantly analyzing samples of Ramona's blood, a further check on her condition at every stage.

8:12 A.M. An operating surgeon starts preparing Ramona's torso. Using sterile gauze pledgets held in slender forceps, he washes it first with soap and water, then with alcohol, then with ether; ending with a coating of tincture of Merthiolate. By 8:19 Ramona is a bright orange color from neck to knees.

Ne
and al
across
has a
sterile
remov
one sic
face. T
8:2
move a
cal tean
The
two fe
tery, th
Throug
venous
and ca
sense c
lifted u
A smal
clampe
dextros
This pr
Mul
through
steady
pump v
coils. A
trouble
Bloc
vessels.
As the
is soppe
of blooc
a heart
dertrans
much bl
8:51
have we
minute
laxes fo
the maj
ation is
have ke

mona's heart, rapidly now but always with care, cleaning away all vestiges of blood with gauze pledgets held in long forceps. Under their manipulation the heart tosses and tumbles, rolls this way and that way, but keeps working with the utmost regularity, never losing a beat.

Now the two men are putting tapes around the *venae cavae* — the two great veins which carry the venous blood into the heart. The anesthesiologist at Ramona's head crouches above her with the alert tensity of a runner poised for the starting signal. His left hand is on Ramona's temple, to get the pulse there, his right hand squeezes the oxygen bag. He watches the surgeons' every move, while also receiving constant reports from the recordings of the oscilloscope and from the blood samplings, to guide him in administering the oxygen.

9:40 A.M. A pause now, while a surgeon applies a miniature stethoscope to Ramona's heart. For a second or more the spectators in the balcony hear the thud, thud of Ramona's heartbeat. In this procedure, Ramona is making a contribution to science, as well as benefiting from one of its ingenious devices. These recordings, from a stethoscope applied directly to the heart, are of tremendous value in making diagnoses and in evaluating the results of heart surgery.

Zero hour is approaching. Ramona is given an injection of heparin, so that her blood will not clot in the pump. At the same time, the bottle of citrated infusion blood is removed from the rack, a bottle of blood containing heparin is substituted.

The chief surgeon is pushing a catheter through the right atrium of Ramona's heart, at the apex of the right chamber, into the inferior *vena cava*, the three other surgeons assisting. Then another catheter into the superior *vena cava*. For a brief period, eight rubber-gloved hands are engaged on and around Ramona's heart. (The inferior *vena cava* is the venous trunk line that brings blood back to the heart from the legs and abdominal region; the superior *vena cava* brings the venous blood from the upper part of the body. Both empty into the right atrium.) By now, the towels tucked around Ramona's heart have taken on the color of Mercurochrome.

One can feel the mounting tension, even though there is no change in the calm precision with which those in the operating theater are doing their work. The heparinized blood collected from this morning's donors is running up through the mixing tube of the pump, spilling over into the debubbler and forming a slender red ribbon down through the plastic coils of the helix reservoir. The pump-oxygenator is being primed.

The four members of the pump team take their stations. One surgeon will manage the connections between Ramona and the ma-hours or longer.) The chief surgeon, who has been Ramona's own doctor for three and a half years, stands on her right, immediately by her heart. Directly across from him at Ramona's left side stands the first assistant. (He also is one of the three surgeons who worked out Columbia's open-heart technique.) Next to him stands the second assistant, the third assistant standing to the right of the chief surgeon. Two operating nurses at the end of the table complete the group.

8:55 A.M. The first cut is made horizontally across Ramona's chest, at a point where the scar will be hidden by her breasts when she is grown. Again there is no feeling of shock, only of absorption in the skill with which the surgeons work, of fascination in the dramatic scene below. For on one side of the sheet there is the tranquil face of the sleeping child; on the other side, the surgeons cutting and sponging away blood, cutting and sponging away blood, gradually making the incision wider and deeper. An electric cauterizer coagulates the small veins and arteries as they are severed. The larger ones are tied off with silk thread. As the surgeons go deeper into the chest wall they seal the area off with moistened sterile towels. Ramona sleeps on quietly, unconscious alike of the six people working with intense concentration on the other side of the sheet that is reared above her head; of the two anesthesiologists, just behind her; of the steady tap, tap on the pump filter.

9:15 A.M. The chest is open. One can see a pink mass — Ramona's lungs — moving up and down, pumping strongly. Its action is due to expert manipulation of the oxygen bag, which keeps the oxygen supply constant. Otherwise the lungs would collapse when the chest cavity is penetrated. The chief surgeon spreads the ribs apart with a metal retractor. Now one gets a glimpse of the heart, covered with a thin membrane called the pericardium, where it lies just below the lung mass. Very gently the surgeons move the lungs aside, exposing Ramona's heart in its entirety.

"That's a big heart for such a little girl," a doctor in the spectators' balcony murmurs. But it beats regularly and strongly while the chief surgeon and the first assistant slit the pericardium; tie long silk threads in the edges of the slit and then with utmost gentleness work the pericardium back and down, freeing the heart surface. As they work, more sterile towels are tucked in at the sides, constantly narrowing the field of view.

9:30 A.M. Now nothing can be seen of Ramona's body except her heart, nestled in its bed of moistened sterile towels; contracting and expanding, contracting and expanding. Receiving the venous blood; pumping the arterial blood through the network of blood vessels. The chief surgeon and the first assistant are both working on Ramona's heart, rapidly now but always with care, cleaning away all vestiges of blood with gauze pledgets held in long forceps. Under their manipulation the heart tosses and tumbles, rolls this way and that way, but keeps working with the utmost regularity, never losing a beat.

Now the two men are putting tapes around the *venae cavae* — the two great veins which carry the venous blood into the heart. The anesthesiologist at Ramona's head crouches above her with the alert tensity of a runner poised for the starting signal. His left hand is on Ramona's temple, to get the pulse there, his right hand squeezes the oxygen bag. He watches the surgeons' every move, while also receiving constant reports from the recordings of the oscilloscope and from the blood samplings, to guide him in administering the oxygen.

9:40 A.M. A pause now, while a surgeon applies a miniature stethoscope to Ramona's heart. For a second or more the spectators in the balcony hear the thud, thud of Ramona's heartbeat. In this procedure, Ramona is making a contribution to science, as well as benefiting from one of its ingenious devices. These recordings, from a stethoscope applied directly to the heart, are of tremendous value in making diagnoses and in evaluating the results of heart surgery.

Zero hour is approaching. Ramona is given an injection of heparin, so that her blood will not clot in the pump. At the same time, the bottle of citrated infusion blood is removed from the rack, a bottle of blood containing heparin is substituted.

The chief surgeon is pushing a catheter through the right atrium of Ramona's heart, at the apex of the right chamber, into the inferior *vena cava*, the three other surgeons assisting. Then another catheter into the superior *vena cava*. For a brief period, eight rubber-gloved hands are engaged on and around Ramona's heart. (The inferior *vena cava* is the venous trunk line that brings blood back to the heart from the legs and abdominal region; the superior *vena cava* brings the venous blood from the upper part of the body. Both empty into the right atrium.) By now, the towels tucked around Ramona's heart have taken on the color of Mercurochrome.

One can feel the mounting tension, even though there is no change in the calm precision with which those in the operating theater are doing their work. The heparinized blood collected from this morning's donors is running up through the mixing tube of the pump, spilling over into the debubbler and forming a slender red ribbon down through the plastic coils of the helix reservoir. The pump-oxygenator is being primed.

The four members of the pump team take their stations. One surgeon will manage the connections between Ramona and the machine. The two other surgeons of this team will watch the operation of the pump itself, a technician standing by to help.

The crucial moment is at hand. The two catheters in the *venae cavae* sprout out from Ramona's heart like willow branches; yet its steady beat has not faltered once. The first assistant ties knot after knot of silk thread around the catheters, so that they cannot possibly slip out of position.

10:07 A.M. The last knot is tied. The chief surgeon adjusts the retractor which holds the sides of the chest apart. An anesthesiologist lowers the spotlight. A voice comes through the amplifier: "Are you ready to go on the pump?" The first assistant answers "Yes."

10:10 A.M. The clamps are being removed from the catheters that will convey Ramona's blood to and from the pump. Except for the watchers at the oscilloscope, all eyes in the operating theater go to the vertical mixing tube. The thin red column is becoming a thick column of dark red blood, filling the tube. The pump is working perfectly. Now it is carrying the full task of oxygenating the blood from the veins, and pumping it back into and through Ramona's body. The dark red blood shoots up strongly through the tall vertical tube, goes through the debubbling chamber and runs down through the coils of the helix reservoir, a lighter, brighter red. Ramona's heart has not lost a single beat, though it beats less strongly now. The tension relaxes. A critical moment has been passed safely.

The chief surgeon makes a single strong, decisive cut into the heart. The first assistant holds the severed sides apart, the two men peer closely into the interior of the organ. The spotlight is lowered again until it all but touches the chief surgeon's bent head. Another careful little cut or two and the hole in the inner heart wall is reached. The chief surgeon sews the sides together with silk thread. This will hold until the tissue joins of itself, in about two weeks' time. (The surgeon used running stitches. Had ordinary stitches been employed, around nine would have been required. A big hole in the heart of so tiny a girl.) All the while Ramona's blood shoots up through the mixing tube in a steady stream, down through the coils, into her left femoral artery and through her body, bypassing the heart.

10:25 A.M. The chief surgeon says, "We're about through." The hole in the heart has been mended. The surgeons are getting ready to sew up the incision in the heart muscle. The spectators' balcony and the passage leading to it are crammed with doctors and nurses, those at the rear standing on tiptoe, trying to get a glimpse of the scene below.

10:29 A.M. Blood is started back into Ramona's heart through the inferior *vena cava*. Another tense moment. But the beat is growing stronger now. Without a miss, Ramona's heart is again taking up its work of pumping her blood.

10:30 A.M. Ramona's special nurse goes to the lounge in Babies' Hospital to report to Ramona's parents and grandparents. She is able to tell them that the most perilous part of the operation is already successfully accomplished.

10:32 A.M. The catheter in the superior *vena cava* is removed gently. The pump is stopped. The surgeons close the holes that were made in inserting the catheters through the right auricle; the tapes on the big veins are removed. The chief surgeon carefully works the pericardium back up over the heart again, tying the slit sides together with the long retaining threads that had been left in them for this purpose. After all the cutting and sewing to which it has been subjected, Ramona's heart is beating as strongly and regularly as before.

"That's a good heart — a very good heart," says one of the doctor spectators approvingly. It was a good heart, but for the one defect. Now that it is a whole heart, it should serve Ramona long and well.

10:45 A.M. The surgeons are gently teasing the lungs back into their proper place. They pause to take a bit of tissue from a lung for biopsy. Often a defective heart has a damaging effect on the lungs. There is no reason to think that Ramona's lungs have suffered as yet. The surgeons sew the cut tissue together; take a full minute to examine the stitching closely, making sure that no gap is left through which air may escape into the chest.

10:51 A.M. The chest contents arranged precisely as they had been before, the head surgeon removes the clamps which held the incision open, pulls the chest together, preparatory to closing it. The severed breastbone is held together firmly with stainless-steel wire, the soft tissues of the chest wall are closed with silk thread.

There are still many things to do. Tests must be made of heart action, blood pressure and many other things. It is 12:05 before Ramona is carried to the recovery room, trailed by technicians bringing the oscilloscope and the temperature-control mattress, both of which must be reinstalled. As the mattress is slipped beneath her, she whimpers and begins to wail softly. This is a good sign. At once, eight doctors surround Ramona's bed. The first assistant begins issuing crisp directions for postoperative care.

1:00 P.M. The first assistant, in street clothes, is sitting in the dining room of Harkness Pavilion, part of the Columbia-Presbyterian Medical Center, bowed head resting on his hands. The stand-by crew, which will watch over Ramona until she is out of danger, has taken stations. Her special nurse will not leave Ramona's side nor remove her eyes from the child. After her eight-hour shift, she will be relieved by other nurses with special training in open-heart cases. A chest surgeon will keep a twenty-four-hour vigil, round the clock, snatching such sleep as he can get on a cot placed beside Ramona's bed. Three anesthesiologists are assigned to Ramona, each on an eight-hour shift. At least one cardiologist will be on duty round the clock. Other cardiologists undoubtedly will be dropping in, for an open-heart patient is of special interest.

The first assistant straightens up briskly as the other guests approach the table.

"An open-heart operation is a strain," he admits. "You don't think about it while the operation is going on. All you think about is the patient and what you are doing. Then after it's all over, you get the impact."

One reason for the extremely complicated procedures in Ramona's case, the chief surgeon explains, is that the open-heart technique is still new. "In a few years' time, we may be doing it in an entirely different way. Perhaps someday it will be simplified to a point where it can be carried out with ordinary operating-room procedures."

Today, though, an open-heart operation is high drama; a succession of daring risks, offset by endless precautions. It requires a very large cast. Counting the workers at the blood bank in Jamaica who found the donors, the workers at the blood bank at Columbia-Presbyterian Medical Hospital who drew the blood, and the diagnostic teams, sixty-three men and women played an immediate part in the operation on Ramona. And back of the incredibly smooth intermeshing of intricate machines and human skills and intelligence lie long years of study and practice; long years of dreaming and experimenting and striving by a multitude of scientists. To the end that a frail, sickly little girl may be able to romp and play; may have the same chance as any other bright, pretty little girl to grow to lovely, radiant womanhood.

And how did it go with Ramona? Within two weeks she was up and playing with the other youngsters in the Children's Ward. This winter, Ramona is riding to school on the school bus, with the other children.

ᴄᴣ THE ABOLITION OF SLAVERY

The Man with the Hoe

EDWIN MARKHAM

Bowed by the weight of centuries he leans
Upon his hoe and gazes on the ground,
The emptiness of ages in his face,
And on his back the burden of the world.
Who made him dead to rapture and despair,
A thing that grieves not and that never hopes,
Stolid and stunned, a brother to the ox?
Who loosened and let down this brutal jaw?
Whose was the hand that slanted back this brow?
Whose breath blew out the light within his brain?

Is this the Thing the Lord God made and gave
To have dominion over sea and land;
To trace the stars and search the heavens for power;
To feel the passion of Eternity?
Is this the dream He dreamed who shaped the suns
And marked their ways upon the ancient deep?
Down all the caverns of Hell to their last gulf
There is no shape more terrible than this —
More tongued with censure of the world's blind greed —
More filled with signs and portents for the soul —
More packt with danger to the universe.

What gulfs between him and the seraphim!
Slave of the wheel of labor, what to him
Are Plato and the swing of Pleiades?
What the long reaches of the peaks of song,
The rift of dawn, the reddening of the rose?
Through this dread shape the suffering ages look;
Time's tragedy is in that aching stoop;
Through this dread shape humanity betrayed,
Plundered, profaned, and disinherited,

Cries protest to the Judges of the World,
A protest that is also prophecy.

O masters, lords and rulers in all lands,
Is this the handiwork you give to God,
This monstrous thing distorted and soul-quenched?
How will you ever straighten up this shape;
Touch it again with immortality;
Give back the upward looking and the light;
Rebuild in it the music and the dream;
Make right the immemorial infamies,
Perfidious wrongs, immedicable woes?

O masters, lords and rulers in all lands,
How will the Future reckon with this man?
How answer his brute question in that hour
When whirlwinds of rebellion shake all shores?
How will it be with kingdoms and with kings —
With those who shaped him to the thing he is —
When this dumb terror shall rise to judge the world,
After the silence of the centuries?

The Child-Slaves of England

BERTRAND RUSSELL

IN RURAL LIFE there were three classes (landowners, farmers, laborers), but in industrial life there were only two. The landowner, as a rule, did not choose to live amid the grime and smoke and squalor of factories and mines; even if, for a while, he lingered in a neighborhood which had been rural in his father's time, he had little contact with the rising class of industrial employers, whom he regarded as vulgar and uneducated. The relations of the land-owning class with the mill-owners were, for the most part, polit-

From *Freedom Versus Organization* by Bertrand Russell. By permission of George Allen and Unwin, Ltd., publishers.

ical rather than social. They had a common interest in suppressing disturbances, but on most points their interests diverged. There
was an import duty on raw cotton which the manufacturers resented. The duty on grain increased the price of bread, and therefore the cost of keeping a laborer alive; the extra wages which this
obliged the manufacturer to pay ultimately found their way into the
pocket of the landowner in the shape of rent for agricultural land.
The manufacturer desired free trade, the landowner believed in
protection; the manufacturer was often a nonconformist, the landowner almost always belonged to the Church of England; the manufacturer had picked up his education as best he could, and had risen
from poverty by thrift and industry, while the landowner had been
at a public school and was the son of his father.

The upper classes, when they stopped to think, were aware that
the new industrial life of the North had its importance. They knew
that our manufacturers had helped to beat Napoleon; some of
them had heard of James Watt, and had a hazy impression that
there were processes in which steam had been found useful. But this
sort of thing seemed to them new-fangled and rather unpleasant;
moreover, if it spread, it might interfere with the foxes and part-
ridges. My grandfather, at one period of his education, had for his
tutor Dr. Cartwright, the inventor of the power loom, which introduced machinery and the factory system into the weaving trade.
His pupil, in later life, observed: "From Dr. Cartwright, who was a
man of much learning and great mechanical ingenuity, I acquired
a taste for Latin poetry, which has never left me." His reminiscences
go on to give some examples of the pedagogue's "mechanical ingenuity," but not a word is said about the power loom, of which, for
aught that appears, my grandfather never heard, although its inventor addressed to him "a volume of letters and sonnets on moral
and other interesting subjects." Abroad England was known for its
machinery, but upper-class England resented this view, and put the
emphasis on agriculture. Even so late as 1844, this feeling is amusingly expressed by Kinglake in *Eothen*, in an imaginary interview
between an English traveler and a Turkish pasha:

PASHA: . . . whirr! whirr! all by wheels! — whizz! whizz! all by
steam!

TRAVELLER (*to the* DRAGOMAN):   What does the Pasha mean by
that whizzing? he does not mean to say, does he, that our Government will ever abandon their pledges to the Sultan?

DRAGOMAN: No, your excellency, but he says the English talk by
wheels and by steam.

TRAVELLER: That's an exaggeration; but say that the English really have carried machinery to great perfection. Tell the Pasha (he'll be struck with that) that whenever we have any disturbances to put down, even at two or three hundred miles from London, we can send troops by the thousands to the scene of action in a few hours.

DRAGOMAN (*recovering his temper and freedom of speech*): His Excellency, this Lord of Mudcombe, observes to your Highness, that whenever the Irish, or the French, or the Indians rebel against the English, whole armies of soldiers and brigades of artillery are dropped into a mighty chasm called Euston Square, and, in the biting of a cartridge, they rise up again in Manchester, or Dublin, or Paris, or Delhi, and utterly exterminate the enemies of England from the face of the earth.

PASHA: I know it — I know all; the particulars have been faithfully related to me, and my mind comprehends locomotives. The armies of the English ride upon the vapors of boiling caldrons, and their horses are flaming coal; — whirr! whirr! all by wheels! — whizz! whizz! all by steam!

TRAVELLER (*to his* DRAGOMAN): I wish to have the opinion of an unprejudiced Ottoman gentleman as to the prospects of our English commerce and manufactures; just ask the Pasha to give me his views on the subject.

PASHA (*after having received the communication of the* DRAGOMAN): The ships of the English swarm like flies; their printed calicoes cover the whole earth, and by the side of their swords the blades of Damascus are blades of grass. All India is but an item in the ledger-books of the merchants, whose lumber-rooms are filled with ancient thrones! — whirr! whirr! all by wheels! — whizz! whizz! all by steam!

DRAGOMAN: The Pasha compliments the cutlery of England, and also the East India Company.

TRAVELLER: The Pasha's right about the cutlery: I tried my scimitar with the common officers' swords belonging to our fellows at Malta, and they cut it like the leaf of a novel. Well (*to the* DRAGOMAN), tell the Pasha I am exceedingly gratified to find that he entertains such a high opinion of our manufacturing energy, but I should like him to know, though, that we have got something in England besides that. These foreigners are always fancying that we have nothing but ships and railways, and East India Companies; do just tell the Pasha that our rural districts deserve his attention, and that even within the last two hundred years there has been an evident improvement in the culture of the turnip; and if he does not take any interest about that, at all events you can explain that we have our virtues in the country —

that we are a truth-telling people, and, like the Osmanlees are faithful in the performance of our promises. Oh, and by-the-by, whilst you are about it, you may just as well just say, at the end, that the British yeoman is still, thank God! the British yeoman.

The British yeoman, as we have seen, was not still the British yeoman; Kinglake's traveler and his friends had transformed him into a starving, terrified pauper. But if the evils of rural England were great, those of industrial England were infinitely greater. The abominations in the mills and mines of those days are a trite theme, and yet one that remains all but unbearable. I have scarcely the heart to embark upon it, and yet something must be said.

Napoleon had been defeated by the snows of Russia and the children of England. The part played by the snows of Russia was acknowledged, since it could be attributed to Providence; but the part played by the children of England was passed over in silence, since it was shameful to the men of England. It was Michelet, in his history, who first gave it due prominence in the shape of an imaginary conversation between Pitt and the employers: when they complain of his war taxes, he replies "Take the children." But it was a very long time after the end of the war before they let the children go again.

There were two systems of child labor: the older system, of pauper apprentices, and the newer system, of "free" children. The older system was as follows: in London, and in various other places, when a man received poor relief, the parish claimed the exclusive right of disposing of his children up to the age of twenty-one. Until 1767, almost all such children died, so that no problem arose for the authorities. In that year, however, a philanthropist named Hanway got an Act passed which caused the children to be boarded out up to the age of six, instead of being kept in the workhouse. The consequence was that large numbers had the misfortune to survive, and the London authorities were faced with the problem of their disposal. The demand for child labor in the Lancashire mills supplied the solution. The children were apprenticed to some mill-owner, and became virtually his property until the age of twenty-one. If the mill worked continuously, day and night, the children were employed in two shifts of twelve hours each, each bed being shared between a day-child and a night-child. These were the more fortunate children. In mills which closed during the night, there was only one shift, and the children might have to work fifteen or sixteen hours every day.

Sometimes the mill-owners would go bankrupt, and the children would be taken in a cart to a lonely spot, and then turned out to shift for themselves. Unless this happened, the children never left the mill, except to go to church on Sundays if the machinery was cleaned in time. The possibility of insufficient religious instruction was almost the only point on which the general conscience of the time was sensitive; it was, however, somewhat moved by the frequent epidemics of which large numbers of the children died.

In the year 1802, Sir Robert Peel (father of the statesman), who had been himself a far from model employer, introduced and carried through Parliament a Bill "for the better preservation of the Health and Morals of Apprentices and others employed in the cotton and other mills and the cotton and other manufactories." The Bill in fact applied only to apprentices, and only to cotton. Sir Robert Peel thought that it "would render the cotton trade as correct and moral as it was important." It prescribed that apprentices were not to work at night, and no more than twelve hours a day; they were to have some education every day, one new suit of clothes a year, and separate rooms for the boys and girls, with a whole bed for each. Every Sunday they were to be taught the Christian religion, and once a year they were to be examined by a clergyman. What could virtuous children want more?

The employers protested that this Act was going to ruin their business. But it turned out that no one was going to force them to obey the law, and in practice little good resulted. Moreover, the employment of apprentices came to be more and more replaced by what were amusingly called "free" children, i.e., those who went to work at the behest of their parents although they had not been deprived of the legal right to starve. The change was due to the substitution of steam for water power, which led to the removal of mills to the towns, where a supply of child labor was available. The authorities refused the aid of the Poor Law to parents who refused to send their children to the mill, and owing to the competition of the new machines there were many weavers on the verge of starvation. The result was that many children were forced to begin earning their living at the age of six or seven, or sometimes even sooner. Their life as wage-earners is described by the Hammonds in *The Town Labourer:*

When once children became wage earners, their working life differed little from that of the apprentices already described. They entered the mill gates at 5 or 6 A.M., they left them (at earliest) at 7 or 8 P.M., Saturdays included. All this time they were shut up in temperature varying from 75° to 85°. The only respite during the fourteen or fifteen hours' confinement was afforded by meal hours, at most half an hour for breakfast and an hour for dinner. But regular meal hours were privileges for adults only: to the children for three or four days a week they meant merely a change of work; instead of tending a machine that was running, they cleaned a machine that was standing still, snatching and swallowing their food as best they could in the midst of dust and flue. Children soon lost all relish for meals eaten in the factory. The flue used to choke their lungs. When spitting failed to expel it, emetics were freely given.

The work on which these children were engaged was often described as light and easy, in fact almost as an amusement, requiring attention but not exertion. Three-fourths of the children were piecers — that is, engaged in joining together or piecing the threads broken in the various roving and spinning machines. Others were employed in sweeping up the waste cotton, or removing and replacing bobbins. Fielden (1784-1849), the enlightened and humane employer who represented Oldham with Cobbett, and shares the laurels that grace the memory of Shaftesbury and Sadler, made an interesting experiment to measure the physical strain that the children endured. Struck with some statements made by factory delegates about the miles a child walked a day in following the spinning machine, he submitted the statements to a practical test in his own factory, and found to his amazement that in twelve hours the distance covered was not less than twenty miles. There were indeed short intervals of leisure, but no seat to sit on, sitting being contrary to rules. The view that the piecers' work was really light was best given by Mr. Tufnell, one of the Factory Commissioners. Three-fourths of the children, he says, are engaged as piecers at mules, and whilst the mules are receding there is nothing to be done and the piecers stand idle for about three-quarters of a minute. From this he deduces the conclusion that if a child is nominally working twelve hours a day, "*for nine hours he performs no actual labour*," or if, as is generally the case, he attends two mules, then "his leisure is six hours instead of nine."

The fourteen or fifteen hours' confinement for six days a week were the "regular" hours: in busy times hours were elastic and sometimes stretched to a length that seems almost incredible. Work from 3 A.M. to 10 P.M. was not unknown; in Mr. Varley's mill, all through the summer, they worked from 3:30 A.M. to 9:30 P.M. At the mill, aptly called "Hell's Bay," for two months at a time, they not only worked regularly from 5 A.M. to 9 P.M., but for two nights each week worked all through the night as well. The more humane employers contented themselves when busy with a spell of sixteen hours (5 A.M. to 9 P.M.).

It was physically impossible to keep such a system working at all except by the driving force of terror. The overseers who gave evidence before Sadler's Committee did not deny that their methods were brutal. They said that they had either to exact the full quota of work, or to be dismissed, and in these circumstances pity was a luxury that men with families could not allow themselves. The punishments for arriving late in the morning had to be made cruel enough to overcome the temptation to tired children to take more than three or four hours in bed. One witness before Sadler's committee had known a child, who had reached home at eleven o'clock one night, get up at two o'clock next morning in panic and limp to the mill gate. In some mills scarcely an hour passed in the long day without the sound of beating and cries of pain. Fathers beat their own children to save them from a worse beating by the overseers. In the afternoon the strain grew so severe that the heavy iron stick known as the billy-roller was in constant use, and, even then, it happened not infrequently that a small child, as he dozed, tumbled into the machine beside him to be mangled for life, or, if he were more fortunate, to find a longer Lethe than his stolen sleep. In one mill indeed, where the owner, a Mr. Gott, had forbidden the use of anything but a ferule, some of the slubbers tried to keep the children awake, when they worked from 5 in the morning to 9 at night, by encouraging them to sing hymns. As the evening wore on the pain and fatigue and tension on the mind became insupportable. Children would implore any one who came near to tell them how many hours there were still before them. A witness told Sadler's Committee that his child, a boy of six, would say to him, " 'Father, what o'clock is it?' I have said perhaps it is seven o'clock. 'Oh, it is two hours to nine o'clock? I cannot bear it.' "

As the circumstances became known, an agitation arose for an Act to prohibit the worst abuses. . . . For the present, I shall only observe that an Act was passed in 1819, but proved wholly ineffective, as the work of inspection was left to magistrates and clergymen. To the relief of employers, experience showed that magistrates and clergymen had no objection to lawbreaking when its purpose was merely the torture of children.

It was not only in cotton mills that children suffered; they were subjected to conditions quite as terrible in the coal mines. There were, for example, the trappers, generally from five to eight years old, who "sat in a little hole, made at the side of the door, holding a string in their hand, for twelve hours. As a rule they were in the dark, but sometimes a good-natured collier would give them a bit of candle." A girl of eight, according to the Report of the Children's Employment Committee in 1842, said: "I have to trap without a light, and I'm scared. I go at four and sometimes at half-past three in the morning and come out at five and half-past (in the afternoon). I never go to sleep. Sometimes I sing when I've light, but not in the dark: I dare not sing them."

It was by the labor of children under such conditions that Lord Melbourne acquired the fortune which enabled him to be civilized and charming. Castlereagh, as Lord Londonderry, was a very important mine-owner. Indeed, the chief difference between mines and cotton was that many of the leading aristocrats of both parties were directly interested in the mines, and they showed themselves quite as callous as the most brutal self-made mill-owners. The agony of tortured children is an undertone to the elegant conversation of Holland House.

I have spoken of the children, because that is the most terrible aspect of industrialism a hundred years ago. But such sufferings for children would have been impossible unless their parents had been in a condition of despair. Hours for adults were almost incredibly long, wages very low, and housing conditions abominable. Industrial workers, many of whom had till recently lived in the country, were herded together in new, ill-built, smoky and insanitary towns, some even lived in cellars, and cholera and typhus were endemic. Skilled handicraftsmen were reduced to destitution by the new machines; weavers, who had formerly been prosperous, could only earn 6s. 6d. a week. Combinations among wage-earners were illegal until 1824, and though trade unions existed, they were necessarily small and ineffectual so long as they had to be kept secret. The Government employed spies whose business it was to induce poor men to utter revolutionary sentiments. The spies themselves, with great trouble, organized little movements, and their dupes were hanged or transported.

The men guilty of these atrocities were human beings: you and I share their human nature, and might, I suppose, in other circumstances have done as they did.

Machines To Do Our Work

EDWARD BELLAMY

WHEN WE ARRIVED HOME Dr. Leete had not yet returned, and Mrs. Leete was not visible. "Are you fond of music, Mr. West?" Edith asked.

I assured her that it was half of life, according to my notion.

"I ought to apologize for inquiring," she said. "It is not a question that we ask one another nowadays; but I have read that in your day, even among the cultured class, there were some who did not care for music."

"You must remember, in excuse," I said, "that we had some rather absurd kinds of music."

"Yes," she said, "I know that; I am afraid I should not have fancied it all myself. Would you like to hear some of ours now, Mr. West?"

"Nothing would delight me so much as to listen to you," I said.

"To me!" she exclaimed, laughing. "Did you think I was going to play or sing to you?"

"I hoped so, certainly," I replied.

Seeing that I was a little abashed, she subdued her merriment and explained. "Of course, we all sing nowadays as a matter of course in the training of the voice, and some learn to play instruments for their private amusement; but the professional music is so much grander and more perfect than any performance of ours, and so easily commanded when we wish to hear it, that we don't think of calling our singing or playing music at all. All the really fine singers and players are in the musical service, and the rest of us hold our peace for the main part. But would you really like to hear some music?"

I assured her once more that I would.

"Come, then, into the music room," she said, and I followed her into an apartment finished, without hangings, in wood, with a floor of polished wood. I was prepared for new devices in musical instruments, but I saw nothing in the room which by any stretch of imagination could be conceived as such. It was evident that my puzzled appearance was affording intense amusement to Edith.

"Please look at today's music," she said, handing me a card, "and

From *Looking Backward 2000-1887* by Edward Bellamy, published 1888.

tell me what you would prefer. It is now five o'clock, you will remember."

The card bore the date "September 12, 2000," and contained the
largest program of music I had ever seen. It was as various as it was
long, including a most extraordinary range of vocal and instrumental
solos, duets, quartets, and various orchestral combinations. I remained bewildered by the prodigious list until Edith's pink finger
tip indicated a particular section of it, where several selections were
bracketed, with the words "5 P.M." against them; then I observed
that this prodigious program was an all-day one, divided into
twenty-four sections answering to the hours. There were but a few
pieces of music in the "5 P.M." section, and I indicated an organ
piece as my preference.

"I am so glad you like the organ," said she. "I think there is
scarcely any music that suits my mood oftener."

She made me sit down comfortably, and crossing the room, so
far as I could see, merely touched one or two screws, and at once
the room was filled with the music of a grand organ anthem; filled,
not flooded, for, by some means, the volume of melody had been
perfectly graduated to the size of the apartment. I listened,
scarcely breathing, to the close. Such music, so perfectly rendered,
I had never expected to hear.

"Grand!" I cried, as the last great wave of sound broke and
ebbed away into silence. "Bach must be at the keys of that organ;
but where is the organ?"

"Wait a moment, please," said Edith; "I want to have you listen
to this waltz before you ask any questions. I think it is perfectly
charming," and as she spoke the sound of violins filled the room
with the witchery of a summer night. When this had also ceased,
she said: "There is nothing in the least mysterious about the music,
as you seem to imagine. It is not made by fairies or genii, but by
good, honest, and exceedingly clever human hands. We have simply
carried the idea of labor-saving by co-operation into our musical
service as into everything else. There are a number of music rooms
in the city, perfectly adapted acoustically to the different sorts of
music. These halls are connected by telephone with all the houses of
the city whose people care to pay the small fee, and there are none,
you may be sure, who do not. The corps of musicians attached to
each hall is so large that, although no individual performer, or group
of performers, has more than a brief part, each day's program lasts
through the twenty-four hours. There are on that card for today,
as you will see if you observe closely, distinct programs of four of
these concerts, each of a different order of music from the others,
being now simultaneously performed, and any one of the four

pieces now going on that you prefer, you can hear by merely pressing the button which will connnect your house wire with the hall
where it is being rendered. The programs are so co-ordinated that
the pieces at any one time simultaneously proceeding in the different halls, usually offer a choice, not only between instrumental and
vocal, and between different sorts of instruments; but also between
different motives from grave to gay, so that all tastes and moods
can be suited."

"It appears to me, Miss Leete," I said, "that if we could have
devised an arrangement for providing everybody with music in
their homes, perfect in quality, unlimited in quantity, suited to
every mood, and beginning and ceasing at will, we should have considered the limit of human felicity already attained, and ceased
to strive for further improvements."

"I am sure I never could imagine how those among you who
depended at all on music managed to endure the old-fashioned system for providing it," replied Edith. "Music really worth hearing
must have been, I suppose, wholly out of the reach of the masses,
and attainable by the most favored only occasionally at great trouble, prodigious expense, and then for brief periods, arbitrarily fixed
by somebody else and in connection with all sorts of undesirable
circumstances. Your concerts, for instance, and operas! How perfectly exasperating it must have been, for the sake of a piece or two
of music that suited you, to have to sit for hours listening to what
you did not care for! Now, at a dinner one can skip the courses one
does not care for. Who would ever dine, however hungry, if required to eat everything brought on the table? and I am sure one's
hearing is quite as sensitive as one's taste. I suppose it was these
difficulties in the way of commanding really good music which
made you endure so much playing and singing in your homes by
people who had only the rudiments of the art."

"Yes," I replied, "it was that sort of music or none for most of
us."

"Ah, well," Edith sighed, "when one really considers, it is not so
strange that people in those days so generally did not care for
music. I daresay I should have detested it, too."

"Did I understand you rightly," I inquired, "that this musical
program covers the entire twenty-four hours? It seems to on this
card, certainly; but who is there to listen to music between say midnight and morning?"

"Oh, many," Edith replied. "Our people keep all hours; but if the
music were provided from midnight to morning for no others, it still
would be for the sleepless, the sick, and the dying. All our bedcham-
bers have a telephone attachment at the head of the bed by which

any person who may be sleepless can command music at pleasure, of the sort suited to the mood."

"Is there such an arrangement in the room assigned to me?"

"Why, certainly; and how stupid, how very stupid, of me not to think to tell you of that last night! Father will show you about the adjustment before you go to bed tonight, however; and with the receiver at your ear, I am quite sure you will be able to snap your fingers at all sorts of uncanny feelings if they trouble you again. . . ."

"You spoke of paying for service to take care of your houses," said I; "that suggests a question I have several times been on the point of asking. How have you disposed of the problem of domestic service? Who are willing to be domestic servants in a community where all are social equals? Our ladies found it hard enough to find such even when there was little pretense of social equality."

"It is precisely because we are all social equals whose equality nothing can compromise, and because service is honorable in a society whose fundamental principle is that all in turn shall serve the rest, that we could easily provide a corps of domestic servants such as you never dreamed of, if we needed them," replied Dr. Leete. "But we do not need them."

"Who does your housework, then?" I asked.

"There is none to do," said Mrs. Leete, to whom I had addressed this question. "Our washing is all done at public laundries at excessively cheap rates, and our cooking at public kitchens. The making and repairing of all we wear are done outside in public shops. Electricity, of course, takes the place of all fires and lighting. We choose houses no larger than we need, and furnish them so as to involve the minimum of trouble to keep them in order. We have no use for domestic servants."

"The fact," said Dr. Leete, "that you had in the poorer classes a boundless supply of serfs on whom you could impose all sorts of painful and disagreeable tasks, made you indifferent to devices to avoid the necessity for them. But now that we all have to do in turn whatever work is done for society, every individual in the nation has the same interest, and a personal one, in devices for lightening the burden. This fact has given a prodigious impulse to labor-saving inventions in all sorts of industry, of which the combination of the maximum of comfort and minimum of trouble in household arrangements was one of the earliest results."

"In case of special emergencies in the household," pursued Dr. Leete, "such as extensive cleaning or renovation, or sickness in the family, we can always secure assistance from the industrial force."

"But how do you recompense these assistants, since you have no money?"

"We do not pay them, of course, but the nation for them. Their services can be obtained by application at the proper bureau, and their value is pricked off the credit card of the applicant."

"What a paradise for womankind the world must be now!" I exclaimed. "In my day, even wealth and unlimited servants did not enfranchise their possessors from household cares, while the women of the merely well-to-do and poorer classes lived and died martyrs to them."

"Yes," said Mrs. Leete, "I have read something of that; enough to convince me that, badly off as the men, too, were in your day, they were more fortunate than their mothers and wives."

"The broad shoulders of the nation," said Dr. Leete, "bear now like a feather the burden that broke the backs of the women of your day. Their misery came, with all your other miseries, from that incapacity for co-operation which followed from the individualism on which your social system was founded, from your inability to perceive that you could make ten times more profit out of your fellow men by uniting with them than by contending with them. The wonder is, not that you did not live more comfortably, but that you were able to live together at all, who were all confessedly bent on making one another your servants, and securing possession of one another's goods."

"There, there, father, if you are so vehement, Mr. West will think you are scolding him," laughingly interposed Edith.

"When you want a doctor," I asked, "do you simply apply to the proper bureau and take any one that may be sent?"

"That rule would not work well in the case of physicians," replied Dr. Leete. "The good a physician can do a patient depends largely on his acquaintance with his constitutional tendencies and condition. The patient must be able, therefore, to call in a particular doctor, and he does so, just as patients did in your day. The only difference is that, instead of collecting his fee for himself, the doctor collects it for the nation by pricking off the amount, according to a regular scale for medical attendance, from the patient's credit card."

"I can imagine," I said, "that if the fee is always the same, and a doctor may not turn away patients, as I suppose he may not, the good doctors are called constantly and the poor doctors left in idleness."

"In the first place, if you will overlook the apparent conceit of the remark from a retired physician," replied Dr. Leete, with a smile, "we have no poor doctors. Anybody who pleases to get a little smattering of medical terms is not now at liberty to practice on the bodies of citizens, as in your day. None but students who have passed the severe tests of the schools, and clearly proved their vocation, are permitted to practice. Then, too, you will observe that there is nowadays no attempt of doctors to build up their practice at the expense of other doctors. There would be no motive for that. For the rest, the doctor has to render regular reports of his work to the medical bureau, and if he is not reasonably well employed, work is found for him."

⊂⊅ *THE CRY OF THE LAND*

The River

PARE LORENTZ

From as far West as Idaho,
　　Down from the glacier peaks of the Rockies —
From as far East as New York,
　　Down from the Turkey ridges of the Alleghenies
Down from Minnesota, twenty-five hundred miles,
　　The Mississippi River runs to the Gulf.
Carrying every drop of water, that flows down two-thirds the continent,
Carrying every brook and rill, rivulet and creek,
Carrying all the rivers that run down two-thirds the continent,
The Mississippi runs to the Gulf of Mexico.
Down the Yellowstone, the Milk, the White and Cheyenne;
The Cannonball, the Musselshell, the James and the Sioux:
Down the Judith, the Grand, the Osage, and the Platte,
The Skunk, the Salt, the Black, and Minnesota;
Down the Rock, the Illinois, and the Kankakee,
The Allegheny, the Monongahela, Kanawha, and Muskingum;
Down the Miami, the Wabash, the Licking, and the Green,
The Cumberland, the Kentucky, and the Tennessee;
Down the Ouchita, the Wichita, the Red, and Yazoo —

From Pare Lorentz: *The River*, originally published 1938 by Stackpole Sons, now The Stackpole Company, Harrisburg, Pennsylvania.